Glencoe Science
Features and Benefits

		Pages
Dynamic Instructional Strategies	**... present clear and comprehensive coverage of middle school science.**	
	■ Each engaging chapter opener includes a *Launch Lab* and *Foldables*™.	7, 39
	■ *National Geographic Visualizing* features illustrate important concepts in middle school science.	22, 50
A Strong Reading Strand	**... encourages active reading and learning for students of all reading levels. In the *Student Edition:***	
	■ as you read gives students a preview of learning objectives and vocabulary for each section;	8, 40
	■ *Reading Checks* help students check their reading comprehension; and	14, 41
	■ *Caption questions* ask students to interpret visuals.	10, 43
	■ *Reading Essentials, An Interactive Student Textbook* is designed to help struggling readers comprehend core content. It is written at a reading level of about two to three grades below the *Student Edition.*	
Meeting the Needs of All Students	**... facilitates understanding of science concepts for students of all learning levels. In the *Teacher Wraparound Edition:***	
	■ *Differentiated Instruction* strategies help meet the needs of students with learning disabilities and physical challenges, or create opportunities to enrich and extend students' learning;	13, 44
	■ *Daily Intervention* provides intervention strategies for struggling students; and	23, 47
	■ *Identifying Misconceptions* helps uncover and address common science misconceptions.	38F
	■ The *English/Spanish Glossary*, also in the *Student Edition,* helps English-language learners comprehend science terms.	227–234
Extensive Standardized Test Practice	**... gives students the opportunity to practice for state and national exams.**	
	■ Each chapter ends with a variety of standardized test practice questions, including *Multiple Choice, Short Response/Grid In*, and *Open Ended.*	64–65
A Variety of Labs	**... gets students excited about being involved in science. The *Student Edition* provides:**	
	■ *MiniLABs,* traditional labs, and *Design Your Own, Model and Invent,* and *Use the Internet* labs; and	25, 52, 58
	■ *Extra Try at Home Labs* provide opportunities for students to practice their science skills at home with adult supervision using materials from the kitchen, junk drawer, or backyard.	198–200
	■ *Virtual Labs* CD-ROM contains an interactive virtual lab for each chapter.	26
	■ *Video Labs* (VHS) reinforce lab techniques and safety skills, offer troubleshooting tips, and give expected outcomes.	11
	■ The *Science Lab Manual, Probeware Lab Manual,* and *Science Inquiry Lab Manual* provide additional opportunities to practice laboratory techniques.	
Multi-Level Review	**... presents multiple opportunities for all students to review and master content.**	
	■ Each section ends with a review that contains a *Summary* of the section's major concepts and a *Self Check* that has questions to assess student learning and practice math or science skills.	28, 47
	■ The *Study Guide* at the end of each chapter can preview, review, summarize, and visualize the chapter's main ideas.	33, 61
	■ *Study Guide* and *Reinforcement* help students grasp core content.	
Teacher Resources	**... provide innovative strategies to help new and experienced teachers.**	
	■ *Chapter Resources Fast File* ™ contains important reproducible masters.	66B
	■ Section Focus, Assessment, and Teaching transparencies accompany each chapter.	96C
	■ *Performance Assessment in the Science Classroom* has assessment guidelines, strategies, sample rubrics, and more.	
Online Resources	**... enrich the learning experience with the click of a mouse.**	
	■ For prescreened Web links, standardized test practice, self-check quizzes, chapter tests, *Vocabulary PuzzleMaker,* extra math practice, science career information, current science news, and *WebQuest* interactive projects, visit **booka.msscience.com.**	
	■ The complete interactive *Student Edition* is available at The McGraw-Hill Learning Network Web site, **mhln.com**.	
Technology	**... provides timesaving products to help teachers creatively engage their students.**	
	■ *MindJogger Videoquizzes* (VHS & DVD) provide a game-show style interactive quiz for each chapter.	
	■ Easy to edit *Interactive Chalkboard* Microsoft® PowerPoint® presentations include step-by-step lessons, an image bank, chapter and section review questions, standardized test practice, and transparencies.	
	■ *ExamView® Pro Testmaker* CD-ROM in English or Spanish allows you to customize assessments.	
	■ *TeacherWorks* CD-ROM is your all-in-one resource center that helps you plan and organize lessons.	
	■ *StudentWorks* CD-ROM solves the heavy backpack problem.	

SAFETY SYMBOLS	HAZARD	EXAMPLES	PRECAUTION	REMEDY
DISPOSAL	Special disposal procedures need to be followed.	certain chemicals, living organisms	Do not dispose of these materials in the sink or trash can.	Dispose of wastes as directed by your teacher.
BIOLOGICAL	Organisms or other biological materials that might be harmful to humans	bacteria, fungi, blood, unpreserved tissues, plant materials	Avoid skin contact with these materials. Wear mask or gloves.	Notify your teacher if you suspect contact with material. Wash hands thoroughly.
EXTREME TEMPERATURE	Objects that can burn skin by being too cold or too hot	boiling liquids, hot plates, dry ice, liquid nitrogen	Use proper protection when handling.	Go to your teacher for first aid.
SHARP OBJECT	Use of tools or glassware that can easily puncture or slice skin	razor blades, pins, scalpels, pointed tools, dissecting probes, broken glass	Practice common-sense behavior and follow guidelines for use of the tool.	Go to your teacher for first aid.
FUME	Possible danger to respiratory tract from fumes	ammonia, acetone, nail polish remover, heated sulfur, moth balls	Make sure there is good ventilation. Never smell fumes directly. Wear a mask.	Leave foul area and notify your teacher immediately.
ELECTRICAL	Possible danger from electrical shock or burn	improper grounding, liquid spills, short circuits, exposed wires	Double-check setup with teacher. Check condition of wires and apparatus.	Do not attempt to fix electrical problems. Notify your teacher immediately.
IRRITANT	Substances that can irritate the skin or mucous membranes of the respiratory tract	pollen, moth balls, steel wool, fiberglass, potassium permanganate	Wear dust mask and gloves. Practice extra care when handling these materials.	Go to your teacher for first aid.
CHEMICAL	Chemicals can react with and destroy tissue and other materials	bleaches such as hydrogen peroxide; acids such as sulfuric acid, hydrochloric acid; bases such as ammonia, sodium hydroxide	Wear goggles, gloves, and an apron.	Immediately flush the affected area with water and notify your teacher.
TOXIC	Substance may be poisonous if touched, inhaled, or swallowed.	mercury, many metal compounds, iodine, poinsettia plant parts	Follow your teacher's instructions.	Always wash hands thoroughly after use. Go to your teacher for first aid.
FLAMMABLE	Flammable chemicals may be ignited by open flame, spark, or exposed heat.	alcohol, kerosene, potassium permanganate	Avoid open flames and heat when using flammable chemicals.	Notify your teacher immediately. Use fire safety equipment if applicable.
OPEN FLAME	Open flame in use, may cause fire.	hair, clothing, paper, synthetic materials	Tie back hair and loose clothing. Follow teacher's instruction on lighting and extinguishing flames.	Notify your teacher immediately. Use fire safety equipment if applicable.

Eye Safety
Proper eye protection should be worn at all times by anyone performing or observing science activities.

Clothing Protection
This symbol appears when substances could stain or burn clothing.

Animal Safety
This symbol appears when safety of animals and students must be ensured.

Handwashing
After the lab, wash hands with soap and water before removing goggles.

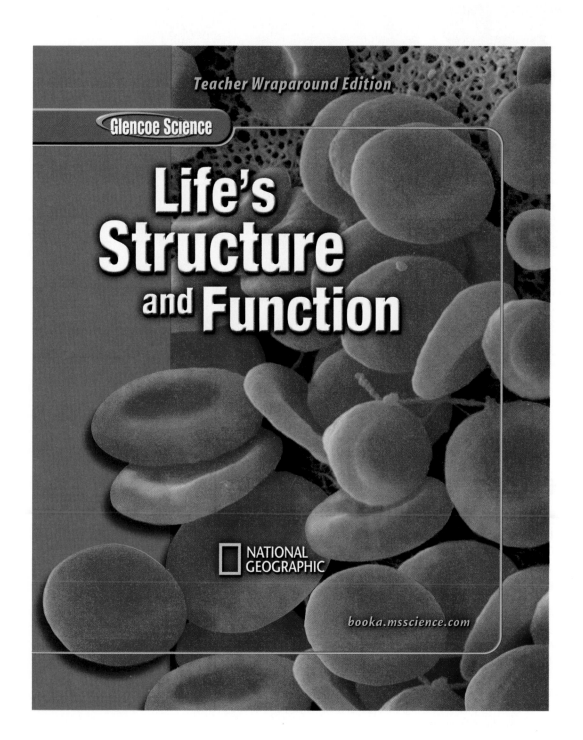

Teacher Wraparound Edition

Glencoe Science

Life's Structure and Function

NATIONAL GEOGRAPHIC

booka.msscience.com

New York, New York   Columbus, Ohio   Chicago, Illinois   Peoria, Illinois   Woodland Hills, California

Glencoe Science

Life's Structure and Function

These human red blood cells are part of a liquid tissue—blood. They deliver oxygen and remove wastes. The protein hemoglobin gives them their red color, and contains iron to transport oxygen and carbon dioxide.

The McGraw-Hill Companies

Send all inquiries to:
Glencoe/McGraw-Hill
8787 Orion Place
Columbus, OH 43240-4027

ISBN 0-07-861734-0 (Student Edition)
ISBN 0-07-861735-9 (Teacher Wraparound Edition)

Printed in the United States of America.

1 2 3 4 5 6 7 8 9 10 027/055 09 08 07 06 05 04

Authors

Education Division
Washington, D.C.

Alton Biggs
Retired Biology Teacher
Allen High School
Allen, TX

Lucy Daniel, PhD
Teacher/Consultant
Rutherford County Schools
Rutherfordton, NC

Dinah Zike
Educational Consultant
Dinah-Might Activities, Inc.
San Antonio, TX

Series Consultants

CONTENT

Connie Rizzo, MD, PhD
Department of Science/Math
Marymount Manhattan College
New York, NY

Dominic Salinas, PhD
Middle School Science Supervisor
Caddo Parish Schools
Shreveport, LA

MATH

Teri Willard, EdD
Mathematics Curriculum Writer
Belgrade, MT

READING

Elizabeth Babich
Special Education Teacher
Mashpee Public Schools
Mashpee, MA

Carol A. Senf, PhD
School of Literature, Communication, and Culture
Georgia Institute of Technology
Atlanta, GA

SAFETY

Sandra West, PhD
Department of Biology
Texas State University-San Marcos
San Marcos, TX

ACTIVITY TESTERS

Nerma Coats Henderson
Pickerington Lakeview Jr. High School
Pickerington, OH

Mary Helen Mariscal-Cholka
William D. Slider Middle School
El Paso, TX

Science Kit and Boreal Laboratories
Tonawanda, NY

Series Reviewers

Maureen Barrett
Thomas E. Harrington Middle School
Mt. Laurel, NJ

Robin Dillon
Hanover Central High School
Cedar Lake, IN

Carolyn Elliott
South Iredell High School
Statesville, NC

Sueanne Esposito
Tipton High School
Tipton, IN

Cory Fish
Burkholder Middle School
Henderson, NV

Linda V. Forsyth
Retired Teacher
Merrill Middle School
Denver, CO

Michelle Mazeika
Whiting Middle School
Whiting, IN

Joe McConnell
Speedway Jr. High School
Indianapolis, IN

Amy Morgan
Berry Middle School
Hoover, AL

Mark Sailer
Pioneer Jr.-Sr. High School
Royal Center, IN

Dee Stout
Penn State University
University Park, PA

Glencoe Science 15-Book Series

Teach science your way!

With the 15 Life, Earth, and Physical Science titles in our modular series, you can select the science topics you want to cover and customize your science curriculum in any way you choose.

A Life's Structure and Function
1 Exploring and Classifying Life
2 Cells
3 Cell Processes
4 Cell Reproduction
5 Heredity
6 Adaptations over Time

B From Bacteria to Plants
1 Bacteria
2 Protists and Fungi
3 Plants
4 Plant Reproduction
5 Plant Processes

C Animal Diversity
1 Introduction to Animals
2 Mollusks, Worms, Arthropods, Echinoderms
3 Fish, Amphibians, and Reptiles
4 Birds and Mammals
5 Animal Behavior

D Human Body Systems
1 Structure and Movement
2 Nutrients and Digestion
3 Circulation
4 Respiration and Excretion
5 Control and Coordination
6 Regulation and Reproduction
7 Immunity and Disease

E Ecology
1 Interactions of Life
2 The Nonliving Environment
3 Ecosystems
4 Conserving Resources
5 Conserving Life

Multi-Level Review and Assessment

Each chapter provides five pages of review and testing to help you evaluate students' knowledge and ability to apply science concepts.

Section Review
- Summary pinpoints important concepts in the section.
- Skill-based questions promote critical thinking skills.

Study Guide
- Main idea summary of each section
- Concept mapping activity to help students visualize the main ideas

Chapter Review
- Using Vocabulary
- Checking Concepts
- Thinking Critically
- Performance Activities
- Applying Math

Standardized Test Practice
- Multiple Choice
- Short Response/ Grid In
- Open-Ended Questions

Dynamic Instruction

The consistent instructional strategies in each chapter strengthen students' learning—from the beginning of each chapter where students see "Chapter Preview," to the end where they have a chance to test the knowledge they have acquired and prepare for the next lesson.

Chapter Opener
- *Chapter Preview* introduces the main concepts.
- *Science Journal* promotes critical-thinking skills
- *Dinah Zike's Foldables*™ let students create interactive study guides.
- *Launch Labs* give students an opportunity to explore new ideas.

Section Opener
- *What You'll Learn* introduces main concepts.
- *Why It's Important* provides an answer to "Why do we have to learn this?"
- *Review Vocabulary* reviews a term that helps students better understand section content.
- *New Vocabulary* highlights new terms students will learn in the section.

Labs
- *Labs* allow students to design their own experiments or follow well-tested procedures, enabling them to learn and practice science processes.
- *MiniLABS* offer students quick and easy-to-do ways to clarify concepts and reinforce skills.

Assessment

Glencoe Science offers the Glencoe Assessment Advantage, a system designed to give you all the tools you need to prepare your students for success in any testing situation.

In the *Student Edition*

Section Review and **Applying Math** questions appear in every chapter.

Chapter Review questions help you evaluate students' knowledge and ability to apply science concepts.

Standardized Test Practice questions at the end of each chapter provide students with additional opportunities to practice their test-taking skills.

In the *Teacher Wraparound Edition*

Assessments located throughout the *Teacher Wraparound Edition* provide methods for assessing students' comprehension with Performance, Process, and Content exercises.

Teacher Classroom Resources

Performance Assessment in the Science Classroom

- Guidelines for assessing the performance of a task
- Reproducible activities for evaluating students
- Sample rubrics and checklists

***Fast File* Chapter Resources** provides six pages of assessement for every chapter including *Testing Concepts, Applying Concepts,* and *Writing Skills.*

Technology Support

MindJogger Videoquizzes are interactive video quizzes set in game show format. Each is designed for the full range of student learning styles.

Exam*View*® Pro Testmaker CD-ROM for Windows® and Macintosh® provides an easy way to create, edit, and customize your tests. Select your own test items by objective from two different levels of difficulty, or write and edit your own. Translate tests from English to Spanish and vice versa.

Rubrics

The following rubrics are sample scoring devices for short response and open-ended questions.

Short Response

Points	Description
2	The student demonstrates a thorough understanding of the science of the task. The response may contain minor flaws that do not detract from the demonstration of a thorough understanding.
1	The student has provided a response that is only partially correct.
0	The student has provided a completely incorrect solution or no response at all.

Open Ended

Points	Description
4	The student demonstrates a thorough understanding of the science of the task. The response may contain minor flaws that do not detract from the demonstration of a thorough understanding.
3	The student demonstrates an understanding of the science of the task. The response is essentially correct and demonstrates an essential but less than thorough understanding of the science.
2	The student demonstrates only a partial understanding of the science of the task. Although the student may have used the correct approach to a solution or may have provided a correct solution, the work lacks an essential understanding of the underlying science concepts.
1	The student demonstrates a very limited understanding of the science of the task. The response is incomplete and exhibits many flaws.
0	The student provides a completely incorrect solution or no response at all.

Time-Saving Teacher Resources

Glencoe Science provides an extensive array of support materials and resources designed to help you create and customize your science course quickly and easily.

FAST FILE Chapter Resources

For each chapter, Chapter Resources contain key reproducible masters along with additional teaching strategies, teacher support, and answer keys.

Teacher Wraparound Edition

The *Teacher Wraparound Edition* is your key to the teaching resources available. In addition to teaching strategies and suggestions, the *Teacher Wraparound Edition* provides a guide for all print and software materials available for each lesson.

Transparencies

Color Transparencies provides three types of transparencies for use while teaching each chapter. The *Section Focus Transparencies* are designed to generate interest and focus students' attention on the topic being presented in the section. The *Teaching Transparency* for each chapter addresses a major concept that will benefit from an extra visual learning aid. The *Assessment Transparency* for each chapter is set up to resemble standardized tests.

Exam*View*® Pro Testmaker CD-ROM

This CD-ROM will help you create, edit, and customize tests. In addition, it will help you create multiple versions of tests, translate tests from English to Spanish and vice versa, and build tests aligned with state standards.

Video Labs

These VHS cassettes contain step-by-step procedures for selected *Student Edition* labs. They also contain lab safety skills, teacher support, and troubleshooting advice.

TeacherWorks™

This CD-ROM is your all-in-one teacher resource center. Personalize a lesson plan, access resources from the *Teacher Wraparound Edition*, connect to the Internet, or make a to-do list. These are only a few of the many features that can assist you in the planning and organizing of your lessons.

StudentWorks™

This CD-ROM is a valuable resource for students to access content online and use online resources to continue learning chapter concepts.

This CD-ROM brings Microsoft® PowerPoint® presentations right to your door. With the large number of graphics provided, students can use a visual approach to learning chapter content.

Virtual Labs CD-ROM Program

The Virtual Labs CD-ROM contains a collection of labs that allow students to complete labs that are too expensive, take too long to complete, or might be too dangerous in a classroom laboratory.

This website is a portal to hundreds of prescreened Internet sites (Web links) that correlate to content in the text. Visit this link to find interactive activities that review chapter concepts and to access the *Student Edition* online.

mhln.com is an online teaching and learning space for teachers, students, and parents.

Differentiated Instruction

Teaching Strategies

Following each suggested assessment and activity, ability levels are supplied to accommodate all students. For a key to the Teaching Strategies designations, see the C page before each chapter.

Identifying Misconceptions

These short, diagnostic, and perscriptive lessons target common science misconceptions.

Multiple Learning Styles

Look for these italicized designations under various activities to help you target your lessons to each student's preferred learning style.

- ***Kinesthetic*** learners learn through touch, movement, and manipulating objects.
- ***Visual-Spatial*** learners think in terms of images, illustrations, and models.
- ***Interpersonal*** learners understand and work well with other people.
- ***Intrapersonal*** learners can analyze their own strengths and weaknesses and may prefer to work on their own.
- ***Linguistic*** learners write clearly and easily understand the written word.
- ***Logical-Mathematical*** learners understand numbers easily and have highly-developed reasoning skills.

Daily Interventions

Found at the end of each chapter section, this feature is designed to intercept students who are struggling and prescribe a system to help them get back on track. *Reteach* provides reinforcement of the section's concepts through visual activities.

Differentiated Instruction

These activities present various teaching strategies designed to help you meet the special needs of students with learning disabilities, physical challenges, visual impairment, and hearing impairment. *Challenge* activities provide opportunities for students who excel to engage in activities and research projects that extend the chapter's concepts. English-language learners in the classroom will also find exercises that bridge the gap between language barriers and the chapter content.

Cultural Diversity

These readings provide insights into the unique ways in which people of different ethnicities and cultural heritage have approached science. The intent of these features is to build awareness and appreciation for the global community in which we live.

Inquiry-Based Science

The call for more inquiry-based science by the *National Science Education Standards* has been met by Glencoe Science.

Glencoe Science recognizes the importance of conducting inquiry-based science activities in the classroom. The process of doing inquiry models actual science practice, encouraging problem-solving strategies and developing critical thinking skills. Inquiry gets students actively involved in the learning process by allowing them to determine materials, procedures, or the topics and questions they want to investigate.

Inquiry can range from a very structured activity for those students who need more guidance to a more open-ended approach where students lead the investigations. Glencoe Science recognizes that the inquiry activities suggested will not look the same in every classroom. We encourage teachers to modify the suggested activities in a manner that best supports your students.

Glencoe also provides teachers with *Alternative Inquiry Labs,* teaching strategies or suggestions for making existing labs more inquiry-based.

Research-Based Learning Strategies

Glencoe Science incorporates the most current and applicable educational research on science learning and follows recommendations from the American Association for the Advancement of Science and the National Science Teachers Association. The following research-based strategies can be found throughout the text.

Learning Strategies

The following research-based strategies can be found throughout the text:

- **Using Prior Knowledge** Glencoe Science encourages students to use their prior knowledge to learn information because this adds relevance to the material. Students are referred back to other parts of the text or to their own real-life experiences.
- **Practicing Important Tasks** By offering students an opportunity to practice important tasks using a variety of labs and activities in the *Student Edition, Teacher Wraparound Edition,* ancillaries and technology, Glencoe Science makes learning fun and relevant for students.
- **Using Visuals to Communicate, Organize, and Reinforce Learning** High-quality art and photos throughout the text communicate concepts more efficiently and reinforce learning, while allowing students to organize information.
- **Motivating Students to Achieve** Active strategies and real-world experiences motivate students to achieve. Throughout Glencoe's programs, students are encouraged to apply their knowledge in ways that will motivate them to learn.
- **Developing Decoding and Reading Comprehension Strategies** Throughout the text, students are supplied with caption questions, reading checks, and other strategies to aid in comprehension.
- **Using Study Strategies** Through the use of highlighting, outlining, note-taking, summarizing, and other such strategies, students can monitor their own progress and organize information more effectively, thereby increasing their scientific literacy. These strategies are found throughout the text and ancillaries.

The use of these strategies within Glencoe Science will help teachers to achieve the goals set forth by the *National Science Education Standards.*

White Paper

The Glencoe Science White Paper outlines the educational strategies on which this program was based. This document provides specific examples from the *Student Edition, Teacher Wraparound Edition,* ancillary program, and technology resources, highlighting extensive use of educationally sound strategies that help students learn science.

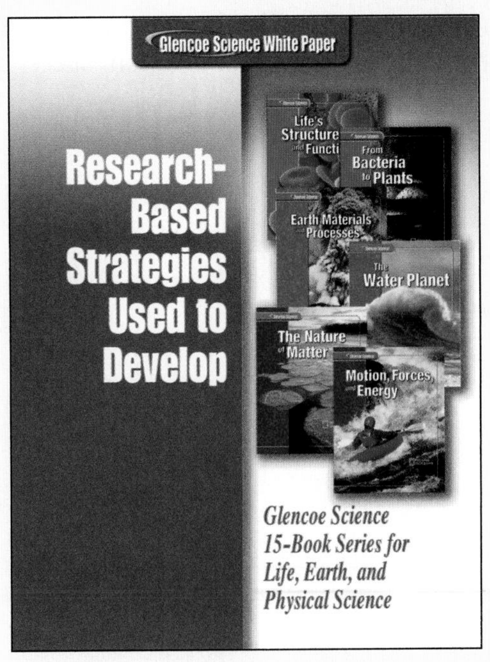

Field Research and Testing

Feedback from students, teachers, curriculum supervisors, department chairpersons, parents, learning specialists, and science content experts was invaluable in the development of this program. The following pre-publication and post-publication research was conducted.

Prior to Publication

- Detailed classroom teacher and curriculum supervisor **surveys** were conducted by independently contracted researchers.
- A **nationwide panel** of science teachers, curriculum supervisors, and department chairpersons provided countless hours of feedback and assistance throughout program development.
- A wide range of **educator and content reviewers** provided in-depth reviews of and suggestions for manuscripts and pre-publication versions of the program.
- **Face-to-face interviews** with science teachers provided insight into teachers' day-to-day challenges.

Field-Test Results

- Field-test research indicates that test scores increased among students using Glencoe Science programs.
- Nine out of ten students earned higher scores after using Glencoe programs.
- Scores improved among both male and female students.
- Scores improved among both minority and non-minority students.
- Overall, the gap between the average pre-test score and a perfect score closed by 33 percent. Stated differently, on average, **scores increased 77 percent after students used the Glencoe program.**

After Publication

- Field tests were conducted in which students and teachers used a pre-publication manuscript in the classroom.
- Follow-up interviews, observations, and surveys of Glencoe Science users provide ongoing opportunities for program development and verification of program success.

KS Studios

National Education Standards

Correlation of *Glencoe Science* to the National Science Education Standards.

Content Standard	Chapter and Section
(UCP) Unifying Concepts and Processes	
1. Systems, order, and organization	A1-1, A1-2, A1-3, A1-4, A2-1, A2-2, A2-3, A3-1, A3-2, A3-3, A4-1, A4-2, A4-3, A5-1, A5-2, A5-3, A6-1, A6-2, A6-3, B1-1, B2-1, B2-2, B4-1, B4-2, B4-3, B5-1, B5-2, C1-1, C2-1, C2-2, C2-3, C2-4, C3-1, C3-2, C3-3, C3-4, C4-1, C4-2, C5-1, C5-2, D1-1, D1-2, D1-3, D2-1, D2-2, D3-1, D3-2, D3-3, D4-1, D4-2, D5-1, D5-2, D6-1, D6-2, D6-3, E1-1, E1-2, E1-3, E2-1, E2-2, E3-1, E3-2, E3-3
2. Evidence, models, and explanation	A1-1, A1-2, A1-3, A1-4, A2-1, A2-2, A2-3, A3-1, A3-2, A3-3, A4-1, A4-2, A4-3, A5-1, A5-2, A5-3, A6-1, A6-2, A6-3, B1-1, B2-1, B2-2, B3-2, B4-1, B4-2, B4-3, B5-1, B5-2, C1-1, C1-2, C1-3, C2-1, C2-2, C2-4, C3-1, C3-2, C3-3, C3-4, C4-1, C4-2, C5-1, C5-2, D1-1, D1-2, D1-3, D2-1, D3-1, D3-2, D3-3, D4-1, D4-2, D5-1, D5-2, D6-1, D6-2, D6-3, D7-1, D7-2, D7-3, E1-1, E1-2, E1-3, E2-1, E2-2, E3-1, E3-2, E3-3, E4-1, E4-2, E4-3, E5-1, E5-2
3. Change, constancy, and measurement	A1-1, A1-2, A1-3, A1-4, A2-1, A2-2, A3-1, A3-2, A3-3, A4-1, A4-3, A5-1, A5-2, A5-3, A6-1, A6-2, A6-3, B2-1, B2-2, B4-1, B4-2, B4-3, B5-1, B5-2, C1-1, C2-1, C2-2, C2-4, C3-1, C3-2, C3-3, C3-4, C4-1, C4-2, C5-1, C5-2, D1-1, D1-2, D1-3, D3-1, D3-2, D3-3, D4-1, D4-2, D5-1, D5-2, D6-1, D6-2, D6-3, E1-1, E1-2, E1-3, E2-1, E2-2, E3-1, E3-2, E3-3, E4-1, E4-2, E4-3, E5-1, E5-2
4. Evolution and equilibrium	A4-3, A5-2, A5-3, A6-1, A6-2, A6-3, B2-1, C3-1, C3-2, C3-3, C3-4, C4-1, C5-1, C5-2, E1-2, E1-3, E2-1, E3-1
5. Form and function	A1-1, A1-2, A1-3, A1-4, A2-1, A2-2, A2-3, A3-1, A3-2, A3-3, A4-3, A5-1, A5-2, A5-3, A6-1, A6-2, A6-3, B1-1, B1-2, B2-1, B2-2, B3-1, B3-2, B3-3, B4-1, B4-2, B4-3, B5-1, B5-2, C1-1, C1-2, C1-3, C2-1, C2-2, C2-3, C2-4, C3-2, C3-3, C3-4, C4-1, C4-2, D1-1, D1-2, D1-3, D3-1, D3-2, D3-3, D4-1, D4-2, D5-1, D5-2, D6-1, D6-2, D6-3, D7-1, D7-2, D7-3, E1-2, E1-3, E2-2, E3-1, E3-2, E3-3, E5-1, E5-2
(A) Science as Inquiry	
1. Abilities necessary to do scientific inquiry	A1-1, A1-2, A1-3, A1-4, A2-1, A2-2, A2-3, A3-1, A3-2, A3-3, A4-1, A4-2, A4-3, A5-1, A5-2, A5-3, A6-1, A6-2, A6-3, B1-1, B1-2, B2-1, B2-2, B3-1, B3-2, B3-3, B4-1, B4-2, B4-3, B5-1, B5-2, C1-1, C1-2, C1-3, C2-1, C2-2, C2-3, C2-4, C3-1, C3-2, C3-3, C3-4, C4-1, C4-2, C5-1, C5-2, D1-1, D1-2, D1-3, D2-1, D2-2, D3-1, D3-2, D3-3, D4-1, D4-2, D5-1, D5-2, D6-1, D6-2, D6-3, D7-1, D7-2, D7-3, E1-1, E1-2, E1-3, E2-1, E2-2, E3-1, E3-2, E3-3, E4-1, E4-2, E4-3, E5-1, E5-2
2. Understandings about scientific theory	A1-1, A1-2, A1-3, A1-4, A2-1, A2-2, A2-3, A3-1, A3-2, A3-3, A4-1, A4-3, A5-1, A5-3, A6-1, A6-2, A6-3, B1-1, B2-1, B2-2, B3-1, B4-1, B4-2, B4-3, B5-1, B5-2, C1-2, C1-3, C2-1, C2-2, C2-3, C2-4, C3-1, C3-2, C3-3, C3-4, C4-1, C4-2, C5-1, C5-2, D1-1, D1-2, D1-3, D2-1, D2-2, D3-1, D3-2, D3-3, D4-1, D4-2, D5-1, D5-2, D6-1, D6-2, D6-3, D7-1, D7-3, E5-1, E5-2, E1-1, E1-2, E1-3, E2-1, E2-2, E3-1, E3-2, E3-3, E4-1, E4-2, E4-3
(B) Physical Science	
1. Properties and changes of properties in matter	A3-1
2. Motions and forces	D1-2
3. Transfer of energy	D1-3, D2-1, D2-2, D6-3, E2-1, E2-2, E2-3
(C) Life Science	
1. Structure and function in living systems	A1-2, A1-3, A2-1, A2-2, A2-3, A3-1, A3-2, A3-3, A4-1, A4-2, A4-3, A5-1, A5-2, A5-3, A6-1, A6-3, B1-1, B2-1, B3-1, B3-2, B3-3, B4-1, B4-2, B4-3, B5-1, B5-2, C1-1, C1-2, C1-3, C2-1, C2-2, C2-3, C2-4, C3-1, C3-2, C3-3, C3-4, C4-1, D1-1, D1-2, D1-3, D2-1, D2-2, D3-1, D3-2, D3-3, D4-1, D4-2, D5-1, D5-2, D6-1, D6-2, D6-3, D7-1, D7-2, D7-3, E1-2, E1-3, E2-2, E2-3, E3-1, E3-2, E3-3, E5-1
2. Reproduction and heredity	A1-2, A2-3, A4-1, A4-2, A4-3, A5-1, A5-2, A5-3, B1-1, B2-1, B3-1, B3-2, B3-3, B4-1, B4-2, B4-3, C1-2, C2-1, C2-2, C2-3, C2-4, C3-1, C3-2, C3-3, C3-4, C4-1, C5-2, D1-1, D1-2, D1-3, D6-1, D6-2, D7-1, D7-2, D7-3, E1-1, E1-2, E1-3
3. Regulation and behavior	A1-2, A2-1, A3-2, A4-1, A4-2, A4-3, B1-1, B1-2, B2-1, B3-1, B3-2, B3-3, B5-1, B5-2, C1-1, C1-2, C1-3, C2-1, C2-2, C2-3, C2-4, C3-1, C3-2, C3-3, C3-4, C4-1, C5-1, D1-2, D1-3, D2-1, D2-2, D3-1, D3-2, D3-3, D4-1, D4-2, D5-1, D5-2, D6-1, D6-2, D6-3, D7-1, D7-2, D7-3, E1-2, E2-2, E3-1, E3-2, E3-3
4. Populations and ecosystems	A6-1, B1-1, B1-2, B2-1, B3-1, B3-2, B3-3, B4-3, C1-2, C1-3, C4-1, C5-2, E1-2, E1-3, E2-2, E3-1, E3-2, E3-3, E5-1
5. Diversity and adaptations of organisms	A1-4, A2-3, A4-2, A6-1, A6-3, B1-1, B1-2, B2-1, B3-1, B3-2, B3-3, B4-1, B4-2, B4-3, B5-2, C1-1, C1-2, C1-3, C2-2, C2-3, C2-4, C3-1, C3-2, C3-3, C3-4, C4-1, C5-1, C5-2, D1-1, D1-2, D1-3, D2-1, D2-2, D3-1, D3-2, D3-3, D5-1, D5-2, D6-3, D7-1, D7-2, D7-3, E1-2, E1-3, E2-2, E2-3, E3-3, E5-1

Content Standard	Chapter and Section
(D) Earth and Space Science	
1. Structure of the Earth system	E2-1, E2-2, E2-3
2. Earth's history	A1-3, A6-1, A6-2
3. Earth and the solar system	E2-3
(E) Science and Technology	
1. Abilities of technological design	B1-2
2. Understandings about science and technology	B1-2
(F) Science in Personal and Social Perspectives	
1. Personal health	A5-2, A6-2, B1-2, B2-2, C3-2, C4-2, D1-1, D1-2, D1-3, D2-1, D2-2, D5-1, D7-1, D7-2, D7-3
2. Populations, resources, and environments	A2-3, B4-3, E1-2, E1-3, E3-3, E4-1, E4-2, E4-3, E5-1, E5-2
3. Natural hazards	A5-3, D7-2
4. Risks and benefits	B1-2, C2-3, C3-4, D7-2, D7-3, E5-1, E5-2
5. Science and technology in society	A5-3, B1-2, C3-4, D7-2, D7-3
(G) History and Nature of Science	
1. Science as a human endeavor	A5-2, A6-1, A6-3, B3-2, D1-3, D2-2, D3-3, D7-3
2. Nature of science	A1-1, A3-3, A5-1, A6-1, A6-2, A6-3, B3-2, B4-3, C1-1, D1-3, D2-2, D3-3, D7-1, D7-3
3. History of science	A1-3, A1-4, A2-2, A2-3, A3-3, A5-1, A6-1, A6-3, B3-2, B4-3, C5-2, D4-2, D5-1

How Glencoe Science Aligns with the National Science Education Standards

The correlations at the left and above show the close alignment between Glencoe Science and the grade-appropriate standards. Glencoe Science allows students to discover concepts within each of the content standards and gives students opportunities to make connections among the science disciplines. Hands-on activities and inquiry-based lessons reinforce the science processes emphasized in the standards.

How Glencoe Science Aligns with the NCTM Standards for Grades 6–8

Throughout Glencoe Science, each Applying Math activity provides students with the opportunity to practice and apply some of the mathematical concepts and applications described in the NCTM Standards. These activities serve to reinforce mathematical skills in real-life situations, thus preparing students to meet their needs in an ever-changing world.

Correlation of *Glencoe Science* to NCTM Standards

Math Standard	Page
1. Number and Operations	A-35, A-46, A-74, A-93, A-123, A-133, A-151, A-181, B-57, B-112, B-119, B-135, B-145, C-25, C-33, C-52, C-67, C-82, C-129, C-155, D-11, D-31, D-59, D-87, D-133, D-141, D-147, D-171, D-201, E-31, E-40, E-59, E-80, E-121, E-150
2. Algebra	A-35, A-46, A-93, A-181, B-57, B-112, B-119, C-25, C-52, D-133, E-40, E-80, E-121
3. Geometry	A-46, D-11
4. Measurement	A-35, A-46, A-63, D-59, E-40, E-80
5. Data Analysis and Probability	A-35, A-93, A-133, A-151, A-181, B-27, B-57, B-89, B-119, B-135, B-145, C-67, C-101, C-129, C-155, D-31, D-59, D-87, D-113, D-141, D-171, D-201, E-40, E-59, E-89, E-121, E-150
6. Problem Solving	A-46, A-93, A-123, B-27, B-89, C-25, C-33, C-101, D-59, D-133, D-201, E-31, E-40, E-59, E-150
7. Reasoning and Proof	C-82, E-31
8. Communication	A-179, D-167
9. Connections	A-35, A-46, A-63, A-74, A-93, A-123, A-133, A-151, A-181, B-27, B-57, B-112, B-119, B-135, B-145, C-25, C-33, C-52, C-67, C-129, C-155, D-59, D-87, D-133, D-141, D-147, D-171, E-40, E-59, E-80, E-121
10. Representation	A-133, E-40

Foldables™

Foldables™ are easy-to-make, three-dimensional, interactive graphic organizers that students create out of simple sheets of paper. These unique hands-on tools for studying and reviewing were created exclusively for Glencoe by education specialist Dinah Zike.

Research Behind Foldables™

According to research (Bransford, 1979; Corno, 1994), study strategies help students understand, organize, remember and apply new information presented in science textbooks. Some study strategies include concept mapping, highlighting, outlining, note taking, summarizing, and underlining (Peverly, Brobst, Graham & Shaw, 2003). Glencoe Science offers Dinah Zike's Foldables™ Study Organizers as an organizational tool and study guide for students.

Foldables™

- Build prereading skills
- Encourage active reading and writing
- Summarize content for review

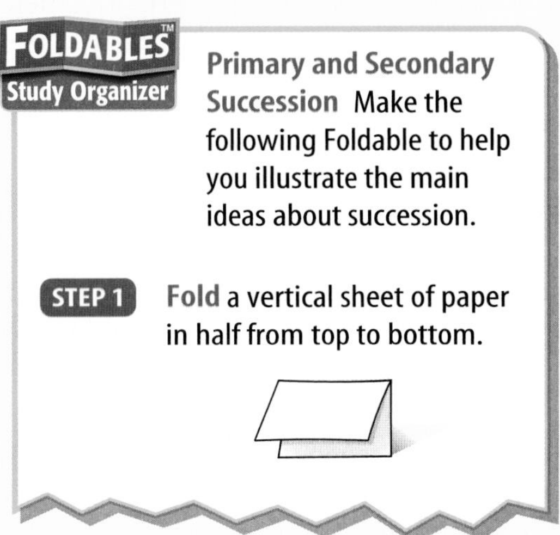

For more ideas on how to incorporate Foldables™ into your lessons consult **Dinah Zike's *Teaching Science with Foldables™***

Educational Partnerships

NATIONAL GEOGRAPHIC

Some topics in the chapter either require or benefit from a larger, more detailed visual explanation. The National Geographic Society has created *Visualizing* features that call out an important concept from the chapter and illustrate it in a way that will inform, excite, and motivate your students.

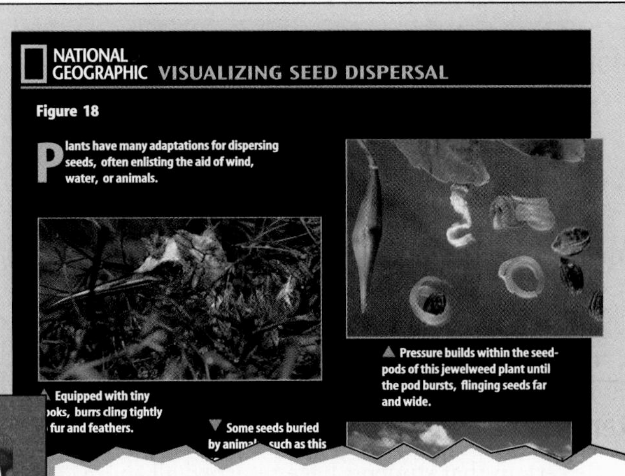

NATIONAL GEOGRAPHIC VISUALIZING SEED DISPERSAL
Figure 18
Plants have many adaptations for dispersing seeds, often enlisting the aid of wind, water, or animals.
Pressure builds within the seedpods of this jewelweed plant until the pod bursts, flinging seeds far and wide.

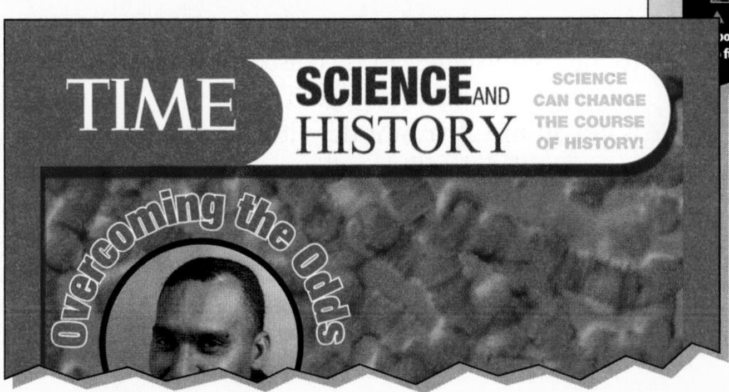

TIME
SCIENCE AND HISTORY
SCIENCE CAN CHANGE THE COURSE OF HISTORY!
Overcoming the Odds

TIME

TIME magazine brings science topics and history together to further explain the chapter's main ideas and show how science relates to real life.

Safety in the Laboratory

All activities are designed to minimize dangers in the laboratory. Careful laboratory planning and management by both the instructor and the student are essential to a safe laboratory experience. **Local, state, and federal laboratory safety laws and regulations must be strictly followed.** The information provided here is one of the many resources to which you can refer for information about laboratory safety.

Classroom and Laboratory Preparation

1. Store equipment properly and securely and other thing.
   a. Clean and dry all equipment before storing.
   b. Protect electronic equipment and microscopes from dust, humidity, and extreme temperatures.
   c. Number, catalog, and organize equipment.
2. Ensure adequate work space for each student.
3. Ensure adequate classroom and storeroom ventilation.
4. Explain and post safety and evacuation guidelines along with expectations of conduct.
5. Ensure that all safety equipment is functioning properly and is clearly visible.
6. Provide hot plates as a heat source whenever possible. If gas burners are used, know where the central gas supply shutoff valve is located.
7. Ensure that each workstation has a GFCI-protected electrical source.
8. Provide safety goggles consistent with ANSI Standard Z87.1 for each student, including students who wear corrective lenses.

Before Each MiniLAB or Lab

1. Arrange the lab in such a way that equipment and supplies are clearly labeled and easily accessible.
2. Have available only equipment and supplies needed to complete the assigned investigation.
3. Review the procedure with students, emphasizing any caution statements or safety symbols that appear.
4. Be sure all students know the proper procedures to follow if an accident should occur.

After the MiniLAB or Lab

1. Be certain that students have returned all equipment and disposed of broken glassware and chemicals properly.
2. Be sure that all hot plates and electrical connections are off.

Storage of Chemicals

Be sure to store all chemicals properly. The following are guidelines commonly used. Your school, city, county, or state may have additional requirements for handling chemicals. It is the responsibility of each teacher to become informed of the rules or guidelines in effect in his or her area.

1. Separate chemicals by reaction type. Strong acids should be stored together. Likewise, strong bases should be stored together and should be separated from acids. Oxidants should be stored away from easily oxidized materials, and so on.
2. Be sure all chemicals are stored in labeled containers indicating contents, concentration, source, date purchased (or prepared), any precautions for handling and storage, and expiration date.
3. Hazardous chemicals require special storage containers and conditions. Be sure to know which chemicals those are and the accepted practices for your area. Some substances must be stored outside the building.

Disposal of Chemicals

Local, state, and federal laws regulate the proper disposal of chemicals. These laws should be consulted before chemical disposal is attempted. Although many substances encountered in the science classroom can be flushed down the drain with plenty of water, it is not safe to assume that this is always true.

DISCLAIMER

Glencoe Publishing Company makes no claims to the completeness of this discussion of laboratory safety and chemical storage. The material presented is not all-inclusive, nor does it address all of the hazards associated with handling, storing, and disposing of chemicals, or with laboratory management.

Preparation of Solutions

It is important to use safe laboratory techniques when handling all chemicals. Always check the MSDS (Material Safety Data Sheet) for each chemical before using it in the classroom. Many substances might appear harmless, but might be toxic, corrosive, or very reactive. Chemicals should never be ingested. Use proper techniques to smell any chemical, wear safety goggles and an apron in the laboratory, and observe the following precautions.

1. **Dilution of Acids and Bases** When diluting acids with water, always add the acids to the water. Never add water to acids. When sulfuric acid and sodium hydroxide are added to water, a large amount of thermal energy is released. Use extra care when handling these substances.

2. **Poisonous and Corrosive Liquids or Vapors** Use a fume hood if possible. Examples include hydrochloric acid, acetic acid, nitric acid, and ammonium hydroxide.

3. **Poisonous and Corrosive to Eyes, Lungs, and Skin** Examples include acids, bases, silver nitrate, iodine, and potassium permanganate.

Bromthymol blue: Add 0.5 g bromthymol blue powder to 500 mL distilled water to make a BTB stock solution. Dilute 40 mL BTB stock solution to 2 L with distilled water. Solution should be bright blue. If not, add one drop of NaOH at a time, swirling to mix. Check color.

Hydrochloric acid (HCL) solution: To make a 5% solution, add 13.6 mL concentrated HCl to 73 mL water while stirring. To make a 0.1*M* solution, add 1 mL concentrated hydrochloric acid to 100 mL water while stirring.

Iodine solution/Iodine stain: Dilute 1 part Lugol's solution with 15 parts water.

Lugol's solution: Dissolve 10 g potassium iodide in 100 mL distilled water. Then add and dissolve 5 g iodine. Store in dark bottle. Keeps indefinitely.

Phenolphthalein indicator: From a drug store, buy a package of any laxative that contains phenolphthalein. To make 1% solution, mash 4 tablets and pour the powder into 10 mL of rubbing alcohol. Let mixture soak for 15 minutes. Pour liquid into and store in a dropper bottle.

Potassium permanganate: For a 0.01*M* solution of potassium permanganate, dissolve 0.15 g $KMnO_4$ in 100 mL water.

Red cabbage concentrate: Put 5 leaves of red cabbage in a pot. Add 1 L of water, bring to a boil, and simmer until water turns a deep purple. Pour liquid through a strainer or piece of cheesecloth into a storage bottle. Keep refrigerated.

Salt solution: For a 3.5% salt (NaCl) solution that simulates the concentration of ocean water, dissolve 35 g of salt (NaCl) in 965 mL of water. For a 1% solution (weak), dissolve 1 g of salt (NaCl) in 99 mL of water. For a 6% solution, dissolve 6 g of salt (NaCl) in 94 mL of water.

Silver nitrate solution: To make a 10% solution, put 5 g of silver nitrate in 50 mL of distilled water.

Sugar solution: Add 1 tablespoon of sugar to 1 cup of warm water in a deep jar or flask. Stir to dissolve.

Sodium hydroxide (dilute): To make a 1% solution, dissolve 1 g NaOH in 99 mL of water.

Equipment and Materials List

Refer to the Chapter Organizer in front of each chapter for a list of equipment and materials used for each laboratory activity in the chapter.

Consumables			
Material	**Launch Lab (Chapter)**	**MiniLAB (Chapter-Section)**	**Lab (Chapter-Section)**
beads			6-1
bean seeds	4		5-1
bromothymol blue solution			3-3
carrot sticks	3		
classified ads	6		
clay, modeling			6-1
corn syrup, light			3-2
egg, unshelled			3-2
food coloring		3-2	
fruit and seeds from one species			6-3
gelatin		2-1, 3-1	
labels			1-4
newspaper		2-2	
paper, black	6		
paper, graph			6-3
pineapple, fresh		3-1	
plastic bag(s), self-sealing	4		
poster board or white paper			5-3
salt	3		
salt solution			1-4
seeds, packaged			1-4
sequins			6-1
slide of an onion root tip			4-1
spoon			1-4, 3-2
water, carbonated			3-3
water, distilled			1-4, 2-3, 3-2
Nonconsumables			
balance		1-1	3-2
compound light microscope			2-3
container		2-1	1-4, 3-2
coverslip(s)			2-1, 2-3
dropper(s)			2-1, 2-3
flashlight		2-1	
forceps			2-1
glass, clear		2-2	
magazine picture of a piece of furniture		1-4	
magnifying lens	2		1-4, 6-3
microscope slide(s)			2-1, 2-3
microscope			2-1, 4-1
petri dishes, plastic			2-3
sponge, dry		1-1	
stereomicroscope			2-3
stirring rod			3-3
test tubes, with stoppers			3-3
test tubes			3-3
test-tube rack			3-3
Biological			
brine shrimp eggs			1-4
Elodea			2-1, 3-3
human cheek cells			2-1

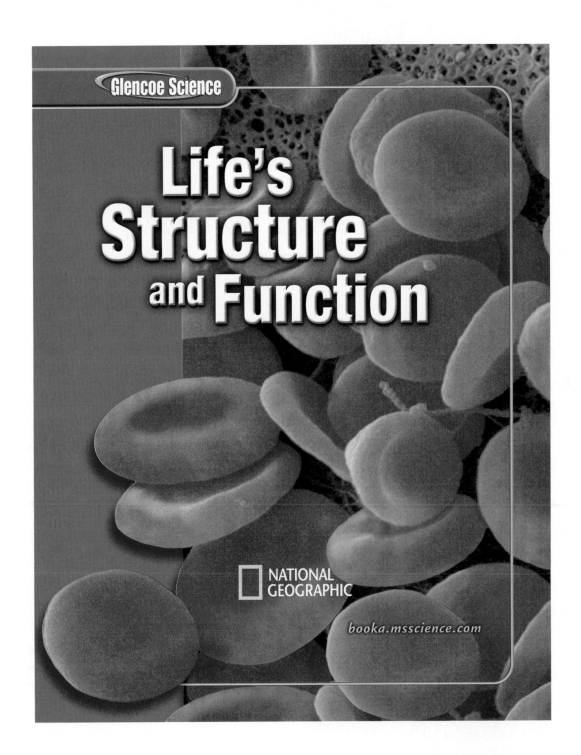

Glencoe Science

Life's Structure and Function

NATIONAL GEOGRAPHIC

booka.msscience.com

New York, New York Columbus, Ohio Chicago, Illinois Peoria, Illinois Woodland Hills, California

HOW TO...

Use Your Science Book

Why do I need my science book?

Have you ever been in class and not understood all of what was presented? Or, you understood everything in class, but at home, got stuck on how to answer a question? Maybe you just wondered when you were ever going to use this stuff?

These next few pages are designed to help you understand everything your science book can be used for . . . besides a paperweight!

Glencoe Science
Life's Structure and Function
NATIONAL GEOGRAPHIC

Before You Read

- **Chapter Opener** Science is occurring all around you, and the opening photo of each chapter will preview the science you will be learning about. The **Chapter Preview** will give you an idea of what you will be learning about, and you can try the **Launch Lab** to help get your brain headed in the right direction. The **Foldables** exercise is a fun way to keep you organized.
- **Section Opener** Chapters are divided into two to four sections. The **As You Read** in the margin of the first page of each section will let you know what is most important in the section. It is divided into four parts. **What You'll Learn** will tell you the major topics you will be covering. **Why It's Important** will remind you why you are studying this in the first place! The **Review Vocabulary** word is a word you already know, either from your science studies or your prior knowledge. The **New Vocabulary** words are words that you need to learn to understand this section. These words will be in **boldfaced** print and highlighted in the section. Make a note to yourself to recognize these words as you are reading the section.

As You Read

- **Headings** Each section has a title in large red letters, and is further divided into blue titles and small red titles at the beginnings of some paragraphs. To help you study, make an outline of the headings and subheadings.
- **Margins** In the margins of your text, you will find many helpful resources. The **Science Online** exercises and **Integrate** activities help you explore the topics you are studying. **MiniLabs** reinforce the science concepts you have learned.
- **Building Skills** You also will find an **Applying Math** or **Applying Science** activity in each chapter. This gives you extra practice using your new knowledge, and helps prepare you for standardized tests.
- **Student Resources** At the end of the book you will find **Student Resources** to help you throughout your studies. These include **Science, Technology,** and **Math Skill Handbooks,** an **English/Spanish Glossary,** and an **Index.** Also, use your **Foldables** as a resource. It will help you organize information, and review before a test.
- **In Class** Remember, you can always ask your teacher to explain anything you don't understand.

FOLDABLES™ Study Organizer

Science Vocabulary Make the following Foldable to help you understand the vocabulary terms in this chapter.

STEP 1 **Fold** a vertical sheet of notebook paper from side to side.

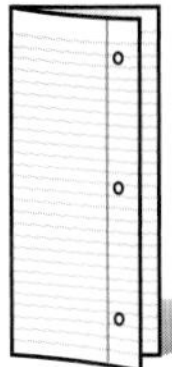

STEP 2 **Cut** along every third line of only the top layer to form tabs.

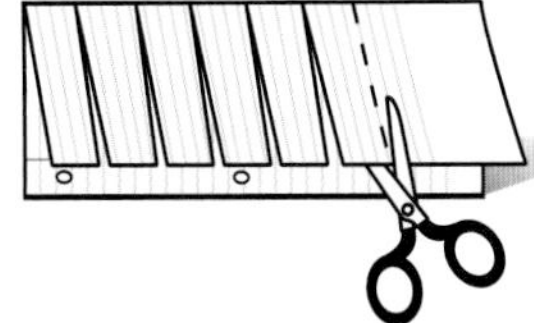

STEP 3 **Label** each tab with a vocabulary word from the chapter.

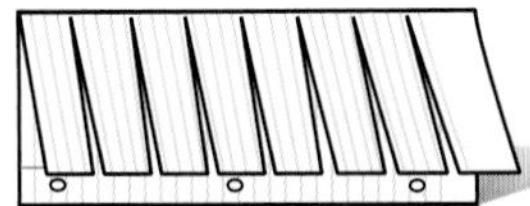

Build Vocabulary As you read the chapter, list the vocabulary words on the tabs. As you learn the definitions, write them under the tab for each vocabulary word.

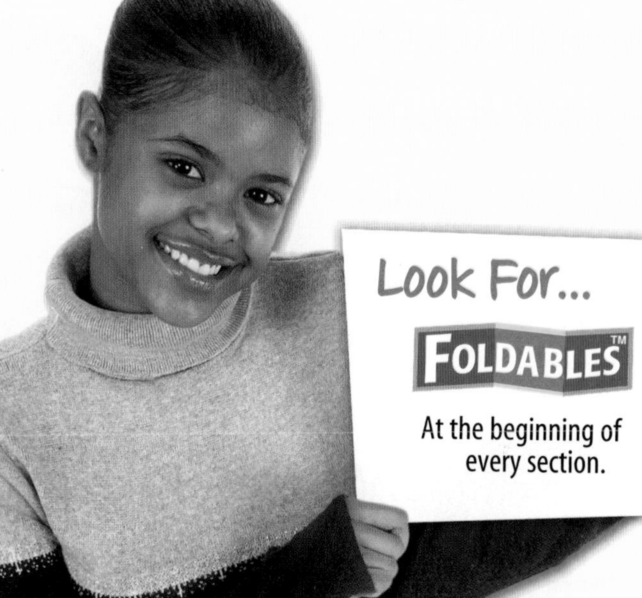

Look For...
FOLDABLES™
At the beginning of every section.

In Lab

Working in the laboratory is one of the best ways to understand the concepts you are studying. Your book will be your guide through your laboratory experiences, and help you begin to think like a scientist. In it, you not only will find the steps necessary to follow the investigations, but you also will find helpful tips to make the most of your time.

- Each lab provides you with a **Real-World Question** to remind you that science is something you use every day, not just in class. This may lead to many more questions about how things happen in your world.
- Remember, experiments do not always produce the result you expect. Scientists have made many discoveries based on investigations with unexpected results. You can try the experiment again to make sure your results were accurate, or perhaps form a new hypothesis to test.
- Keeping a **Science Journal** is how scientists keep accurate records of observations and data. In your journal, you also can write any questions that may arise during your investigation. This is a great method of reminding yourself to find the answers later.

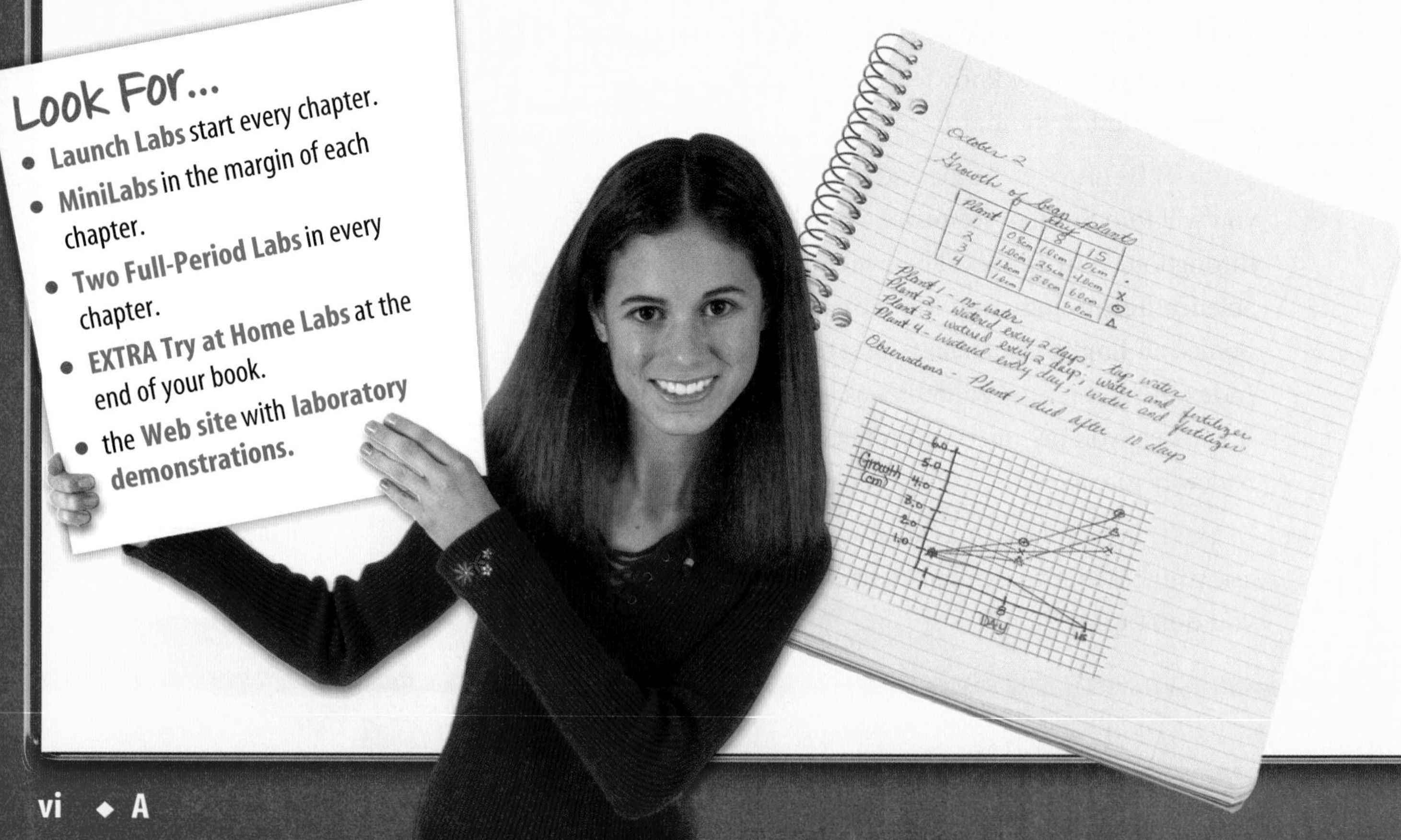

Look For...
• Launch Labs start every chapter.
• MiniLabs in the margin of each chapter.
• Two Full-Period Labs in every chapter.
• EXTRA Try at Home Labs at the end of your book.
• the Web site with laboratory demonstrations.

Before a Test

Admit it! You don't like to take tests! However, there *are* ways to review that make them less painful. Your book will help you be more successful taking tests if you use the resources provided to you.

- Review all of the **New Vocabulary** words and be sure you understand their definitions.
- Review the notes you've taken on your **Foldables,** in class, and in lab. Write down any question that you still need answered.
- Review the **Summaries** and **Self Check questions** at the end of each section.
- Study the concepts presented in the chapter by reading the **Study Guide** and answering the questions in the **Chapter Review.**

a or b?
?
T or F?

Look For...

- **Reading Checks** and **caption questions** throughout the text.
- the **Summaries** and **Self Check questions** at the end of each section.
- the **Study Guide** and **Review** at the end of each chapter.
- the **Standardized Test Practice** after each chapter.

Let's Get Started

To help you find the information you need quickly, use the Scavenger Hunt below to learn where things are located in Chapter 1.

1. What is the title of this chapter?
2. What will you learn in Section 1?
3. Sometimes you may ask, "Why am I learning this?" State a reason why the concepts from Section 2 are important.
4. What is the main topic presented in Section 2?
5. How many reading checks are in Section 1?
6. What is the Web address where you can find extra information?
7. What is the main heading above the sixth paragraph in Section 2?
8. There is an integration with another subject mentioned in one of the margins of the chapter. What subject is it?
9. List the new vocabulary words presented in Section 2.
10. List the safety symbols presented in the first Lab.
11. Where would you find a Self Check to be sure you understand the section?
12. Suppose you're doing the Self Check and you have a question about concept mapping. Where could you find help?
13. On what pages are the Chapter Study Guide and Chapter Review?
14. Look in the Table of Contents to find out on which page Section 2 of the chapter begins.
15. You complete the Chapter Review to study for your chapter test. Where could you find another quiz for more practice?

Teacher Advisory Board

The Teacher Advisory Board gave the authors, editorial staff, and design team feedback on the content and design of the Student Edition. They provided valuable input in the development of the 2005 edition of ***Glencoe Science.***

John Gonzales
Challenger Middle School
Tucson, AZ

Rachel Shively
Aptakisic Jr. High School
Buffalo Grove, IL

Roger Pratt
Manistique High School
Manistique, MI

Kirtina Hile
Northmor Jr. High/High School
Galion, OH

Marie Renner
Diley Middle School
Pickerington, OH

Nelson Farrier
Hamlin Middle School
Springfield, OR

Jeff Remington
Palmyra Middle School
Palmyra, PA

Erin Peters
Williamsburg Middle School
Arlington, VA

Rubidel Peoples
Meacham Middle School
Fort Worth, TX

Kristi Ramsey
Navasota Jr. High School
Navasota, TX

Student Advisory Board

The Student Advisory Board gave the authors, editorial staff, and design team feedback on the design of the Student Edition. We thank these students for their hard work and creative suggestions in making the 2005 edition of ***Glencoe Science*** student friendly.

Jack Andrews
Reynoldsburg Jr. High School
Reynoldsburg, OH

Peter Arnold
Hastings Middle School
Upper Arlington, OH

Emily Barbe
Perry Middle School
Worthington, OH

Kirsty Bateman
Hilliard Heritage Middle School
Hilliard, OH

Andre Brown
Spanish Emersion Academy
Columbus, OH

Chris Dundon
Heritage Middle School
Westerville, OH

Ryan Manafee
Monroe Middle School
Columbus, OH

Addison Owen
Davis Middle School
Dublin, OH

Teriana Patrick
Eastmoor Middle School
Columbus, OH

Ashley Ruz
Karrer Middle School
Dublin, OH

The Glencoe middle school science Student Advisory Board taking a timeout at COSI, a science museum in Columbus, Ohio.

Contents

In each chapter, look for these opportunities for review and assessment:
- Reading Checks
- Caption Questions
- Section Review
- Chapter Study Guide
- Chapter Review
- Standardized Test Practice
- Online practice at booka.msscience.com

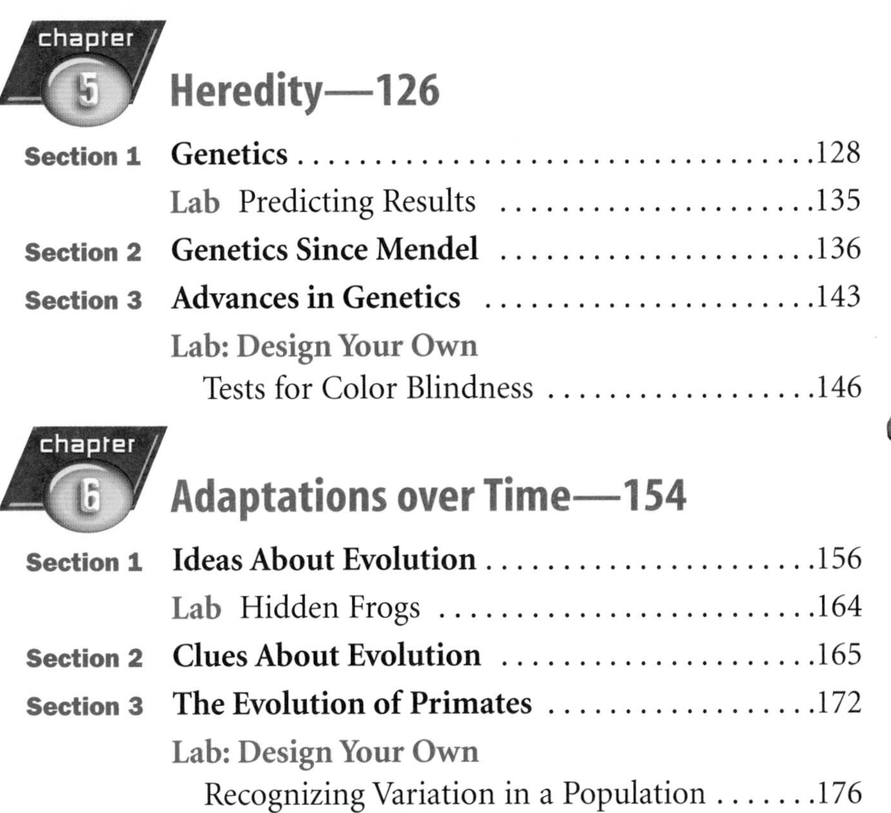

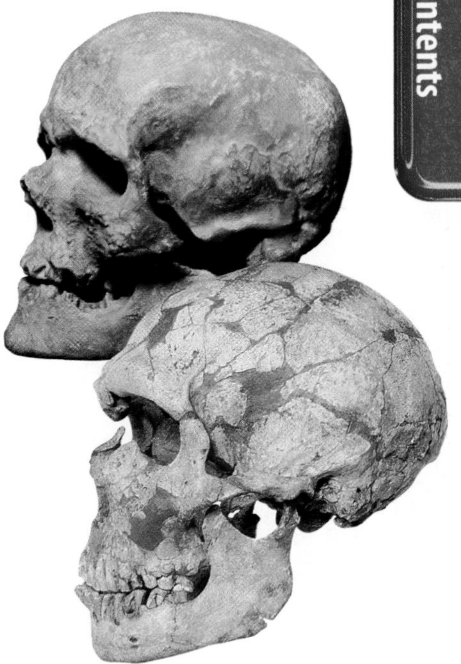

chapter 5 Heredity—126

chapter 6 Adaptations over Time—154

Student Resources

Cross-Curricular Readings/Labs

available as a video lab

NATIONAL GEOGRAPHIC VISUALIZING

TIME SCIENCE AND Society

TIME SCIENCE AND HISTORY

Oops! Accidents in SCIENCE

Science and Language Arts

SCIENCE Stats

Launch LAB

Mini LAB

Mini LAB Try at Home

One-Page Labs

Two-Page Labs

Labs/Activities

Design Your Own Labs

Use the Internet Labs

Applying Math

Applying Science

INTEGRATE

Science Online

Standardized Test Practice

The NATURE OF SCIENCE

Genome Sequencing

Introduction

This feature introduces students to scientific inquiry by discussing the sequencing of genomes. It is important to note that scientists who have sequenced the genomes of various organisms could complete their work only because of the background work done by generations of chemists and biologists. Sequencing of genomes is an excellent example of the interdependent nature of the different fields of science. Scientists who have developed and refined computers and software are vital to rapid, high-volume sequencing. Genome sequencing will benefit scientists in many fields, as well as the general public. Advances in medicine and agriculture due to genome research have the potential to enhance life for the human race.

1 Motivate

Have students discuss potential advantages and disadvantages of genome sequencing. Encourage students to think creatively. Record student's responses in two side-by-side lists on the board or overhead. Discuss the relative number of positive and negative responses.

The NATURE OF SCIENCE

Science Today

Genome Sequencing

Your genome determines your traits—everything from your eye color and blood type to the likelihood that you might get certain diseases. A genome is all of the DNA in a one-celled or many-celled organism. Each gene plays a part in the expression of a specific trait. Organisms like protists, fungi, plants, and animals have their genes on chromosomes in the nucleus of cells. In the human genome, there are about 30,000 genes on 23 pairs of chromosomes.

Sequencing the genome of any organism—bacteria, protist, fungus, plant, or animal—is complex. Each gene's message involves four chemicals called bases—adenine (A), cytosine (C), guanine (G), and thymine (T). The bases are linked in pairs—adenine with thymine and cytosine with guanine. Each gene is a unique chain of paired bases. The average size of a human gene is about 3,000 paired bases. The sequence carries instructions for making a specific protein. Depending on the string of bases in a gene, the protein might control the formation of a certain type of tissue or it might be an enzyme that drives a biochemical reaction. Many human disorders and diseases, including Huntington's Disease and sickle-cell disease, are the result of a person's genetic makeup.

Figure 1 The DNA in your cells makes up your genetic material.

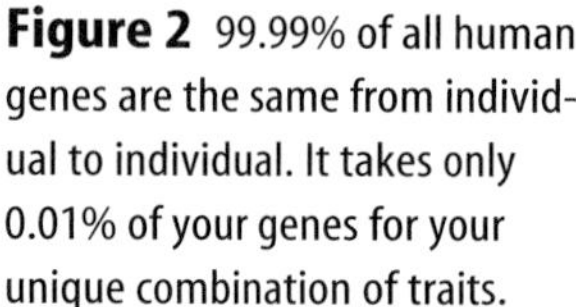

Figure 2 99.99% of all human genes are the same from individual to individual. It takes only 0.01% of your genes for your unique combination of traits.

Curriculum Connection

Mathematics The great variety of genes that make up the genome of organisms are formed using only four different chemical bases in varying sequences. Have students determine the number of possible sequences of an eight-base length of DNA. Because there are four possible bases at each position of the sequence, the students can find the answer by using the formula $4 \times 4 \times 4 \times 4 \times 4 \times 4 \times 4 \times 4$; or 4^8. Students should find that there are 65,536 combinations possible in an eight-base length of DNA.

Decoding the Genome

To decode a genome, scientists first have to identify the bases and their correct sequence. Then they must determine which parts of the sequence are genes. Only a small percentage of the human genome are useful genes.

Powerful supercomputers and inventive software make it possible to collect, sequence, and analyze genetic data faster than ever before. In one method, scientists mark chromosomes and then cut them into manageable fragments. Through chemical processes, each of the bases is dyed a different color then displayed in a pattern read by super-fast machines. The machines convert the base sequences into digital data. A supercomputer then puts the fragments in the proper sequence, using markers from the first stage of the process.

By March 2001, the complete genome of some organisms in every kingdom—eubacteria, archaebacteria, protists, fungi, plants, and animals—was known, including the human genome. These accomplishments would not have been possible without modern computer technology and the research of many scientists worldwide.

Figure 3 The genetic material passed from parents to offspring determines individual characteristics.

2 Teach

Content Background

Decoding the genomes of organisms has been possible only because of advances in sequencing technology. The first practical sequencing methods, called the Sanger method and the Maxam-Gilbert method, provide accurate results, but are time and labor intensive. These methods are still being used to sequence small areas of high interest, but would have been impractical for sequencing an entire genome. The estimated cost per base sequenced using these methods is between $1.00 and $2.00. Newer methods of sequencing include resonance ionization spectroscopy, florescence detection of bases in flow cytometry, and scanning tunnel microscopy. These methods all increase the possible rate of sequencing. The cost per base is decreased with these newer, more efficient methods.

Discussion

Why are scientists interested in sequencing the genomes of organisms other than humans? Answers will vary. Students should note that comparisons of different genomes will help scientists discover the function of different genes and the relationships between various organisms.

Science Journal

Genomes of Different Organisms Have students consider ways that the human genome might be similar to and different from the genome of other organisms. In a paragraph in their Science Journals, have the students discuss some of the expected similarities and differences. L3 LS **Linguistic**

Fun Fact

The complexity of an organism is not related to the size of the organism's genome. Both mice and humans have about 3 billion paired bases in their entire genome.

Activity

Have students consider how scientists in different fields have contributed to the technology of genome sequencing. Remind students that the work being performed today would not be possible without the previous work of other scientists. Have small groups of students select a specific scientist (anyone from Gregor Mendel to Craig Venter) or group of scientists (biologists, engineers, computer scientists, and so on) to research. Have each student group write a newspaper article describing the contributions their subject has made to the sequencing process. L2 COOP LEARN IN Interpersonal

Extension

Have interested students monitor information about progress in sequencing the Human Genome and the genomes of other organisms on a weekly basis. Have students report major breakthroughs and milestones to the class. Encourage students to continue this project throughout the school year. L2

The NATURE OF SCIENCE

Science

Scientists often collect and analyze data to find answers to questions or solve problems. When you collect data and analyze it to answer questions or solve problems, you are doing science.

Genetics is a part of life science, the study of all Earth's living organisms. It includes zoology and botany. In this book, you'll learn about the structures that make up organisms, including genes and their functions.

Science Today

Through science, scientists now have a better understanding than ever before of the world and its inhabitants. New scientific discoveries build on many that came before them. Future scientists might work to understand the long lines of genetic code that today's scientists have uncovered. Each step in decoding genomes will add to the understanding of what each of the genes does. Understanding the human genome is an important key to solving many medical problems. Some day, it might be possible to genetically identify health problems in advance and treat them before they develop.

Improved technology is another important part of science. Many advances in science would not be possible without new equipment to perform experiments and collect data. Sequencing the human genome would be impossible without the technology that allows scientists to see, manipulate, and record the genetic material. Sequencing machines and supercomputers have allowed scientists to map the human genome more quickly and accurately than was previously possible. The transfer of computerized data over the Internet also has made it possible for the Human Genome Project's scientists to share the details of their results instantly.

Figure 4 These machines, called 3700s, ran nonstop to sequence the human genome. They filter the DNA and digitally record it.

Benefits for Society

New scientific discoveries often benefit society. Science has made work easier, has helped to keep people safer, and led to medical advances that allow people to live longer and healthier lives. Scientists working on the Human Genome Project hope that their work will help provide a better explanation of how living organisms are constructed and how they function. A complete understanding of the genome will tell us more about the physical makeup of humans than we have ever known before.

Differentiated Instruction

Learning Disabled Reinforce that all living things—plants, animals, protists, bacteria, and fungi—have DNA in their cells. Scientists are interested in sequencing the genomes of many living things. Remind students that every characteristic of their bodies is affected by their DNA, even those things we can't see, such as digestive enzymes, structure of bones, and make up of blood.

Where Do Scientists Work?

Scientists work in a variety of places for a variety of reasons. Most of the American scientists who sequenced the human genome worked for either the United States government as part of the federally funded Human Genome Project, or for private companies. Both groups have the same goal even though their methods vary. These scientists worked with sensitive equipment in university laboratories and research centers. Scientists, who apply genetic research to medicine, work with the data provided by the new genetic maps. They might test hypotheses about genetic therapy through clinical experimentation.

Figure 5 Some results from the Human Genome Project are available on the Internet.

A Geneticist

Dr. John Carpten is a molecular geneticist working on the Human Genome Project. His focus is on the gene that causes some men to be at higher risk for developing prostate cancer. Geneticists like Dr. Carpten may do research in laboratories, analyze data in lab settings, or do diagnostic work with patients.

Dr. John Carpten

Figure 6 Some day, a physician might consult a patient's genome before prescribing medicine or other treatment for a disease.

You Do It

The human genome is sequenced and the locations of genes for human traits and illnesses are known. If you had the power to choose a project that uses the genome map to create something new or solve a problem, what would you choose to do and why? How would the sequenced genome help you?

Discussion

Imagine that a doctor knew that a patient's genetic makeup caused that person to be more likely to develop a disease. How could the doctor use this information to help the patient? The doctor may be able to advise the patient on preventative medicine or lifestyle changes, such as diet or exercise, that might help the patient avoid the disease. The patient may also have time to prepare for the onset of symptoms of the disease. Students may also point out the negative aspects of knowing in advance the possibility of being afflicted with a disease or illness.

Use Science Words

Word Origin Genome is a word constructed from two root words. Have students determine the language origin of the word genome, and the meanings of the two root words that were combined in the 1930's to develop this term. Students should find that the term *genome* was developed by combining the German words for *gene* and *chromosome.*

3 Assess

Use the questions in the You Do It to assess understanding. Answers should relate to the use of the completed genome map to solve a problem or to make something new and should be a specific as possible.

You Do It

Lead students through this exercise as a class. Remind students that while the sequencing of the Human Genome is an achievement unto itself, there are many ways that this application will lead to advances in many areas of science. List student's responses on the board or overhead. Emphasize that there are no right or wrong answers. Encourage students to think creatively.

chapter 1 Organizer

Section/Objectives	Standards		Labs/Features
	National	State/Local	
Chapter Opener	See pp. 16T–17T for a Key to Standards.		**Launch Lab:** Classify Organisms, p. 7 **Foldables,** p. 7
Section 1 What is science? 2 sessions 1 block 1. **Apply** scientific methods to problem solving. 2. **Demonstrate** how to measure using scientific units.	National Content Standards: UCP.1–UCP.3, UCP.5, A.1, A.2, G.2		**Science Online,** p. 10 **MiniLAB:** Analyzing Data, p. 11 **Applying Science:** Does temperature affect the rate of bacterial reproduction?, p. 13
Section 2 Living Things 2 sessions 1 block 3. **Distinguish** between living and nonliving things. 4. **Identify** what living things need to survive.	National Content Standards: UCP.1–UCP.3, UCP.5, A.1, A.2, C.1–C.3		**Science Online,** p. 15 **Integrate Social Studies,** p. 17
Section 3 Where does life come from? 1 session 0.5-block 5. **Describe** experiments about spontaneous generation. 6. **Explain** how scientific methods led to the idea of biogenesis.	National Content Standards: UCP.1–UCP.3, UCP.5, A.1, A.2, C.1, G.3		**Visualizing the Origins of Life,** p. 22 **Integrate Earth Science,** p. 23
Section 4 How are living things classified? 3 sessions 1.5 block 7. **Describe** how early scientists classified living things. 8. **Explain** how similarities are used to classify organisms. 9. **Explain** the system of binomial nomenclature. 10. **Demonstrate** how to use a dichotomous key.	National Content Standards: UCP.1–UCP.3, UCP.5, A.1, A.2, C.5, G.3		**Science Online,** p. 25 **MiniLAB:** Communicating Ideas, p. 27 **Lab:** Classifying Seeds, p. 29 **Lab:** Using Scientific Methods, p. 30 **Science and Society:** Monkey Business, p. 32

Lab Materials	Reproducible Resources	Section Assessment	Technology
Launch Lab: insect collection	**Chapter *Fast File* Resources** Foldables Worksheet, p. 15 Directed Reading Overview, p. 17 Note-taking Worksheets, pp. 33–35	Glencoe's Assessment Advantage	Teacher**Works** includes: • Interactive Teacher Edition • Lesson Planner with calendar • Access to all program blacklines • Correlations to standards • Web links
MiniLAB: pan balance, dry sponge, water, Science Journal	**Chapter *Fast File* Resources** Transparency Activity, p. 44 MiniLAB, p. 3 Enrichment, p. 29 Reinforcement, p. 25 Lab Activity, pp. 9–10 Directed Reading, p. 18	Portfolio Science Journal, p. 9 Performance MiniLAB, p. 11 Applying Science, p. 13 Applying Skills, p. 15 Content Section Review, p. 15	Section Focus Transparency Virtual Labs CD-ROM Guided Reading Audio Program Interactive Chalkboard CD-ROM Video Lab
	Chapter *Fast File* Resources Transparency Activity, p. 45 Enrichment, p. 30 Reinforcement, p. 26 Directed Reading, p. 18	Portfolio Curriculum Connection, p. 18 Performance Applying Skills, p. 20 Content Section Review, p. 20	Section Focus Transparency Virtual Labs CD-ROM Guided Reading Audio Program Interactive Chalkboard CD-ROM
	Chapter *Fast File* Resources Transparency Activity, p. 46 Enrichment, p. 31 Reinforcement, p. 27 Directed Reading, p. 19	Portfolio Reteach, p. 23 Performance Applying Skills, p. 23 Content Section Review, p. 23	Section Focus Transparency Virtual Labs CD-ROM Guided Reading Audio Program Interactive Chalkboard CD-ROM
MiniLAB: magazine picture of a piece of furniture **Lab:** packets of seeds (10 different kinds), metric ruler, magnifying lens **Lab:** 3 500-mL, wide-mouthed containers; brine shrimp eggs; small, plastic spoon; distilled water; weak salt solution; strong salt solution; 3 labels; magnifying lens	**Chapter *Fast File* Resources** Transparency Activity, p. 47 MiniLAB, p. 4 Enrichment, p. 32 Reinforcement, p. 28 Directed Reading, pp. 19, 20 Transparency Activity, pp. 49–50 Lab Activity, pp. 11–13 Lab Worksheets, pp. 5–6, 7–8	Portfolio Assessment, p. 28 Performance MiniLAB, p. 27 Applying Skills, p. 28 Content Section Review, p. 28	Section Focus Transparency Teaching Transparency Virtual Labs CD-ROM Guided Reading Audio Program Interactive Chalkboard CD-ROM

Need materials? Contact Science Kit at 1-800-828-7777 or www.sciencekit.com on the Internet.

End of Chapter Assessment

Glencoe's Assessment Advantage

Blackline Masters	Technology	Professional Series
Chapter *Fast File* Resources Chapter Review, pp. 37–38 Chapter Tests, pp. 39–42 **Standardized Test Practice,** pp. 7–10	MindJogger Videoquiz Virtual Labs CD-ROM Exam*View*® Pro Testmaker TeacherWorks CD-ROM Interactive Chalkboard CD-ROM	**Performance Assessment in the Science Classroom (PASC)**

Exploring and Classifying Life

Transparencies

Section Focus

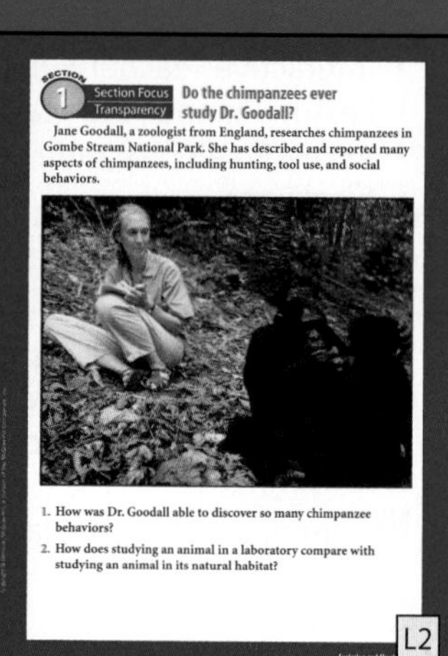

Section 1 Section Focus Transparency

Do the chimpanzees ever study Dr. Goodall?

Jane Goodall, a zoologist from England, researches chimpanzees in Gombe Stream National Park. She has described and reported many aspects of chimpanzees, including hunting, tool use, and social behaviors.

1. How was Dr. Goodall able to discover so many chimpanzee behaviors?
2. How does studying an animal in a laboratory compare with studying an animal in its natural habitat?

L2

Section 2 Section Focus Transparency

Most Enlightening

Have you ever seen a house plant growing toward the window? Most plants grow toward the light. This bending is caused by a plant hormone that makes plant cells stretch and grow in the direction of the light source.

1. Why do plants need light?
2. What would happen if you gave the pot a half turn?
3. What does this plant need to live?

L2

Section 3 Section Focus Transparency

How About a Field Trip?

Is there life on other planets? If there is, it probably doesn't resemble the aliens we see in the movies. Some scientists believe that Europa, one of Jupiter's moons (pictured in the center of the image below), is a candidate for supporting extraterrestrial life.

1. What general resources are needed to sustain life on Earth?
2. Is it possible that other planets or moons in our galaxy might have the resources to support life? Explain.

L2

This is a representation of key blackline masters available in the Teacher Classroom Resources. See Resource Manager boxes within the chapter for additional information.

Assessment

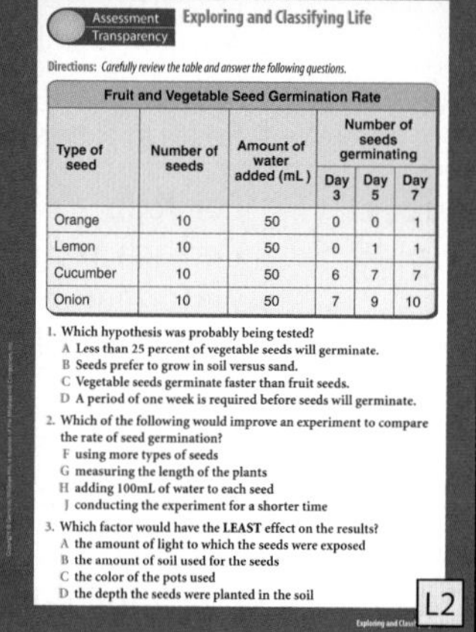

Assessment Transparency

Exploring and Classifying Life

Directions: *Carefully review the table and answer the following questions.*

Fruit and Vegetable Seed Germination Rate

Type of seed	Number of seeds	Amount of water added (mL)	Number of seeds germinating		
			Day 3	Day 5	Day 7
Orange	10	50	0	0	1
Lemon	10	50	0	1	1
Cucumber	10	50	6	7	7
Onion	10	50	7	9	10

1. Which hypothesis was probably being tested?
   A Less than 25 percent of vegetable seeds will germinate.
   B Seeds prefer to grow in soil versus sand.
   C Vegetable seeds germinate faster than fruit seeds.
   D A period of one week is required before seeds will germinate.
2. Which of the following would improve an experiment to compare the rate of seed germination?
   F using more types of seeds
   G measuring the length of the plants
   H adding 100mL of water to each seed
   J conducting the experiment for a shorter time
3. Which factor would have the **LEAST** effect on the results?
   A the amount of light to which the seeds were exposed
   B the amount of soil used for the seeds
   C the color of the pots used
   D the depth the seeds were planted in the soil

L2

Teaching

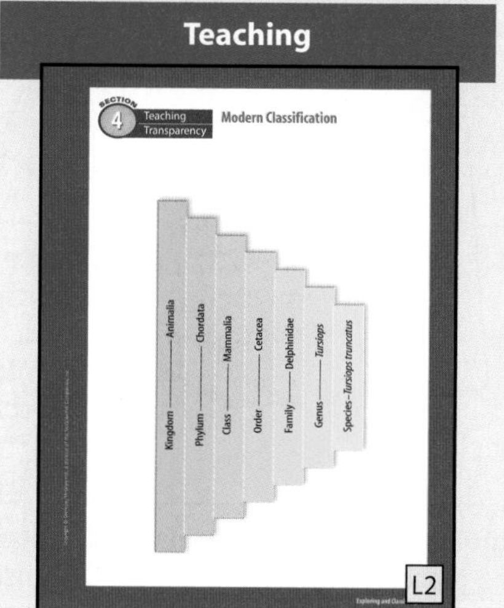

Section 4 Teaching Transparency

Modern Classification

L2

Key to Teaching Strategies

The following designations will help you decide which activities are appropriate for your students.

L1 Level 1 activities should be appropriate for students with learning difficulties.

L2 Level 2 activities should be within the ability range of all students.

L3 Level 3 activities are designed for above-average students.

ELL ELL activities should be within the ability range of English-Language Learners.

COOP LEARN Cooperative Learning activities are designed for small group work.

LS Multiple Learning Styles logos, as described on page 12T, are used throughout to indicate strategies that address different learning styles.

P These strategies represent student products that can be placed into a best-work portfolio.

PBL Problem-Based Learning activities apply real-world situations to learning.

Hands-on Activities

Student Text Lab Worksheet

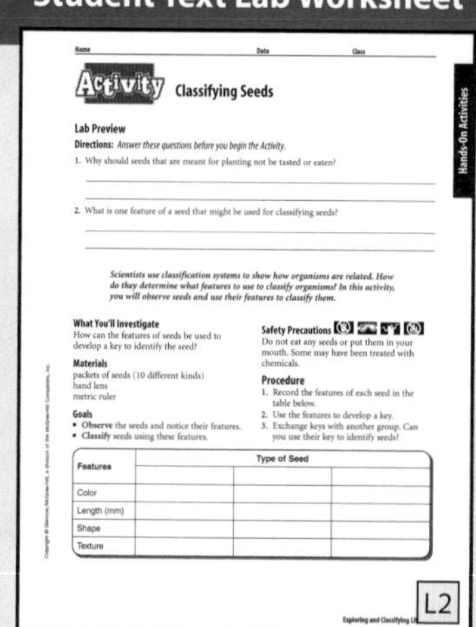

Name Date Class

Activity Classifying Seeds

Lab Preview

Directions: *Answer these questions before you begin the Activity.*

1. Why should seeds that are meant for planting not be tasted or eaten?
2. What is one feature of a seed that might be used for classifying seeds?

Scientists use classification systems to show how organisms are related. How do they determine what features to use to classify organisms? In this activity, you will observe seeds and use their features to classify them.

What You'll Investigate
How can the features of seeds be used to develop a key to identify the seed?

Materials
packets of seeds (10 different kinds)
hand lens
metric ruler

Goals
- **Observe** the seeds and notice their features.
- **Classify** seeds using these features.

Safety Precautions
Do not eat any seeds or put them in your mouth. Some may have been treated with chemicals.

Procedure
1. Record the features of each seed in the table below.
2. Use the features to develop a key.
3. Exchange keys with another group. Can you use their key to identify seeds?

Features	Type of Seed		
Color			
Length (mm)			
Shape			
Texture			

L2

Laboratory Activities

Name Date Class

Lab 1 Laboratory Activity

Scientific Methods

When scientists are asked questions, they may not know the answers. They think of the possible answers, called hypotheses, and experiment to find the correct answers. Using the results of the experiment, they may need to form another hypothesis and test it. This way of solving a problem is called scientific methods.

Strategy
You will predict whether or not red cabbage juice will remain red when chemicals are added to it.
You will test your prediction with an experiment.
You will observe what happens and record your observations.
You will draw conclusions based on your observations.

Materials
apron
goggles
4 test tubes (18 × 150 mm)
test tube rack
labels
3 droppers
graduated cylinder (25 mL)
40 mL red cabbage juice
chemical X (vinegar)
chemical Y (ammonia)
chemical Z (baking soda solution)

Procedure
1. In the space below, predict what will happen to the red cabbage juice when chemicals X, Y and Z are added to it.
2. Label four test tubes, 1, 2, 3, and 4.
3. Add 10 mL of red cabbage juice to each test tube. **CAUTION:** *Do not spill chemicals X, Y, or Z on clothes or skin. Rinse with water if spilled.*
4. Add 10 drops of chemical X to test tube 1.
5. Add 10 drops of chemical Y to test tube 2.
6. Add 10 drops of chemical Z to test tube 3.
7. Do not add anything to test tube 4. This is the control. The control is part of the experiment that is not tested.
8. Record your observations in Table 1.

Data and Observations

Table 1

Test tube	Substance added	Color
1		
2		
3		
4		

L2

Meeting Different Ability Levels

Content Outline

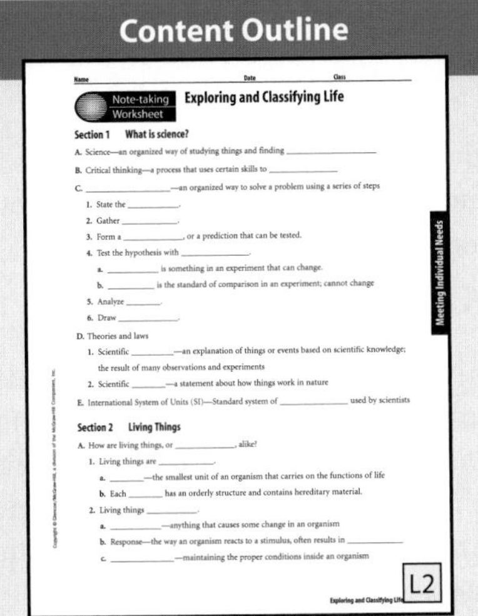
Name Date Class

Note-taking Worksheet **Exploring and Classifying Life**

Section 1 What is science?

A. Science—an organized way of studying things and finding ________

B. Critical thinking—a process that uses certain skills to ________

C. ________—an organized way to solve a problem using a series of steps

1. State the ________.
2. Gather ________.
3. Form a ________, or a prediction that can be tested.
4. Test the hypothesis with ________.
   a. ________ is something in an experiment that can change.
   b. ________ is the standard of comparison in an experiment; cannot change
5. Analyze ________.
6. Draw ________.

D. Theories and laws

1. Scientific ________—an explanation of things or events based on scientific knowledge; the result of many observations and experiments
2. Scientific ________—a statement about how things work in nature

E. International System of Units (SI)—Standard system of ________ used by scientists

Section 2 Living Things

A. How are living things, or ________, alike?

1. Living things are ________.
   a. ________—the smallest unit of an organism that carries on the functions of life
   b. Each ________ has an orderly structure and contains hereditary material.
2. Living things ________.
   a. ________—anything that causes some change in an organism
   b. Response—the way an organism reacts to a stimulus, often results in ________
   c. ________—maintaining the proper conditions inside an organism

Meeting Individual Needs

Exploring and Classifying Life

L2

Reinforcement

Name Date Class

Section 1 Reinforcement **What is science?**

Directions: *List the steps that are usually followed in scientific methods in the order in which they should be performed.*

1. ________
2. ________
3. ________
4. ________
5. ________
6. ________
7. ________
8. What does SI stand for?

Directions: *Match the SI unit with what it measures by writing the correct letter in the space provided.*

____ 9. meter a. length

____ 10. liter b. mass

____ 11. kilogram c. volume

Directions: *Answer the following questions on the lines provided.*

12. Suppose a scientist wants to test a new drug to fight the flu. The scientist injects the drug into three people with the flu. The scientist injects a harmless solution into three other people with the flu. In this experiment, what is the variable group and what is the control group?
13. Why is it necessary to follow safety rules in the science laboratory?
14. What is the difference between a theory and a scientific law?

Meeting Individual Needs

Exploring and Classifying Life

L2

Enrichment

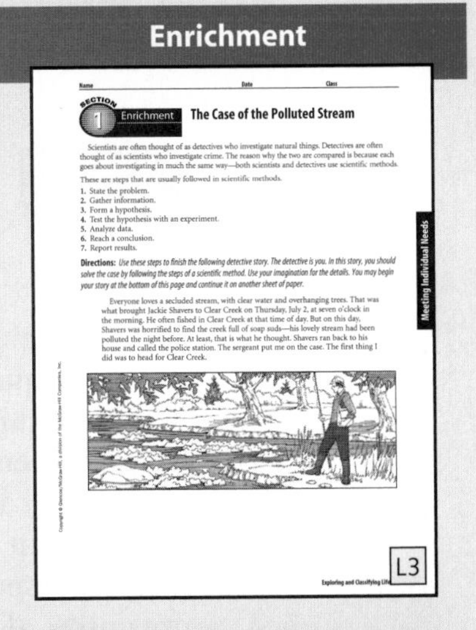
Name Date Class

Section 1 Enrichment **The Case of the Polluted Stream**

Scientists are often thought of as detectives who investigate natural things. Detectives are often thought of as scientists who investigate crime. The reason why the two are compared is because each goes about investigating in much the same way—both scientists and detectives use scientific methods.

These are steps that are usually followed in scientific methods.

1. State the problem.
2. Gather information.
3. Form a hypothesis.
4. Test the hypothesis with an experiment.
5. Analyze data.
6. Reach a conclusion.
7. Report results.

Directions: *Use these steps to finish the following detective story. The detective is you. In this story, you should solve the case by following the steps of a scientific method. Use your imagination for the details. You may begin your story at the bottom of this page and continue it on another sheet of paper.*

Everyone loves a secluded stream, with clear water and overhanging trees. That was what brought Jackie Shavers to Clear Creek on Thursday, July 2, at seven o'clock in the morning. He often fished in Clear Creek at that time of day. But on this day, Shavers was horrified to find the creek full of soap suds—his lovely stream had been polluted the night before. At least, that is what he thought. Shavers ran back to his house and called the police station. The sergeant put me on the case. The first thing I did was to head for Clear Creek.

Meeting Individual Needs

Exploring and Classifying Life

L3

Directed Reading (English/Spanish)

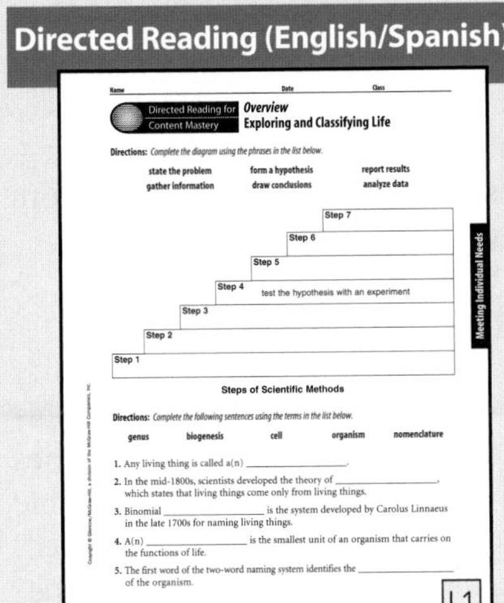
Name Date Class

Directed Reading for Content Mastery **Overview** **Exploring and Classifying Life**

Directions: *Complete the diagram using the phrases in the list below.*

state the problem, form a hypothesis, report results, gather information, draw conclusions, analyze data

Step 7

Step 6

Step 5

Step 4 test the hypothesis with an experiment

Step 3

Step 2

Step 1

Steps of Scientific Methods

Directions: *Complete the following sentences using the terms in the list below.*

genus, biogenesis, cell, organism, nomenclature

1. Any living thing is called a(n) ________.
2. In the mid-1800s, scientists developed the theory of ________, which states that living things come only from living things.
3. Binomial ________ is the system developed by Carolus Linnaeus in the late 1700s for naming living things.
4. A(n) ________ is the smallest unit of an organism that carries on the functions of life.
5. The first word of the two-word naming system identifies the ________ of the organism.

Meeting Individual Needs

Exploring and Classifying Life

L1

Study Guide

Study Guide
Features
• Contains a study guide page for each section of the chapter
• Reviews key concepts
• Includes answer pages
L2

Reading Essentials

Reading Essentials for Glencoe Science
An Interactive Student Workbook
Features
• Condensed core content
• Actively involves students in reading
• Reinforces key vocabulary
L1

Assessment

Test Practice Workbook

Name: Date: Class:

Chapter 1 *Exploring and Classifying Life* Chapter Test

DIRECTIONS

Choose the best answer choice for each of the following questions.

A	Form a hypothesis
B	Gather information
C	Perform an experiment
D	State the problem
E	Analyze the data

1. Below is a list of steps in the scientific method. Which sequence shows the correct order?
   a. A, B, C, D, E
   b. D, C, A, E, B
   c. D, B, A, C, E
   d. C, B, A, D, E
2. Which of these statements about cells is true?
   f. All cells respond to light.
   g. They do not make up most living things.
   h. They take in materials from their surroundings.
   j. They do not contain any hereditary material.
3. Even though the weather is cold, the squirrel maintains a constant body temperature. What is this trait called?
   a. stimuli
   b. biogenesis
   c. homeostasis
   d. hypothesis
4. Organisms need all of the following things EXCEPT ________.
   f. energy
   g. water
   h. a place to live
   j. hunting skills

GO ON

Glencoe Life Science

L2

Chapter Review

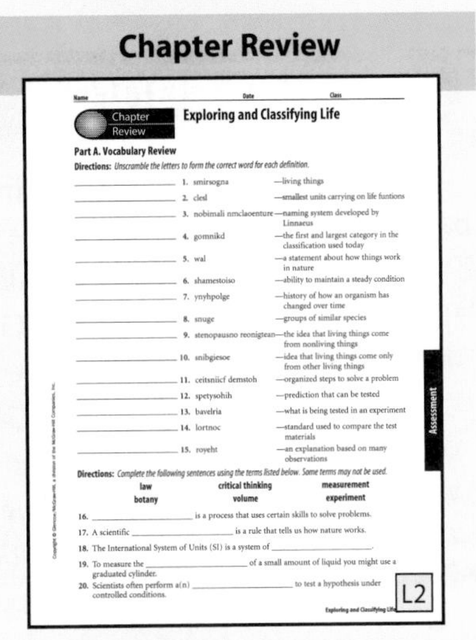
Name Date Class

Chapter Review **Exploring and Classifying Life**

Part A. Vocabulary Review

Directions: *Unscramble the letters to form the correct word for each definition.*

1. smirsogna —living things
2. sled —smallest units carrying on life funtions
3. nobimali nmclaoenture —naming system developed by Linnaeus
4. gommikd —the first and largest category in the classification used today
5. wal —a statement about how things work in nature
6. shamentoiso —ability to maintain a steady condition
7. yoyhpolge —history of how an organism has changed over time
8. sruge —groups of similar species
9. atenopausno reonigtean —the idea that living things come from nonliving things
10. snibgieseo —idea that living things come only from other living things
11. ceitsniicf demtoh —organized steps to solve a problem
12. spetysohih —prediction that can be tested
13. bareiria —what is being tested in an experiment
14. lortnoc —standard used to compare the test materials
15. royeht —an explanation based on many observations

Directions: *Complete the following sentences using the terms listed below. Some terms may not be used.*

law, critical thinking, measurement, botany, volume, experiment

16. ________ is a process that uses certain skills to solve problems.
17. A scientific ________ is a rule that tells us how nature works.
18. The International System of Units (SI) is a system of ________.
19. To measure the ________ of a small amount of liquid you might use a graduated cylinder.
20. Scientists often perform a(n) ________ to test a hypothesis under controlled conditions.

Assessment

Exploring and Classifying Life

L2

Chapter Tests

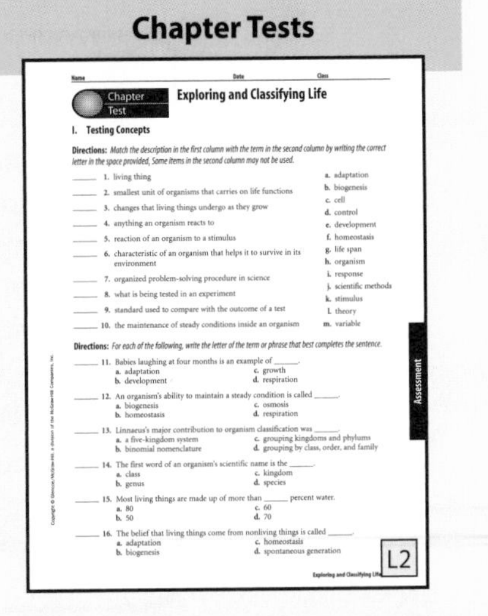
Name Date Class

Chapter Test **Exploring and Classifying Life**

I. Testing Concepts

Directions: *Match the description in the first column with the term in the second column by writing the correct letter in the space provided. Some items in the second column may not be used.*

1. living thing
2. smallest unit of organisms that carries on life functions
3. changes that living things undergo as they grow
4. anything an organism reacts to
5. reaction of an organism to a stimulus
6. characteristic of an organism that helps it to survive in its environment
7. organized problem-solving procedure in science
8. what is being tested in an experiment
9. standard used to compare with the outcome of a test
10. the maintenance of steady conditions inside an organism

a. adaptation
b. biogenesis
c. cell
d. control
e. development
f. homeostasis
g. life span
h. organism
i. response
j. scientific methods
k. stimulus
l. theory
m. variable

Directions: *For each of the following, write the letter of the term or phrase that best completes the sentence.*

11. Babies laughing at four months is an example of ________.
    a. adaptation c. growth
    b. development d. respiration
12. An organism's ability to maintain a steady condition is called ________.
    a. biogenesis c. osmosis
    b. homeostasis d. respiration
13. Linnaeus's major contribution to organism classification was ________.
    a. a five-kingdom system c. grouping kingdoms and phylums
    b. binomial nomenclature d. grouping by class, order, and family
14. The first word of an organism's scientific name is the ________.
    a. class c. kingdom
    b. genus d. species
15. Most living things are made up of more than ________ percent water.
    a. 80 c. 60
    b. 50 d. 70
16. The belief that living things come from nonliving things is called ________.
    a. adaptation c. homeostasis
    b. biogenesis d. spontaneous generation

Assessment

Exploring and Classifying Life

L2

Science Content Background

section 2 Living Things

Living Versus Nonliving

Living organisms consist of highly organized systems that interact and are dependent upon one another. Living systems require a constant source of energy. All living organisms have metabolic processes by which the energy in carbohydrates is released for use. All living organisms respond to their environment in adaptive ways, including physiological responses as well as behaviors. Living organisms also have a means of reproduction, growth, and development.

section 4 How are living things classified?

Modern Classification

This textbook uses a combination of phenetics and cladistics to classify organisms. Phenetics is based on particular features. Cladistics uses shared, derived characteristics to classify organisms. By comparing DNA nucleotide sequences between species and by measuring the amount of bonding between DNA from different species, taxonomists infer the degree of similarity between organisms. Scientists hypothesize that organisms with similar proteins are closely related. A comparison of the amino acid sequences between species' proteins provides objective, quantitative data for taxonomists because the structure of proteins is genetically determined.

Domains

Most taxonomists currently divide the six-kingdom system into groups called domains. The three domains are Eubacteria, Archaea, and Eukarya. The domains Eubacteria and Archaea contain Kingdom Eubacteria and Kingdom Archaebacteria, respectively.

Kingdom Eubacteria and Kingdom Archaebacteria differ. Eubacteria have muramic acid in their cell walls, but archaebacteria do not. The RNA sequences of the two groups also differ.

Domain Eukarya contains four kingdoms—Kingdom Protista, Kingdom Fungi, Kingdom Plantae, and Kingdom Animalia.

Scientific Names

A system of classification avoids ambiguity among species, reflects the phylogeny (evolutionary history) of organisms, and provides clues about the organism's habits and possible features shared with similar organisms. The second word of a scientific name is called the specific epithet, usually an adjective that describes the organism, indicates the organism's place of origin, or is a Latinized surname to honor someone. Subspecies have two specific epithets.

chapter content resources

Internet Resources

For additional content background, visit **booka.msscience.com** to:

- access your book online
- find references to related articles in popular science magazines
- access Web links with related content background
- access current events with science journal topics

Print Resources

The Science of Life: Projects and Principles for Beginning Biologists, by Frank G. Bottone, Chicago Review Press, 2001

The Origins of Life, by Roy A. Gallant, Marshall Cavendish, 2000

Carl Linnaeus: Father of Classification, by Margaret Jean Anderson, Enslow Publishers, 1997

National Audubon Society First Field Guide: Reptiles, by John L. Behler, Scholastic Inc., 1999

IDENTIFYING Misconceptions

Find Out What Students Think

Students may think that . . .

All things that move are alive.

Students generally define "living" according to the characteristics of large animals. Hence they associate "living" with movement. Students often do not consider plants and fungi to be alive because they do not appear to move, but may classify rivers or clouds as living because they do move. Students may add other mammalian characteristics to their definitions of life such as eating, breathing, or the presence of a heartbeat.

Clouding the concept further is the confusion between "nonliving" and "dead." Students may classify both a dead animal and a rock as "nonliving" objects, even though they classify animals in general as alive.

Discussion

Place a rock, a houseplant, and a living animal (such as a caged hamster or a volunteer student) in view of the class. Ask students if they think any of the three items are alive. As students respond, ask them why they think the item is or is not alive. From this, generate a list of characteristics that students believe belong to all living organisms. Students will probably recognize that the animal is alive. Some will understand that the plant is alive, but have difficulty explaining why. Most will know that the rock is not alive.

Promote Understanding

Activity

Have the students read **Section 2** in this chapter, then review the list they generated in the discussion suggestion above. Ask the students if they want to change anything on the list.

Next, place a candle in full view of the class and light it. Ask students if they think the flame is alive. Then do the following:

- Blow gently on the flame to show that it responds.
- Light another candle or a match from the flame to show that the flame can reproduce.
- Point out that the wax of the candle is being consumed, showing that the flame uses energy.

Remind students that many nonliving things have some characteristics of living things.

- Ask the class what characteristics the candle flame lacks. Students should recognize that the flame is not highly organized, it is not made up of organic molecules, and it contains no cells. L2

Assess

After completing the chapter, see *Identifying Misconceptions* in the Study Guide at the end of the chapter.

chapter 1

Chapter Vocabulary

scientific methods, p. 9
hypothesis, p. 10
control, p. 11
variable, p. 11
theory, p. 12
law, p. 12
organism, p. 16
cell, p. 16
homeostasis, p. 17
spontaneous generation, p. 21
biogenesis, p. 21
phylogeny, p. 25
kingdom, p. 25
binomial nomenclature, p. 26
genus, p. 26

Science Journal Students' answers will vary. Characteristics might include method of movement, shape of body, and what they eat.

PowerPoint® Presentations

This CD-ROM is an editable Microsoft® PowerPoint® presentation that includes:

- a pre-made presentation for every chapter
- interactive graphics
- animations
- audio clips
- image bank
- all new section and chapter questions
- Standardized Test Practice
- transparencies
- pre-lab questions for all labs
- Foldables directions
- links to booka.msscience.com

chapter 1

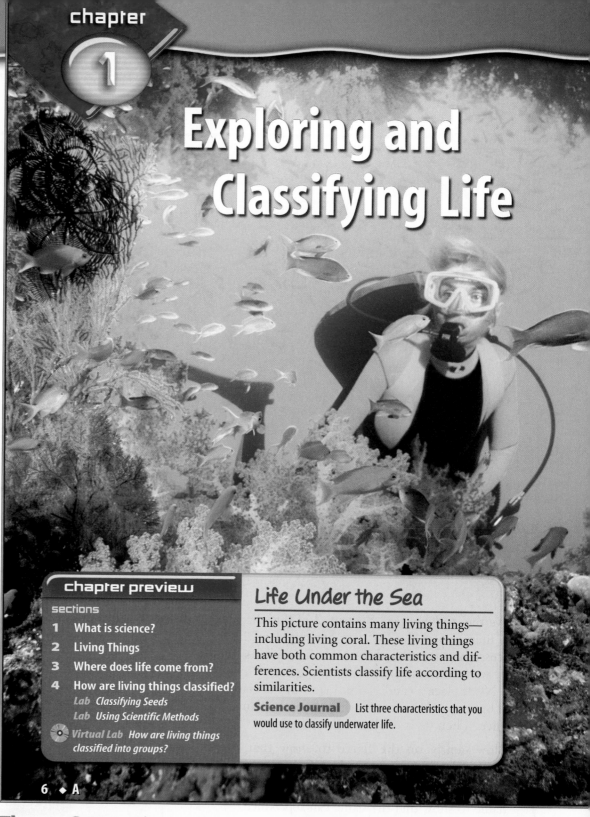

Exploring and Classifying Life

chapter preview

sections

1 What is science?
2 Living Things
3 Where does life come from?
4 How are living things classified?
Lab Classifying Seeds
Lab Using Scientific Methods
Virtual Lab How are living things classified into groups?

Life Under the Sea

This picture contains many living things—including living coral. These living things have both common characteristics and differences. Scientists classify life according to similarities.

Science Journal List three characteristics that you would use to classify underwater life.

Theme Connection

Systems and Interactions Scientists have devised systems for classifying organisms. These systems use an organism's traits, which have changed over time often as a result of natural selection as organisms interact with the environment.

About the Photo

Diversity of Life The diver is surrounded by a wide variety of living organisms. Some are easily recognizable as living, while others may look more like nonliving rocks. While all the organisms, including the diver, share characteristics that classify them as living, those that are more closely classified share the most characteristics.

Start-Up Activities

Classify Organisms

Life scientists discover, describe, and name hundreds of organisms every year. How do they decide if a certain plant belongs to the iris or orchid family of flowering plants, or if an insect is more like a grasshopper or a beetle?

1. Observe the organisms on the opposite page or in an insect collection in your class.
2. Decide which feature could be used to separate the organisms into two groups, then sort the organisms into the two groups.
3. Continue to make new groups using different features until each organism is in a category by itself.
4. **Think Critically** How do you think scientists classify living things? List your ideas in your Science Journal.

Preview this chapter's content and activities at booka.msscience.com

Vocabulary Make the following Foldable to help you understand the vocabulary terms in this chapter.

STEP 1 **Fold** a vertical sheet of notebook paper from side to side.

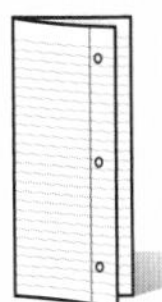

STEP 2 **Cut** along every third line of only the top layer to form tabs.

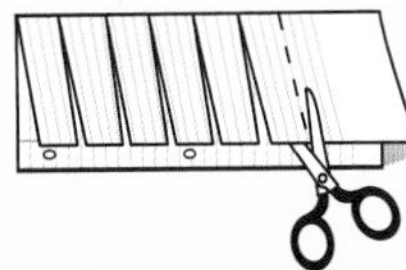

STEP 3 **Label** each tab.

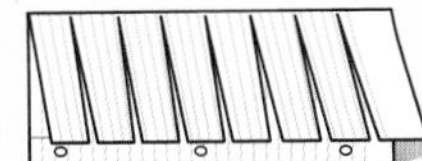

Build Vocabulary As you read the chapter, write the vocabulary words on the tabs. As you learn the definitions, write them under the tab for each vocabulary word.

A ◆ 7

Purpose Use the Launch Lab to introduce students to classification. In this chapter students will learn how characteristics of organisms are used in classification. L2 COOP LEARN LS **Interpersonal**

Preparation Use the opening photo to promote a discussion of how organisms are classified. If insect collections are available, use them to supplement the discussion.

Materials chapter-opening photo or an insect collection

Alternate Materials collection of leaves

Teaching Strategies

- Make sure students can identify the differences between the organisms in the coral reef or in the insect collection.
- Accept any logical classification groupings devised by students.

Think Critically

Scientists identify the traits of an organism. They compare these traits with those of other living things. The organism is then placed into a group of living things with similar traits.

Assessment

Oral Have students explain the reasons behind the choices they made.

Dinah Zike Study Fold

Student preparation materials for this Foldable are available in the Chapter *Fast File* Resources.

1 Motivate

Bellringer

Section Focus Transparencies also are available on the Interactive Chalkboard CD-ROM.

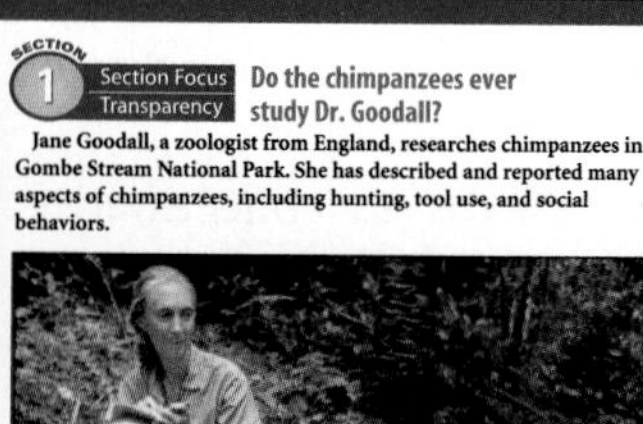

1. How was Dr. Goodall able to discover so many chimpanzee behaviors?
2. How does studying an animal in a laboratory compare with studying an animal in its natural habitat?
Exploring and Classifying Life

Tie to Prior Knowledge

Daily Decisions Students use problem-solving skills daily. Discuss how they solve everyday problems, such as deciding what outfit to wear or how to manage homework with extra-curricular activities. Relate solving everyday problems to scientific methods.

Text Question Answer

bacteria

section 1

What is science?

as you read

What **You'll Learn**

- **Apply** scientific methods to problem solving.
- **Demonstrate** how to measure using scientific units.

Why **It's Important**

Learning to use scientific methods will help you solve ordinary problems in your life.

Review Vocabulary
experiment: using controlled conditions to test a prediction

New Vocabulary
- scientific methods
- hypothesis
- control
- variable
- theory
- law

The Work of Science

Movies and popcorn seem to go together. So before you and your friends watch a movie, sometimes you pop some corn in a microwave oven. When the popping stops, you take out the bag and open it carefully. You smell the mouthwatering, freshly popped corn and avoid hot steam that escapes from the bag. What makes the popcorn pop? How do microwaves work and make things hot? By the way, what are microwaves anyway?

Asking questions like these is one way scientists find out about anything in the world and the universe. Science is often described as an organized way of studying things and finding answers to questions.

Types of Science Many types of science exist. Each is given a name to describe what is being studied. For example, energy and matter have a relationship. That's a topic for physics. A physicist could answer most questions about microwaves.

On the other hand, a life scientist might study any of the millions of different animals, plants, and other living things on Earth. Look at the objects in **Figure 1.** What do they look like to you? A life scientist could tell you that some of the objects are living plants and some are just rocks. Life scientists who study plants are botanists, and those who study animals are zoologists. What do you suppose a bacteriologist studies?

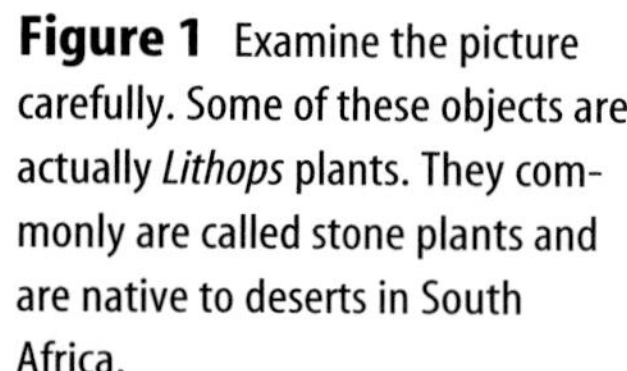

Figure 1 Examine the picture carefully. Some of these objects are actually *Lithops* plants. They commonly are called stone plants and are native to deserts in South Africa.

Section 1 Resource Manager

Chapter *Fast File* Resources
- Transparency Activity, p. 44
- Directed Reading for Content Mastery, pp. 17, 18
- Note-taking Worksheets, pp. 33–35
- MiniLAB, p. 3
- Reinforcement, p. 25
- Enrichment, p. 29
- Lab Activity, pp. 9–10

Life Science Critical Thinking/Problem Solving, p. 4
Mathematics Skill Activities, p. 33
Reading and Writing Skill Activities, pp. 17, 33

Critical Thinking

Whether or not you become a trained scientist, you are going to solve problems all your life. You probably solve many problems every day when you sort out ideas about what will or won't work. Suppose your CD player stops playing music. To figure out what happened, you have to think about it. That's called critical thinking, and it's the way you use skills to solve problems.

If you know that the CD player does not run on batteries and must be plugged in to work, that's the first thing you check to solve the problem. You check and the player is plugged in so you eliminate that possible solution. You separate important information from unimportant information—that's a skill. Could there be something wrong with the first outlet? You plug the player into a different outlet, and your CD starts playing. You now know that it's the first outlet that doesn't work. Identifying the problem is another skill you have.

Solving Problems

Scientists use the same types of skills that you do to solve problems and answer questions. Although scientists don't always find the answers to their questions, they always use critical thinking in their search. Besides critical thinking, solving a problem requires organization. In science, this organization often takes the form of a series of procedures called **scientific methods. Figure 2** shows one way that scientific methods might be used to solve a problem.

State the Problem Suppose a veterinary technician wanted to find out whether different types of cat litter cause irritation to cats' skin. What would she do first? The technician begins by observing something she cannot explain. A pet owner brings his four cats to the clinic to be boarded while he travels. He leaves his cell phone number so he can be contacted if any problems arise. When they first arrive, the four cats seem healthy. The next day however, the technician notices that two of the cats are scratching and chewing at their skin. By the third day, these same two cats have bare patches of skin with red sores. The technician decides that something in the cats' surroundings or their food might be irritating their skin.

Figure 2 The series of procedures shown below is one way to use scientific methods to solve a problem.

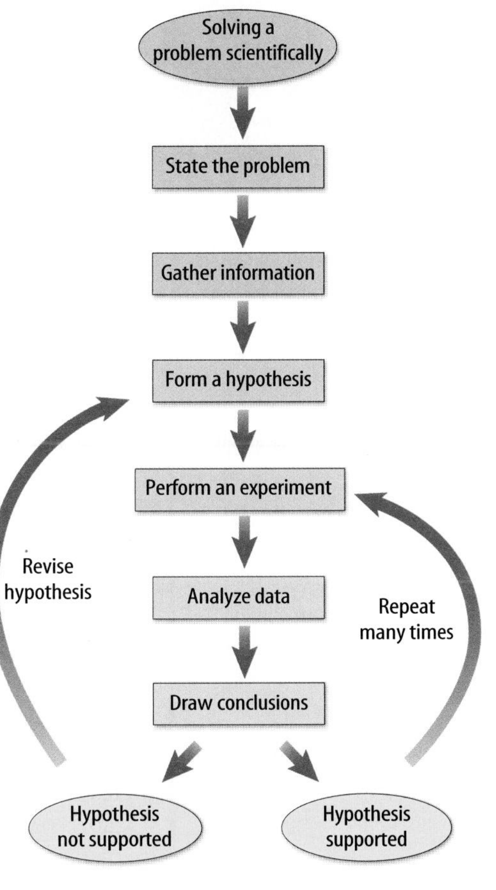

2 Teach

Activity

Life Scientists Divide the class into small groups. Ask: What do you think life scientists do? Where might they work? Allow time for groups to discuss the questions and record their responses. Have each group use their results to write a Help Wanted advertisement seeking a life scientist. Ask groups to present their advertisements to the class.
L2 COOP LEARN LS **Interpersonal**

IDENTIFYING Misconceptions

Science for Everybody Science is often thought of as a discipline out of reach of most people. Many believe that only well-educated or specially trained people can practice science. Explain that science is a process of understanding and that anyone can use the methods of science in daily life.

Visual Learning

Figure 2 Are all the steps shown here always followed in the exact same sequence? No; if a hypothesis is not supported, the scientist starts over by forming a new hypothesis. Sometimes, only a few of the steps are used.

Science Journal

Critical-Thinking Log Ask students to keep in their journals a log of instances in which they used critical thinking to solve problems. Logs should note the date, problem, and solution. At the end of one week, have students share their logs with classmates. Guide students in recognizing that critical thinking is a life skill. L2 LS **Interpersonal** P

SECTION 1 What is science? A ◆ 9

Quick Demo

Testing a Hypothesis

Materials 2-L clear container, pond water

Estimated Time 20 minutes

Procedure Fill the container with pond water and place it in a well-lighted area. Have students write a hypothesis about how the water will appear in ten days. Collect the hypotheses and in ten days, have students check their hypotheses against the conditions in the jar.

Fun Fact

Scientists use computer models to study how cloud cover affects Earth's climate.

Caption Answer

Figure 3 Accept any reasonable answers. Possible answers include: an observatory, space station, rain forest, or underwater.

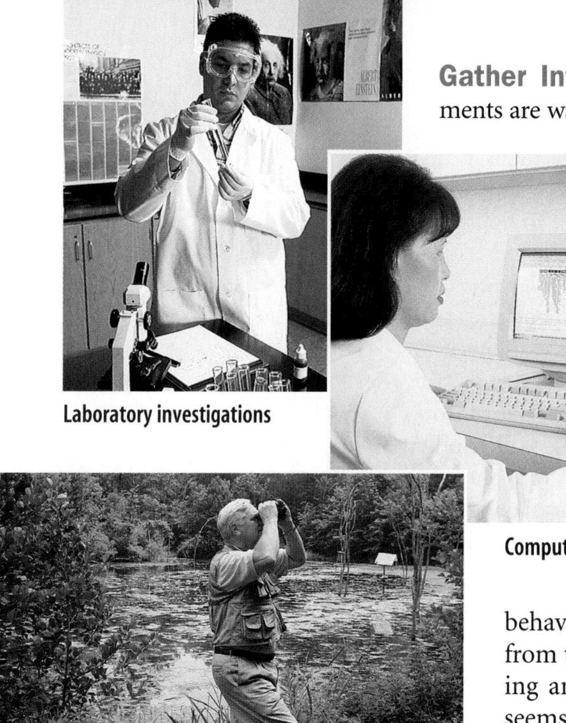

Laboratory investigations

Computer models

Fieldwork

Figure 3 Observations can be made in many different settings. **List** *three other places where scientific observations can be made.*

Gather Information Laboratory observations and experiments are ways to collect information. Some data also are gathered from fieldwork. Fieldwork includes observations or experiments that are done outside of the laboratory. For example, the best way to find out how a bird builds a nest is to go outside and watch it. **Figure 3** shows some ways data can be gathered.

The technician gathers information about the problem by watching the cats closely for the next two days. She knows that cats sometimes change their behavior when they are in a new place. She wants to see if the behavior of the cats with the skin sores seems different from that of the other two cats. Other than the scratching and chewing at their skin, all four cats' behavior seems to be the same.

The technician calls the owner and tells him about the problem. She asks him what brand of cat food he feeds his cats. Because his brand is the same one used at the clinic, she decides that food is not the cause of the skin irritation. She decides that the cats probably are reacting to something in their surroundings. There are many things in the clinic that the cats might react to. How does she decide what it is?

During her observations she notices that the cats seem to scratch and chew themselves most after using their litter boxes. The cat litter used by the clinic contains a deodorant. The technician calls the owner and finds out that the cat litter he buys does not contain a deodorant.

Topic: Controlled Experiments

Visit booka.msscience.com for Web links to information about how scientists use controlled experiments.

Activity List the problem, hypothesis, and how the hypothesis was tested for a recently performed controlled experiment.

Form a Hypothesis Based on this information, the next thing the veterinary technician does is form a hypothesis. A **hypothesis** is a prediction that can be tested. After discussing her observations with the clinic veterinarian, she hypothesizes that something in the cat litter is irritating the cats' skin.

Test the Hypothesis with an Experiment The technician gets the owner's permission to test her hypothesis by performing an experiment. In an experiment, the hypothesis is tested using controlled conditions. The technician reads the labels on two brands of cat litter and finds that the ingredients of each are the same except that one contains a deodorant.

LAB DEMONSTRATION

Purpose to compare observations and inferences

Materials one red apple

Alternate Materials one purple grape for each student pair

Preparation Wash the fruit.

Procedure Have students record visual observations of the fruit and then classify the following statements as observations or inferences. 1. The apple's covering is red. 2. The apple is edible. 3. There are seeds inside the apple.

Expected Outcome 1 is an observation; 2 and 3 are inferences.

Assessment

How are observations and inferences different? Observations are information gathered through the senses. Inferences result from past observations.  L2

Controls The technician separates the cats with sores from the other two cats. She puts each of the cats with sores in a cage by itself. One cat is called the experimental cat. This cat is given a litter box containing the cat litter without deodorant. The other cat is given a litter box that contains cat litter with deodorant. The cat with deodorant cat litter is the control.

A **control** is the standard to which the outcome of a test is compared. At the end of the experiment, the control cat will be compared with the experimental cat. Whether or not the cat litter contains deodorant is the variable. A **variable** is something in an experiment that can change. An experiment should have only one variable. Other than the difference in the cat litter, the technician treats both cats the same.

Reading Check *How many variables should an experiment have?*

Analyze Data The veterinary technician observes both cats for one week. During this time, she collects data on how often and when the cats scratch or chew, as shown in **Figure 4.** These data are recorded in a journal. The data show that the control cat scratches and chews more often than the experimental cat does. The sores on the skin of the experimental cat begin to heal, but those on the control cat do not.

Draw Conclusions The technician then draws the conclusion—a logical answer to a question based on data and observation—that the deodorant in the cat litter probably irritated the skin of the two cats. To accept or reject the hypothesis is the next step. In this case, the technician accepts the hypothesis. If she had rejected it, new experiments would have been necessary.

Although the technician decides to accept her hypothesis, she realizes that to be surer of her results she should continue her experiment. She should switch the experimental cat with the control cat to see what the results are a second time. If she did this, the healed cat might develop new sores. She makes an ethical decision and chooses not to continue the experiment. Ethical decisions, like this one, are important in deciding what science should be done.

Analyzing Data

Procedure

1. Obtain a **pan balance.** Follow your teacher's instructions for using it.
2. Record all data in your **Science Journal.**
3. Measure and record the mass of a **dry sponge.**
4. Soak this sponge in **water.** Measure and record its mass.
5. Calculate how much water your sponge absorbed.
6. Combine the class data and calculate the average amount of water absorbed.

Analysis

What other information about the sponges might be important when analyzing the data from the entire class?

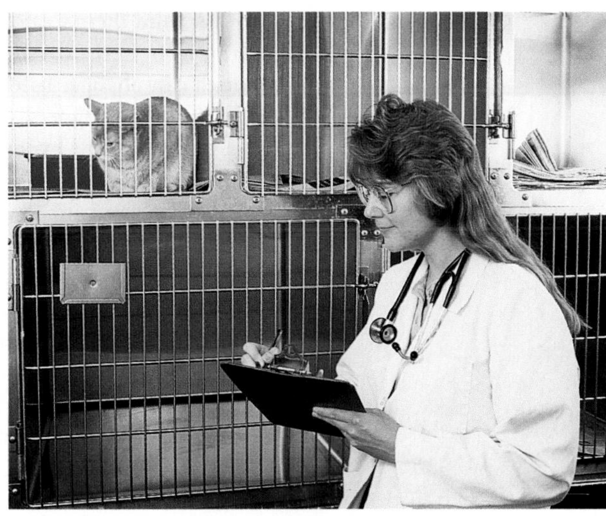

Figure 4 Collecting and analyzing data is part of scientific methods.

Discussion

Observation First Is it possible to form a hypothesis without first making observations? Explain. No; a hypothesis is formed from observations. L2

Reading Check

Answer one

Purpose to obtain data using a pan balance L1 IS **Logical-Mathematical**

Materials pan balance, sponge, water, Science Journal

Teaching Strategies

- Demonstrate the use of a balance.
- Review techniques for transporting a balance: be sure all riders are back to the zero point; place one hand under the balance and the other hand on the beam's support to carry the balance.

Analysis

Accept all reasonable answers. Students may suggest that the size of the sponges or how long each was soaked in water would affect results.

Assessment

Performance Have students use a meterstick to measure the length and width of their lab tables. Ask them to explain how they decided which units of measure to use. Use **Performance Assessment in the Science Classroom,** p. 97.

Teacher FYI

Galileo One of the first scientists credited with using the scientific method was Galileo. In his investigation of falling objects, the steps he used were (1) observation, (2) hypothesis, (3) mathematical analysis or deduction from hypothesis, (4) experimental test, and (5) revision of hypothesis.

Curriculum Connection

Language Arts Have students research a major discovery in life science and the person who made the discovery. Possible research subjects include Francesco Redi, William Harvey, Alexander Fleming, Barbara McClintock, and George Washington Carver. Have students use their findings to write newspaper articles describing their discoveries. L2 IS **Linguistic**

IDENTIFYING Misconceptions

Scientific Theory The word *theory* is used outside of science to mean "speculation" or "an idea that is uncertain." People often use the word when they are referring to a hypothesis, for example, *I have a theory about why I didn't do well on the test*, or *I have a theory that wearing blue brings me good luck.* Reinforce that a scientific theory is an accepted fact that scientists do not usually question until new evidence is presented.

Reading Check

Answer scientific knowledge resulting from observations and experiments

Teacher FYI

Scientist's Methods Scientists use many methods of investigation. They approach problems from a variety of perspectives and structure their research based on available data, tools, and time. Observations often generate new hypotheses that lead to additional testing.

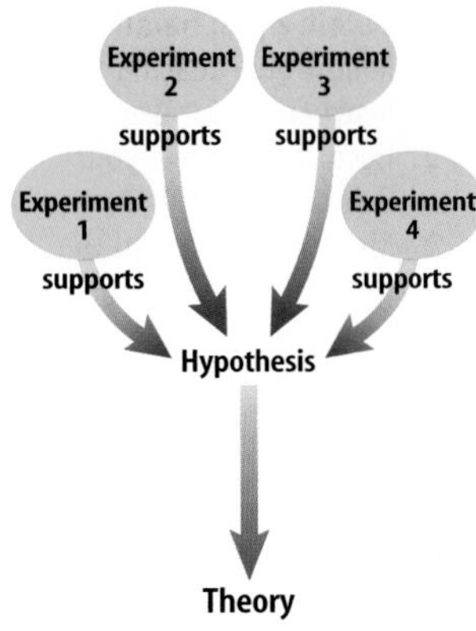

Figure 5 If data collected from several experiments over a period of time all support the hypothesis, it finally can be called a theory.

Report Results When using scientific methods, it is important to share information. The veterinary technician calls the cats' owner and tells him the results of her experiment. She tells him she has stopped using the deodorant cat litter.

The technician also writes a story for the clinic's newsletter that describes her experiment and shares her conclusions. She reports the limits of her experiment and explains that her results are not final. In science it is important to explain how an experiment can be made better if it is done again.

Developing Theories

After scientists report the results of experiments supporting their hypotheses, the results can be used to propose a scientific theory. When you watch a magician do a trick you might decide you have an idea or "theory" about how the trick works. Is your idea just a hunch or a scientific theory? A scientific **theory** is an explanation of things or events based on scientific knowledge that is the result of many observations and experiments. It is not a guess or someone's opinion. Many scientists repeat the experiment. If the results always support the hypothesis, the hypothesis can be called a theory, as shown in **Figure 5.**

Reading Check *What is a theory based on?*

A theory usually explains many hypotheses. For example, an important theory in life sciences is the cell theory. Scientists made observations of cells and experimented for more than 100 years before enough information was collected to propose a theory. Hypotheses about cells in plants and animals are combined in the cell theory.

A valid theory raises many new questions. Data or information from new experiments might change conclusions and theories can change. Later in this chapter you will read about the theory of spontaneous generation and how this theory changed as scientists used experiments to study new hypotheses.

Laws A scientific **law** is a statement about how things work in nature that seems to be true all the time. Although laws can be modified as more information becomes known, they are less likely to change than theories. Laws tell you what will happen under certain conditions but do not necessarily explain why it happened. For example, in life science you might learn about laws of heredity. These laws explain how genes are inherited but do not explain how genes work. Due to the great variety of living things, laws that describe them are few. It is unlikely that a law about how all cells work will ever be developed.

Active Reading

Learning Journal In this strategy, students analyze their own learning processes. Have students fold a paper in half. On the left, have them record what they have learned about a topic. On the right, have them record the page number of the text and any illustrations that helped them learn it. Have students write a Learning Journal about scientific methods. L2

Cultural Diversity

Development of Cell Theory One theory in life science that has been widely accepted by scientists is the cell theory. The cell theory originated through the work of English scientist Robert Hooke in 1665. Almost two hundred years later, the works of three German scientists—Matthias Schleiden, Theodor Schwann, and Rudolph Virchow—were incorporated to form the modern cell theory.

Scientific Methods Help Answer Questions You can use scientific methods to answer all sorts of questions. Your questions may be as simple as "Where did I leave my house key?" or as complex as "Will global warming cause the polar ice caps to melt?" You probably have had to find the answer to the first question. Someday you might try to find the answer to the second question. Using these scientific methods does not guarantee that you will get an answer. Often scientific methods just lead to more questions and more experiments. That's what science is about—continuing to look for the best answers to your questions.

Applying Science

Does temperature affect the rate of bacterial reproduction?

Some bacteria make you sick. Other bacteria, however, are used to produce foods like cheese and yogurt. Understanding how quickly bacteria reproduce can help you avoid harmful bacteria and use helpful bacteria. It's important to know things that affect how quickly bacteria reproduce. How do you think temperature will affect the rate of bacterial reproduction? A student makes the hypothesis that bacteria will reproduce more quickly as the temperature increases.

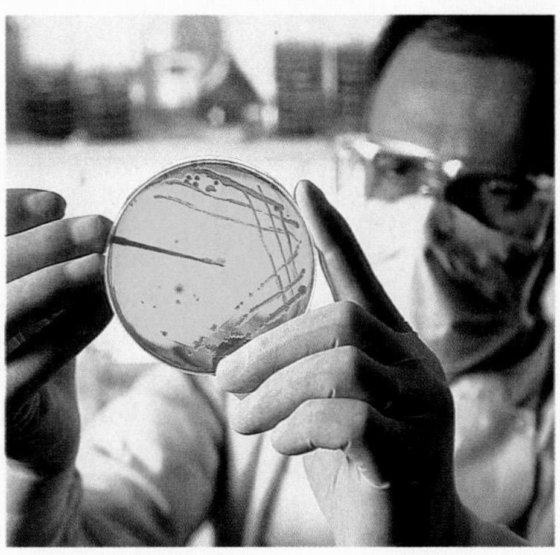

Identifying the Problem

The table below lists the reproduction-doubling rates at specific temperatures for one type of bacteria. A rate of 2.0 means that the number of bacteria doubled two times that hour (e.g., 100 to 200 to 400).

Bacterial Reproductive Rates

Temperature (°C)	Doubling Rate per Hour
20.5	2.0
30.5	3.0
36.0	2.5
39.2	1.2

Look at the table. What conclusions can you draw from the data?

Solving the Problem

1. Do the data in the table support the student's hypothesis?
2. How would you write a hypothesis about the relationship between bacterial reproduction and temperature?
3. Make a list of other factors that might have influenced the results in the table.
4. Are you satisfied with these data? List other things that you wish you knew.
5. Describe an experiment that would help you test these other ideas.

Activity

Article Review Have students obtain articles from science magazines, journals, or newspapers that describe scientific studies. As they read their articles, have students circle passages that describe the use of scientific methods. Ask them each to prepare an oral report that summarizes the content of the article and describes how scientific methods were used. L2 LS **Logical-Mathematical**

Applying Science

Answers

1. Not completely; doubling increases to a certain temperature, and then decreases.
2. Possible answer: Bacteria reproduce more quickly as temperature rises until a certain temperature is reached; then rate falls.
3. Other possible influences: Was the light always the same? Did the bacteria have the same amount of space to grow? Were the bacteria always in the same medium? Check that students' experiments test only one variable at a time.
4. Answers will vary. Accept reasonable responses.
5. Answers will vary depending on responses to question 4. Look for variables and controls in student descriptions.

Differentiated Instruction

Learning Disabled Invite students to design a bulletin board showing the steps in scientific methods using pictures from magazines. L2 LS **Visual-Spatial**

Challenge Students can investigate how the use of electron microscopes changed theories about cell structure. Have them observe labeled photomicrographs of plant or animal cells taken by light and electron microscopes. They can make a table that compares and contrasts structures seen in both photos. L3

Quick Demo

Measuring Coins

Materials nickel, dime, other coins, calipers, triple-beam balance

Estimated Time 20 minutes

Procedure Show students a nickel and a dime. Tell them the nickel has a mass of about 5 g and the dime is 1 mm thick. Using a triple-beam balance and calipers, have students determine the mass and thickness of other coins they have. L2

IDENTIFYING Misconceptions

Gravity and Weight Students may not understand that the weight of an object can vary, depending on the force of gravity. Explain that an object on the moon weighs less than an object on Earth because the pull of gravity is weaker on the moon than on Earth. However, the amount of matter (mass) that makes up the object does not change with location.

Reading Check

Answer to be able to repeat an experiment; to have valid results

Discussion

Safety Symbols What is the purpose of safety symbols? Each safety symbol alerts experimenters to a potential danger associated with a particular situation. L2

Figure 6 Your food often is measured in metric units. Nutritional information on the label is listed in grams or milligrams.

The label of this juice bottle shows you that it contains 473 mL of juice.

Measuring with Scientific Units

An important part of most scientific investigations is making accurate measurements. Think about things you use every day that are measured. Ingredients in your hamburger, hot dog, potato chips, or soft drink are measured in units such as grams and milliliters, as shown in **Figure 6.** The water you drink, the gas you use, and the electricity needed for a CD player are measured, too.

Reading Check *Why is it important to make accurate measurements?*

In your classroom or laboratory this year, you will use the same standard system of measurement scientists use to communicate and understand each other's research and results. This system is called the International System of Units, or SI. For example, you may need to calculate the distance a bird flies in kilometers. Perhaps you will be asked to measure the amount of air your lungs can hold in liters or the mass of an automobile in kilograms. Some of the SI units are shown in **Table 1.**

Table 1 Common SI Measurements

Measurement	Unit	Symbol	Equal to
Length	1 millimeter 1 centimeter 1 meter 1 kilometer	mm cm m km	0.001 (1/1,000) m 0.01 (1/100) m 100 cm 1,000 m
Volume	1 milliliter 1 liter	mL L	0.001 (1/1,000) L 1,000 mL
Mass	1 gram 1 kilogram 1 tonne	g kg t	1,000 mg 1,000 g 1,000 kg = 1 metric ton

Teacher FYI

SI in the U.S. The U.S. is the only industrialized country that has not officially adopted SI. To compete in world markets, many products made in the U.S. are labeled in SI and customary units. Students can hunt for five items from their homes marked with both types of measures.

Cultural Diversity

Ancient Measurements The ancient Chinese system of weights and measures included an acoustical dimension. The quantity of content in a vessel was defined by both weight and by the pitch produced when the vessel was struck. Have students research and report on other measurement instruments and systems. Students might investigate the cubit and thermoscope or the history of the metric system. L3

14 ◆ A CHAPTER 1 Exploring and Classifying Life

Safety First

Doing science is usually much more interesting than just reading about it. Some of the scientific equipment that you will use in your classroom or laboratory is the same as what scientists use. Laboratory safety is important. In many states, a student can participate in a laboratory class only when wearing proper eye protection. Don't forget to wash your hands after handling materials. Following safety rules, as shown in **Figure 7,** will protect you and others from injury during your lab experiences. Symbols used throughout your text will alert you to situations that require special attention. Some of these symbols are shown below. A description of each symbol is in the Safety Symbols chart at the front of this book.

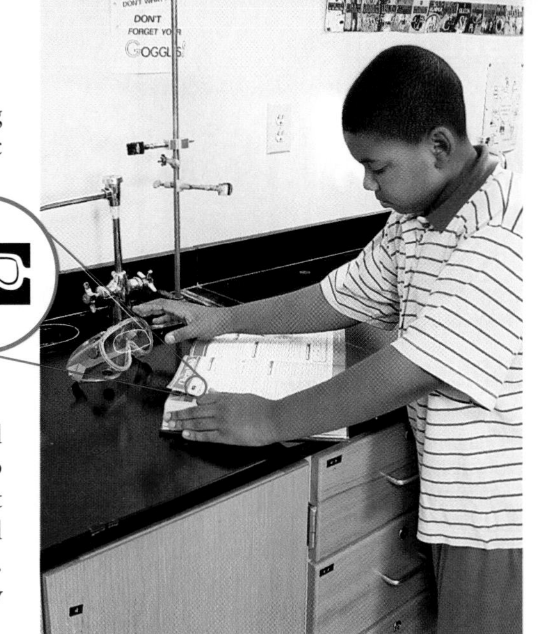

Figure 7 Proper eye protection should be worn whenever you see this safety symbol.
Predict *what might happen if you do not wear eye protection in the lab.*

section  review

Summary

The Work of Science

- Science is an organized way of studying things and finding answers to questions.

Solving Problems and Developing Theories

- Scientific methods are procedures used to solve problems and answer questions.
- A theory is an explanation based on many scientific observations.

Measuring with Scientific Units

- Scientists use the SI system for measurements.

Safety First

- Follow safety rules in the lab.

Self Check

1. **Describe** scientific methods.
2. **Infer** why it is important to test only one variable at a time during an experiment.
3. **Identify** the SI unit you would use to measure the width of your classroom.
4. **Compare and contrast** a theory with a hypothesis.
5. **Think Critically** Can the veterinary technician in this section be sure that deodorant caused the cats' skin problems? How could she improve her experiment?

Applying Skills

6. **Write a paper** that explains what the veterinary technician discovered from her experiment.

Caption Answer

Figure 7 something might accidentally enter the eye and cause permanent damage resulting in a loss of vision

3 Assess

DAILY INTERVENTION

Check for Understanding

Intrapersonal Have students make a set of flash cards they can use to review important terms from this section. L1

Reteach

Scientific Methods Divide the class into groups. Give each student in a group a slip of paper labeled with a step of a scientific method. After all the papers have been distributed, have students arrange themselves in a line that shows the order in which the steps are often carried out. Have groups compare their results and discuss why each group may not necessarily have the steps in the same order. L2

Assessment

Portfolio Safety is just as important at home as it is in the laboratory. For each safety symbol in the chart at the front of the book, have students write one safety rule to follow at home in the kitchen, bathroom, or outdoors. Use **Performance Assessment in the Science Classroom,** p. 157. L1

section 1 review

1. State the problem, gather information, form a hypothesis, experiment to test the hypothesis, analyze data, and draw conclusions.
2. so the scientist can understand which condition caused the results
3. meters
4. theory—an explanation based on many observations; hypothesis—a testable prediction
5. Possible answer: Both cats may not be allergic to the same thing. She could repeat the experiment, this time giving the other cat non-deodorized litter. If the skin problem clears up, she has likely identified the problem.
6. The paper should include observations that led to stating the problem, how she gathered the information to form the hypothesis, how she experimented to test the hypothesis, analyzed the data, drew conclusions, and reported the results.

1 Motivate

INTERACTIVE CHALKBOARD
PowerPoint® Presentations

Bellringer

Section Focus Transparencies also are available on the Interactive Chalkboard CD-ROM.  

Section 2 Section Focus Transparency **Most Enlightening**

Have you ever seen a house plant growing toward the window? Most plants grow toward the light. This bending is caused by a plant hormone that makes plant cells stretch and grow in the direction of the light source.

1. Why do plants need light?
2. What would happen if you gave the pot a half turn?
3. What does this plant need to live?

Tie to Prior Knowledge

Living Things Students will have ideas about characteristics and needs of all living things. Ask them to name traits and needs that all organisms share. Record responses on the board. L2

section 2

Living Things

as you read

***What* You'll Learn**

- **Distinguish** between living and nonliving things.
- **Identify** what living things need to survive.

***Why* It's Important**

All living things, including you, have many of the same traits.

Review Vocabulary
raw materials: substances needed by organisms to make other necessary substances

New Vocabulary
- organism
- cell
- homeostasis

What are living things like?

What does it mean to be alive? If you walked down your street after a thunderstorm, you'd probably see earthworms on the sidewalk, birds flying, clouds moving across the sky, and puddles of water. You'd see living and nonliving things that are alike in some ways. For example, birds and clouds move. Earthworms and water feel wet when they are touched. Yet, clouds and water are nonliving things, and birds and earthworms are living things. Any living thing is called an **organism.**

Organisms vary in size from the microscopic bacteria in mud puddles to gigantic oak trees and are found just about everywhere. They have different behaviors and food needs. In spite of these differences, all organisms have similar traits. These traits determine what it means to be alive.

Living Things Are Organized If you were to look at almost any part of an organism, like a plant leaf or your skin, under a microscope, you would see that it is made up of small units called cells. A **cell** is the smallest unit of an organism that carries on the functions of life. Some organisms are composed of just one cell while others are composed of many cells. Cells take in materials from their surroundings and use them in complex ways. Each cell has an orderly structure and contains hereditary material. The hereditary material contains instructions for cellular organization and function. **Figure 8** shows some organisms that are made of many cells. All the things that these organisms can do are possible because of what their cells can do.

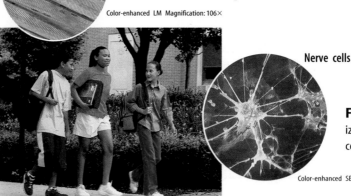

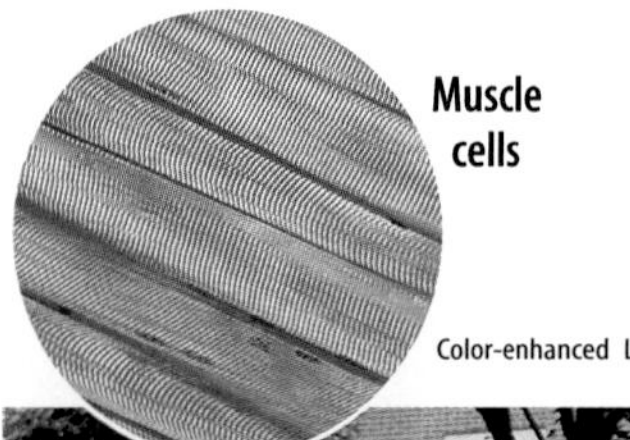
Muscle cells

Color-enhanced LM Magnification: 106×

Nerve cells

Color-enhanced SEM Magnification: 2500×

Figure 8 Your body is organized into many different types of cells. Two types are shown here.

Section 2 Resource Manager

Chapter *FAST FILE* Resources
- Transparency Activity, p. 45
- Directed Reading for Content Mastery, p. 18
- Enrichment, p. 30
- Reinforcement, p. 26

Cultural Diversity, pp. 7, 9

Living Things Respond Living things interact with their surroundings. Watch your cat when you use your electric can opener. Does your cat come running to find out what's happening even when you're not opening a can of cat food? The cat in **Figure 9** ran in response to a stimulus—the sound of the can opener. Anything that causes some change in an organism is a stimulus (plural, *stimuli*). The reaction to a stimulus is a response. Often that response results in movement, such as when the cat runs toward the sound of the can opener. To carry on its daily activity and to survive, an organism must respond to stimuli.

Living things also respond to stimuli that occur inside them. For example, water or food levels in organisms' cells can increase or decrease. The organisms then make internal changes to keep the right amounts of water and food in their cells. Their temperature also must be within a certain range. An organism's ability to keep the proper conditions inside no matter what is going on outside the organism is called **homeostasis.** Homeostasis is a trait of all living things.

Figure 9 Some cats respond to a food stimulus even when they are not hungry.
Infer *why a cat comes running when it hears a can opener.*

What are some internal stimuli living things respond to?

Living Things Use Energy Staying organized and carrying on activities like homeostasis require energy. The energy used by most organisms comes either directly or indirectly from the Sun. Plants and some other organisms use the Sun's energy and the raw materials carbon dioxide and water to make food. You and most other organisms can't use the energy of sunlight directly. Instead, you take in and use food as a source of energy. You get food by eating plants or other organisms that ate plants. Most organisms, including plants, also must take in oxygen in order to release the energy of foods.

Some bacteria live at the bottom of the oceans and in other areas where sunlight cannot reach. They can't use the Sun's energy to produce food. Instead, the bacteria use energy stored in some chemical compounds and the raw material carbon dioxide to make food. Unlike most other organisms, many of these bacteria do not need oxygen to release the energy that is found in their food.

Topic: Homeostasis
Visit booka.msscience.com for Web links to information about homeostasis.

Activity Describe the external stimuli and the corresponding internal changes for three different situations.

2 Teach

Quick Demo

Plant Responses

Materials mimosa plant

Estimated Time 5 minutes

Procedure Responses in plants are usually less obvious than in animals. However, if you touch a mimosa plant, all the small leaflets on the branch fold upward. Use a mimosa plant to demonstrate this rapid response.

Caption Answer

Figure 9 The cat is responding to the stimulus of the sound of the can opener which means food to the cat.

Reading Check

Answer water and food levels, temperature

Use an Analogy

Car Necessities Compare the homeostasis that must be maintained by the body to the conditions necessary for a car to function. For example, a car must have fuel, oil, and other fluids in proper balance in order to run. In the same way, organisms must have fuel and other materials in order to remain alive. L2

Differentiated Instruction

Learning Disabled Have students choose and draw a scene on poster board or mural paper. Have them label the objects in the drawing as living or nonliving. L1 LS **Visual-Spatial**

Fun Fact

Some bacteria can use petroleum as a food source. These bacteria have been used to help clean up oil spills.

Discussion

Seed Development How does an acorn grow and develop? An acorn sprouts and produces roots, stems, and leaves that continue to grow for years. As it grows, it takes in substances from the air and soil and changes those substances into living cells. It continues to add new cells and tissues to replace those that wear out. L2

Nonliving Movement Students may think that all things that move are alive. Refer to page 6F for teaching strategies that address this misconception.

Teacher FYI

Energy Uses Nonliving things use energy just as living things do. Windmills, solar calculators, solar panels, and thunderclouds all use energy from their environments and change it into different forms. However, living things take in energy from their environments and use it for specialized purposes such as growth, development, and reproduction.

Living Things Grow and Develop When a puppy is born, it might be small enough to hold in one hand. After the same dog is fully grown, you might not be able to hold it at all. How does this happen? The puppy grows by taking in raw materials, like milk from its female parent, and making more cells. Growth of many-celled organisms, such as the puppy, is mostly due to an increase in the number of cells. In one-celled organisms, growth is due to an increase in the size of the cell.

Organisms change as they grow. Puppies can't see or walk when they are born. In eight or nine days, their eyes open, and their legs become strong enough to hold them up. All of the changes that take place during the life of an organism are called development. **Figure 10** shows how four different organisms changed as they grew.

The length of time an organism is expected to live is its life span. Adult dogs can live for 20 years and a cat for 25 years. Some organisms have a short life span. Mayflies live only one day, but a land tortoise can live for more than 180 years. Some bristlecone pine trees have been alive for more than 4,600 years. Your life span is about 80 years.

Figure 10 Complete development of an organism can take a few days or several years. The pictures below show the development of a dog, a human, a pea plant, and a butterfly.

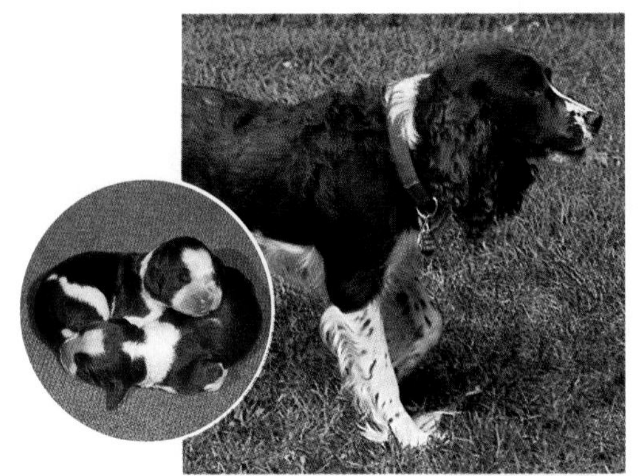

Science Journal

Characteristics of Living Things Have students choose an animal that they have observed. In their Science Journals, have them write an essay explaining how their observations show that the animal is a living organism. L1 IN **Linguistic**

Curriculum Connection

Math Have students obtain data that illustrates how they have changed as they have grown older. Ask them to research their heights at three different ages. (If this information is not available at home, have students obtain the data from their school records.) Then have students work in pairs to measure their current heights. Ask students to present their results as bar graphs. L2 IN **Logical-Mathematical** P

Figure 11 Living things reproduce themselves in many different ways. A *Paramecium* reproduces by dividing into two. Beetles, like most insects, reproduce by laying eggs. Every spore released by the puffballs can grow into a new fungus.

Living Things Reproduce Cats, dogs, alligators, fish, birds, bees, and trees eventually reproduce. They make more of their own kind. Some bacteria reproduce every 20 minutes while it might take a pine tree two years to produce seeds. **Figure 11** shows some ways organisms reproduce.

Without reproduction, living things would not exist to replace those individuals that die. An individual cat can live its entire life without reproducing. However, if cats never reproduced, all cats soon would disappear.

Reading Check *Why is reproduction important?*

What do living things need?

What do you need to live? Do you have any needs that are different from those of other living things? To survive, all living things need a place to live and raw materials. The raw materials that they require and the exact place where they live can vary.

A Place to Live The environment limits where organisms can live. Not many kinds of organisms can live in extremely hot or extremely cold environments. Most cannot live at the bottom of the ocean or on the tops of mountains. All organisms also need living space in their surroundings. For example, thousands of penguins build their nests on an island. When the island becomes too crowded, the penguins fight for space and some may not find space to build nests. An organism's surroundings must provide for all of its needs.

Social Development Human infants quickly develop their first year of life. Research to find out how infants interact socially at different stages of development. Make a chart that shows changes from birth to one year old.

Visual Learning

Figure 11 How do these organisms reproduce? Beetles lay eggs, a fungus releases spores, and a paramecium undergoes cell division to become two organisms. L2

Activity

Illustrate Living Things Label five sheets of paper with one of the subheads in this section. Divide the class into five groups. Give each group a sheet of paper. Ask group members to cut pictures from magazines that illustrate the subhead, to paste the pictures on the paper, and write a caption for each picture. When all groups have finished their tasks, combine the pages into a booklet titled "How Living Things Are Alike." L1 COOP LEARN

Reading Check

Answer Organisms must reproduce to replace members of their species that die, or the species will become extinct.

Development 1 month: movements are clumsy, throaty sounds can be made; 3 months: can sit up with assistance and laugh; 6 months: birth weight doubles, can roll over, sit alone and babble; 9 months: can crawl and repeat syllables; 1 year: birth weight triples, can walk and speak first words

Teacher FYI

Survival All the characteristics of living things are needed for survival of the individual, except for reproduction. Reproduction is needed for survival of the species.

Differentiated Instruction

English-Language Learners Have students name the characteristics and needs of living things that can be observed in a classroom aquarium or terrarium. Have them make a poster that shows two of the organisms and their characteristics. L1

Caption Answer

Figure 12 Plants take in water through their roots.

3 Assess

DAILY INTERVENTION

Check for Understanding

Linguistic Have students use information in the chapter to compare and contrast characteristics of life of plants and animals. They should then write a paragraph concerning their findings. L2

Reteach

Cards of Life Write the characteristics of living things on 3" × 5" cards. Have students draw a card and give an example of the characteristic. L1

Assessment

Process Have students heat water in a beaker and dissolve as much sugar in the beaker as they can. Tie a string around a stirring rod. Place the rod across the top of the beaker so the string is immersed in the cooled water. Leave the string in the beaker until sugar crystals begin to grow. Ask students why these crystals are not alive. They have none of the other characteristics of living things. Use **Performance Assessment in the Science Classroom,** p. 89. L1

Figure 12 You and a corn plant each take in and give off about 2 L of water in a day. Most of the water you take in is from water you drink or from foods you eat. **Infer** *where plants get water to transport materials.*

Raw Materials Water is important for all living things. Plants and animals take in and give off large amounts of water each day, as shown in **Figure 12.** Organisms use homeostasis to balance the amounts of water lost with the amounts taken in. Most organisms are composed of more than 50 percent water. You are made of 60 to 70 percent water. Organisms use water for many things. For example, blood, which is about 90 percent water, transports digested food and wastes in animals. Plants have a watery sap that transports materials between roots and leaves.

Living things are made up of substances such as proteins, fats, and sugars. Animals take in most of these substances from the foods they eat. Plants and some bacteria make them using raw materials from their surroundings. These important substances are used over and over again. When organisms die, substances in their bodies are broken down and released into the soil or air. The substances can then be used again by other living organisms. Some of the substances in your body might once have been part of a butterfly or an apple tree.

At the beginning of this section, you learned that things such as clouds, sidewalks, and puddles of water are not living things. Now do you understand why? Clouds, sidewalks, and water do not reproduce, use energy, or have other traits of living things.

section 2 review

Summary

What are living things like?

- A cell is the smallest unit of an organism that carries on the functions of life.
- Anything that causes some change in an organism is a stimulus.
- Organisms use energy to stay organized and perform activities like homeostasis.
- All of the changes that take place during an organism's life are called development.

What do living things need?

- Living things need a place to live, water, and food.

Self Check

1. **Identify** the source of energy for most organisms.
2. **List** five traits that most organisms have.
3. **Infer** why you would expect to see cells if you looked at a section of a mushroom cap under a microscope.
4. **Determine** what most organisms need to survive.
5. **Think Critically** Why is homeostasis important to organisms?

Applying Skills

6. **Use a Database** Use references to find the life span of ten animals. Use your computer to make a database. Then, graph the life spans from shortest to longest.

  booka.msscience.com/self_check_quiz

section 2 review

1. the Sun
2. Living things are organized, respond, take in and use energy, grow and develop, and reproduce.
3. All living things are made of cells.
4. Organisms need raw materials and a place to live.
5. Without homeostasis—the maintaining of proper conditions inside an organism regardless of external conditions—the organism would die.
6. Life spans will vary in different references. Sample data (in years): humans: 76; horses: 30; cows: 24; dogs: 15; cats: 12; turtles: 125; elephants: 60; penguins: 23; shrews: 1, snakes: 11; spiders: 3

section 3

Where does life come from?

Life Comes from Life

You've probably seen a fish tank, like the one in **Figure 13,** that is full of algae. How did the algae get there? Before the seventeenth century, some people thought that insects and fish came from mud, that earthworms fell from the sky when it rained, and that mice came from grain. These were logical conclusions at that time, based on repeated personal experiences. The idea that living things come from nonliving things is known as **spontaneous generation.** This idea became a theory that was accepted for several hundred years. When scientists began to use controlled experiments to test this theory, the theory changed.

Reading Check *Why did the theory of spontaneous generation change?*

Spontaneous Generation and Biogenesis From the late seventeenth century through the middle of the eighteenth century, experiments were done to test the theory of spontaneous generation. Although these experiments showed that spontaneous generation did not occur in most cases, they did not disprove it entirely.

It was not until the mid-1800s that the work of Louis Pasteur, a French chemist, provided enough evidence to disprove the theory of spontaneous generation. It was replaced with **biogenesis** (bi oh JE nuh suss), which is the theory that living things come only from other living things.

Figure 13 The sides of this tank were clean and the water was clear when the aquarium was set up. Algal cells, which were not visible on plants and fish, reproduced in the tank. So many algal cells are present now that the water is cloudy.

as you read

***What* You'll Learn**

- **Describe** experiments about spontaneous generation.
- **Explain** how scientific methods led to the idea of biogenesis.

***Why* It's Important**

You can use scientific methods to try to find out about events that happened long ago or just last week. You can even use them to predict how something will behave in the future.

Review Vocabulary

contaminate: to make impure by coming into contact with an unwanted substance

New Vocabulary

- spontaneous generation
- biogenesis

Section 3 Resource Manager

Chapter *FAST FILE* Resources

Transparency Activity, p. 46

Directed Reading for Content Mastery, p. 19

Enrichment, p. 31

Reinforcement, p. 27

Earth Science Critical Thinking/Problem Solving, pp. 1, 12, 14

1 Motivate

Bellringer

Section Focus Transparencies also are available on the Interactive Chalkboard CD-ROM. L2 ELL

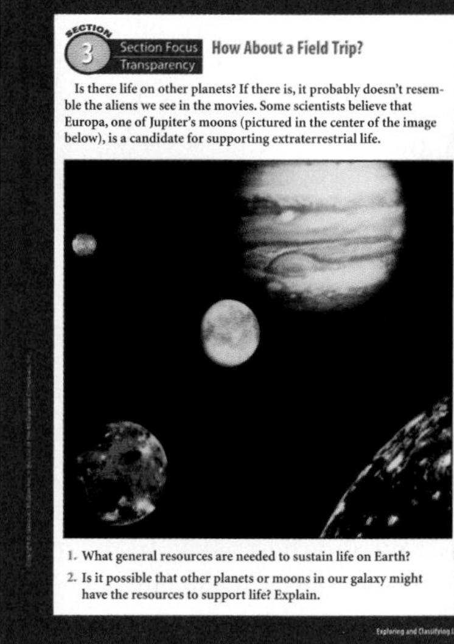

Section 3 Section Focus Transparency **How About a Field Trip?**

Is there life on other planets? If there is, it probably doesn't resemble the aliens we see in the movies. Some scientists believe that Europa, one of Jupiter's moons (pictured in the center of the image below), is a candidate for supporting extraterrestrial life.

1. What general resources are needed to sustain life on Earth?
2. Is it possible that other planets or moons in our galaxy might have the resources to support life? Explain.

Tie to Prior Knowledge

Life's Origins Review the characteristics and needs of living things. Elicit from volunteers their ideas on where organisms possessing such characteristics and needs came from. L2

2 Teach

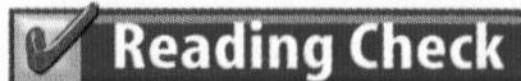

Reading Check

Answer experiments did not support it

Discussion

Keeping Foods Safe How did Pasteur's experiments lead to the development of pasteurization? He showed that heating killed bacteria that caused food to spoil. L2

SECTION 3 Where does life come from? A ◆ 21

Visualizing the Origins of Life

Have students examine the pictures and read the captions. Then ask the following questions.

What are the similarities of Spallanzani's and Redi's work? Students should note that both Spallanzani and Redi did experiments that questioned the idea of spontaneous generation.

What must have been present in the neck of the S-necked flasks used by Pasteur in his experiments? The necks of the S-neck flasks must have contained microorganisms, which contaminated the broth when the flask was tilted.

Activity

Matching Game Students should work in small groups to create and play a matching game based on the scientists in the this feature and their work. In the game, points should be awarded for correctly matching a scientist with his work. Have students explain the rules of their game to the class.

Fun Fact

A seventeenth-century recipe for mice called for sweaty underwear and wheat to be placed in an open container for 21 days.

Visual Learning

Figure 14 Have students create a poster showing the progression of scientific thought on life origins, as evidenced by the experiments in this feature.

NATIONAL GEOGRAPHIC **VISUALIZING THE ORIGINS OF LIFE**

Figure 14

For centuries scientists have theorized about the origins of life. As shown on this timeline, some examined spontaneous generation—the idea that nonliving material can produce life. More recently, scientists have proposed theories about the origins of life on Earth by testing hypotheses about conditions on early Earth.

1668 Francesco Redi put decaying meat in some jars, then covered half of them. When fly maggots appeared only on the uncovered meat (see below, left), Redi concluded that they had hatched from fly eggs and had not come from the meat.

1745 John Needham heated broth in sealed flasks. When the broth became cloudy with microorganisms, he mistakenly concluded that they developed spontaneously from the broth.

1768 Lazzaro Spallanzani boiled broth in sealed flasks for a longer time than Needham did. Only the ones he opened became cloudy with contamination.

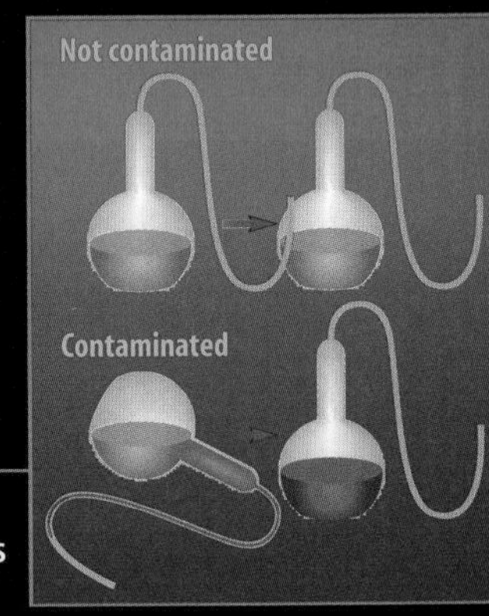

1859 Louis Pasteur disproved spontaneous generation by boiling broth in S-necked flasks that were open to the air. The broth became cloudy (see above, bottom right) only when a flask was tilted and the broth was exposed to dust in the S-neck.

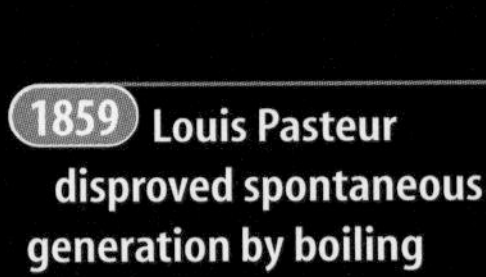

Gases of Earth's early atmosphere
Electric current
Oceanlike mixture forms
Cools
Materials in present-day cells

1953 Stanley Miller and Harold Urey sent electric currents through a mixture of gases like those thought to be in Earth's early atmosphere. When the gases cooled, they condensed to form an oceanlike liquid that contained materials such as amino acids, found in present-day cells.

1924 Alexander Oparin hypothesized that energy from the Sun, lightning, and Earth's heat triggered chemical reactions early in Earth's history. The newly-formed molecules washed into Earth's ancient oceans and became a part of what is often called the primordial soup.

Differentiated Instruction

Challenge Have students research world events that occurred in the years the experiments shown in this feature took place. Students can construct an expanded time line showing these events, and share their findings with the class. L3

Hearing Impaired Have students pantomime the work of one of the scientists who studied life's origins. Other students must guess which scientist is being represented.

Life's Origins

If living things can come only from other living things, how did life on Earth begin? Some scientists hypothesize that about 5 billion years ago, Earth's solar system was a whirling mass of gas and dust. They hypothesize that the Sun and planets were formed from this mass. It is estimated that Earth is about 4.6 billion years old. Rocks found in Australia that are more than 3.5 billion years old contain fossils of once-living organisms. Where did these living organisms come from?

Oparin's Hypothesis In 1924, a Russian scientist named Alexander I. Oparin suggested that Earth's early atmosphere had no oxygen but was made up of the gases ammonia, hydrogen, methane, and water vapor. Oparin hypothesized that these gases could have combined to form the more complex compounds found in living things.

Using gases and conditions that Oparin described, American scientists Stanley L. Miller and Harold Urey set up an experiment to test Oparin's hypothesis in 1953. Although the Miller-Urey experiment showed that chemicals found in living things could be produced, it did not prove that life began in this way.

For many centuries, scientists have tried to find the origins of life, as shown in **Figure 14.** Although questions about spontaneous generation have been answered, some scientists still are investigating ideas about life's origins.

Oceans Scientists hypothesize that Earth's oceans originally formed when water vapor was released into the atmosphere from many volcanic eruptions. Once it cooled, rain fell and filled Earth's lowland areas. Identify five lowland areas on Earth that are now filled with water. Record your answer in your Science Journal.

section 3 review

Summary

Life Comes from Life

- Spontaneous generation is the idea that living things come from nonliving things.
- The work of Louis Pasteur in 1859 disproved the theory of spontaneous generation.
- Biogenesis is the theory that living things come only from other living things.

Life's Origins

- Alexander I. Oparin hypothesized about the origin of life.
- The Miller-Urey experiment did not prove that Oparin's hypothesis was correct.

Self Check

1. **Compare and contrast** spontaneous generation with biogenesis.
2. **Describe** three controlled experiments that helped disprove the theory of spontaneous generation and led to the theory of biogenesis.
3. **Summarize** the results of the Miller-Urey experiment.
4. **Think Critically** How do you think life on Earth began?

Applying Skills

5. **Draw Conclusions** Where could the organisms have come from in the 1768 broth experiment described in **Figure 14?**

Science Online booka.msscience.com/self_check_quiz

Oceans Students may list five of Earth's oceans and seas.

Career Explore the jobs of oceanographers and what they might study.

Teacher FYI

Oparin's Theory When Oparin first presented his hypotheses on the origins of life, they received negative responses. It was only after continued retesting that his ideas began to be accepted.

3 Assess

DAILY INTERVENTION

Check for Understanding

Interpersonal Have groups of students write true and false statements concerning spontaneous generation and biogenesis and share them with each other. L2

Reteach

Making Charts Have students make a three-column chart to summarize the experiments described in this section. Columns should be headed *Experimenter*, *Summary of Experiment*, and *Conclusions*. L2 P

Assessment

Performance Have students review the results of Redi's experiment and write their interpretation. Jars left open to the air attracted flies, and maggots appeared on the meat. Flies could not get to the meat in the covered jars. Use **Performance Assessment in the Science Classroom,** p. 99.

section 3 review

1. spontaneous generation: living things come from nonliving matter; biogenesis: living things come only from other living things of the same kind
2. Students should describe the experiments performed by Redi, Pasteur, and Spallanzani.
3. Miller and Urey passed electricity through gasses as suggested by Oparin's hypothesis and produced chemicals found in living things.
4. Students' answers will vary. Accept all reasonable responses.
5. The organisms could have come from the air.

1 Motivate

Bellringer

Section Focus Transparencies also are available on the Interactive Chalkboard CD-ROM.

L2 ELL

Tie to Prior Knowledge

Real-Life Classification Ask students to identify real-life situations in which they need to classify a group of items. Possible responses may include organizing a collection of tapes or CDs, arranging canned goods in a pantry, and sorting beads used to make jewelry. Have volunteers explain the process they use in these instances. L2

Caption Answer

Figure 15 Possible answer: amphibians and all invertebrates

section 4

How are living things classified?

as you read

What You'll Learn

- **Describe** how early scientists classified living things.
- **Explain** how similarities are used to classify organisms.
- **Explain** the system of binomial nomenclature.
- **Demonstrate** how to use a dichotomous key.

Why It's Important

Knowing how living things are classified will help you understand the relationships that exist among all living things.

Review Vocabulary

common name: a nonscientific term that may vary from region to region

New Vocabulary

- phylogeny
- kingdom
- binomial nomenclature
- genus

Classification

If you go to a library to find a book about the life of Louis Pasteur, where do you look? Do you look for it among the mystery or sports books? You expect to find a book about Pasteur's life with other biography books. Libraries group similar types of books together. When you place similar items together, you classify them. Organisms also are classified into groups.

History of Classification When did people begin to group similar organisms together? Early classifications included grouping plants that were used in medicines. Animals were often classified by human traits such as courageous—for lions—or wise—for owls.

More than 2,000 years ago, a Greek named Aristotle observed living things. He decided that any organism could be classified as either a plant or an animal. Then he broke these two groups into smaller groups. For example, animal categories included hair or no hair, four legs or fewer legs, and blood or no blood. **Figure 15** shows some of the organisms Aristotle would have grouped together. For hundreds of years after Aristotle, no one way of classifying was accepted by everyone.

Figure 15 Using Aristotle's classification system, all animals without hair would be grouped together.
List *other animals without hair that Aristotle would have put in this group.*

Section 4 Resource Manager

Chapter *Fast File* Resources

- Transparency Activity, pp. 47, 49–50
- Directed Reading for Content Mastery, pp. 19, 20
- Enrichment, p. 32
- Reinforcement, p. 28
- MiniLAB, p. 4
- Lab Worksheets, pp. 5–6, 7–8
- Lab Activity, pp. 11–13

Lab Management and Safety, p. 65

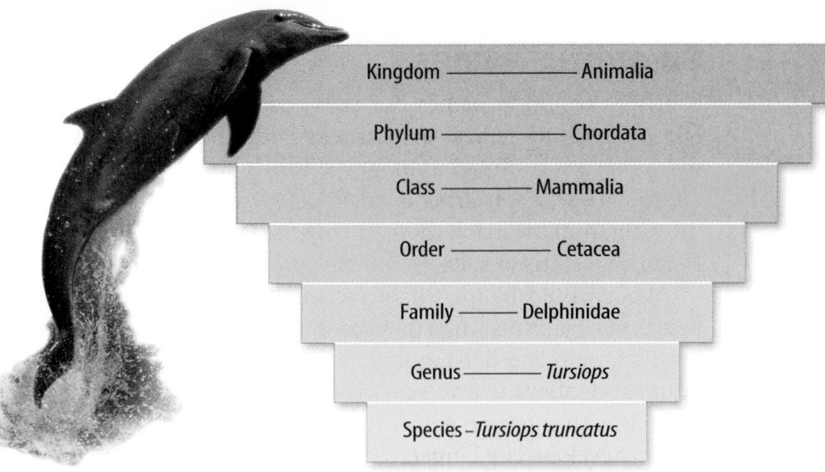

Figure 16 The classification of the bottle-nosed dolphin shows that it is in the order Cetacea. This order includes whales and porpoises.

Linnaeus In the late eighteenth century, Carolus Linnaeus, a Swedish naturalist, developed a new system of grouping organisms. His classification system was based on looking for organisms with similar structures. For example, plants that had similar flower structure were grouped together. Linnaeus's system eventually was accepted and used by most other scientists.

Modern Classification Like Linnaeus, modern scientists use similarities in structure to classify organisms. They also use similiarities in both external and internal features. Specific characteristics at the cellular level, such as the number of chromosomes, can be used to infer the degree of relatedness among organisms. In addition, scientists study fossils, hereditary information, and early stages of development. They use all of this information to determine an organism's phylogeny. **Phylogeny** (fi LAH juh nee) is the evolutionary history of an organism, or how it has changed over time. Today, it is the basis for the classification of many organisms.

Reading Check ***What information would a scientist use to determine an organism's phylogeny?***

Six Kingdoms A classification system commonly used today groups organisms into six kingdoms. A **kingdom** is the first and largest category. Organisms are placed into kingdoms based on various characteristics. Kingdoms can be divided into smaller groups. The smallest classification category is a species. Organisms that belong to the same species can mate and produce fertile offspring. To understand how an organism is classified, look at the classification of the bottle-nosed dolphin in **Figure 16.** Some scientists propose that before organisms are grouped into kingdoms, they should be placed in larger groups called domains. One proposed system groups all organisms into three domains.

Topic: Domains
Visit booka.msscience.com for Web links to information about domains.

Activity List all the domains and give examples of organisms that are grouped in each domain.

2 Teach

Inquiry Lab

Classifying with Bones

Question While excavating for a new building, the skeleton of a large animal is found. How could scientists determine the classification of this animal?

Possible Materials photos of skeletons of mammoth, elephant, dinosaurs, and other large animals; real or model skeletons of smaller animals; books concerning fossils and animal structure

Estimated Time 1 class session

Teaching Strategies

- Students can look at photos of animal skeletons and determine how to use them to gain information about classification.
- Students can compare photos of mammoth and elephant skeletons and note similarities.
- Students can hypothesize what animals would have similar skeletons and then use pictures or bones of the animals to collect data; they can research to find out what scientists think.
- A trip to a museum may be planned to look at skeletons of larger animals. L2

For additional inquiry activities, see *Science Inquiry Labs.*

Reading Check

Answer similar structures, fossils, hereditary information, and early stages of development

Fun Fact

Amber is the hardened resin of some trees. Some amber contains fossils of insects that became trapped in the resin.

Differentiated Instruction

English-Language Learners Have students listen to a variety of songs and determine how the songs might be classified into different categories. L2

SECTION 4 How are living things classified? A ◆ 25

Quick Demo

Latin's Origins

Materials world map

Estimated Time 5 minutes

Procedure Use the map to point out the Roman Empire. Tell students that Latin originated there thousands of years ago. Explain that Latin was the basis of the Romance languages—Spanish, French, Italian, and Portuguese.

Use Science Words

Word Origin Have students find what language the word *genus* is from and its meaning in that language. Genus is Latin for "kind." L2

Use an Analogy

Chinese Naming The two-word naming system is similar to the structure of Chinese names. The first word in a Chinese name is that of the family and the second and third words are those of the individual. American and European names represent the same idea in reverse order. L2

Discussion

Classification Trivia Which classification group has the most members? Which has the fewest? Kingdom has the most; species has the fewest. L2

Caption Answer

Figure 17 Possible answers: Sea horses are not horses that live in the sea; wolverines are not small wolves.

Virtual Labs

Classification *How are living things classified into groups?*

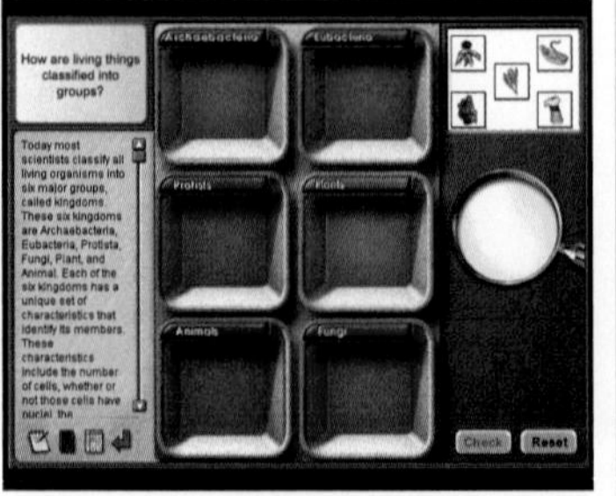

Scientific Names

Using common names can cause confusion. Suppose that Diego is visiting Jamaal. Jamaal asks Diego if he would like a soda. Diego is confused until Jamaal hands him a soft drink. At Diego's house, a soft drink is called pop. Jamaal's grandmother, listening from the living room, thought that Jamaal was offering Diego an ice-cream soda.

What would happen if life scientists used only common names of organisms when they communicated with other scientists? Many misunderstandings would occur, and sometimes health and safety are involved. In **Figure 17,** you see examples of animals with common names that can be misleading. A naming system developed by Linnaeus helped solve this problem. It gave each species a unique, two-word scientific name.

Figure 17 Common names can be misleading.

Sea lions are more closely related to seals than to lions. **Identify** *another misleading common name.*

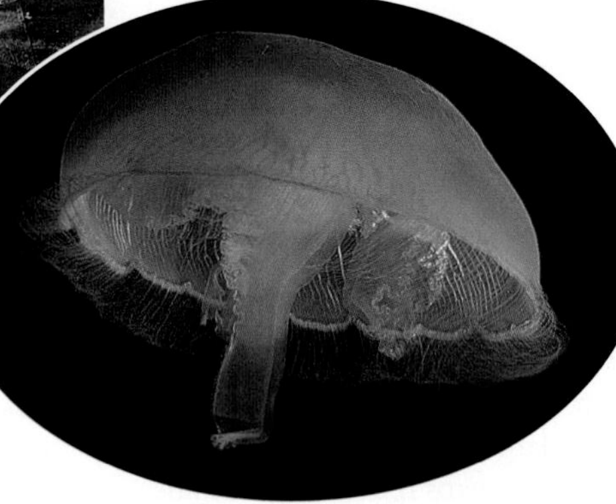

Jellyfish are neither fish nor jelly.

Binomial Nomenclature The two-word naming system that Linnaeus used to name the various species is called **binomial nomenclature** (bi NOH mee ul • NOH mun klay chur). It is the system used by modern scientists to name organisms. The first word of the two-word name identifies the genus of the organism. A **genus** is a group of similar species. The second word of the name might tell you something about the organism—what it looks like, where it is found, or who discovered it.

In this system, the tree species commonly known as red maple has been given the name *Acer rubrum.* The maple genus is *Acer.* The word *rubrum* is Latin for red, which is the color of a red maple's leaves in the fall. The scientific name of another maple is *Acer saccharum.* The Latin word for sugar is *saccharum.* In the spring, the sap of this tree is sweet.

Curriculum Connection

Math Ask students to explain how numbers are classified. Answers may include odd and even, real and imaginary, whole numbers and fractions, decimals and percents, and rational and irrational. L2

Teacher FYI

Classification Systems Aristotle's classification system remained in use for almost two thousand years. In the 16th and 17th centuries, there was renewed interest in classification when European explorers returned with unidentified species from other lands. In the 17th century, John Ray classified plants according to the structure of their seeds.

Figure 18 These two lizards have the same common name, iguana, but are two different species.

Uses of Scientific Names Two-word scientific names are used for four reasons. First, they help avoid mistakes. Both of the lizards shown in **Figure 18** have the name *iguana.* Using binomial nomenclature, the green iguana is named *Iguana iguana.* Someone who studied this *iguana,* shown in the left photo, would not be confused by information he or she read about *Dispsosaurus dorsalis,* the desert iguana, shown in the right photo. Second, organisms with similar evolutionary histories are classified together. Because of this, you know that organisms in the same genus are related. Third, scientific names give descriptive information about the species, like the maples mentioned earlier. Fourth, scientific names allow information about organisms to be organized easily and efficiently. Such information may be found in a book or a pamphlet that lists related organisms and gives their scientific names.

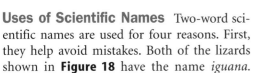

Reading Check *What are four functions of scientific names?*

Tools for Identifying Organisms

Tools used to identify organisms include field guides and dichotomous (di KAH tuh mus) keys. Using these tools is one way you and scientists solve problems scientifically.

Many different field guides are available. You will find some field guides at the back of this book. Most have descriptions and illustrations of organisms and information about where each organism lives. You can identify species from around the world using the appropriate field guide.

Communicating Ideas

Procedure

1. Find a **magazine picture of a piece of furniture** that can be used as a place to sit and to lie down.
2. Show the picture to ten people and ask them to tell you what word they use for this piece of furniture.
3. Keep a record of the answers in your **Science Journal.**

Analysis

1. In your Science Journal, infer how using common names can be confusing.
2. How do scientific names make communication among scientists easier?

Purpose Students ask people to give them the name of a common piece of furniture seen in a photo. L2 LS **Visual-Spatial**

Materials photo from magazine

Teaching Strategy Review how to collect and record data.

Analysis

1. More than one name might be used for the same object.
2. Each organism has a specific, unique name.

Assessment

Oral To further assess students' abilities to identify characteristic features, ask them to list traits of other common objects. L2

Reading Check

Answer to avoid mistakes, classify organisms with similar evolutionary histories together, give descriptive information about a species, help organize information about species

Make a Model

Object Dichotomy Have students list the characteristics of several related objects such as shoes, animals, or foods. Then have students use their lists to make a model dichotomous key. L1

Visual Learning

Figure 18 What traits do the desert iguana and green iguana share? clawed toes, scaly skin L2

Differentiated Instruction

Challenge Challenge students to identify an organism from its scientific name. Use *Musca domestica* (housefly), *Equus zebra* (zebra), and *Camelus dromedarius* (dromedary camel). Have students find other scientific names to present to their classmates. L3 LS

Activity

Using Keys Pass out taxonomic keys or field guides. Ask students to describe how these tools are used. Have them use the keys to identify a particular organism. Note that students may try to skip steps in keys. Point out that skipping steps often leads to the wrong identification. L2

Text Question Answer

Microtus pinetorum

3 Assess

DAILY INTERVENTION

Check for Understanding

Auditory-Musical Have students write a poem that demonstrates their understanding of binomial nomenclature and scientific names. L2

Reteach

Classification Develop understanding of modern classification by asking students to name the lowest taxonomic category for the organisms described. Ask: Which level contains a spider plant? species Which level contains all willow trees? genus Which level contains all plants? kingdom L2

Assessment

Performance Have students make a concept map to show how an address is like a classification system. The first step should be Country—United States. Use **Performance Assessment in the Science Classroom,** p. 161. L2 P

Dichotomous Keys A dichotomous key is a detailed list of identifying characteristics that includes scientific names. Dichotomous keys are arranged in steps with two descriptive statements at each step. If you learn how to use a dichotomous key, you can identify and name a species.

Did you know many types of mice exist? You can use **Table 2** to find out what type of mouse is pictured to the left. Start by choosing between the first pair of descriptions. The mouse has hair on its tail, so you go to 2. The ears of the mouse are small, so you go on to 3. The tail of the mouse is less that 25 mm. What is the name of this mouse according to the key?

Table 2 Key to Some Mice of North America

1. Tail hair	**a.** no hair on tail; scales show plainly; house mouse, *Mus musculus* **b.** hair on tail, go to 2
2. Ear size	**a.** ears small and nearly hidden in fur, go to 3 **b.** ears large and not hidden in fur, go to 4
3. Tail length	**a.** less than 25 mm; woodland vole, *Microtus pinetorum* **b.** more than 25 mm; prairie vole, *Microtus ochrogaster*
4. Tail coloration	**a.** sharply bicolor, white beneath and dark above; deer mouse, *Peromyscus maniculatus* **b.** darker above than below but not sharply bicolor; white-footed mouse, *Peromyscus leucopus*

section 4 review

Summary

Classification

- Organisms are classified into groups based on their similarities.
- Scientists today classify organisms into six kingdoms.
- Species is the smallest classification category.

Scientific Names

- Binomial nomenclature is the two-word naming system that gives organisms their scientific names.

Tools for Identifying Organisms

- Field guides and dichotomous keys are used to identify organisms.

Self Check

1. **State** Aristotle's and Linnaeus' contributions to classifying living things.
2. **Identify** a specific characteristic used to classify organisms.
3. **Describe** what each of the two words identifies in binomial nomenclature.
4. **Think Critically** Would you expect a field guide to have common names as well as scientific names? Why or why not?

Applying Skills

5. **Classify** Create a dichotomous key that identifies types of cars.

booka.msscience.com/self_check_quiz

section 4 review

1. Aristotle—two kingdoms: plants and animals; Linnaeus—binomial nomenclature
2. Students' answers will vary. Accept all reasonable responses.
3. first word is the genus and second word tells something about the organism
4. Yes. Field guides are also used by non-scientists.
5. Students' keys will vary and may divide cars by color, make, size, or other variable characteristics.

Classifying Seeds

Scientists use classification systems to show how organisms are related. How do they determine which features to use to classify organisms? In this lab, you will observe seeds and use their features to classify them.

Real-World Question

How can the features of seeds be used to develop a key to identify the seed?

Goals

- **Observe** the seeds and notice their features.
- **Classify** seeds using these features.

Materials

packets of seeds (10 different kinds)
magnifying lens
metric ruler

Safety Precautions

WARNING: *Some seeds may have been treated with chemicals. Do not put them in your mouth.*

Procedure

1. Copy the following data table in your Science Journal and record the features of each seed. Your table will have a column for each different type of seed you observe.

Seed Data

Feature	Type of Seed		
	corn	kidney bean	wheat
Color	yellow	dark brown	light brown
Length (mm)	10	17	5
Shape	triangle	oval	oval
Texture	smooth	smooth	smooth

2. Use the features to develop a key.
3. Exchange keys with another group. Can you use their key to identify seeds?

Conclude and Apply

1. **Determine** how different seeds can be classified.
2. **Explain** how you would classify a seed you had not seen before using your data table.
3. **Explain** why it is an advantage for scientists to use a standardized system to classify organisms. What observations did you make to support your answer?

Communicating Your Data

Compare your conclusions with those of other students in your class. **For more help, refer to the** Science Skill Handbook.

Real-World Question

Purpose Students observe seed features and then classify the seeds. L2 LS **Kinesthetic**

Process Skills observe and infer, classify, form operational definitions, communicate, make and use tables, compare and contrast

Time Required 45 minutes

Procedure

Alternate Materials Any objects may be used, but biological specimens should be used if possible.

Safety Precautions Use only edible seeds, not seeds that have been treated for planting.

Teaching Strategy Prepare packets of ten different kinds of easily classified seeds, such as black-eyed peas, squash, beans (lima, kidney, pinto, black), green peas, popcorn, seed corn, and sunflower.

Conclude and Apply

1. color, shape, size, texture, how they are attached to the plant
2. You would use the data table to categorize identifying characteristics of seeds.
3. Different classification systems could result in confusion. Answers should be based on the observation that students classified the same seeds in different ways.

Communicating Your Data

Comparisons may or may not result in agreement. If one group can use another group's key, the second group was successful.

Assessment

Performance Give students photocopies of ten different leaves. Have them devise and describe a classification system for the leaves. Use **Performance Assessment in the Science Classroom**, p. 121.

Real-World Question

Purpose Design and carry out an experiment using scientific methods to infer why brine shrimp live in salty waters. L2
COOP LEARN IN Interpersonal

Process Skills observe and infer, compare and contrast, recognize cause and effect, interpret data, hypothesize, communicate, make and use tables, make and use graphs, design an experiment, separate and control variables, measure in SI

Time Required 50 minutes on Day 1, 5 minutes a day for 3 days, 30 minutes to summarize

Materials Purchase brine shrimp eggs from a pet store or a biological supply house. Do not place too many brine shrimp eggs in each container. Brine shrimp are orange-colored and swim with a jerking motion. To maintain the brine shrimp, add a pinch of yeast to the container two or three times a week.

Safety Precautions Students should use care when working with live animals.

Form a Hypothesis

Possible Hypothesis Brine shrimp will best grow in a strong salt solution since they naturally live in salty lakes.

Test Your Hypothesis

Possible Procedures The same amount of brine shrimp eggs can be added to the three solutions and observed.

Design Your Own

Using Scientific Methods

Goals
- **Design** and carry out an experiment using scientific methods to infer why brine shrimp live in the ocean.
- **Observe** the jars for one week and notice whether the brine shrimp eggs hatch.

Possible Materials
500-mL, widemouthed containers (3)
brine shrimp eggs
small, plastic spoon
distilled water (500 mL)
weak salt solution (500 mL)
strong salt solution (500 mL)
labels (3)
magnifying lens

Safety Precautions

WARNING: *Protect eyes and clothing. Be careful when working with live organisms.*

Real-World Question

Brine shrimp are relatives of lobsters, crabs, crayfish, and the shrimp eaten by humans. They are often raised as a live food source in aquariums. In nature, they live in the oceans where fish feed on them. They can hatch from eggs that have been stored in a dry condition for many years. How can you use scientific methods to determine whether salt affects the hatching and growth of brine shrimp?

Brine shrimp

Form a Hypothesis

Based on your observations, form a hypothesis to explain how salt affects the hatching and growth of brine shrimp.

Test Your Hypothesis

Make a Plan

1. As a group, agree upon the hypothesis and decide how you will test it. Identify what results will confirm the hypothesis.

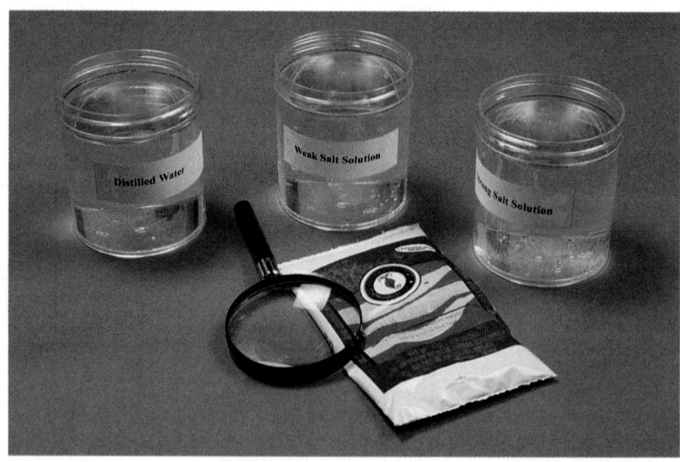

Alternative Inquiry Lab

Environmental Change Have students investigate how other environmental conditions, like temperature and light, might affect the development and growth of brine shrimp. Allow students to prepare variable salt solutions. Since brine shrimp are an important food for birds, have students hypothesize how changing salinity levels might affect both shrimp and bird populations. L2

2. **List** steps that you need to test your hypothesis. Be specific. Describe exactly what you will do at each step.
3. **List** your materials.
4. **Prepare** a data table in your Science Journal to record your data.
5. Read over your entire experiment to make sure that all planned steps are in logical order.
6. **Identify** any constants, variables, and controls of the experiment.

Follow Your Plan

1. Make sure your teacher approves your plan before you start.
2. Carry out the experiment as planned by your group.
3. While doing the experiment, record any observations and complete the data table in your Science Journal.
4. Use a bar graph to plot your results.

Analyze Your Data

1. **Describe** the contents of each jar after one week.
2. **Identify** your control in this experiment.
3. **Identify** your variable in this experiment.

Conclude and Apply

1. **Explain** whether or not the results support your hypothesis.
2. **Predict** the effect that increasing the amount of salt in the water would have on the brine shrimp eggs.
3. **Compare** your results with those of other groups.

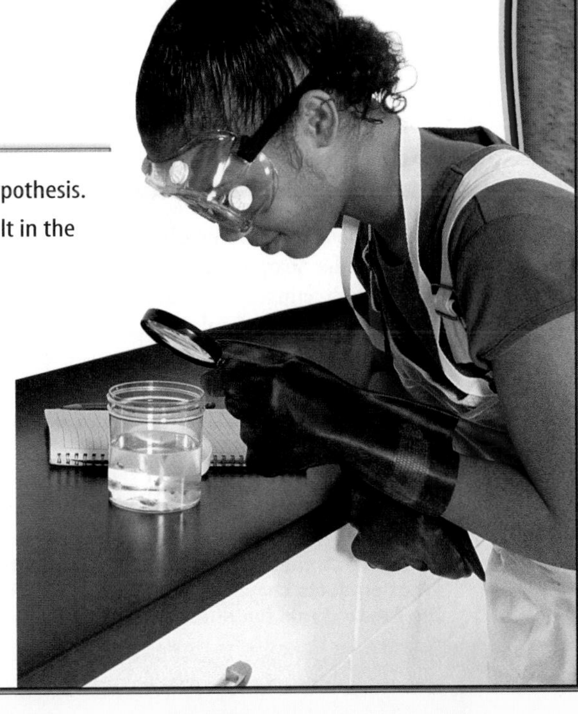

Communicating Your Data

Prepare a set of instructions on how to hatch brine shrimp to use to feed fish. Include diagrams and a step-by-step procedure.

Teaching Strategies

Prepare the solutions as follows:

- Dechlorinated water: Allow tap water to stand for 48 hours.
- Weak salt solution: Add 20 mL non-iodized salt to 4 L dechlorinated water. Stir until dissolved.
- Strong salt solution: Add 75 mL non-iodized salt to 4 L dechlorinated water. Stir until dissolved.

Expected Outcome Results likely will reflect that the brine shrimp grew best in the strong salt solution.

Analyze Your Data

Answers to Questions

1. There were no shrimp in the distilled water or weak salt solution. There were many shrimp in the strong salt solution.
2. The dechlorinated water without salt was the control.
3. The amount of salt in the water was the variable.

Error Analysis Have students compare their results and their hypotheses and explain any differences.

Conclude and Apply

1. Answers will be determined by students' hypotheses.
2. Answers will vary. Some may predict that more brine shrimp will hatch.
3. Results will vary.

Communicating Your Data

Instructions should include information on the amount of salt to add to the water, light conditions, and so on. Students can use word-processing software programs to write their instructions.

Assessment

Performance Have students design an experiment to determine how ocean currents affect brine shrimp. Use **Performance Assessment in the Science Classroom,** p. 95.

Content Background

The rain forests of the world are home to fifty percent of all species of plants and animals. Some insect species evolve and become extinct without ever having been seen alive by humans. Most rain forest species live in the forest canopy between 18 to 46 meters (60–150 ft) above the ground. While observing wildlife in the canopy is extremely difficult, the need for extensive study is pressing as logging and slash and burn agriculture destroys more forest habitat.

One method being attempted to halt uncontrolled agriculture is the development of programs that preserve wild areas by attracting tourists, or ecotourism. Building an economy based on service industries can relieve pressure to clear more land for farming. One version of ecotourism is the canopy tour ranging from climbing harnesses to walkways and aerial tramways. A benefit of these tours is that canopy research can be conducted from these structures.

Discussion

Invisible Species What features of the rain forest cause a large number species to remain unknown? Possible answer: The difficulty of travel and the remoteness of some areas make observation points difficult to get to. The fact that most of the species live in the canopy further complicates surveys. L2

Investigate the Issue

Numbers of Species Direct students to research the estimated number of plant and animal species worldwide and chart their distribution on a map using colored pins. How many species are in the rain forests? How will deforestation affect these species? L2

TIME SCIENCE AND Society

SCIENCE ISSUES THAT AFFECT YOU!

Acari marmoset

Manicore marmoset

Monkey BUSINESS

In 2000, a scientist from Brazil's Amazon National Research Institute came across two squirrel-sized monkeys in a remote and isolated corner of the rain forest, about 2,575 km from Rio de Janeiro.

It turns out that the monkeys had never been seen before, or even known to exist.

Acari marmoset

The new species were spotted by a scientist who named them after two nearby rivers the Manicore and the Acari, where the animals were discovered. Both animals are marmosets, which is a type of monkey found only in Central and South America. Marmosets have claws instead of nails, live in trees, and use their extraordinarily long tail like an extra arm or leg. Small and light, both marmosets measure about 23 cm in length with a 38 cm tail, and weigh no more than 0.4 kg.

The Manicore marmoset has a silvery-white upper body, a light-gray cap on its head, a yellow-orange underbody, and a black tail.

The Acari marmoset's upper body is snowy white, its gray back sports a stripe running to the knee, and its black tail flashes a bright-orange tip.

Amazin' Amazon

The Amazon Basin is a treasure trove of unique species. The Amazon River is Earth's largest body of freshwater, with 1,100 smaller tributaries. And more than half of the world's plant and animal species live in its rain forest ecosystems.

Research and Report Working in small groups, find out more about the Amazon rain forest. Which plants and animals live there? What products come from the rain forest? How does what happens in the Amazon rain forest affect you? Prepare a multimedia presentation.

For more information, visit booka.msscience.com/time

Research and Report As an extension, have students discuss the pros and cons of ecotourism in light of their research of current rain forest uses and conditions.

Resources for Teachers and Students

Rain Forests of the World: Water, Fire, Earth, Air, by Art Wolfe and Sir Ghillean Prance, New York: Crown Publishers, 1998

Amazonia: the Land, the Wildlife, the River, the People, by Afonso Capelas, Firefly Books, 2003

Reviewing Main Ideas

Section 1 What is science?

1. Scientists use problem-solving methods to investigate observations about living and nonliving things.
2. Scientists use SI measurements to gather measurable data.
3. Safe laboratory practices help you learn more about science.

Section 2 Living Things

1. Organisms are made of cells, use energy, reproduce, respond, grow, and develop.
2. Organisms need energy, water, food, and a place to live.

Section 3 Where does life come from?

1. Controlled experiments finally disproved the theory of spontaneous generation.
2. Pasteur's experiment proved biogenesis.

Section 4 How are living things classified?

1. Classification is the grouping of ideas, information, or objects based on their similar characteristics.
2. Scientists today use phylogeny to group organisms into six kingdoms.
3. All organisms are given a two-word scientific name using binomial nomenclature.

Visualizing Main Ideas

Copy and complete this events-chain concept map that shows the order in which you might use a scientific method. Use these terms: analyze data, perform an experiment, *and* form a hypothesis.

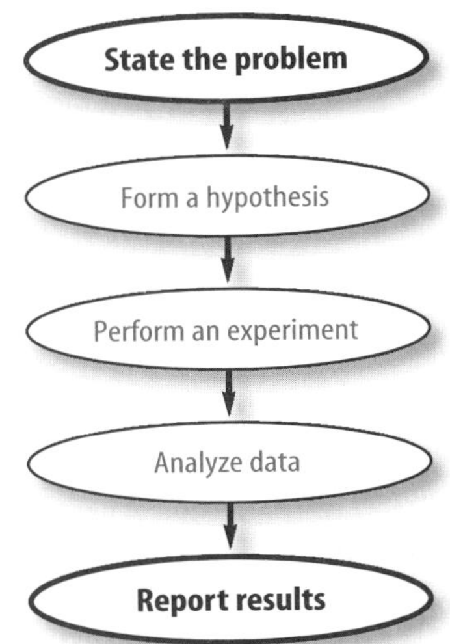

Identifying Misconceptions

Assess

Activity Have students record whether items in several pictures are living or nonliving and their reason. Have students share ideas and generate a list of characteristics that they think describe living things. Compare this list to the list in **Section 2** and ask the class if they would like to make any changes in their list.

Expected Outcome Most students should be forming a more sophisticated definition that includes characteristics from the text. L2

Reviewing Main Ideas

Summary statements can be used by students to review the major concepts of the chapter.

Visualizing Main Ideas

See student page.

Visit booka.msscience.com
/self_check_quiz
/interactive_tutor
/vocabulary_puzzlemaker
/chapter_review
/standardized_test

Assessment Transparency

For additional assessment questions, use the *Assessment Transparency* located in the transparency book.

Assessment

Assessment Transparency — Exploring and Classifying Life

Directions: *Carefully review the table and answer the following questions.*

Fruit and Vegetable Seed Germination Rate

Type of seed	Number of seeds	Amount of water added (mL)	Number of seeds germinating Day 3	Day 5	Day 7
Orange	10	50	0	0	1
Lemon	10	50	0	1	1
Cucumber	10	50	6	7	7
Onion	10	50	7	9	10

1. Which hypothesis was probably being tested?
   A Less than 25 percent of vegetable seeds will germinate.
   B Seeds prefer to grow in soil versus sand.
   C Vegetable seeds germinate faster than fruit seeds.
   D A period of one week is required before seeds will germinate.
2. Which of the following would improve an experiment to compare the rate of seed germination?
   F using more types of seeds
   G measuring the length of the plants
   H adding 100mL of water to each seed
   J conducting the experiment for a shorter time
3. Which factor would have the LEAST effect on the results?
   A the amount of light to which the seeds were exposed
   B the amount of soil used for the seeds
   C the color of the pots used
   D the depth the seeds were planted in the soil

Using Vocabulary

1. variable—condition tested; control—standard used to compare with outcome of the test
2. theory—explanation of things or events based on many observations; law—a statement about how things work in nature
3. The theory of spontaneous generation (living things come from non-living things) was replaced with the theory of biogenesis (living things come only from other living things).
4. Phylogeny is the evolutionary history of an organism; binomial nomenclature is a naming system based on phylogeny.
5. A cell is the smallest unit of an organism that carries out the functions of life. All organisms are made of cells.
6. Phylogeny is the basis for placing organisms into kingdoms.
7. Forming a hypothesis is an important part of solving a problem with scientific methods.
8. Homeostasis—keeping proper internal conditions no matter what external conditions are—is a trait of all organisms.
9. A genus is a subgroup of a kingdom.
10. If the results of repeated experiments always support the same hypothesis, the hypothesis may be called a theory.

Checking Concepts

11. D	16. D
12. D	17. A
13. A	18. B
14. D	19. D
15. C	20. B

Using Vocabulary

binomial nomenclature p. 26
biogenesis p. 21
cell p. 16
control p. 11
genus p. 26
homeostasis p. 17
hypothesis p. 10
kingdom p. 25
law p. 12
organism p. 16
phylogeny p. 25
scientific methods p. 9
spontaneous generation p. 21
theory p. 12
variable p. 11

Explain the differences in the vocabulary words in each pair below. Then explain how they are related.

1. control—variable
2. law—theory
3. biogenesis—spontaneous generation
4. binomial nomenclature—phylogeny
5. organism—cell
6. kingdom—phylogeny
7. hypothesis—scientific methods
8. organism—homeostasis
9. kingdom—genus
10. theory—hypothesis

Checking Concepts

Choose the word or phrase that best answers the question.

11. What category of organisms can mate and produce fertile offspring?
 A) family C) genus
 B) class D) species

12. What is the closest relative of *Canis lupus?*
 A) *Quercus alba* C) *Felis tigris*
 B) *Equus zebra* D) *Canis familiaris*

13. What is the source of energy for plants?
 A) the Sun C) water
 B) carbon dioxide D) oxygen

14. What makes up more than 50 percent of all living things?
 A) oxygen C) minerals
 B) carbon dioxide D) water

15. Who finally disproved the theory of spontaneous generation?
 A) Oparin C) Pasteur
 B) Aristotle D) Miller

16. What gas do some scientists think was missing from Earth's early atmosphere?
 A) ammonia C) methane
 B) hydrogen D) oxygen

17. What is the length of time called that an organism is expected to live?
 A) life span C) homeostasis
 B) stimulus D) theory

18. What is the part of an experiment that can be changed called?
 A) conclusion C) control
 B) variable D) data

19. What does the first word in a two-word name of an organism identify?
 A) kingdom C) phylum
 B) species D) genus

Use the photo below to answer question 20.

20. What SI unit is used to measure the volume of soda shown above?
 A) meter C) gram
 B) liter D) degree

 booka.msscience.com/vocabulary_puzzlemaker

Use the Exam*View*® Pro Testmaker CD-ROM to:

- create multiple versions of tests
- create modified tests with one mouse click for inclusion students
- edit existing questions and add your own questions
- build tests aligned with state standards using built-in State Curriculum Tags
- change English tests to Spanish with one mouse click and vice versa

Thinking Critically

21. Predict what *Lathyrus odoratus,* the scientific name for a sweet pea plant, tells you about one of its characteristics.

Use the photo below to answer question 22.

22. Determine what problem-solving techniques this scientist would use to find how dolphins learn.

Use the graph below to answer question 23.

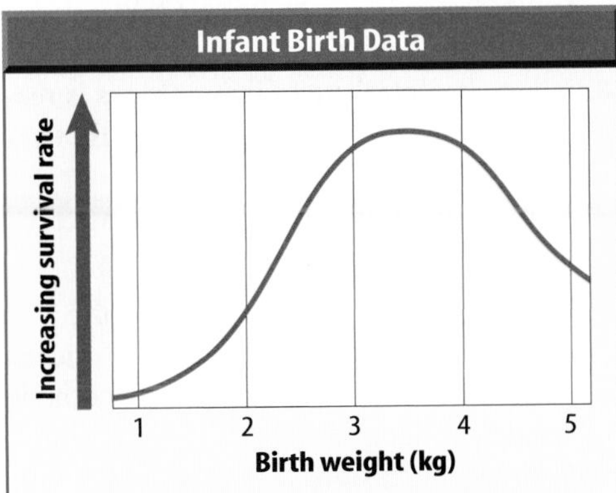

23. Interpret Data Do the data in the graph above support the hypothesis that babies with a birth weight of 2.5 kg have the best chance of survival? Explain.

24. List advantages of using SI units.

25. Form a Hypothesis A lima bean plant is placed under green light, another is placed under red light, and a third under blue light. Their growth is measured for four weeks to determine which light is best for plant growth. What are the variables in this experiment? State a hypothesis for this experiment.

Performance Activities

26. Bulletin Board Interview people in your community whose jobs require a knowledge of life science. Make a Life Science Careers bulletin board. Summarize each person's job and what he or she had to study to prepare for that job.

Applying Math

27. Body Temperature Normal human body temperature is 98.6°F. What is this temperature in degrees Celsius? Use the following expression, 5/9(°F–32), to find degrees Celsius.

Use the graph below to answer question 28.

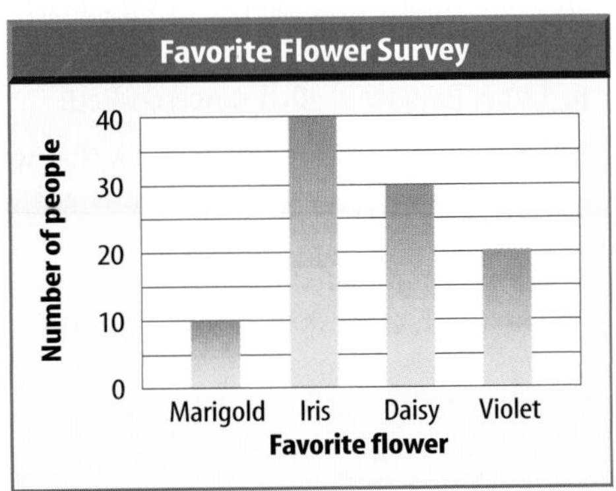

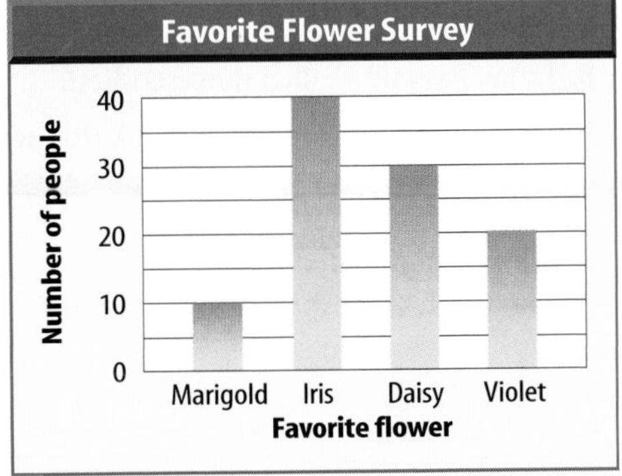

28. Favorite Flower The graph above shows how many people selected a certain type of flower as their favorite. According to the graph, what percentage of the people picked daisy as their favorite?

Thinking Critically

21. The name *odoratus* tells you that the sweet pea probably has an odor.

22. critical thinking including scientific methods of observation, forming hypotheses, performing experiments, and analyzing data

23. No. The graph indicates that a birth weight of 3.5 kg is best for survival.

24. Scientists can compare and repeat experiments; they have a common tool for measurement.

25. The colors of light used are variables. A possible hypothesis is that plants will grow better under some colors of light than under other colors.

Performance Activities

26. Careers could include farmers, produce clerks, florists, veterinary technicians, health care workers, and teachers. Use **Performance Assessment in the Science Classroom,** p. 131.

Applying Math

National Math Standards

1, 2, 4, 5, 9

27. 5/9(98.6–32) = 37°C

28. 30 people out of the 100 surveyed chose the daisy or 30/100 = 0.3 = 30%

Assessment Resources

Reproducible Masters

Chapter *Fast File* Resources
- Chapter Review, pp. 37–38
- Chapter Tests, pp. 39–42
- Assessment Transparency Activity, p. 51

Glencoe Science Web site
- Chapter Review Test
- Standardized Test Practice

Glencoe Technology

- Assessment Transparency
- Exam*View*® Pro Testmaker
- MindJogger Videoquiz
- Interactive Chalkboard

chapter 1 Standardized Test Practice

Answer Sheet A practice answer sheet can be found at booka.msscience.com/answer_sheet.

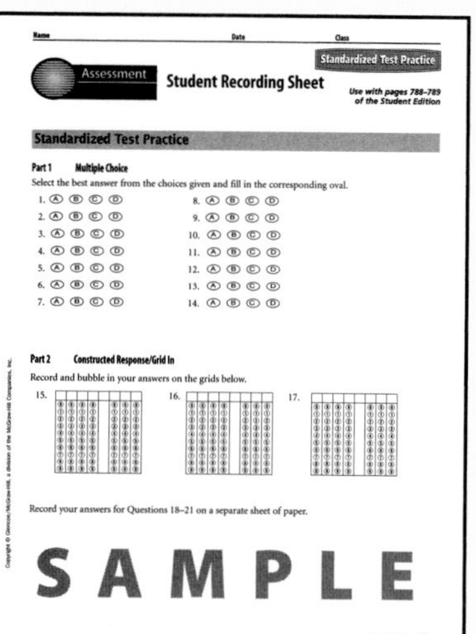
Name Date Class

Assessment **Student Recording Sheet** — Standardized Test Practice — *Use with pages 788–789 of the Student Edition*

Standardized Test Practice

Part 1 Multiple Choice

Select the best answer from the choices given and fill in the corresponding oval.

Part 2 Constructed Response/Grid In

Record and bubble in your answers on the grids below.

Record your answers for Questions 18–21 on a separate sheet of paper.

SAMPLE

Part 1 Multiple Choice

1. C	**6.** C
2. B	**7.** A
3. B	**8.** A
4. C	**9.** D
5. B	**10.** A

chapter 1 Standardized Test Practice

Part 1 Multiple Choice

Record your answers on the answer sheet provided by your teacher or on a sheet of paper.

1. A prediction that can be tested is a
- **A.** conclusion.
- **B.** variable.
- **C.** hypothesis.
- **D.** theory.

2. Which of the following units would a scientist likely use when measuring the length of a mouse's tail?
- **A.** kilometers
- **B.** millimeters
- **C.** grams
- **D.** milliliters

Use the illustrations below to answer questions 3 and 4.

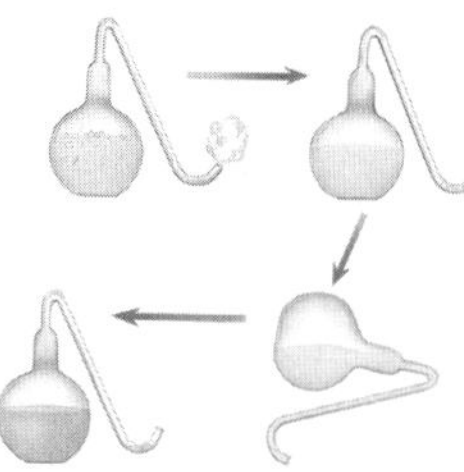

3. What scientist used the flasks pictured above to support the theory of biogenesis?
- **A.** John Needham
- **B.** Louis Pasteur
- **C.** Lazzaro Spallanzani
- **D.** Francesco Redi

4. Why did only the broth in the flask that was tilted become cloudy and contaminated?
- **A.** The broth was not boiled.
- **B.** Flies contaminated the broth.
- **C.** The broth was exposed to dust in the neck of the flask.
- **D.** Decaying meat caused the broth to be contaminated.

Test-Taking Tip

Practice Skills Remember that test-taking skills can improve with practice. If possible, take at least one practice test and familiarize yourself with the test format and instructions.

Use the photos below to answer questions 5 and 6.

5. The dog pictured above has increased in size. How did most of this size increase take place?
- **A.** an increase in cell size
- **B.** an increase in the number of cells
- **C.** an increase in cell water
- **D.** an increase in cell energy

6. What characteristic of life is illustrated by the change in the dog?
- **A.** reproduction
- **B.** homeostasis
- **C.** growth and development
- **D.** response to stimulus

7. What gas must most organisms take in to release the energy of foods?
- **A.** oxygen
- **B.** carbon dioxide
- **C.** water vapor
- **D.** hydrogen

8. What characteristic of living things is represented by a puffball releasing millions of spores?
- **A.** reproduction
- **B.** development
- **C.** organization
- **D.** use of energy

9. When using scientific methods to solve a problem, which of the following is a scientist most likely to do after forming a hypothesis?
- **A.** analyze data
- **B.** draw conclusions
- **C.** state a problem
- **D.** perform an experiment

10. What are the smallest units that make up your body called?
- **A.** cells
- **B.** organisms
- **C.** muscles
- **D.** fibers

Part 2 Short Response/Grid In

11. They use energy stored in chemical compounds.

12. process of homeostasis

13. The theory would state that earthworms come from other earthworms not from the rain or sky.

14. similarities in structure, study of fossils, study of hereditary information, or study of early stages of development

15. the hypothesis that plants grow toward light

16. Remove the boxes over the plants.

Part 2 Short Response/Grid In

Record your answers on the answer sheet provided by your teacher or on a sheet of paper.

11. From where do bacteria that live in areas where there is no sunlight obtain energy?

12. Organisms take in and give off large amounts of water each day. What process do they use to balance the amount of water lost with the amount taken in?

13. After a rain storm, earthworms may be seen crawling on the sidewalk or road. How would the theory of spontaneous generation explain the origin of the worms?

14. List three things modern scientists study when they classify organisms.

Use the illustrations below to answer questions 15 and 16.

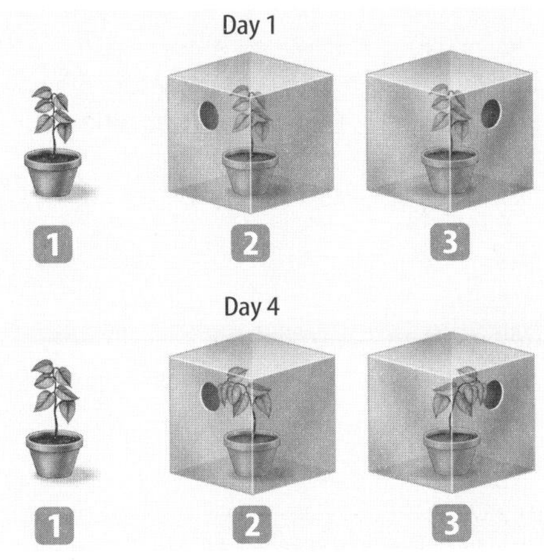

15. A science class set up the experiment above to study the response of plants to the stimulus of light. What hypothesis is likely being tested by this experiment?

16. After day 4, Fatima wanted to find out how plant 2 and plant 3 would grow in normal light. What did she have to do to find out?

Part 3 Open Ended

Record your answers on a sheet of paper.

17. Describe several different ways scientists gather information. Which of these ways would likely be used to collect data about which foods wild alligators eat in Florida?

18. Some scientists think that lightning may have caused chemicals in the Earth's early atmosphere to combine to begin the origin of life. Explain how the experiment of Miller and Urey does not prove this hypothesis.

Use the photo below to answer questions 19 and 20.

19. Both of these living things use energy. Describe the difference between the source of energy for each. In what similar ways would each of these organisms use energy?

20. How are the needs of the two organisms alike? Explain why the plant is raw material for the beetle. When the beetle dies, how could it be raw material for the plant?

21. Explain stimulus and response. How is response to a stimulus related to homeostasis?

22. What information would you need to write a field guide used to identify garden plants? What other information would you need if the guide included a dichotomous key?

23. Explain the difference between a kingdom and a species in the classification system commonly used.

Part 3 Open Ended

17. Information may be gathered in the laboratory, from field work, or by computer models. Fieldwork would be the best way to study the alligator's diet.

18. Using an electric current and a mixture of gasses, chemicals found in present-day cells were produced. However, the experiment did not produce living things.

19. Plants use the Sun's energy. Since the beetles eat plants for energy they also indirectly use the Sun. Both use energy for organization and homeostasis.

20. Both need an environment with proper conditions and the raw materials water and oxygen. Plants need carbon dioxide and soil minerals. The beetles need plants for food. Dead beetles will be broken down into substances in the soil which plants use as raw materials.

21. The cause of any change in an organism is a stimulus. Reaction to a stimulus is a response. Living things respond to internal and external stimuli. Keeping proper internal conditions is homeostasis.

22. You would need to collect information describing each plant, pictures of each plant, and information about where each plant grows. A dichotomous key would include scientific names of each plant and detailed identifying characteristics.

23. A kingdom is the first and largest of seven classification categories. One system includes six kingdoms. A species is the smallest category. Every type of living thing is a separate species.

Rubrics

For more help evaluating open-ended assessment questions, see the rubric on p. 10T.

chapter 2 Organizer

Section/Objectives	Standards		Labs/Features
	National	**State/Local**	
Chapter Opener	See pp. 16T–17T for a Key to Standards.		**Launch Lab:** Magnifying Cells, p. 39 **Foldables,** p. 39 A data-collection lab using Probeware technology can be found in the **Probeware Lab Manual,** pp. 1–4
Section 1 Cell Structure 2 sessions 1 block 1. **Identify** names and functions of each part of a cell. 2. **Explain** how important a nucleus is in a cell. 3. **Compare** tissues, organs, and organ systems.	National Content Standards: UCP.1–UCP.3, UCP.5, A.1, A.2, C.1, C.3		**MiniLAB:** Modeling Cytoplasm, p. 42 **Integrate Environment,** p. 46 **Applying Math:** Cell Ratio, p. 46 **Lab:** Comparing Cells, p. 48
Section 2 Viewing Cells 2 sessions 1 block 4. **Compare** the differences between the compound light microscope and the electron microscope. 5. **Summarize** the discoveries that led to the development of the cell theory.	National Content Standards: UCP.1–UCP.3, UCP.5, A.1, A.2, C.1, G.3		**Visualizing Microscopes,** p. 50 **MiniLAB:** Observing Magnified Objects, p. 52 **Integrate Career,** p. 52
Section 3 Viruses 3 sessions 1.5 blocks 6. **Explain** how a virus makes copies of itself. 7. **Identify** the benefits of vaccines. 8. **Investigate** some uses of viruses.	National Content Standards: UCP.1, UCP.2, UCP.5, A.1, A.2, C.1, C.2, C.5, F.2, G.3		**Science Online,** p. 55 **Science Online,** p. 56 **Lab:** Comparing Light Microscopes, p. 58 **Science and History:** Cobb Against Cancer, p. 60

Lab Materials	Reproducible Resources	Section Assessment	Technology
Launch Lab: hand lens, metric ruler	**Chapter *Fast File* Resources** Foldables Worksheet, p. 17 Directed Reading Overview, p. 19 Note-taking Worksheets, pp. 33–35	Glencoe's Assessment Advantage	TeacherWorks includes: • Interactive Teacher Edition • Lesson Planner with calendar • Access to all program blacklines • Correlations to standards • Web links
MiniLAB: water, clear container, unflavored gelatin, flashlight, stirring rod **Lab:** microscope, microscope slide, coverslip, forceps, tap water, dropper, *Elodea* plant, prepared slide of human cheek cells	**Chapter *Fast File* Resources** Transparency Activity, p. 44 MiniLAB, p. 3 Enrichment, p. 30 Reinforcement, p. 27 Directed Reading, p. 20 Transparency Activity, pp. 47–48 Lab Worksheet, pp. 5–6 **Mathematics Skill Activities,** p. 5	Portfolio Visual Learning, p. 43 Performance MiniLAB, p. 43 Applying Math, p. 46 Applying Skills, p. 47 Content Section Review, p. 47	Section Focus Transparency Teaching Transparency Virtual Labs CD-ROM Guided Reading Audio Program Interactive Chalkboard CD-ROM Video Lab
MiniLAB: newspaper, clear empty glass, clear empty glass bowl, water, magnifying lens *Need materials?* Contact Science Kit at 1-800-828-7777 or www.sciencekit.com on the Internet.	**Chapter *Fast File* Resources** Transparency Activity, p. 45 MiniLAB, p. 4 Enrichment, p. 31 Reinforcement, p. 28 Directed Reading, p. 20 Lab Activity, pp. 9–12, 13–16	Portfolio Assessment, p. 53 Performance MiniLAB, p. 52 Applying Math, p. 53 Content Section Review, p. 53	Section Focus Transparency Virtual Labs CD-ROM Guided Reading Audio Program Interactive Chalkboard CD-ROM
Lab: compound light microscope, stereomicroscope, 8 classroom items to view, microscope slides and coverslips, plastic petri dishes, distilled water, dropper	**Chapter *Fast File* Resources** Transparency Activity, p. 46 Enrichment, p. 32 Reinforcement, p. 29 Directed Reading, pp. 21, 22 Lab Worksheet, pp. 7–8 **Lab Management and Safety,** p. 58 **Reading and Writing Skill Activities,** p. 31	Performance Applying Skills, p. 57 Content Section Review, p. 57	Section Focus Transparency Virtual Labs CD-ROM Guided Reading Audio Program Interactive Chalkboard CD-ROM Probeware Lab

End of Chapter Assessment

Glencoe's Assessment Advantage

Blackline Masters	Technology	Professional Series
Chapter *Fast File* Resources Chapter Review, pp. 37–38 Chapter Tests, pp. 39–42 **Standardized Test Practice,** pp. 11–14	MindJogger Videoquiz Virtual Labs CD-ROM Exam*View*® Pro Testmaker TeacherWorks CD-ROM Interactive Chalkboard CD-ROM	**Performance Assessment in the Science Classroom (PASC)**

Transparencies

Section Focus

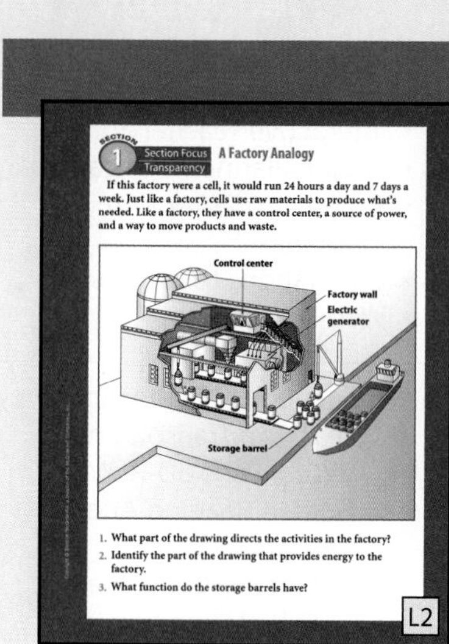
Section 1 Section Focus Transparency — A Factory Analogy

If this factory were a cell, it would run 24 hours a day and 7 days a week. Just like a factory, cells use raw materials to produce what's needed. Like a factory, they have a control center, a source of power, and a way to move products and waste.

1. What part of the drawing directs the activities in the factory?
2. Identify the part of the drawing that provides energy to the factory.
3. What function do the storage barrels have?

L2

Section 2 Section Focus Transparency — At Home in the Salt

The Dead Sea has very high salt concentrations, and people have used it as a salt resource since ancient times. But is the Dead Sea really dead? The concentration of salt is too high for most living things, but bacteria like the ones below are able to live in its waters.

1. Why might ancient people have thought the Dead Sea was totally without life?
2. What tool would you use to show there really is life in the Dead Sea?
3. Do you think the living thing pictured is simple or complex? Defend your answer.

L2

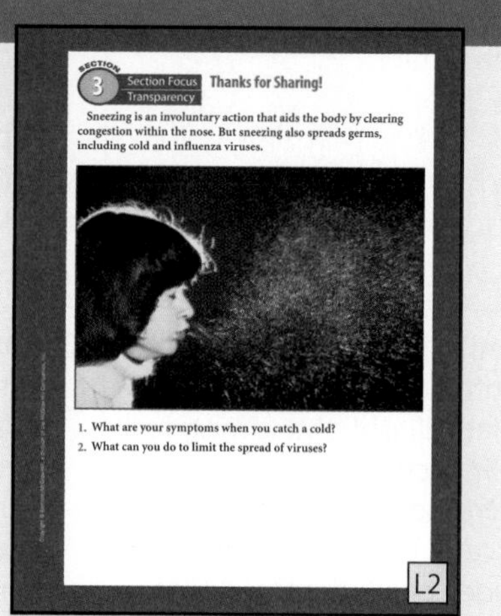
Section 3 Section Focus Transparency — Thanks for Sharing!

Sneezing is an involuntary action that aids the body by clearing congestion within the nose. But sneezing also spreads germs, including cold and influenza viruses.

1. What are your symptoms when you catch a cold?
2. What can you do to limit the spread of viruses?

L2

This is a representation of key blackline masters available in the Teacher Classroom Resources. See Resource Manager boxes within the chapter for additional information.

Assessment

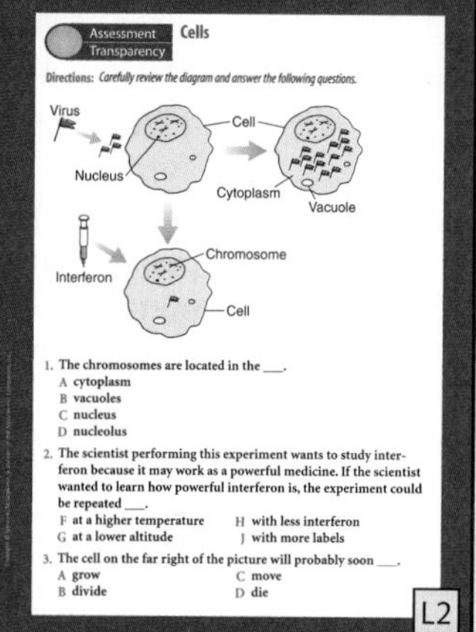
Assessment Transparency — Cells

Directions: Carefully review the diagram and answer the following questions.

1. The chromosomes are located in the ___.
   A cytoplasm
   B vacuoles
   C nucleus
   D nucleolus
2. The scientist performing this experiment wants to study interferon because it may work as a powerful medicine. If the scientist wanted to learn how powerful interferon is, the experiment could be repeated ___.
   F at a higher temperature
   G at a lower altitude
   H with less interferon
   J with more labels
3. The cell on the far right of the picture will probably soon ___.
   A grow
   B divide
   C move
   D die

L2

Teaching

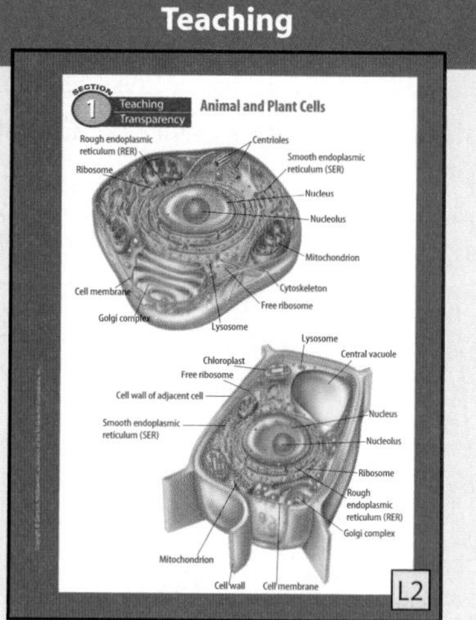
Section 1 Teaching Transparency — Animal and Plant Cells

L2

Key to Teaching Strategies

The following designations will help you decide which activities are appropriate for your students.

L1 Level 1 activities should be appropriate for students with learning difficulties.

L2 Level 2 activities should be within the ability range of all students.

L3 Level 3 activities are designed for above-average students.

ELL ELL activities should be within the ability range of English-Language Learners.

COOP LEARN Cooperative Learning activities are designed for small group work.

LS Multiple Learning Styles logos, as described on page 12T, are used throughout to indicate strategies that address different learning styles.

P These strategies represent student products that can be placed into a best-work portfolio.

PBL Problem-Based Learning activities apply real-world situations to learning.

Hands-on Activities

Student Text Lab Worksheet

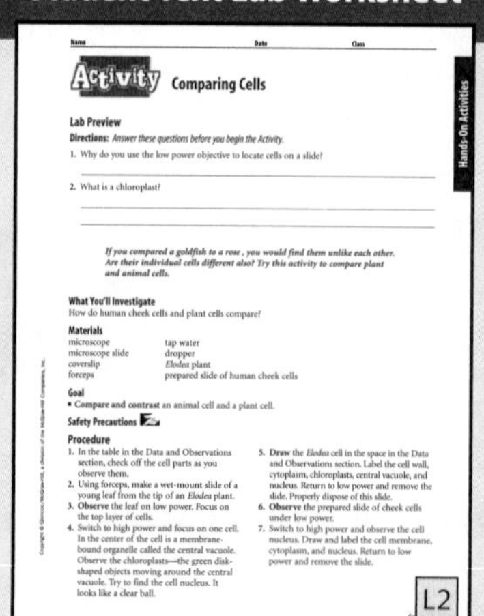
Name Date Class

Activity — Comparing Cells

Hands-On Activities

Lab Preview

Directions: *Answer these questions before you begin the Activity.*

1. Why do you use the low power objective to locate cells on a slide?
2. What is a chloroplast?

If you compared a goldfish to a rose, you would find them unlike each other. Are their individual cells different also? Try this activity to compare plant and animal cells.

What You'll Investigate
How do human cheek cells and plant cells compare?

Materials
microscope, microscope slide, coverslip, forceps, tap water, dropper, *Elodea* plant, prepared slide of human cheek cells

Goal
- **Compare and contrast** an animal cell and a plant cell.

Safety Precautions

Procedure
1. In the table in the Data and Observations section, check off the cell parts as you observe them.
2. Using forceps, make a wet-mount slide of a young leaf from the tip of an *Elodea* plant.
3. **Observe** the leaf on low power. Focus on the top layer of cells.
4. Switch to high power and focus on one cell. In the center of the cell is a membrane-bound organelle called the central vacuole. Observe the chloroplasts—the green disk-shaped objects moving around the central vacuole. Try to find the cell nucleus. It looks like a clear ball.
5. **Draw** the *Elodea* cell in the space in the Data and Observations section. Label the cell wall, cytoplasm, chloroplasts, central vacuole, and nucleus. Return to low power and remove the slide. Properly dispose of this slide.
6. **Observe** the prepared slide of cheek cells under low power.
7. Switch to high power and observe the cell nucleus. Draw and label the cell membrane, cytoplasm, and nucleus. Return to low power and remove the slide.

L2

Laboratory Activities

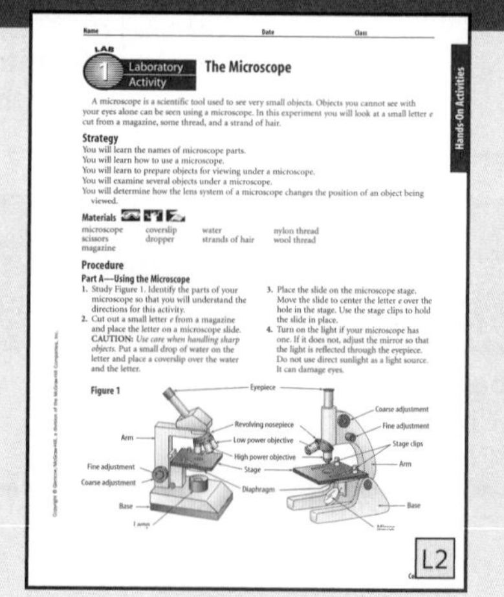
Name Date Class

Lab 1 Laboratory Activity — The Microscope

Hands-On Activities

A microscope is a scientific tool used to see very small objects. Objects you cannot see with your eyes alone can be seen using a microscope. In this experiment you will look at a small letter *e* cut from a magazine, some thread, and a strand of hair.

Strategy
You will learn the names of microscope parts.
You will learn how to use a microscope.
You will learn to prepare objects for viewing under a microscope.
You will examine several objects under a microscope.
You will determine how the lens system of a microscope changes the position of an object being viewed.

Materials
microscope, scissors, magazine, coverslip, dropper, water, strands of hair, nylon thread, wool thread

Procedure

Part A—Using the Microscope
1. Study Figure 1. Identify the parts of your microscope so that you will understand the directions for this activity.
2. Cut out a small letter *e* from a magazine and place the letter on a microscope slide. **CAUTION:** *Use care when handling sharp objects.* Put a small drop of water on the letter and place a coverslip over the water and the letter.
3. Place the slide on the microscope stage. Move the slide to center the letter *e* over the hole in the stage. Use the stage clips to hold the slide in place.
4. Turn on the light if your microscope has one. If it does not, adjust the mirror so that the light is reflected through the eyepiece. Do not use direct sunlight as a light source. It can damage eyes.

Figure 1

L2

Meeting Different Ability Levels

Content Outline

Name Date Class

Note-taking Worksheet **Cells**

Section 1 Cell Structure

A. Common cell structures—outer covering called _____________ and internal gelatinlike _____________

1. Comparing cells—size and shape relate to _____________
2. Two cell types
   a. _____________ cells lack membrane-bound internal structures.
   b. _____________ cells contain membrane-bound internal structures.

B. Cell organization

1. Composed of cellulose, a **cell wall** grows, changes shape, and protects the cells of _____________, algae, fungi, and most bacteria.
2. Cell _____________—protective layer around all cells
   a. For cells with cell _____________, the cell membrane is inside the cell wall
   b. A cell _____________ allows food and oxygen into the cell and waste products out of the cell.
3. Cytoplasm—gelatinlike substance inside cell membrane
   a. _____________—scaffolding-like structure in cytoplasm which helps cell keep its shape
   b. In the cytoplasm, eukaryotic cells have _____________ which help with cell life processes.
4. **Nucleus**—contains instructions for everything cell does; includes DNA
5. Energy-processing organelles—help cells do their _____________
   a. Green organelles in plant cells contain _____________ to make food.
   b. Organelles which release _____________ from food are called **mitochondria.**
6. Manufacturing organelles
   a. **Ribosomes** make _____________ for cell activities.
   b. Some ribosomes attach to the rough part of the **endoplasmic reticulum,** a series of smooth or rough _____________ that move materials around in a cell.

Meeting Individual Needs

L2

Reinforcement

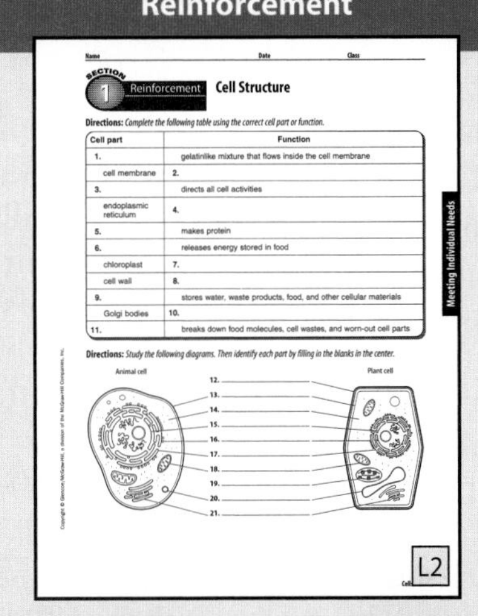

Name Date Class

Section 1 Reinforcement **Cell Structure**

Directions: *Complete the following table using the correct cell part or function.*

Cell part	Function
1.	gelatinlike mixture that flows inside the cell membrane
cell membrane	2.
3.	directs all cell activities
endoplasmic reticulum	4.
5.	makes protein
6.	releases energy stored in food
chloroplast	7.
cell wall	8.
9.	stores water, waste products, food, and other cellular materials
Golgi bodies	10.
11.	breaks down food molecules, cell wastes, and worn-out cell parts

Directions: *Study the following diagrams. Then identify each part by filling in the blanks in the center.*

Enrichment

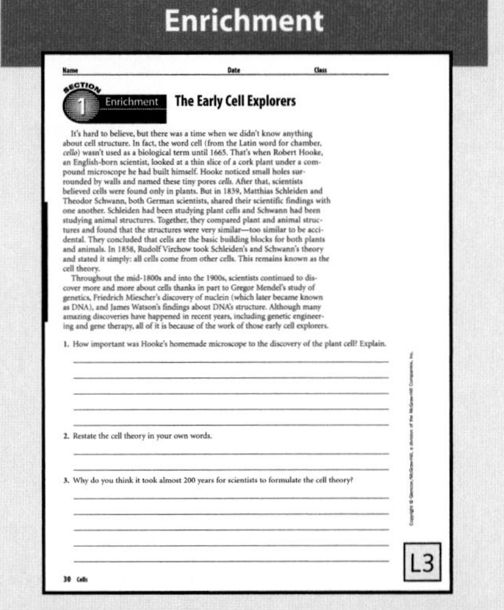

Name Date Class

Section 1 Enrichment **The Early Cell Explorers**

It's hard to believe, but there was a time when we didn't know anything about cell structure. In fact, the word cell (from the Latin word for chamber, cello) wasn't used as a biological term until 1665. That's when Robert Hooke, an English-born scientist, looked at a thin slice of a cork plant under a compound microscope he had built himself. Hooke noticed small holes surrounded by walls and named these tiny pores cells. After that, scientists believed cells were found only in plants. But in 1839, Matthias Schleiden and Theodor Schwann, both German scientists, shared their scientific findings with one another. Schleiden had been studying plant cells and Schwann had been studying animal structures. Together, they compared plant and animal structures and found that the structures were very similar—too similar to be accidental. They concluded that cells are the basic building blocks for both plants and animals. In 1858, Rudolf Virchow took Schleiden's and Schwann's theory and stated it simply: all cells come from other cells. This remains known as the cell theory.

Throughout the mid-1800s and into the 1900s, scientists continued to discover more and more about cells thanks in part to Gregor Mendel's study of genetics, Friedrich Miescher's discovery of nuclein (which later became known as DNA), and James Watson's findings about DNA's structure. Although many amazing discoveries have happened in recent years, including genetic engineering and gene therapy, all of it is because of the work of those early cell explorers.

1. How important was Hooke's homemade microscope to the discovery of the plant cell? Explain.
2. Restate the cell theory in your own words.
3. Why do you think it took almost 200 years for scientists to formulate the cell theory?

Directed Reading (English/Spanish)

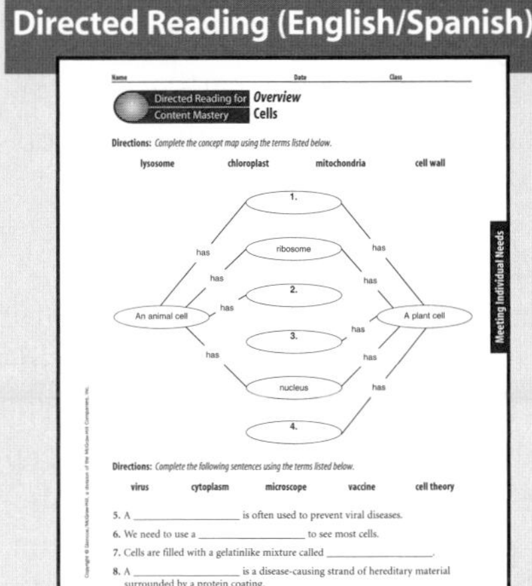

Name Date Class

Directed Reading for Content Mastery ***Overview* Cells**

Directions: *Complete the concept map using the terms listed below.*

lysosome chloroplast mitochondria cell wall

Directions: *Complete the following sentences using the terms listed below.*

virus cytoplasm microscope vaccine cell theory

5. A _____________ is often used to prevent viral diseases.
6. We need to use a _____________ to see most cells.
7. Cells are filled with a gelatinlike mixture called _____________.
8. A _____________ is a disease-causing strand of hereditary material surrounded by a protein coating.
9. The _____________ was developed from the observations and conclusions of several scientists.

L1

Study Guide

Reading Essentials

Assessment

Test Practice Workbook

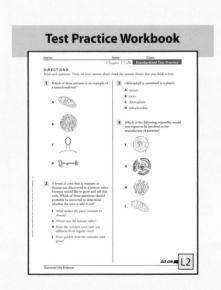

Name: Date: Class:

Chapter 2 Cells **Standardized Test Practice**

DIRECTIONS

Read each question. Then, on your answer sheet, mark the answer choice that you think is best.

1 Which of these pictures is an example of a mitochondrion?

A B C D

2 A breed of corn that is resistant to disease was discovered in a remote valley. Farmers would like to grow and sell this corn. Which of these questions should probably be answered to determine whether the corn is safe to eat?

F What makes the plant resistant to disease?
G Where was the remote valley?
H Does the resistant corn taste any different from regular corn?
J How quickly does the resistant corn grow?

3 Chlorophyll is contained in a plant's

A viruses
B roots
C chloroplasts
D mitochondria

4 Which of the following organelles would you expect to be involved in the manufacture of proteins?

F G H J

GO ON

Glencoe Life Science

L2

Chapter Review

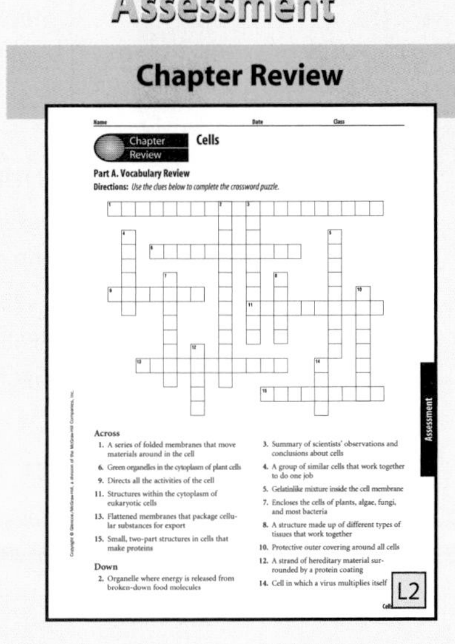

Name Date Class

Chapter Review **Cells**

Part A. Vocabulary Review

Directions: *Use the clues below to complete the crossword puzzle.*

Across

1. A series of folded membranes that move materials around in the cell
6. Green organelles in the cytoplasm of plant cells
9. Directs all the activities of the cell
11. Structures within the cytoplasm of eukaryotic cells
13. Flattened membranes that package cellular substances for export
15. Small, two-part structures in cells that make proteins

Down

2. Organelle where energy is released from broken-down food molecules
3. Summary of scientists' observations and conclusions about cells
4. A group of similar cells that work together to do one job
5. Gelatinlike mixture inside the cell membrane
7. Encloses the cells of plants, algae, fungi, and most bacteria
8. A structure made up of different types of tissues that work together
10. Protective outer covering around all cells
12. A strand of hereditary material surrounded by a protein coating
14. Cell in which a virus multiplies itself

Chapter Tests

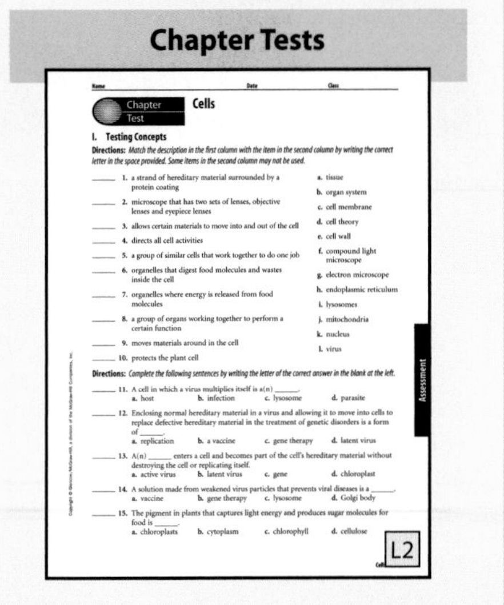

Name Date Class

Chapter Test **Cells**

I. Testing Concepts

Directions: *Match the description in the first column with the item in the second column by writing the correct letter in the space provided. Some items in the second column may not be used.*

_____ 1. a strand of hereditary material surrounded by a protein coating
_____ 2. microscope that has two sets of lenses, objective lenses and eyepiece lenses
_____ 3. allows certain materials to move into and out of the cell
_____ 4. directs all cell activities
_____ 5. a group of similar cells that work together to do one job
_____ 6. organelles that digest food molecules and wastes inside the cell
_____ 7. organelles where energy is released from food molecules
_____ 8. a group of organs working together to perform a certain function
_____ 9. moves materials around in the cell
_____ 10. protects the plant cell

a. tissue
b. organ system
c. cell membrane
d. cell theory
e. cell wall
f. compound light microscope
g. electron microscope
h. endoplasmic reticulum
i. lysosomes
j. mitochondria
k. nucleus
l. virus

Directions: *Complete the following sentences by writing the letter of the correct answer in the blank at the left.*

_____ 11. A cell in which a virus multiplies itself is a(n) _____.
a. host b. infection c. lysosome d. parasite

_____ 12. Enclosing normal hereditary material in a virus and allowing it to move into cells to replace defective hereditary material in the treatment of genetic disorders is a form of _____.
a. replication b. a vaccine c. gene therapy d. latent virus

_____ 13. A(n) _____ enters a cell and becomes part of the cell's hereditary material without destroying the cell or replicating itself.
a. active virus b. latent virus c. gene d. chloroplast

_____ 14. A solution made from weakened virus particles that prevents viral diseases is a _____.
a. vaccine b. gene therapy c. lysosome d. Golgi body

_____ 15. The pigment in plants that captures light energy and produces sugar molecules for food is _____.
a. chloroplasts b. cytoplasm c. chlorophyll d. cellulose

Science Content Background

section 1 Cell Structure

Common Cell Traits

The two kinds of cells are prokaryotes and eukaryotes. Each type is surrounded by a cell membrane and contains cytoplasm, DNA, and ribosomes. Prokaryotes have a relatively uniform cytoplasm that is not divided into separate compartments by interior membranes. The ribosomes of prokaryotes are different from those of eukaryotes. Prokaryotic DNA is a single molecule and is found floating freely in the cell's cytoplasm. The nucleus is the organelle that contains the eukaryotic cell's many molecules of DNA. All prokaryotic cells are one-celled organisms. Eukaryotic cells make up all multicellular organisms and some one-celled organisms.

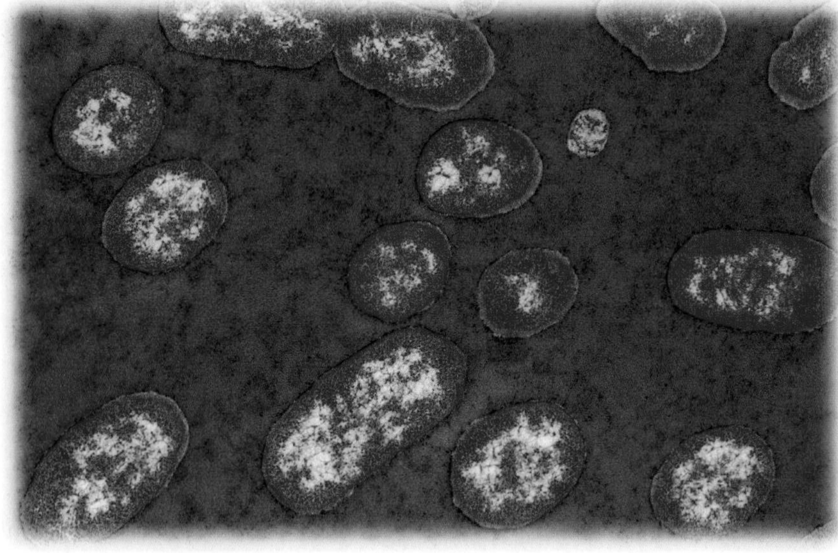

Dwight R. Kuhn/DRK Photo

Cell Wall

Although structurally they resemble plant cell walls, the walls of fungi cells are chemically quite different. Some contain cellulose, but most fungal cell walls are made up of chitin, a polysaccharide that also is found in the exoskeletons of insects. Just like cellulose in plants, the chitin is laid down in bundles of fibers that make the fungal cell walls tough and able to support the fungal body.

Bacterial cell walls are different from those found in either plants or fungi. Bacterial cell walls are composed in large part of a compound called peptidoglycan. Various other substances coat and bind to the cell wall. Other bacteria have an outer membrane that surrounds the peptidoglycan cell wall.

Cell Organization

The cytoskeleton, found only in eukaryotic cells, anchors cell organelles. This "scaffolding" cannot be seen with a normal light microscope but stands out clearly when special fluorescent dyes are used on the cell. Three different kinds of protein fibers—microfilaments, microtubules, and intermediate fibers—make up the cytoskeleton.

Teacher to Teacher

Steve Federman, 6th Grade Teacher
Loveland Middle School
Loveland, Ohio

"I reinforce the concepts of cell structures and functions by having students create a cell from a light colored flavored gelatin mixed with unflavored gelatin (6-oz. package will make 5 cells). Pour into a small cup or petri dish. Students then use items such as cake sprinkles for ribosomes, hot tamale candies for mitochondria, a gumball for the nucleus, and so on."

Steve Federman

section 2

Viewing Cells

Magnifying Cells

Microscopes enlarge the image of an object and show its details. The change of an object's apparent size is magnification. The power to show details is resolution. The resolution power of light microscopes is limited by the wavelengths of visible light. Unless the wavelength of light can pass between two objects, the objects are seen as one unit, not two. The electron microscope allows for greater resolution because it uses a beam of electrons to generate an image of the specimen. Because they move in waves that have extremely short wavelengths, electron waves can easily pass through microscopic spaces that visible light cannot enter.

Development of the Cell Theory

The cell theory is sometimes called the cell doctrine. Those scientists who use the term *cell doctrine* want to make it clear that extensive data support the cell theory and that it is universally accepted by biologists.

Internet Resources
For additional content background, visit **booka.msscience.com** to:

- access your book online
- find references to related articles in popular science magazines
- access Web links with related content background
- access current events with science journal topics

Print Resources

Cells (The Kidhaven Science Library), by Jeanne Duprau, Kidhaven, 2001

Science Experiments with a Microscope, by Shar Levine and Leslie Johnstone, Sterling Publications, 2002

Influenza and Other Viruses (Perspectives on Disease and Illness), by Judy Monroe, Lifematters Press, 2001

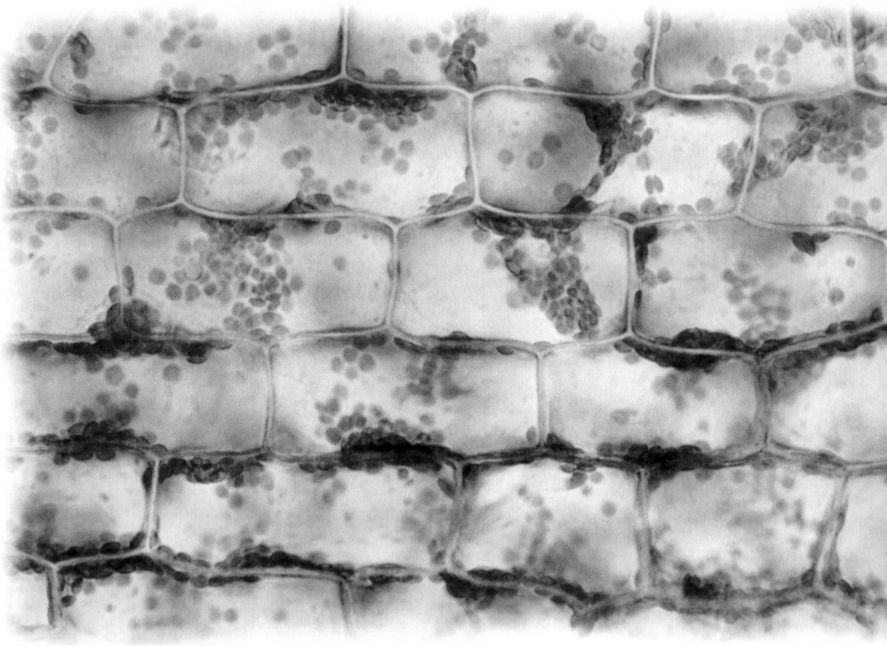

Telegraph Colour Library/FPG International

section 3

Viruses

Living or Not?

To a biologist, living organisms are cellular and are able to grow and reproduce independently. The smallest organisms that satisfy these criteria are bacteria. Viruses do not meet most criteria for being a living organism.

Viruses are segments of DNA or RNA wrapped in a protein coat. A membranous envelope surrounds many animal viruses. The lipids of the envelope are taken from the host cell, but the proteins are coded by the virus's genetic material. Viruses cannot reproduce on their own but multiply only within host cells using the cellular machinery of the host cell. The host cells often are destroyed when viruses multiply. For the host organism, infection by a virus may have a minor effect like a cold or may be devastating like AIDS. Several types of cancer, including some skin and cervical cancers, are now known to be caused by viruses. Viruses continue to have a major impact on the living world.

Chapter Vocabulary

cell membrane, p. 40
cytoplasm, p. 40
cell wall, p. 41
organelle, p. 42
nucleus, p. 42
chloroplast, p. 44
mitochondrion, p. 44
ribosome, p. 44
endoplasmic reticulum, p. 45
Golgi body, p. 45
tissue, p. 47
organ, p. 47
cell theory, p. 53
virus, p. 54
host cell, p. 54

Science Journal Student responses will vary, but may include how they became a scientist, how can cancer be treated, and when will there be a cure for cancer.

PowerPoint® Presentations

This CD-ROM is an editable Microsoft® PowerPoint® presentation that includes:

- a pre-made presentation for every chapter
- interactive graphics
- animations
- audio clips
- image bank
- all new section and chapter questions
- Standardized Test Practice
- transparencies
- pre-lab questions for all labs
- Foldables directions
- links to booka.msscience.com

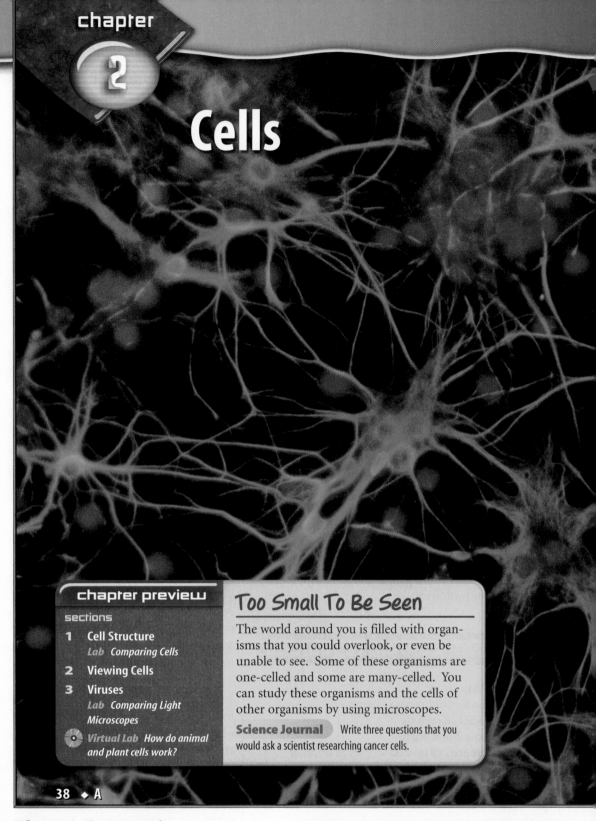

chapter 2

Cells

chapter preview

sections

1 Cell Structure
Lab Comparing Cells
2 Viewing Cells
3 Viruses
Lab Comparing Light Microscopes
Virtual Lab How do animal and plant cells work?

Too Small To Be Seen

The world around you is filled with organisms that you could overlook, or even be unable to see. Some of these organisms are one-celled and some are many-celled. You can study these organisms and the cells of other organisms by using microscopes.

Science Journal Write three questions that you would ask a scientist researching cancer cells.

38 ◆ A

Theme Connection

Scale and Structure All organisms are made up of cells, which are the basic unit organisms. Cells are made up of many types of smaller structures, or organelles. This idea wasn't conceived of until the invention of the microscope.

About the Photo

Brain Cells These are brain cells from the cortex of a mammalian brain. Astrocytes are star-shaped cells that might play a role in the storage of information. A technique called immunofluorescence was used to stain the cells shown here. Fluorescent dyes are attached to antibodies that recognize specific molecules in the cells. Under ultraviolet light, the dye fluoresces. Each cell's cytoplasm appears green, and each astrocyte's nucleus and other neighboring cells appear blue.

Start-Up Activities

Magnifying Cells

If you look around your classroom, you can see many things of all sizes. Using a magnifying lens, you can see more details. You might examine a speck of dust and discover that it is a living or dead insect. In the following lab, use a magnifying lens to search for the smallest thing you can find in the classroom.

1. Obtain a magnifying lens from your teacher. Note its power (the number followed by ×, shown somewhere on the lens frame or handle).
2. Using the magnifying lens, look around the room for the smallest object that you can find.
3. Measure the size of the image as you see it with the magnifying lens. To estimate the real size of the object, divide that number by the power. For example, if it looks 2 cm long and the power is 10×, the real length is about 0.2 cm.
4. **Think Critically** Write a paragraph that describes what you observed. Did the details become clearer? Explain.

Cells Make the following Foldable to help you illustrate the main parts of cells.

STEP 1 **Fold** a vertical sheet of paper in half from top to bottom.

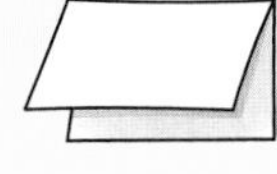

STEP 2 **Fold** in half from side to side with the fold at the top.

STEP 3 **Unfold** the paper once. **Cut** only the fold of the top flap to make two tabs.

STEP 4 **Turn** the paper vertically and **write** on the front tabs as shown.

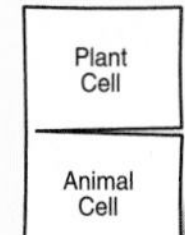

Illustrate and Label As you read the chapter, draw and identify the parts of plant and animal cells under the appropriate tab.

Preview this chapter's content and activities at booka.msscience.com

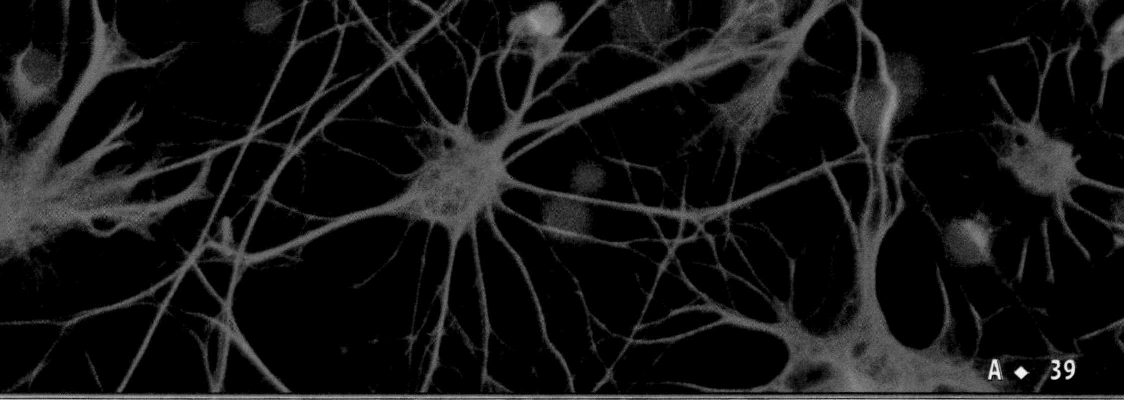

Purpose Students will use a magnifying lens to study very small objects. Students will calculate the actual size of the object from a measured size seen through the magnifying lens. L2

Preparation Obtain magnifying lenses and make sure the power is clearly visible on each one.

Materials magnifying lenses, rulers

Teaching Strategy Have some very small objects, such as grains of sand, salt, sugar, etc., available for students to study with their magnifying lenses.

Think Critically

Details of small objects will become larger and clearer when seen through a magnifying lens.

Assessment

Oral Have students describe aloud additional features of small objects, such as sand, salt, sugar, dust particles, etc., that they can observe through a magnifying lens. Use **Performance Assessment in the Science Classroom,** p. 89. L2

Dinah Zike Study Fold

Student preparation materials for this Foldable are available in the **Chapter *Fast File* Resources.**

Probeware Labs

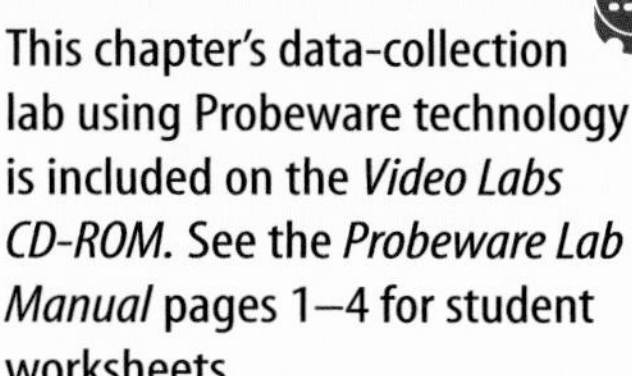

This chapter's data-collection lab using Probeware technology is included on the *Video Labs CD-ROM*. See the *Probeware Lab Manual* pages 1–4 for student worksheets.

1 Motivate

Bellringer

Section Focus Transparencies also are available on the Interactive Chalkboard CD-ROM.

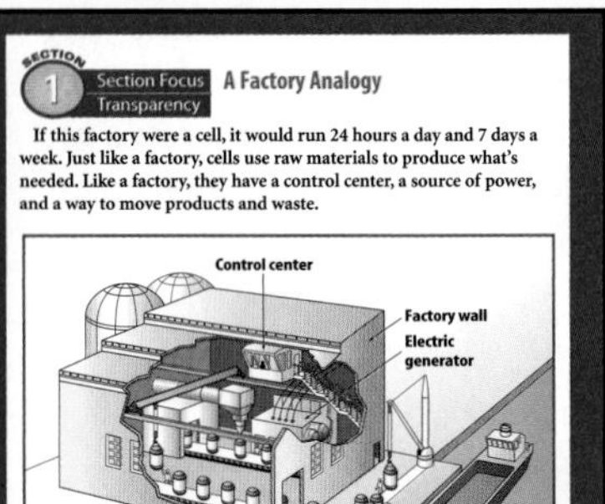

Section Focus Transparency 1 — A Factory Analogy

If this factory were a cell, it would run 24 hours a day and 7 days a week. Just like a factory, cells use raw materials to produce what's needed. Like a factory, they have a control center, a source of power, and a way to move products and waste.

1. What part of the drawing directs the activities in the factory?
2. Identify the part of the drawing that provides energy to the factory.
3. What function do the storage barrels have?

Tie to Prior Knowledge

Body Systems Ask students what body systems they need to live. Write their responses on the board or overhead projector. Use this list to help students understand that the functions of life are carried out in the cell. L2

section 1

Cell Structure

as you read

What You'll Learn

- **Identify** names and functions of each part of a cell.
- **Explain** how important a nucleus is in a cell.
- **Compare** tissues, organs, and organ systems.

Why It's Important

If you know how organelles function, it's easier to understand how cells survive.

Review Vocabulary

photosynthesis: process by which most plants, some protists, and many types of bacteria make their own food

New Vocabulary

- cell membrane
- cytoplasm
- cell wall
- organelle
- nucleus
- chloroplast
- mitochondrion
- ribosome
- endoplasmic reticulum
- Golgi body
- tissue
- organ

Common Cell Traits

Living cells are dynamic and have several things in common. A cell is the smallest unit that is capable of performing life functions. All cells have an outer covering called a **cell membrane.** Inside every cell is a gelatinlike material called **cytoplasm** (SI tuh pla zum). In the cytoplasm of every cell is hereditary material that controls the life of the cell.

Comparing Cells Cells come in many sizes. A nerve cell in your leg could be a meter long. A human egg cell is no bigger than the dot on this *i*. A human red blood cell is about one-tenth the size of a human egg cell. A bacterium is even smaller—8,000 of the smallest bacteria can fit inside one of your red blood cells.

A cell's shape might tell you something about its function. The nerve cell in **Figure 1** has many fine extensions that send and receive impulses to and from other cells. Though a nerve cell cannot change shape, muscle cells and some blood cells can. In plant stems, some cells are long and hollow and have openings at their ends. These cells carry food and water throughout the plant.

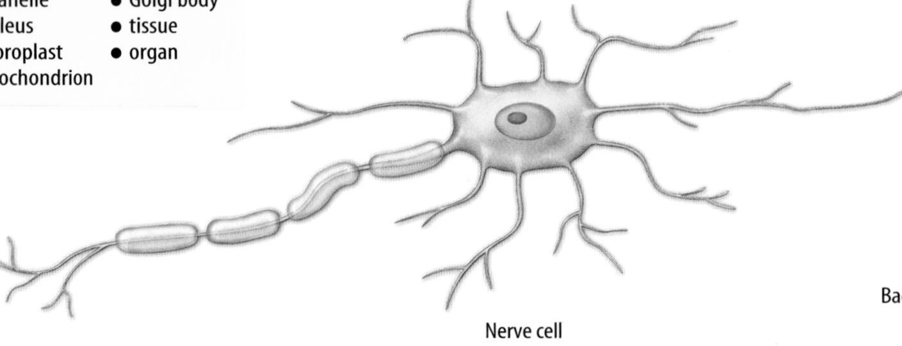

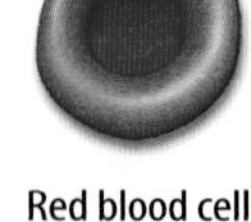

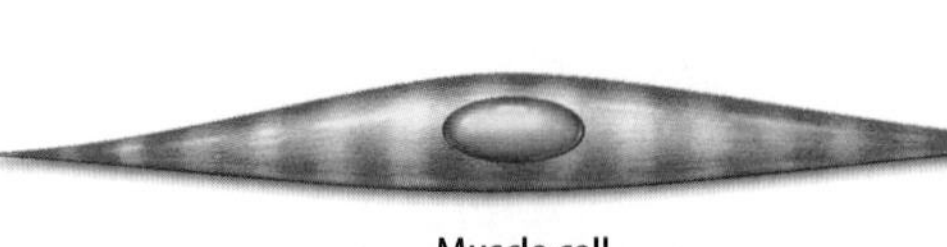

Figure 1 The shape of the cell can tell you something about its function. These cells are drawn 700 times their actual size.

Section 1 Resource Manager

Chapter *FAST FILE* Resources

- Transparency Activity, pp. 44, 47–48
- Directed Reading for Content Mastery, pp. 19, 20
- Note-taking Worksheets, pp. 33–35
- MiniLAB, p. 3
- Enrichment, p. 30
- Lab Worksheet, pp. 5–6
- Reinforcement, p. 27

Life Science Critical Thinking/Problem Solving, p. 1

Mathematics Skill Activities, p. 5

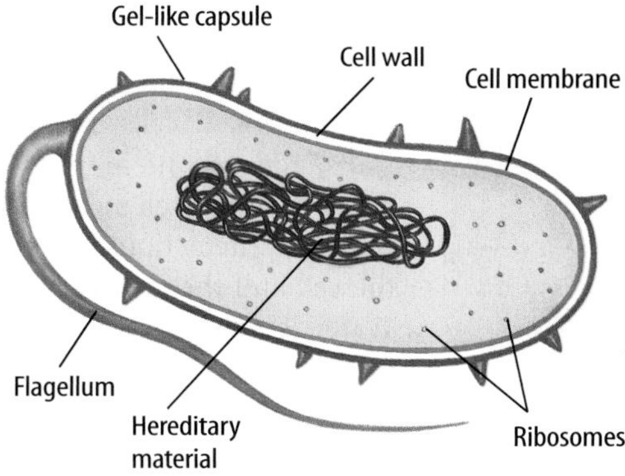

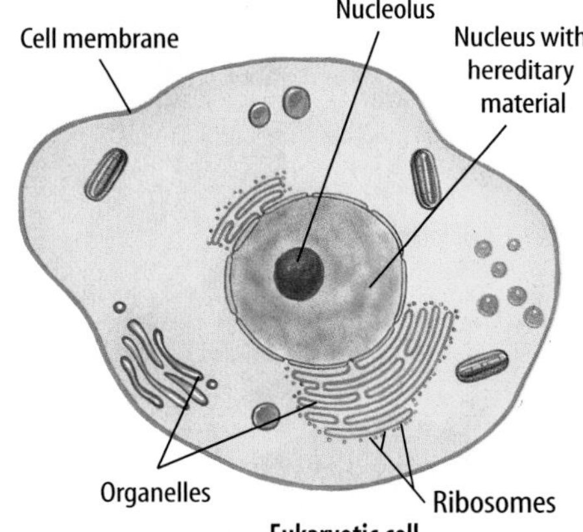

Cell Types Scientists have found that cells can be separated into two groups. One group has no membrane-bound structures inside the cell and the other group does, as shown in **Figure 2.** Cells without membrane-bound structures are called prokaryotic (proh KAYR ee yah tihk) cells. Cells with membrane-bound structures are called eukaryotic (yew KAYR ee yah tihk) cells.

Reading Check *Into what two groups can cells be separated?*

Figure 2 Examine these drawings of cells. Prokaryotic cells are only found in one-celled organisms, such as bacteria. Protists, fungi, plants, and animals are made of eukaryotic cells.
Describe *differences you see between them.*

Cell Organization

Each cell in your body has a specific function. You might compare a cell to a busy delicatessen that is open 24 hours every day. Raw materials for the sandwiches are brought in often. Some food is eaten in the store, and some customers take their food with them. Sometimes food is prepared ahead of time for quick sale. Wastes are put into trash bags for removal or recycling. Similarly, your cells are taking in nutrients, secreting and storing chemicals, and breaking down substances 24 hours every day.

Cell Wall Just like a deli that is located inside the walls of a building, some cells are enclosed in a cell wall. The cells of plants, algae, fungi, and most bacteria are enclosed in a cell wall. **Cell walls** are tough, rigid outer coverings that protect the cell and give it shape.

A plant cell wall, as shown in **Figure 3,** mostly is made up of a carbohydrate called cellulose. The long, threadlike fibers of cellulose form a thick mesh that allows water and dissolved materials to pass through it. Cell walls also can contain pectin, which is used in jam and jelly, and lignin, which is a compound that makes cell walls rigid. Plant cells responsible for support have a lot of lignin in their walls.

Figure 3 The protective cell wall of a plant cell is outside the cell membrane.

Color-enhanced TEM Magnification: 9000×

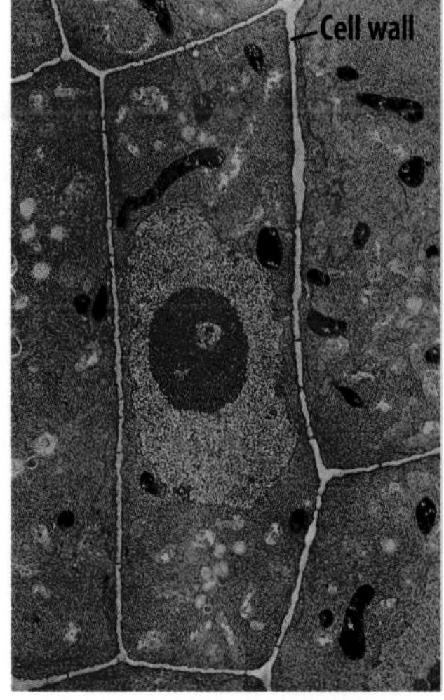

2 Teach

Quick Demo

Different Cell

Materials microprojector, prepared slides of plant, animal, and bacterial cells

Estimated Time 10 minutes

Procedure Show the prepared slides to students using the microprojector. Have students identify the characteristics of each cell shown. L2 LS **Visual-Spatial**

Caption Answer

Figure 2 Answers may include the prokaryotic cell has no membrane-bound structures inside; the eukaryotic cell does have membrane-bound structures.

Reading Check

Answer prokaryotic and eukaryotic

Use an Analogy

Cell Wall To show how a plant cell wall provides strength, inflate a balloon and place it inside a small cardboard box. The balloon represents the cell membrane and the box represents the cell wall.

Discussion

Similarities How are prokaryotic and eukaryotic cells similar? Both have cell membranes, cytoplasm, and DNA as their genetic material.

Fun Fact

Creatures 20–150 nanometers in length were found living in sandstone from the Australian seabed. They are smaller than any other known living organism. They contain DNA and distinct cell membranes.

Curriculum Connection

Health Cellulose, found in all plant cell walls, is not digestible by humans. However, it provides fiber, which is important because it helps in the elimination of wastes. Have students make a list of foods that contain fiber. Lists should include fruits, grains, and leafy vegetables. L2

Discussion

Damaged Cells What would happen if the nucleus of a cell were damaged? The cell would no longer function correctly because the nucleus controls all the cell's activities.

Answer It helps the cell maintain or change its shape.

Purpose Students model cytoplasm. L2 ELL LS **Kinesthetic**

Materials 250-mL beaker, unflavored gelatin (one package per student group), water, flashlight, stirring rod

Teaching Strategy Be certain students stir the gelatin well before shining the light on the beaker.

Analysis

1. particles suspended in the gelatin, which represent organelles suspended in the cytoplasm
2. A model is a representation of an abstract object that is used to help visualize and better understand it.

Assessment

Oral Have students infer how the chemical composition of cytoplasm compares to that of gelatin. Both are water-based suspensions. Cytoplasm is 80% water. Use **Performance Assessment in the Science Classroom,** p. 89.

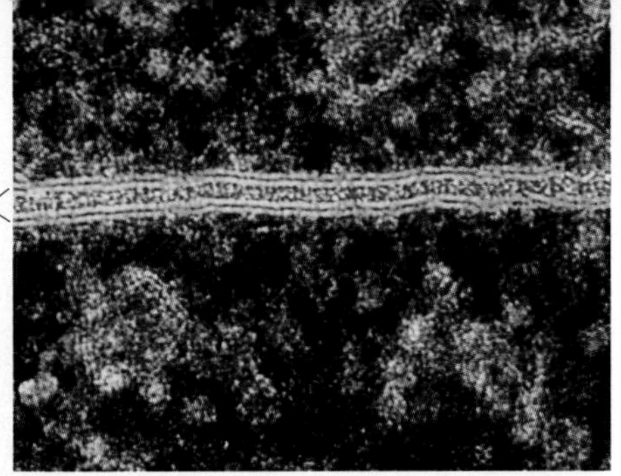

Figure 4 A cell membrane is made up of a double layer of fatlike molecules.

Cell Membrane The protective layer around all cells is the cell membrane, as shown in **Figure 4.** If cells have cell walls, the cell membrane is inside of it. The cell membrane regulates interactions between the cell and the environment. Water is able to move freely into and out of the cell through the cell membrane. Food particles and some molecules enter and waste products leave through the cell membrane.

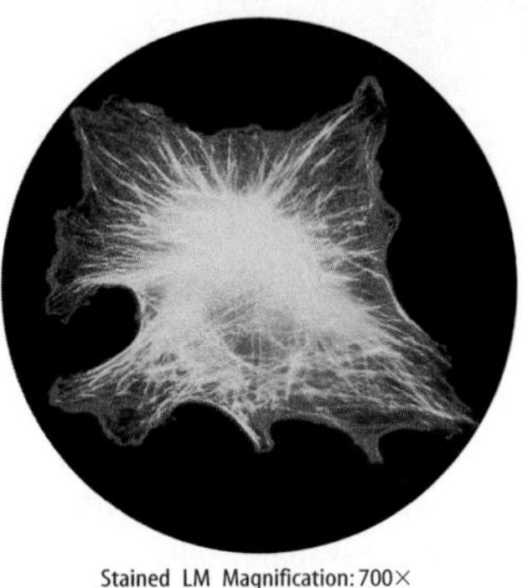

Figure 5 Cytoskeleton, a network of fibers in the cytoplasm, gives cells structure and helps them maintain shape.

Cytoplasm Cells are filled with a gelatinlike substance called cytoplasm that constantly flows inside the cell membrane. Many important chemical reactions occur within the cytoplasm.

Throughout the cytoplasm is a framework called the cytoskeleton, which helps the cell maintain or change its shape. Cytoskeletons enable some cells to move. An amoeba, for example, moves by stretching and contracting its cytoskeleton. The cytoskeleton is made up of thin, hollow tubes of protein and thin, solid protein fibers, as shown in **Figure 5.** Proteins are organic molecules made up of amino acids.

Reading Check *What is the function of the cytoskeleton?*

Most of a cell's life processes occur in the cytoplasm. Within the cytoplasm of eukaryotic cells are structures called **organelles.** Some organelles process energy and others manufacture substances needed by the cell or other cells. Certain organelles move materials, while others act as storage sites. Most organelles are surrounded by membranes. The nucleus is usually the largest organelle in a cell.

Modeling Cytoplasm

Procedure

1. Add 100 mL of **water** to a **clear container.**
2. Add **unflavored gelatin** and stir.
3. Shine a **flashlight** through the solution.

Analysis

1. Describe what you see.
2. How does a model help you understand what cytoplasm might be like?

Nucleus The nucleus is like the deli manager who directs the store's daily operations and passes on information to employees. The **nucleus,** shown in **Figure 6,** directs all cell activities and is separated from the cytoplasm by a membrane. Materials enter and leave the nucleus through openings in the membrane. The nucleus contains the instructions for everything the cell does. These instructions are found on long, threadlike, hereditary material made of DNA. DNA is the chemical that contains the code for the cell's structure and activities. During cell division, the hereditary material coils tightly around proteins to form structures called chromosomes. A structure called a nucleolus also is found in the nucleus.

Teacher FYI

Electron Microscopes Before electron microscopes, scientists could only theorize about many cell structures and their makeups. Even the best compound microscope cannot reveal what can be seen with electron microscopes.

Curriculum Connection

Health Students may think that any cholesterol in the body presents a health risk. Cholesterol is an important component of the cell membrane. It creates a health risk only when it is present in high levels in the blood, where it builds up in arteries and obstructs blood flow. Ask students to investigate cholesterol to differentiate between blood cholesterol and dietary cholesterol. L3

Figure 6 Refer to these diagrams of a typical animal cell (top) and plant cell (bottom) as you read about cell structures and their functions. **Determine** *which structures a plant cell has that are not found in animal cells.*

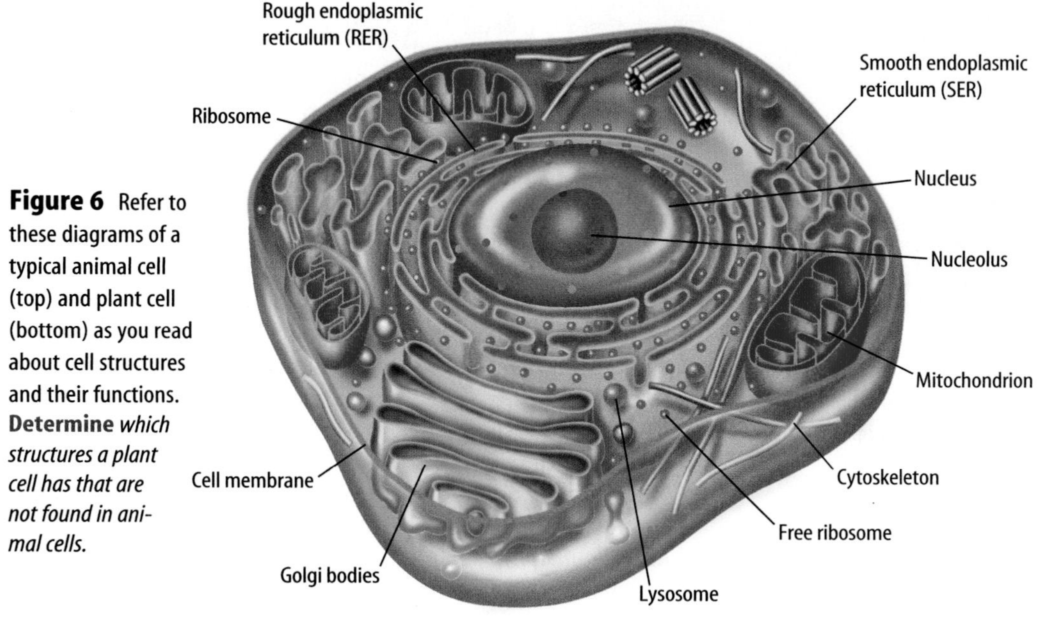

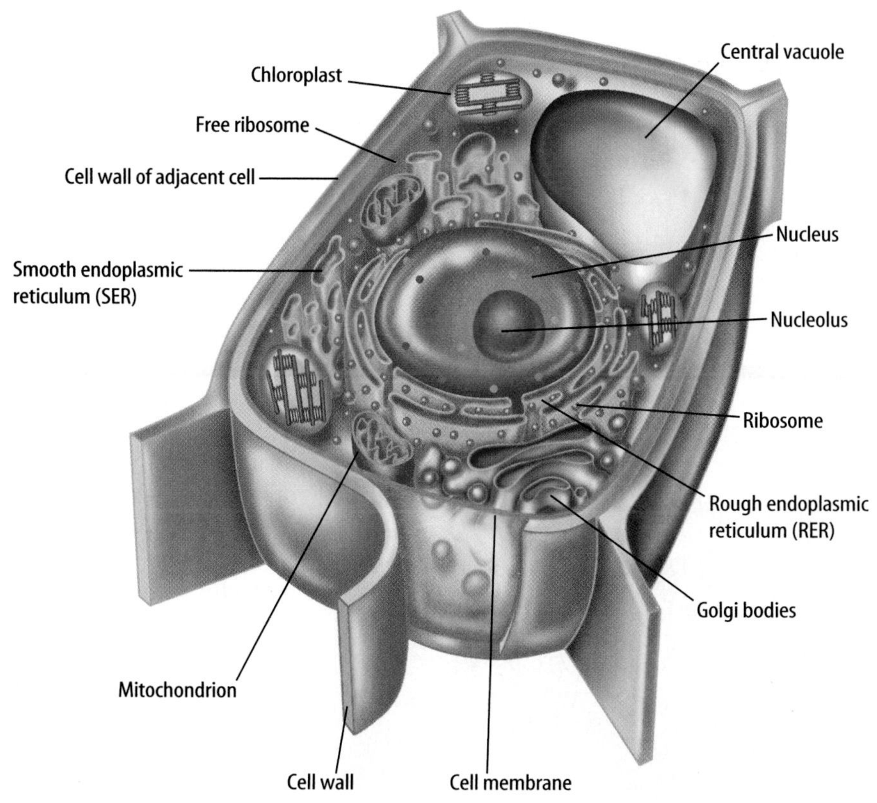

Use an Analogy

Organelle Functions Point out that just as each part of a car engine performs a different function to enable the car to run, each organelle performs a different function in the cell.

Use Science Words

Word Origin Greek and Latin words are used in naming cell parts. Have students make a list of cell parts and use a dictionary to find the origins of the words and their meanings. L2 LS **Linguistic**

Visual Learning

Figure 6 Have students create a network tree concept map comparing and contrasting plant and animal cells. Diagrams should make clear which organelles appear in both cells and which are specific to only one type of cell. L2 LS **Visual-Spatial** P

IDENTIFYING Misconceptions

Water in Cells Students may think that cells are solid. Explain that almost 80 percent of a cell is water. The water is enclosed in a membrane that allows certain materials to enter and leave.

Caption Answer

Figure 6 cell wall, central vacuole, chloroplast

Differentiated Instruction

Challenge Have students do research on the cylindrical organelles in animal cells that are called centrioles. Have students discuss the function of these organelles. How many centrioles are contained within a cell? What is their function in mitosis and meiosis? Students can draw what they learn and share their findings. L3

Teacher FYI

Mitochondria A liver cell has hundreds of mitochondria, which makes up about 25% of the cell's volume. The high number of mitochondria reflects the high level of energy a liver cell requires.

IDENTIFYING Misconceptions

Plant Mitochondria Students may think that because plant cells carry out photosynthesis, they do not have mitochondria. Explain that plants also carry out cellular respiration.

Discussion

Cell Color What color are most cells? Most cells are colorless. Photographs of cells are usually color-enhanced; prepared slides of cells are usually stained so cell parts are visible.

Text Question Answer

Mitochondria provide energy, and active cells would be more in need of energy than inactive cells.

Caption Answer

Figure 8 Possible answer: muscle cells

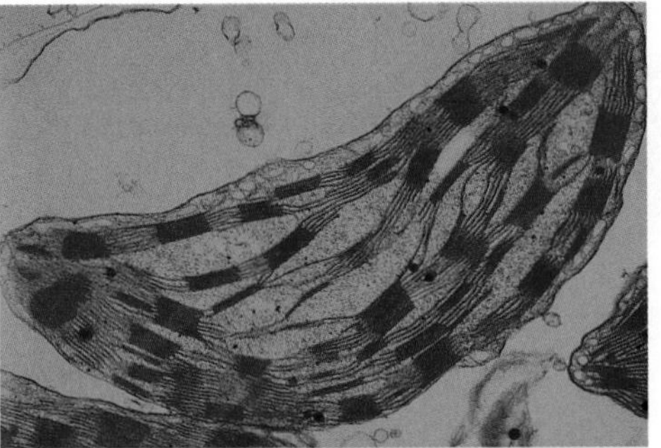

Figure 7 Chloroplasts are organelles that use light energy to make sugar from carbon dioxide and water.

Energy-Processing Organelles Cells require a continuous supply of energy to process food, make new substances, eliminate wastes, and communicate with each other. In plant cells, food is made in green organelles in the cytoplasm called **chloroplasts** (KLOR uh plasts), as shown in **Figure 7.** Chloroplasts contain the green pigment chlorophyll, which gives many leaves and stems their green color. Chlorophyll captures light energy that is used to make a sugar called glucose. Glucose molecules store the captured light energy as chemical energy. Many cells, including animal cells, do not have chloroplasts for making food. They must get food from their environment.

The energy in food is stored until it is released by the mitochondria. **Mitochondria** (mi tuh KAHN dree uh) (singular, *mitochondrion*), such as the one shown in **Figure 8,** are organelles where energy is released from breaking down food into carbon dioxide and water. Just as the gas or electric company supplies fuel for the deli, a mitochondrion releases energy for use by the cell. Some types of cells, such as muscle cells, are more active than other cells. These cells have large numbers of mitochondria. Why would active cells have more or larger mitochondria?

Figure 8 Mitochondria are known as the powerhouses of the cell because they release energy that is needed by the cell from food.
Name *the cell types that might contain many mitochondria.*

Manufacturing Organelles One substance that takes part in nearly every cell activity is protein. Proteins are part of cell membranes. Other proteins are needed for chemical reactions that take place in the cytoplasm. Cells make their own proteins on small structures called **ribosomes.** Even though ribosomes are considered organelles, they are not membrane bound. Some ribosomes float freely in the cytoplasm; others are attached to the endoplasmic reticulum. Ribosomes are made in the nucleolus and move out into the cytoplasm. Ribosomes receive directions from the hereditary material in the nucleus on how, when, and in what order to make specific proteins.

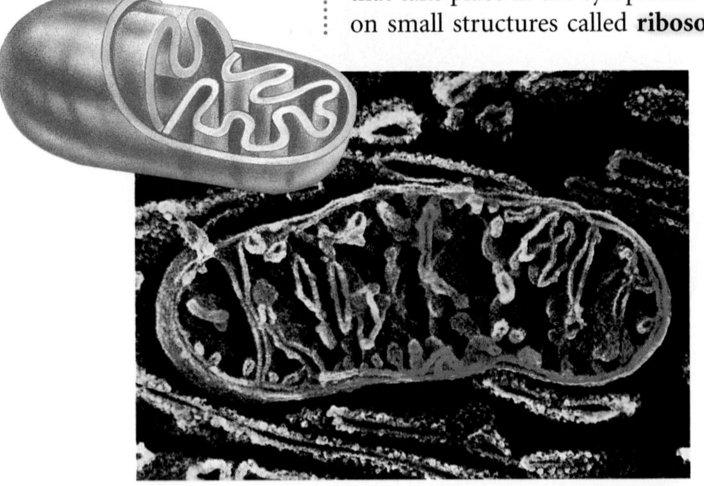

Cultural Diversity

Cell Function Ernest Everett Just, an African American biologist in the early 1900s, studied cells and how they function. His research showed that all parts of the cell influence its activities, not just the nucleus, as scientists then believed. This idea changed scientific opinion concerning the basis of life. Discuss how Just's research is important to the study of cells today.

Differentiated Instruction

Learning Disabled Provide pairs of students with an unlabeled drawing of an animal cell. Have students print small stick-on labels and place them appropriately on the drawing. The labels can be folded to conceal the words and removed as the students learn the cell structures, then replaced for review. L1

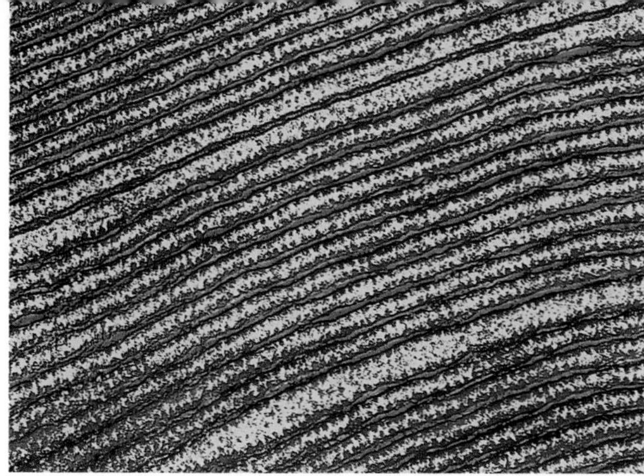
Color-enhanced TEM Magnification: 65000×

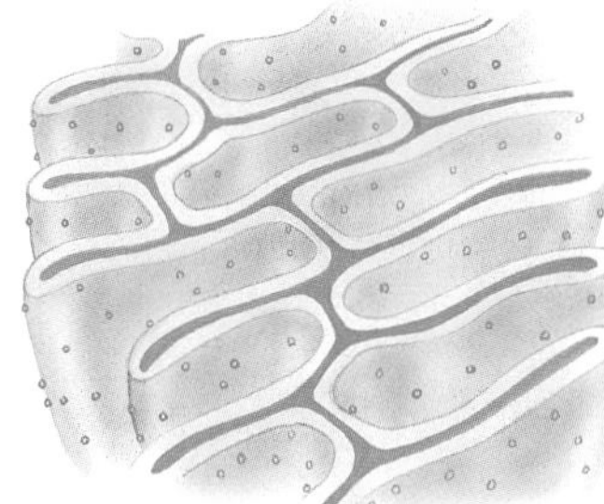

Figure 9 Endoplasmic reticulum (ER) is a complex series of membranes in the cytoplasm of the cell.
Infer *what smooth ER would look like.*

Processing, Transporting, and Storing Organelles

The **endoplasmic reticulum** (en duh PLAZ mihk • rih TIHK yuh lum) or ER, as shown in **Figure 9,** extends from the nucleus to the cell membrane. It is a series of folded membranes in which materials can be processed and moved around inside of the cell. The ER takes up a lot of space in some cells.

The endoplasmic reticulum may be "rough" or "smooth." ER that has no attached ribosomes is called smooth endoplasmic reticulum. This type of ER processes other cellular substances such as lipids that store energy. Ribsomes are attached to areas on the rough ER. There they carry out their job of making proteins that are moved out of the cell or used within the cell.

Reading Check *What is the difference between rough ER and smooth ER?*

After proteins are made in a cell, they are transferred to another type of cell organelle called the Golgi (GAWL jee) bodies. The **Golgi bodies,** as shown ion **Figure 10,** are stacked, flattened membranes. The Golgi bodies sort proteins and other cellular substances and package them into membrane-bound structures called vesicles. The vesicles deliver cellular substances to areas inside the cell. They also carry cellular substances to the cell membrane where they are released to the outside of the cell.

Just as a deli has refrigerators for temporary storage of some of its foods and ingredients, cells have membrane-bound spaces called vacuoles for the temporary storage of materials. A vacuole can store water, waste products, food, and other cellular materials. In plant cells, the vacuole may make up most of the cell's volume.

Figure 10 The Golgi body packages materials and moves them to the outside of the cell.
Explain *why materials are removed from the cell.*

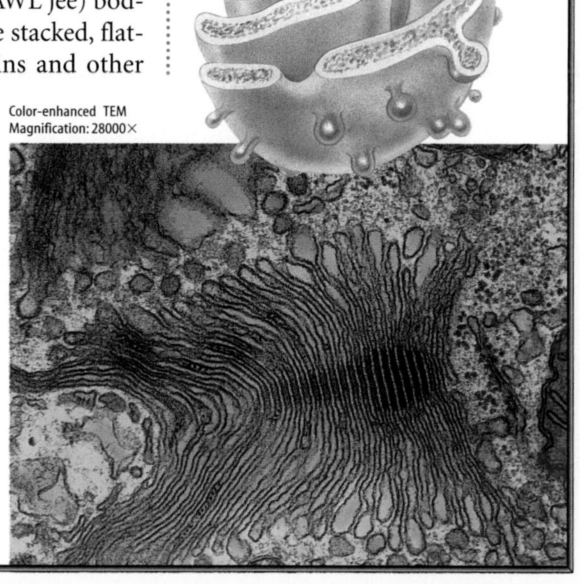
Color-enhanced TEM Magnification: 28000×

Caption Answer

Figure 9 Smooth ER looks the same as rough ER, only without ribosomes attached to it.

Make a Model

Cell Cutaway Have students make a cutaway model of a eukaryotic cell, using a clear plastic bag for the cell membrane, gelatin for cytoplasm, kidney beans for mitochondria, small seeds for ribosomes, noodles for ER and Golgi bodies, a lemon for the nucleus, and peppercorns for lysosomes. Sealed plastic bags full of water can be used for vacuoles. To make a model of a plant cell, green peas can be used for chloroplasts, and licorice for cell walls. L2 LS **Kinesthetic**

Reading Check

Answer Rough endoplasmic reticulum has ribosomes attached to it and makes proteins; smooth ER has no ribosomes and processes cellular substances.

Caption Answer

Figure 10 Materials are removed from a cell because they are waste products of the cell, or are to be used in other parts of the organism.

Activity

Cell Magnification Have students study a cell under increasing magnifications. A microprojector or photos can be used if microscopes are not available. Have them describe the cells at each magnification. Students can make drawings based on their descriptions. L2

Recycling Posters will vary.

Research Have students research the different methods that are used in recycling. Methods could include those for paper, plastic, aluminum, steel, and glass. Students' research should also include what products are made from recycled material and the benefits of recycling. Information from students' research can be included on their promotional poster. L2

Reading Check

Answer to prevent digestive chemicals from leaking into the cytoplasm and destroying the cell

Applying Math

National Math Standards

Correlation to Mathematics Objectives

1, 2, 4, 6, 9

Answers to Practice Problems

1. $A = 2\text{ cm} \times 2\text{ cm} \times 6 = 24\text{ cm}^2$
   $V = 2\text{ cm} \times 2\text{ cm} \times 2\text{ cm} = 8\text{ cm}^3$
   $R = 24\text{ cm}^2/8\text{ cm}^3 = 3\text{ cm}^2/\text{cm}^3$
   As the size of the cube decreases, the ratio increases.
2. $A = 2(4\text{ cm} \times 4\text{ cm}) + 4(4\text{ cm} \times 8\text{ cm}) = 160\text{ cm}^2$
   $V = 4\text{ cm} \times 4\text{ cm} \times 8\text{ cm} = 128\text{ cm}^3$
   $R = 160\text{ cm}^2/128\text{ cm}^3 = 1.25\text{ cm}^2/\text{cm}^3$
   The ratio decreases.

INTEGRATE Environment

Recycling Just like a cell, you can recycle materials. Paper, plastics, aluminum, and glass are materials that can be recycled into usable items. Make a promotional poster to encourage others to recycle.

Recycling Organelles Active cells break down and recycle substances. Organelles called lysosomes (LI suh sohmz) contain digestive chemicals that help break down food molecules, cell wastes, and worn-out cell parts. In a healthy cell, chemicals are released into vacuoles only when needed. The lysosome's membrane prevents the digestive chemicals inside from leaking into the cytoplasm and destroying the cell. When a cell dies, a lysosome's membrane disintegrates. This releases digestive chemicals that allow the quick breakdown of the cell's contents.

Reading Check *What is the function of the lysosome's membrane?*

Applying Math — Calculate a Ratio

CELL RATIO Assume that a cell is like a cube with six equal sides. Find the ratio of surface area to volume for a cube that is 4 cm high.

Solution

1. *This is what you know:* A cube has 6 equal sides of $4\text{ cm} \times 4\text{ cm}$.
2. *This is what you need to find out:* What is the ratio (R) of surface area to volume for the cube?
3. *These are the equations you use:*
   - surface area (A) = width × length × 6
   - volume (V) = length × width × height
   - $R = A/V$
4. *This is the procedure you need to use:*
   - Substitute in known values and solve the equations

   $A = 4\text{ cm} \times 4\text{ cm} \times 6 = 96\text{ cm}^2$

   $V = 4\text{ cm} \times 4\text{ cm} \times 4\text{ cm} = 64\text{ cm}^3$

   $R = 96\text{ cm}^2/64\text{ cm}^3 = 1.5\text{ cm}^2/\text{cm}^3$
5. *Check your answer:* Multiply the ratio by the volume. Did you calculate the surface area?

Practice Problems

1. Calculate the ratio of surface area to volume for a cube that is 2 cm high. What happens to this ratio as the size of the cube decreases?
2. If a 4-cm cube doubled just one of its dimensions, what would happen to the ratio of surface area to volume?

For more practice, visit booka.msscience.com/math_practice

Active Reading

ReQuest To improve listening skills, have students listen carefully as you read an interesting article or story aloud. After the reading, have students construct discussion questions. Have students participate in a ReQuest with the chapter feature or another interesting article related to cell structure or function. L2

46 ◆ A CHAPTER 2 Cells

From Cell to Organism

Many one-celled organisms perform all their life functions by themselves. Cells in a many-celled organism, however, do not work alone. Each cell carries on its own life functions while depending in some way on other cells in the organism.

In **Figure 11,** you can see cardiac muscle cells grouped together to form a tissue. A **tissue** is a group of similar cells that work together to do one job. Each cell in a tissue does its part to keep the tissue alive.

Tissues are organized into organs. An **organ** is a structure made up of two or more different types of tissues that work together. Your heart is an organ made up of cardiac muscle tissue, nerve tissue, and blood tissues. The cardiac muscle tissue contracts, making the heart pump. The nerve tissue brings messages that tell the heart how fast to beat. The blood tissue is carried from the heart to other organs of the body.

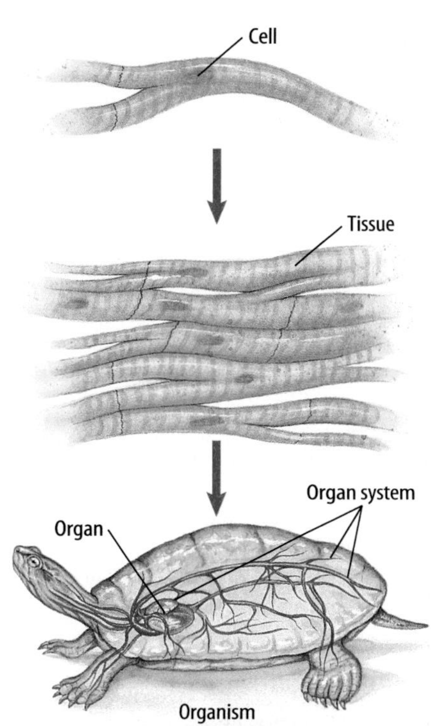

Figure 11 In a many-celled organism, cells are organized into tissues, tissues into organs, organs into systems, and systems into an organism.

Reading Check *What types of tissues make up your heart?*

A group of organs working together to perform a certain function is an organ system. Your heart, arteries, veins, and capillaries make up your cardiovascular system. In a many-celled organism, several systems work together in order to perform life functions efficiently. Your nervous, circulatory, respiratory, muscular, and other systems work together to keep you alive.

section 1 review

Summary

Common Cell Traits

- All cells have an outer covering called a cell membrane.
- Cells can be classified as prokaryotic or eukaryotic.

Cell Organization

- Each cell in your body has a specific function.
- Most of a cell's life processes occur in the cytoplasm.

From Cell to Organism

- In a many-celled organism, several systems work together to perform life functions.

Self Check

1. **Explain** why the nucleus is important in the life of a cell.
2. **Determine** why digestive enzymes in a cell are enclosed in a membrane-bound organelle.
3. **Discuss** how cells, tissues, organs, and organ systems are related.
4. **Think Critically** How is the cell of a one-celled organism different from the cells in many-celled organisms?

Applying Skills

5. **Interpret Scientific Illustrations** Examine **Figure 6.** Make a list of differences and similarities between the animal cell and the plant cell.

Science Online booka.msscience.com/self_check_quiz

section 1 review

1. It directs the activities of the cell and stores hereditary information.
2. It prevents the digestive chemicals inside from destroying the cell.
3. Organ systems are made of organs, which are made of tissues. Tissues are made of cells.
4. one-celled—performs all life functions; multicellular—cells depend on each other
5. Plant cells have chloroplasts and cell walls which animal cells do not have. Unlike plant cells, animal cells have centrioles.

IDENTIFYING Misconceptions

Cell Size Students may assume that the larger an organism is, the larger its cells. Explain that while cells vary in shape and size, most are only about 0.0025 cm in diameter. The number of cells, not how large they are, determines an organism's size.

Reading Check

Answer cardiac muscle tissue, nerve tissue, and blood tissue

3 Assess

DAILY INTERVENTION

Check for Understanding

Visual-Kinesthetic Have students make a bulletin board showing unlabeled parts of an animal cell. As students review each cell part, have a student place a label by it on the bulletin board. L2

Reteach

Cell Differences What are the differences between plant and animal cells? Most plant cells contain chloroplasts and cell walls; animal cells do not. What is the difference between a prokaryotic and eukaryotic cell? Eukaryoticcells have membrane-bound structures; prokaryotic cells do not. L2

Assessment

Process To further assess students' abilities to compare and contrast different cell types, have them write statements in their Science Journals comparing animal and plant cells. Use **Performance Assessment in the Science Classroom,** p. 175. L2

Real-World Question

Purpose Students identify and compare the parts of a plant and animal cell. L2 ELL LS **Visual-Spatial**

Process Skills observe, identify, infer, diagram, compare and contrast, classify

Time Required 45 minutes

Procedure

Alternate Materials If *Elodea* is unavailable, the thin, newest leaves of a coleus plant or similar houseplant.

Safety Precautions Caution students to use extreme care when working with a microscope and microscope slides.

Teaching Strategies

- Have students work in pairs. One student obtains and sets up the microscope while the other prepares the wet mount and obtains the cheek-cell slide. Both observe the slides and record data.
- Have students clean slides and coverslips after use.

Troubleshooting To see movement of cytoplasm, use only leaves from the tips of *Elodea*. Help students focus so they will see cell layers. Students may not be able to see the nucleus. Many students may mistake the chloroplast for the cells.

Conclude and Apply

1. The *Elodea* cell is rectangular; the cheek cell is oval.
2. Only plant cells have a cell wall and chloroplasts.

Comparing Cells

If you compared a goldfish to a rose, you would find them unlike each other. Are their individual cells different also?

Real-World Question

How do human cheek cells and plant cells compare?

Goals

- **Compare and contrast** an animal cell and a plant cell.

Materials

microscope
microscope slide
coverslip
forceps
tap water
dropper
Elodea plant
prepared slide of human cheek cells

Safety Precautions

Procedure

1. Copy the data table in your Science Journal. Check off the cell parts as you observe them.

Cell Observations

Cell Part	Cheek	*Elodea*
Cytoplasm	✔	✔
Nucleus	✔	✔
Chloroplasts		✔
Cell wall		✔
Cell membrane	✔	✔

2. Using forceps, make a wet-mount slide of a young leaf from the tip of an *Elodea* plant.
3. **Observe** the leaf on low power. Focus on the top layer of cells.
4. Switch to high power and focus on one cell. In the center of the cell is a membrane-bound organelle called the central vacuole. Observe the chloroplasts—the green, disk-shaped objects moving around the central vacuole. Try to find the cell nucleus. It looks like a clear ball.
5. **Draw** the *Elodea* cell. Label the cell wall, cytoplasm, chloroplasts, central vacuole, and nucleus. Return to low power and remove the slide. Properly dispose of the slide.
6. **Observe** the prepared slide of cheek cells under low power.
7. Switch to high power and observe the cell nucleus. Draw and label the cell membrane, cytoplasm, and nucleus. Return to low power and remove the slide.

Conclude and Apply

1. **Compare and contrast** the shapes of the cheek cell and the *Elodea* cell.
2. **Draw conclusions** about the differences between plant and animal cells.

Communicating Your Data

Draw the two kinds of cells on one sheet of paper. Use a green pencil to label the organelles found only in plants, a red pencil to label the organelles found only in animals, and a blue pencil to label the organelles found in both. **For more help, refer to the** Science Skill Handbook.

Assessment

Performance To further assess students' abilities to compare plant and animal cells, have them examine cells from lettuce leaves and other types of animal cells on prepared slides. Use **Performance Assessment in the Science Classroom,** p. 97. L2

Communicating Your Data

Chloroplasts and cell walls should be labeled in green on the plant cell. No organelles are labeled red. Cytoplasm, nuclei, and cell membranes should be labeled in blue on plant and animal cells. L2

section 2

Viewing Cells

Magnifying Cells

The number of living things in your environment that you can't see is much greater than the number that you can see. Many of the things that you cannot see are only one cell in size. To see most cells, you need to use a microscope.

Trying to see separate cells in a leaf, like the ones in **Figure 12,** is like trying to see individual photos in a photo mosaic picture that is on the wall across the room. As you walk toward the wall, it becomes easier to see the individual photos. When you get right up to the wall, you can see details of each small photo. A microscope has one or more lenses that enlarge the image of an object as though you are walking closer to it. Seen through these lenses, the leaf appears much closer to you, and you can see the individual cells that carry on life processes.

Early Microscopes In the late 1500s, the first microscope was made by a Dutch maker of reading glasses. He put two magnifying glasses together in a tube and got an image that was larger than the image that was made by either lens alone.

In the mid 1600s, Antonie van Leeuwenhoek, a Dutch fabric merchant, made a simple microscope with a tiny glass bead for a lens, as shown in **Figure 13.** With it, he reported seeing things in pond water that no one had ever imagined. His microscope could magnify up to 270 times. Another way to say this is that his microscope could make the image of an object 270 times larger than its actual size. Today you would say his lens had a power of 270×. Early compound microscopes were crude by today's standards. The lenses would make an image larger, but it wasn't always sharp or clear.

as you read

What **You'll Learn**

- **Compare** the differences between the compound light microscope and the electron microscope.
- **Summarize** the discoveries that led to the development of the cell theory.

Why **It's Important**

Humans are like other living things because they are made of cells.

Review Vocabulary
magnify: to increase the size of something

New Vocabulary
- cell theory

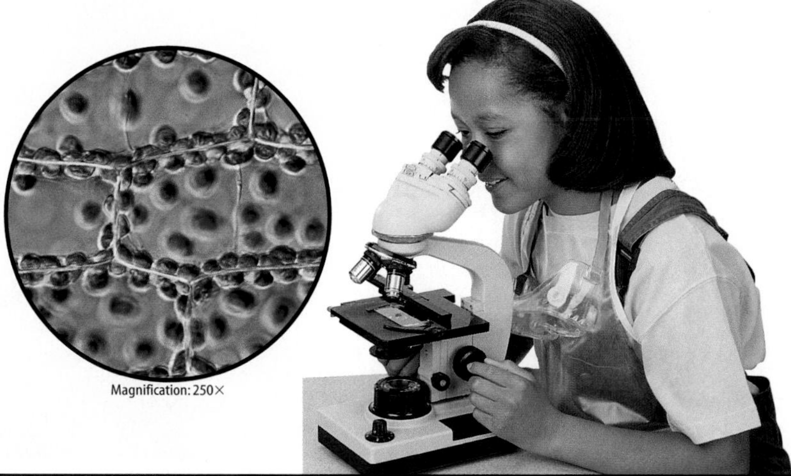

Figure 12 Individual cells become visible when a plant leaf is viewed using a microscope with enough magnifying power.

1 Motivate

Bellringer

Section Focus Transparencies also are available on the Interactive Chalkboard CD-ROM. L2 ELL

Tie to Prior Knowledge

Magnification Students may have used magnifying glasses and binoculars. Explain that a microscope magnifies in the same way.

Section 2 Resource Manager

Chapter *FAST FILE* Resources
- Transparency Activity, p. 45
- Directed Reading for Content Mastery, p. 20
- Enrichment, p. 31
- Lab Activity, pp. 9–12, 13–16
- MiniLAB, p. 4
- Reinforcement, p. 28

Visualizing Microscopes

Have students examine the pictures and read the captions. Then ask the following questions.

What are the similarities and differences between a fluorescence microscope and a phase-contrast microscope? Possible answers: Both microscopes magnify up to 1500×. With the fluorescence microscope, the specimen must be stained and can be viewed through the scope directly. With the phase-contrast microscope, the specimen is not stained and can only be viewed on a monitor or in a photograph. Phase-contrast microscopes are good for viewing living things.

Compare and contrast the features of a TEM and an SEM. Possible answers: Both microscopes use electrons to help produce the magnified image. Also, with both microscopes the specimen can only be viewed on a monitor or in a photograph. In a TEM the electrons go through the specimen and the magnification is up to 1,000,000×. With an SEM, the electrons sweep over the surface of the specimen and a three-dimensional image is produced. The magnification of an SEM is only up to 200,000×.

Activity

Microscope Types Have students identify the type of microscope(s) they use in science class. Then have students view different slides under the microscope (e.g. onion slices, hair, sliver from a grass blade, color-comics section of the newspaper). Have students draw what they observe. If possible, use several types of microscopes and a magnifying glass and have students compare how the same slide looks under each one. Ask students to list the similarities and differences between them, and hypothesize what accounts for these differences. L2

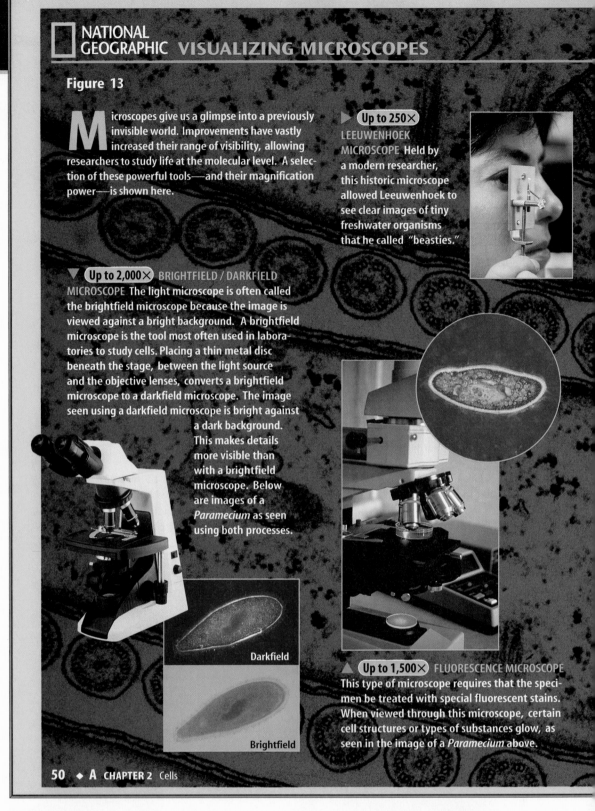

NATIONAL GEOGRAPHIC VISUALIZING MICROSCOPES

Figure 13

Microscopes give us a glimpse into a previously invisible world. Improvements have vastly increased their range of visibility, allowing researchers to study life at the molecular level. A selection of these powerful tools—and their magnification power—is shown here.

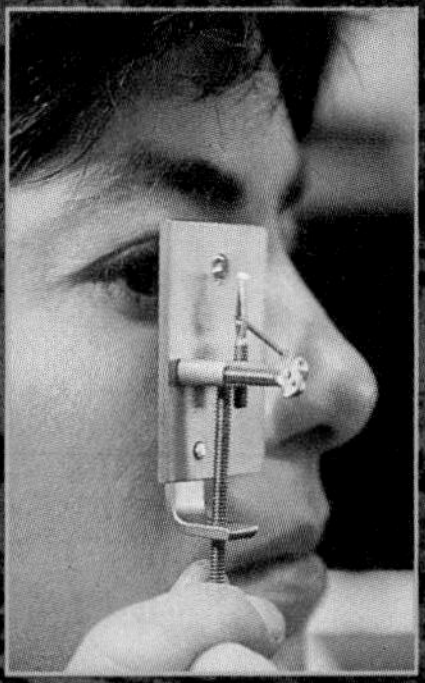

▶ Up to 250× LEEUWENHOEK MICROSCOPE Held by a modern researcher, this historic microscope allowed Leeuwenhoek to see clear images of tiny freshwater organisms that he called "beasties."

▼ Up to 2,000× BRIGHTFIELD / DARKFIELD MICROSCOPE The light microscope is often called the brightfield microscope because the image is viewed against a bright background. A brightfield microscope is the tool most often used in laboratories to study cells. Placing a thin metal disc beneath the stage, between the light source and the objective lenses, converts a brightfield microscope to a darkfield microscope. The image seen using a darkfield microscope is bright against a dark background. This makes details more visible than with a brightfield microscope. Below are images of a *Paramecium* as seen using both processes.

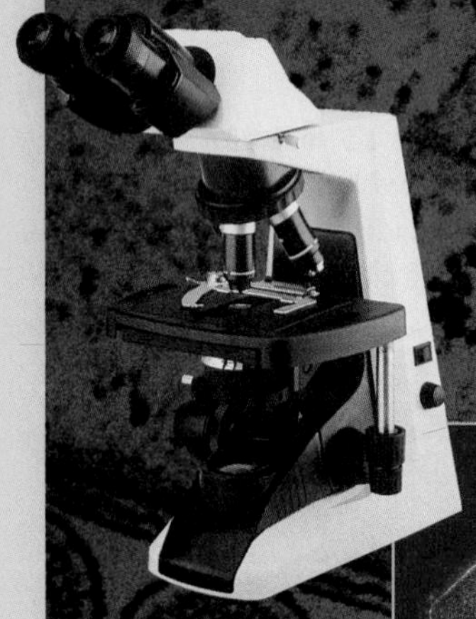

Darkfield

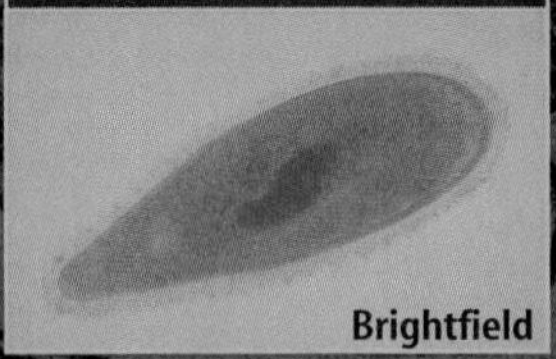

Brightfield

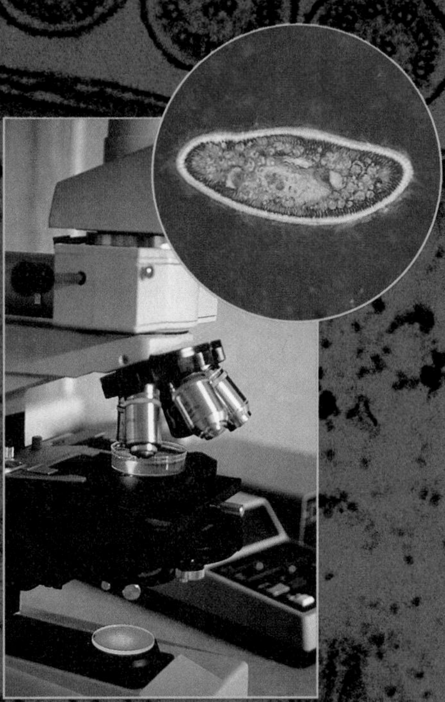

▲ Up to 1,500× FLUORESCENCE MICROSCOPE This type of microscope requires that the specimen be treated with special fluorescent stains. When viewed through this microscope, certain cell structures or types of substances glow, as seen in the image of a *Paramecium* above.

50 ◆ A CHAPTER 2 Cells

Science Journal

Magnification Have students make a time line showing discoveries made with the light microscope, beginning with Robert Hooke (1665) identifying and drawing cells. L2

Teacher FYI

Artifacts Any phenomenon that occurs as a result of the fixing or staining procedure used to prepare a specimen to be viewed on a slide is called an artifact. An artifact is not a feature of the living organism. Sometimes an artifact can be a simple air bubble; other times the procedure can change the shape of a particular feature.

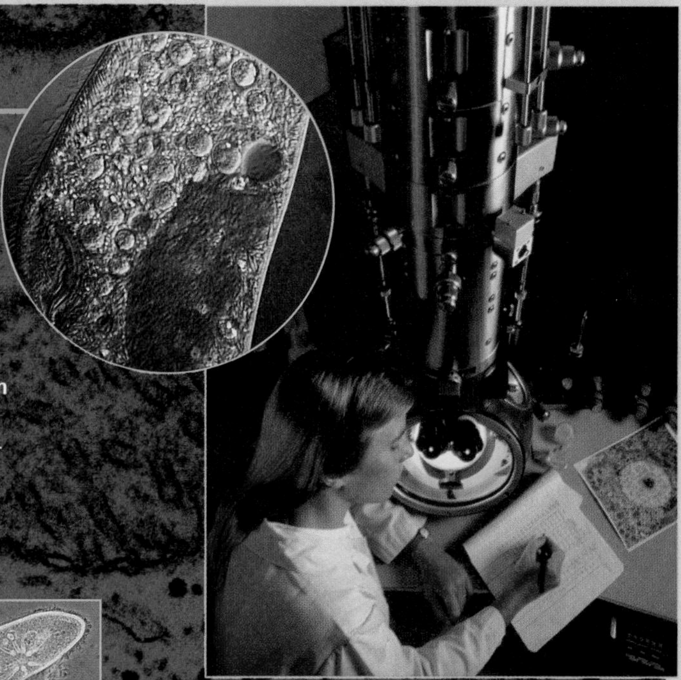

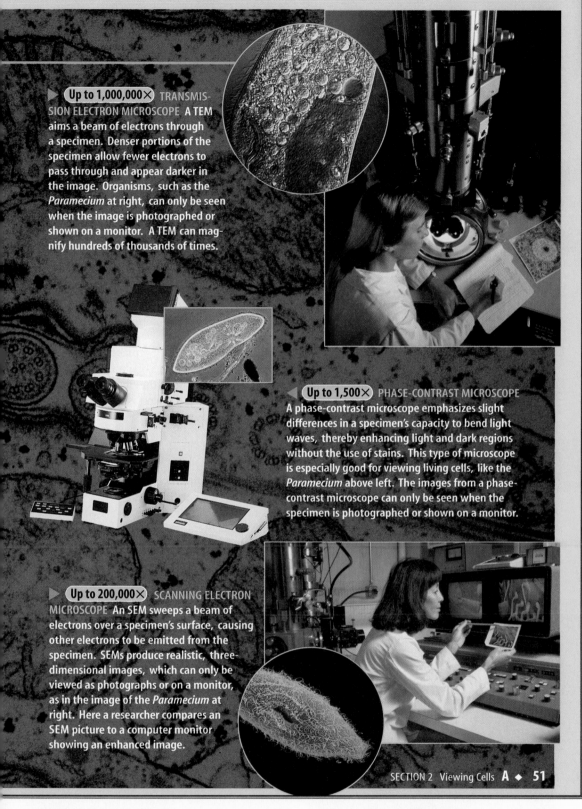

Up to 1,000,000× TRANSMISSION ELECTRON MICROSCOPE A TEM aims a beam of electrons through a specimen. Denser portions of the specimen allow fewer electrons to pass through and appear darker in the image. Organisms, such as the *Paramecium* at right, can only be seen when the image is photographed or shown on a monitor. A TEM can magnify hundreds of thousands of times.

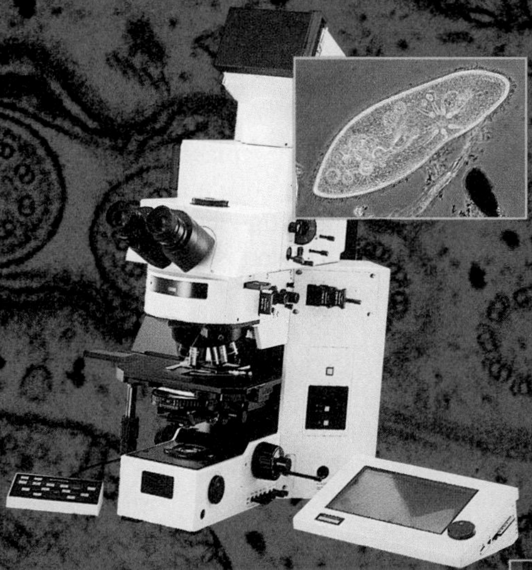

Up to 1,500× PHASE-CONTRAST MICROSCOPE A phase-contrast microscope emphasizes slight differences in a specimen's capacity to bend light waves, thereby enhancing light and dark regions without the use of stains. This type of microscope is especially good for viewing living cells, like the *Paramecium* above left. The images from a phase-contrast microscope can only be seen when the specimen is photographed or shown on a monitor.

Up to 200,000× SCANNING ELECTRON MICROSCOPE An SEM sweeps a beam of electrons over a specimen's surface, causing other electrons to be emitted from the specimen. SEMs produce realistic, three-dimensional images, which can only be viewed as photographs or on a monitor, as in the image of the *Paramecium* at right. Here a researcher compares an SEM picture to a computer monitor showing an enhanced image.

SECTION 2 Viewing Cells A ◆ 51

Visualizing Microscopes

Content Background

Microscopes are used by many different types of scientists, including biologists, microbiologists, botanists, geologists, and epidemiologists. In 1665, Robert Hooke was the first person to see cells through a microscope of his creation. The idea of cell theory—that all living things are made of cells—was borne from his discovery. Although Hooke could see the individual cells clearly, he did not stain any of his specimens; therefore, he would not have been able to see other single-celled organisms such as bacteria. It was Antoni van Leeuwenhoek who first examined living organisms through a simple microscope in the late seventeenth century. He found organisms in the rain-water he collected, as well as in the scrapings he took from the surface of his teeth.

Differentiated Instruction

English-Language Learners Have students work in pairs to create an advertisement for a microscope. Students should discuss all of the parts of a microscope in their advertisement. The advertisement should also include all of the parts of a cell that can be visualized using the microscope. L2

Visual Learning

Figure 13 Have students make a chart comparing and contrasting the different types of microscopes in this figure. They should include information on lenses and the uses of each. L2
LS **Visual-Spatial**

Observing Magnified Objects

Procedure

1. Look at a **newspaper** through the curved side and through the flat bottom of an **empty, clear glass.**
2. Look at the newspaper through a **clear glass bowl filled with water** and then with a **magnifying lens.**

Analysis

In your Science Journal, compare how well you can see the newspaper through each of the objects.

Try at Home

Modern Microscopes Scientists use a variety of microscopes to study organisms, cells, and cell parts that are too small to be seen with the human eye. Depending on how many lenses a microscope contains, it is called simple or compound. A simple microscope is similar to a magnifying lens. It has only one lens. A microscope's lens makes an enlarged image of an object and directs light toward your eye. The change in apparent size produced by a microscope is called magnification. Microscopes vary in powers of magnification. Some microscopes can make images of individual atoms.

The microscope you probably will use to study life science is a compound light microscope, similar to the one in the Reference Handbook at the back of this book. The compound light microscope has two sets of lenses—eyepiece lenses and objective lenses. The eyepiece lenses are mounted in one or two tubelike structures. Images of objects viewed through two eyepieces, or stereomicroscopes, are three-dimensional. Images of objects viewed through one eyepiece are not. Compound light microscopes usually have two to four movable objective lenses.

Magnification The powers of the eyepiece and objective lenses determine the total magnifications of a microscope. If the eyepiece lens has a power of 10× and the objective lens has a power of 43×, then the total magnification is 430× (10× times 43×). Some compound microscopes, like those in **Figure 13,** have more powerful lenses that can magnify an object up to 2,000 times its original size.

Electron Microscopes Things that are too small to be seen with other microscopes can be viewed with an electron microscope. Instead of using lenses to direct beams of light, an electron microscope uses a magnetic field in a vacuum to direct beams of electrons. Some electron microscopes can magnify images up to one million times. Electron microscope images must be photographed or electronically produced.

Several kinds of electron microscopes have been invented, as shown in **Figure 13.** Scanning electron microscopes (SEM) produce a realistic, three-dimensional image. Only the surface of the specimen can be observed using an SEM. Transmission electron microscopes (TEM) produce a two-dimensional image of a thinly-sliced specimen. Details of cell parts can be examined using a TEM. Scanning tunneling microscopes (STM) are able to show the arrangement of atoms on the surface of a molecule. A metal probe is placed near the surface of the specimen and electrons flow from the tip. The hills and valleys of the specimen's surface are mapped.

INTEGRATE Career

Cell Biologist Microscopes are important tools for cell biologists as they research diseases. In your Science Journal, make a list of diseases for which you think cell biologists are trying to find effective drugs.

2 Teach

Mini LAB

Purpose Students discover objects that can be used to magnify. L2 ELL LS **Kinesthetic**

Materials clear drinking glass, clear glass bowl, water, magnifying lens, newspaper pages

Teaching Strategy Try this lab with the glasses students will use. Determine beforehand the amount of water that will be needed.

Analysis

Each of the objects magnifies the newsprint.

Assessment

Performance Cover newsprint with clear plastic wrap. Place a drop of water on the plastic wrap. Have students explain what they see and why. The words appear magnified because the water drop acts like a convex lens. Use **Performance Assessment in the Science Classroom,** p. 89.

INTEGRATE Career

Cell Biologist The field of cell biology is very diverse. Many techniques require the use of different microscopes. As students research the drugs that cell biologists are studying, also have them identify techniques that require microscopes, and the types of microscopes that cell biologists use.

Curriculum Connection

Art Discuss the use of art in science before the camera was invented. Photocopy a picture of Hooke's drawing of cells for each student. Ask them to compare it with the photographs of cells throughout the chapter and write in their Science Journals their opinions of the advantages and disadvantages of using artwork and photography. L2 LS **Linguistic and Visual-Spatial**

Differentiated Instruction

Challenge Have students research the Italian scientist who discover the Golgi body. Their research should include how this discovery was made possible and why this organelle was not seriously studied until the 1950s. Students can use references to find electron micrographs of the Golgi body to learn about it in greater depth. Students can write a biographical report on Camillo Golgi and the Golgi body. L3

Cell Theory

During the seventeenth century, scientists used their new invention, the microscope, to explore the newly discovered microscopic world. They examined drops of blood, scrapings from their own teeth, and other small things. Cells weren't discovered until the microscope was improved. In 1665, Robert Hooke cut a thin slice of cork and looked at it under his microscope. To Hooke, the cork seemed to be made up of empty little boxes, which he named cells.

Table 1 The Cell Theory

All organisms are made up of one or more cells.	An organism can be one cell or many cells like most plants and animals.
The cell is the basic unit of organization in organisms.	Even in complex organisms, the cell is the basic unit of structure and function.
All cells come from cells.	Most cells can divide to form two new, identical cells.

In the 1830s, Matthias Schleiden used a microscope to study plants and concluded that all plants are made of cells. Theodor Schwann, after observing different animal cells, concluded that all animals are made up of cells. Eventually, they combined their ideas and became convinced that all living things are made of cells.

Several years later, Rudolf Virchow hypothesized that cells divide to form new cells. Virchow proposed that every cell came from a cell that already existed. His observations and conclusions and those of others are summarized in the **cell theory,** as described in **Table 1.**

Who first concluded that all animals are made of cells?

section 2 review

Summary

Magnifying Cells

- The powers of the eyepiece and objective lenses determine the total magnification of a microscope.
- An electron microscope uses a magnetic field in a vacuum to direct beams of electrons.

Development of the Cell Theory

- In 1665, Robert Hooke looked at a piece of cork under his microscope and called what he saw cells.
- The conclusions of Rudolf Virchow and those of others are summarized in the cell theory.

Self Check

1. **Determine** why the invention of the microscope was important in the study of cells.
2. **State** the cell theory.
3. **Compare** a simple and a compound light microscope.
4. **Explain** Virchow's contribution to the cell theory.
5. **Think Critically** Why would it be better to look at living cells than at dead cells?

Applying Math

6. **Solve One-Step Equations** Calculate the magnifications of a microscope that has an 8× eyepiece and 10× and 40× objectives.

Science Online booka.msscience.com/self_check_quiz

section 2 review

1. Microscopes made cells visible, which established them as a scientific fact. This led to the understanding that all living things are made of cells.
2. All organisms are made of one or more cells. The cell is the basic unit of organization in organisms. All cells come from other cells.
3. A simple light microscope has one lens. A compound light microscope has two or more lenses.
4. Virchow proposed that every cell came from a cell that already existed.
5. Possible answer: some cell parts disintegrate when the cell dies.
6. The low-power magnification is 80× = (8 × 10) and the high-power magnification is 320× = (8 × 40).

Teacher FYI

Dead Cells Hooke saw only cell walls. When plant cells die, the cell wall remains. Tree bark is dead tissue. The cork that Hooke examined comes from the bark of an oak tree.

Reading Check

Answer Theodor Schwann

3 Assess

DAILY INTERVENTION

Check for Understanding

Visual-Spatial Have students make a time line that describes the discoveries that have led up to the modern microscopes used today. Students can include information about the key parts of a microscope, how each type of microscope works, and what each is used for. L2

Reteach

Compound Microscope Place a large drawing of a compound microscope on the bulletin board. Write the functions of each part on a 3-in × 5-in card. Have students select a card, name the part, and find it on the drawing. L1 COOP LEARN IN **Visual-Spatial**

Assessment

Portfolio Have students write a paragraph describing the limitations as they understand them of each microscope presented in this section. Use **Performance Assessment in the Science Classroom,** p. 157. L2 P

1 Motivate

Bellringer

Section Focus Transparencies also are available on the Interactive Chalkboard CD-ROM.

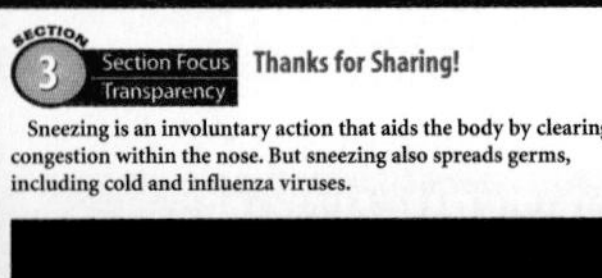

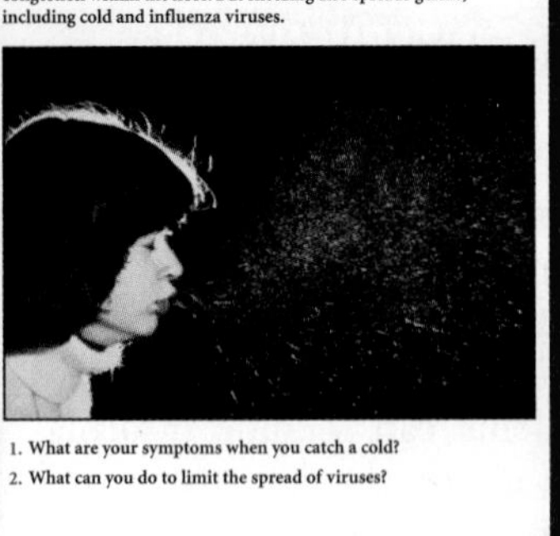

1. What are your symptoms when you catch a cold?
2. What can you do to limit the spread of viruses?

Tie to Prior Knowledge

Viral Symptoms Most students will be familiar with at least one viral disease (chicken pox, cold sores, the common cold). Have them list its symptoms on the board.

section 3

Viruses

as you read

***What* You'll Learn**

- **Explain** how a virus makes copies of itself.
- **Identify** the benefits of vaccines.
- **Investigate** some uses of viruses.

***Why* It's Important**

Viruses infect nearly all organisms, usually affecting them negatively yet sometimes affecting them positively.

Review Vocabulary

disease: a condition that results from the disruption in function of one or more of an organism's normal processes

New Vocabulary

- virus
- host cell

What are viruses?

Cold sores, measles, chicken pox, colds, the flu, and AIDS are diseases caused by nonliving particles called viruses. A **virus** is a strand of hereditary material surrounded by a protein coating. Viruses don't have a nucleus or other organelles. They also lack a cell membrane. Viruses, as shown in **Figure 14,** have a variety of shapes. Because they are too small to be seen with a light microscope, they were discovered only after the electron microscope was invented. Before that time, scientists only hypothesized about viruses.

How do viruses multiply?

All viruses can do is make copies of themselves. However, they can't do that without the help of a living cell called a **host cell.** Crystalized forms of some viruses can be stored for years. Then, if they enter an organism, they can multiply quickly.

Once a virus is inside of a host cell, the virus can act in two ways. It can either be active or it can become latent, which is an inactive stage.

Figure 14 Viruses come in a variety of shapes.

Color-enhanced TEM Magnification: 160000×

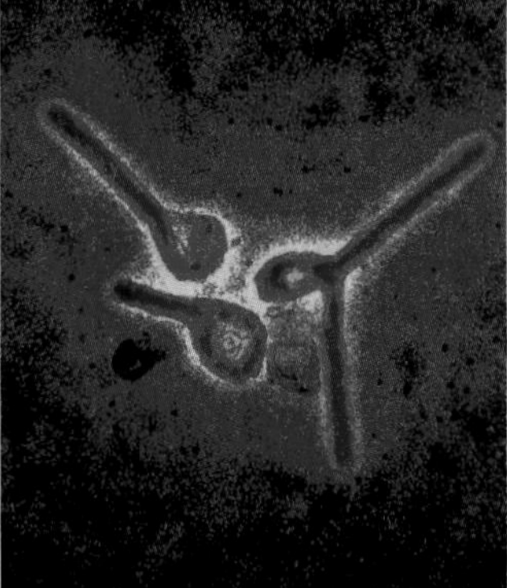

Filoviruses do not have uniform shapes. Some of these *Ebola* viruses have a loop at one end.

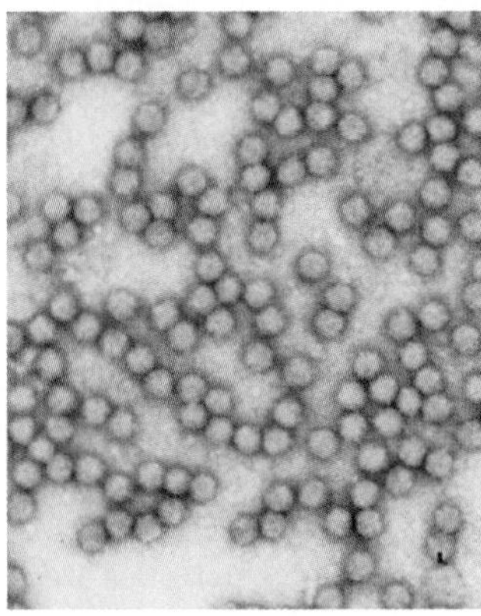

The potato leafroll virus, *Polervirus,* damages potato crops worldwide.

Color-enhanced SEM Magnification: 140000×

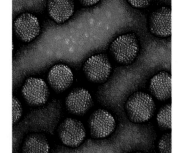

This is just one of the many adenoviruses that can cause the common cold.

Section 3 Resource Manager

Chapter *FAST FILE* Resources

Transparency Activity, p. 46

Directed Reading for Content Mastery, pp. 21, 22

Enrichment, p. 32

Reinforcement, p. 29

Lab Worksheet, pp. 7–8

Reading and Writing Skill Activities, p. 31

Home and Community Involvement, p. 26

Lab Management and Safety, p. 58

Figure 15 An active virus multiplies and destroys the host cell.

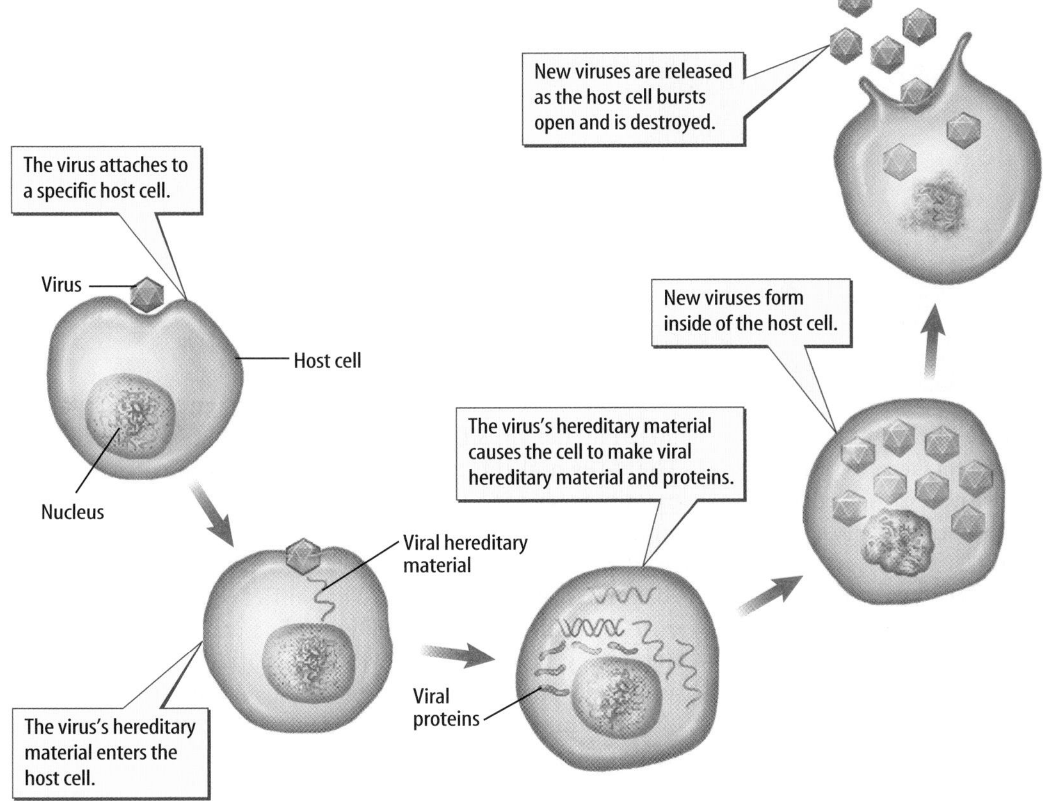

The virus attaches to a specific host cell.
Virus
Host cell
Nucleus
The virus's hereditary material enters the host cell.
Viral hereditary material
The virus's hereditary material causes the cell to make viral hereditary material and proteins.
Viral proteins
New viruses form inside of the host cell.
New viruses are released as the host cell bursts open and is destroyed.

Active Viruses When a virus enters a cell and is active, it causes the host cell to make new viruses. This process destroys the host cell. Follow the steps in **Figure 15** to see one way that an active virus functions inside a cell.

Latent Viruses Some viruses can be latent. That means that after the virus enters a cell, its hereditary material can become part of the cell's hereditary material. It does not immediately make new viruses or destroy the cell. As the host cell reproduces, the viral DNA is copied. A virus can be latent for many years. Then, at any time, certain conditions, either inside or outside your body, can activate the virus.

If you have had a cold sore on your lip, a latent virus in your body has become active. The cold sore is a sign that the virus is active and destroying cells in your lip. When the cold sore disappears, the virus has become latent again. The virus is still in your body's cells, but it is hiding and doing no apparent harm.

Topic: Virus Reactivation
Visit booka.msscience.com for Web links to information about viruses.

Activity In your Science Journal, list five stimuli that might activate a latent virus.

2 Teach

Visual Learning

Figure 15 Have students make a concept map outlining the steps of viral infection and replication shown in this figure. L2

Inquiry Lab

Visualizing Microscopes

Purpose To understand refraction, have students design and construct a simple refracting device.

Possible Materials cup of water, glass jar or beaker, ruler, cooking oil, rubbing alcohol

Estimated Time 30 minutes

Teaching Strategies

- Students can refract light by layering oil and alcohol on top of water.
- The refraction of light can be demonstrated by placing a ruler in the beaker containing layered water, oil, and alcohol.
- Students can observe the refraction of light as evidenced by the ruler appearing as though it is misshapen.
- Refraction can be researched and related to what is seen.
- Allow students to explore other questions that arise. L2

For additional inquiry activities, see Science Inquiry Labs.

LAB DEMONSTRATION

Purpose to model two viruses

Materials two bolts with nuts, two 14-cm pieces of #22-gauge wire, polystyrene ball 4.5 cm in diameter, craft sticks cut in 2-cm lengths

Preparation Prepare materials and provide photos of a bacteriophage and a flu virus.

Procedure Have students use the bacteriophage photo, the bolt, nuts, and wire to make a model bacteriophage. Have them use the polystyrene ball and craft sticks to make a model flu virus.

Expected Outcome Students should observe that virus structures differ.

Assessment

In a real virus, what would make up the threaded part of the bolt and the wires? protein If your flu virus were a real virus, what would you expect to find inside the ball? hereditary material

Use Science Words

Word Usage Have students use the word *vaccine* in a sentence describing its characteristics. LS **Linguistic**

Caption Answer

Figure 16 Answers may include the common cold, measles, smallpox, and chicken pox.

Fun Fact

Scientist have found small spore-like cells in mammal tissues that are involved in tissue repair. They have been used to repair breaks in the spinal cords of rats.

Reading Check

Answer a preparation of weakened virus particles that helps prevent disease

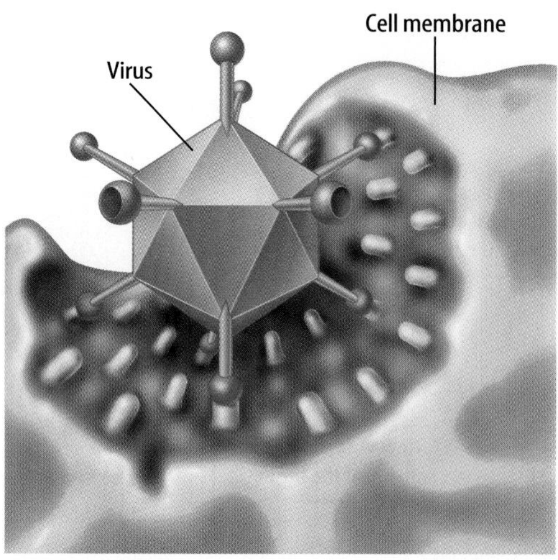

Figure 16 Viruses and the attachment sites of the host cell must match exactly. That's why most viruses infect only one kind of host cell.
Identify *diseases caused by viruses.*

How do viruses affect organisms?

Viruses attack animals, plants, fungi, protists, and all prokaryotes. Some viruses can infect only specific kinds of cells. For instance, many viruses, such as the potato leafroll virus, are limited to one host species or to one type of tissue within that species. A few viruses affect a broad range of hosts. An example of this is the rabies virus. Rabies can infect humans and many other animal hosts.

A virus cannot move by itself, but it can reach a host's body in several ways. For example, it can be carried onto a plant's surface by the wind or it can be inhaled by an animal. In a viral infection, the virus first attaches to the surface of the host cell. The virus and the place where it attaches must fit together exactly, as shown in **Figure 16.** Because of this, most viruses attack only one kind of host cell.

Viruses that infect bacteria are called bacteriophages (bak TIHR ee uh fay jihz). They differ from other kinds of viruses in the way that they enter bacteria and release their hereditary material. Bacteriophages attach to a bacterium and inject their hereditary material. The entire cycle takes about 20 min, and each virus-infected cell releases an average of 100 viruses.

Fighting Viruses

Vaccines are used to prevent disease. A vaccine is made from weakened virus particles that can't cause disease anymore. Vaccines have been made to prevent many diseases, including measles, mumps, smallpox, chicken pox, polio, and rabies.

Reading Check *What is a vaccine?*

The First Vaccine Edward Jenner is credited with developing the first vaccine in 1796. He developed a vaccine for smallpox, a disease that was still feared in the early twentieth century. Jenner noticed that people who got a disease called cowpox didn't get smallpox. He prepared a vaccine from the sores of people who had cowpox. When injected into healthy people, the cowpox vaccine protected them from smallpox. Jenner didn't know he was fighting a virus. At that time, no one understood what caused disease or how the body fought disease.

Science Online

Topic: Filoviruses
Visit booka.msscience.com for Web links to information about the virus family *Filoviridae*.

Activity Make a table that displays the virus name, location, and year of the initial outbreaks associated with the *Filoviridae* family.

Curriculum Connection

Math A common unit of measure for viruses is the nanometer (nm), which is 1,000 times smaller than a micrometer (µm) and 1 million times smaller than a millimeter. A typical virus is 20 nm in size. What part of a millimeter is that? 0.000 02 mm A virus of 0.3 micrometers is how many nanometers? 300 nm LS **Logical-Mathematical**

Differentiated Instruction

Challenge Have students do research on the use of viruses in genetic engineering. Students should research how genetic engineering works and what specific genetic disorders have been or could be treated using genetically engineered viruses. Students can write a newspaper article that describes their findings. L3

Treating Viral Diseases Antibiotics treat bacterial infections but are not effective against viral diseases. One way your body can stop viral infections is by making interferons. Interferons are proteins that are produced rapidly by virus-infected cells and move to noninfected cells in the host. They cause the noninfected cells to produce protective substances.

Antiviral drugs can be given to infected patients to help fight a virus. A few drugs show some effectiveness against viruses but some have limited use because of their adverse side effects.

Preventing Viral Diseases Public health measures for preventing viral diseases include vaccinating people, improving sanitary conditions, quarantining patients, and controlling animals that spread disease. For example, annual rabies vaccinations of pets and farm animals protect them and humans from infection. To control the spread of rabies in wild animals such as coyotes and wolves, wildlife workers place bait containing an oral rabies vaccine, as shown in **Figure 17,** where wild animals will find it.

Figure 17 This oral rabies bait is being prepared for an aerial drop by the Texas Department of Health as part of their Oral Rabies Vaccination Program. This five-year program has prevented the expansion of rabies into Texas.

Research with Viruses

You might think viruses are always harmful. However, through research, scientists are discovering helpful uses for some viruses. One use, called gene therapy, substitutes normal hereditary material for a cell's defective hereditary material. The normal material is enclosed in viruses that "infect" targeted cells. The new hereditary material enters the cells and replaces the defective hereditary material. Using gene therapy, scientists hope to help people with genetic disorders and find a cure for cancer.

section 3 review

Summary

What are viruses?

- A virus is a strand of hereditary material surrounded by a protein coating.

How do viruses multiply?

- An active virus immediately destroys the host cell but a latent virus does not.

Fighting Viruses and Research with Viruses

- Antiviral drugs can be given to infected patients to help fight a virus.
- Scientists are discovering helpful uses for some viruses.

Self Check

1. **Describe** how viruses multiply.
2. **Explain** how vaccines are beneficial.
3. **Determine** how some viruses might be helpful.
4. **Discuss** how viral diseases might be prevented.
5. **Think Critically** Explain why a doctor might not give you any medication if you have a viral disease.

Applying Skills

6. **Concept Map** Make an events-chain concept map to show what happens when a latent virus becomes active.

Science Online booka.msscience.com/self_check_quiz

Teacher FYI

Virus Invasion Even though bacteriophages typically inject their DNA into the host cell, not all viruses invade a host cell in this way. Many animal viruses enter the host cell through endocytosis, the binding of the virus to the cell membrane. Once inside the host cell, the virus sheds its protein coat and either undergoes replication or becomes part of the host's DNA.

Use Science Words

Word Meaning Have students look up the terms *lysis*, *virion*, and *virology*. Have them write a paragraph about the relevance of each to the study of viruses. L2 LS **Linguistic**

3 Assess

DAILY INTERVENTION

Check for Understanding

Visual-Kinesthetic Have students make a puzzle that shows the steps of viral infection and replication. Students can exchange puzzles to test each other's knowledge of the information. L2

Reteach

Viruses Have students write a paragraph that describes the differences between active and latent viruses. L1 LS **Linguistic**

Assessment

Oral How does a virus invade a cell? The virus's hereditary material enters the cell, which becomes infected and eventually replicates the virus.

section 3 review

1. An active virus enters a cell and causes the host cell to make new viruses. When a latent virus enters a cell, its DNA is copied as the host cell reproduces. Under certain conditions, the body can activate the virus.
2. Vaccines, when properly administered, help prevent many viral infections.
3. They may be used to transfer normal DNA into a cell.
4. vaccinating people, improving sanitary conditions, quarantining patients, and controlling animals that spread disease
5. No medications cure a viral disease.
6. Maps should show the following: latent virus enters cell; virus becomes part of cell's DNA; cell divides; virus reproduces as part of cell division; virus becomes active; virus forms new virus particles; cell is destroyed.

Real-World Question

Purpose Students will design an experiment to compare uses of stereomicroscopes and compound light microscopes.
L2 COOP LEARN
Logical-Mathematical

Process Skills observe, identify, recognize and use spatial relationships, classify, communicate

Time Required 15 minutes to plan and 45 minutes to do the experiment

Safety Precautions Caution students to use care when working with microscope slides and coverslips.

Form a Hypothesis

Possible Hypothesis Students may hypothesize that large items can be viewed with the stereomicroscope and small objects can be viewed with the compound light microscope.

Test Your Hypothesis

Possible Procedures Separate items into two groups: those that can be viewed with the stereomicroscope, and those that can be viewed with the light microscope.

Teaching Strategies

- Demonstrate how to make a wet-mount.
- If microscopes have mirrors, explain how to use them.

Design Your Own

Comparing Light Microscopes

Goals

- **Learn** how to correctly use a stereo-microscope and a compound light microscope.
- **Compare** the uses of the stereomicroscope and compound light microscope.

Possible Materials

compound light microscope
stereomicroscope
items from the classroom—include some living or once-living items (8)
microscope slides and coverslips
plastic petri dishes
distilled water
dropper

Safety Precautions

Real-World Question

You're a technician in a police forensic laboratory. You use a stereomicroscope and a compound light microscope in the laboratory. A detective just returned from a crime scene with bags of evidence. You must examine each piece of evidence under a microscope. How do you decide which microscope is the best tool to use? Will all of the evidence that you've collected be viewable through both microscopes?

Form a Hypothesis

Compare the items to be examined under the microscopes. Form a hypothesis to predict which microscope will be used for each item and explain why.

58 ◆ A CHAPTER 2 Cells

Alternative Inquiry Lab

Comparing Light Microscopes To make this Lab an Inquiry Lab, tell students that they are forensics technicians. They are leading a crime scene investigation, and they need to determine the best way to examine the evidence. Have them determine what sorts of evidence would be collected at a crime scene. They also should evaluate which type of microscope would be used with each piece of evidence to help with their examination. Which microscope works best to view a piece of clothing? For examining blood samples, hair, or clothing fibers, which microscope(s) could be used? This can be expanded to include predicting what microscopes, other than a compound light microscope or stereomicroscope, could be used by forensics technicians.

Using Scientific Methods

Test Your Hypothesis

Make a Plan

1. As a group, decide how you will test your hypothesis.
2. **Describe** how you will carry out this experiment using a series of specific steps. Make sure the steps are in a logical order. Remember that you must place an item in the bottom of a plastic petri dish to examine it under the stereomicroscope and you must make a wet mount of any item to be examined under the compound light microscope. For more help, see the Reference Handbook.
3. If you need a data table or an observation table, design one in your Science Journal.

Follow Your Plan

1. Make sure your teacher approves the objects you'll examine, your plan, and your data table before you start.
2. Carry out the experiment.
3. While doing the experiment, record your observations and complete the data table.

Analyze Your Data

1. **Compare** the items you examined with those of your classmates.
2. **Classify** the eight items you observed based on this experiment.

Conclude and Apply

1. **Infer** which microscope a scientist might use to examine a blood sample, fibers, and live snails.
2. **List** five careers that require people to use a stereomicroscope. List five careers that require people to use a compound light microscope. Enter the lists in your Science Journal.
3. **Infer** how the images would differ if you examined an item under a compound light microscope and a stereomicroscope.
4. **Determine** which microscope is better for looking at large, or possibly live, items.

Communicating Your Data

In your Science Journal, **write** a short description of an imaginary crime scene and the evidence found there. Sort the evidence into two lists—items to be examined under a stereomicroscope and items to be examined under a compound light microscope. **For more help, refer to the** Science Skill Handbook.

Troubleshooting Place slides and coverslips for each group in a plastic petri dish to prevent breakage.

Expected Outcome The stereomicroscope is used for items that are too large to fit under a coverslip on a slide. The compound light microscope reveals greater detail. Students should note that the image produced by the compound light microscope is upside down and reversed left to right.

Analyze Your Data

Answers to Questions

1. Answers will vary.
2. Large items should be classified together, and items small enough to fit on a slide should be grouped together.

Error Analysis Have students compare their results and their hypotheses and explain why differences occurred.

Conclude and Apply

1. A scientist might use a stereomicroscope to examine live snails and a compound light microscope to examine blood and fibers.
2. Answers will vary, but may include lab technicians, forensic scientists, and cell biologists for the compound light microscope and surgeons, botanists, entomologists, geologists, and gemologists for the stereomicroscope.
3. The image under the compound light microscope will be magnified more, show greater detail, be upside down, and reversed left to right.
4. stereomicroscope

Communicating Your Data

Items small enough to fit under a coverslip should be examined with a compound light microscope; larger items should be examined with a stereomicroscope.

Assessment

Performance To further assess students' understanding of the differences in microscopes, provide other items and have students demonstrate how to use the appropriate microscope to view each item. Use **Performance Assessment in the Science Classroom,** p. 97. L2

Content Background

Jewel Plummer Cobb hoped to discover if there was a particular drug or combination of drugs which would be effective in destroying specific types of cancer. She would also need to determine whether these drugs would also destroy healthy tissues. Cobb exposed cells from both cancerous and non-cancerous tissues to chemotherapy drugs.

Her results demonstrated that some drugs could stop the uncontrolled growth of certain types of cancer cells. Although normal cells were also harmed, they never showed the dramatic destruction produced in some cancer cells.

Discussion

Experimental Results Using Cobb's research as an example, discuss the value of experiments even if the results do not meet the researcher's specific goals. Possible answer: Science is a continuing process of discovery. Cobb's work is a necessary first step to new approaches to treatment like Levy's.

Historical Significance

The structure and function of DNA were not discovered until 1953. Cobb's research began shortly thereafter, long before the role of genes in the development of cancer was understood. Research like Cobb's leads to questions about how certain drugs can stop the unchecked growth of tumors. In combination with an increasing understanding of how genes work, these results allow scientists to refine the methods of administering treatments and to target the development of drugs specifically aimed at preventing the replication of DNA, a process that all cells require.

TIME **SCIENCE** AND HISTORY

SCIENCE CAN CHANGE THE COURSE OF HISTORY!

Cobb Against Cancer

This colored scanning electron micrograph (SEM) shows two breast cancer cells in the final stage of cell division.

Jewel Plummer Cobb is a cell biologist who did important background research on the use of drugs against cancer in the 1950s. She removed cells from cancerous tumors and cultured them in the lab. Then, in a controlled study, she tried a series of different drugs against batches of the same cells. Her goal was to find the right drug to cure each patient's particular cancer. Cobb never met that goal, but her research laid the groundwork for modern chemotherapy—the use of chemicals to treat cancer.

Jewel Cobb also influenced science in another way. She was a role model, especially in her role as dean or president of several universities. Cobb promoted equal opportunity for students of all backgrounds, especially in the sciences.

Light Up a Cure

Vancouver, British Columbia 2000. While Cobb herself was only able to infer what was going on inside a cell from its reactions to various drugs, her work has helped others go further. Building on Cobb's work, Professor Julia Levy and her research team at the University of British Columbia actually go inside cells, and even organelles, to work against cancer. One technique they are pioneering is the use of light to guide cancer drugs to the right cells. First, the patient is given a chemotherapy drug that reacts to light. Then, a fiber optic tube is inserted into the tumor. Finally, laser light is passed through the tube, which activates the light-sensitive drug—but only in the tumor itself. This will hopefully provide a technique to keep healthy cells healthy while killing sick cells.

Write Report on Cobb's experiments on cancer cells. What were her dependent and independent variables? What would she have used as a control? What sources of error did she have to guard against? Answer the same questions about Levy's work.

For more information, visit booka.msscience.com/time

Write Levy and Cobb were both targeting cancer cells and working to avoid harming normal cells. In both studies, the control group would be normal human cells that were exposed to the chemotherapeutic drugs. The independent variables were the specific drugs administered to the cells. The dependent variables were the response of the cells to the treatment.

Resources for Teachers and Students

Advancing Current Treatments for Cancer, by Samuel Hellman and Everett E. Vokes, Scientific American, September 2000

How Cancer Arises, by Robert A. Weinberg, Scientific American, September 2001

Reviewing Main Ideas

Section 1 Cell Structure

1. Prokaryotic and eukaryotic are the two cell types.
2. The DNA in the nucleus controls cell functions.
3. Organelles such as mitochondria and chloroplasts process energy.
4. Most many-celled organisms are organized into tissues, organs, and organ systems.

Section 2 Viewing Cells

1. A simple microscope has just one lens. A compound light microscope has an eyepiece and objective lenses.
2. To calculate the magnification of a microscope, multiply the power of the eyepiece by the power of the objective lens.
3. According to the cell theory, the cell is the basic unit of life. Organisms are made of one or more cells, and all cells come from other cells.

Section 3 Viruses

1. A virus is a structure containing hereditary material surrounded by a protein coating.
2. A virus can make copies of itself only when it is inside a living host cell.

Visualizing Main Ideas

Copy and complete the following concept map of the basic units of life.

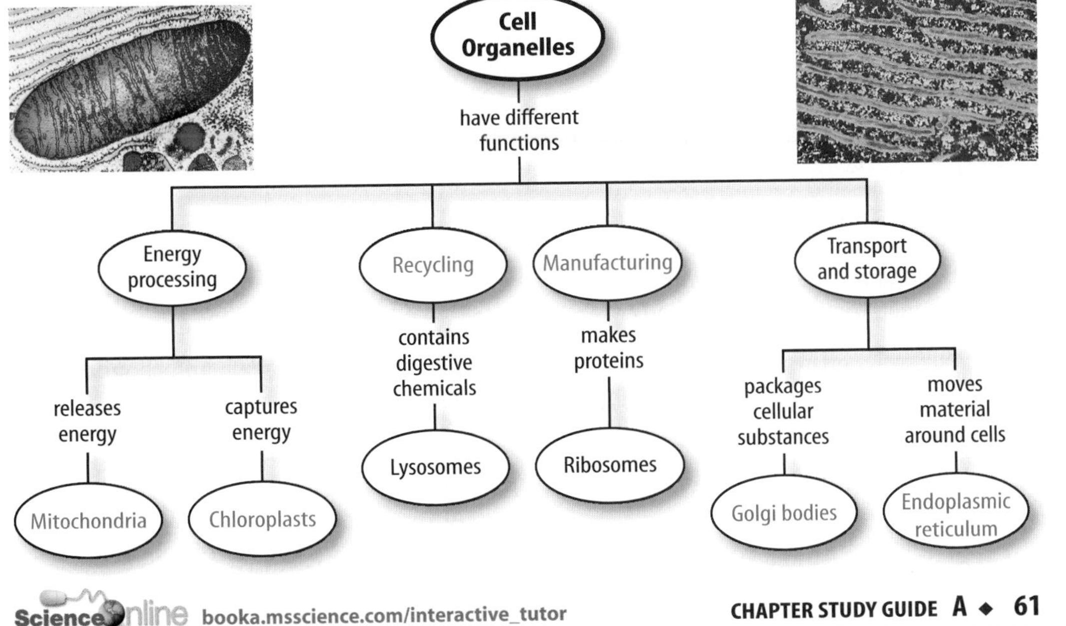

chapter 2 Study Guide

Reviewing Main Ideas

Summary statements can be used by students to review the major concepts of the chapter.

Visualizing Main Ideas

See student page.

Science Online

Visit booka.msscience.com
/self_check_quiz
/interactive_tutor
/vocabulary_puzzlemaker
/chapter_review
/standardized_test

Assessment Transparency

For additional assessment questions, use the *Assessment Transparency* located in the transparency book.

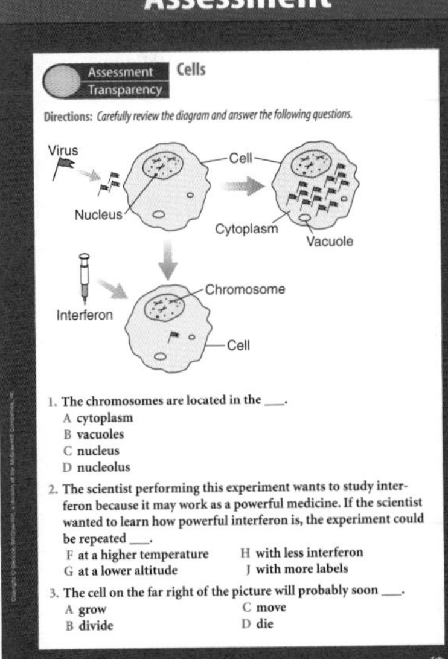
Assessment

Assessment Transparency **Cells**

Directions: *Carefully review the diagram and answer the following questions.*

1. The chromosomes are located in the ___.
   A cytoplasm
   B vacuoles
   C nucleus
   D nucleolus
2. The scientist performing this experiment wants to study interferon because it may work as a powerful medicine. If the scientist wanted to learn how powerful interferon is, the experiment could be repeated ___.
   F at a higher temperature
   G at a lower altitude
   H with less interferon
   J with more labels
3. The cell on the far right of the picture will probably soon ___.
   A grow
   B divide
   C move
   D die

Cells

Using Vocabulary

1. tissue
2. chloroplast, ER, Golgi body, mitochondrion, nucleus, organelle, ribosome, or virus
3. chloroplast, ER, Golgi body, nucleus, or ribosome
4. cell membrane or cytoplasm
5. mitochondrion
6. cell theory
7. cytoplasm, nucleus, or virus
8. cell membrane or cell wall
9. host cell
10. organ or tissue

Checking Concepts

11. B	15. C
12. D	16. C
13. B	17. A
14. A	18. A

Thinking Critically

19. Once a virus infects a cell, it uses the cell to produce more viruses. No drugs will kill viruses.
20. Answers may vary, but a stereomicroscope would enable you to view a large specimen as well as to look closely at the mold.
21. The plant cell would die or become dependent on other cells to provide its food.

chapter 2 Review

Using Vocabulary

cell membrane p. 40	host cell p. 54
cell theory p. 53	mitochondrion p. 44
cell wall p. 41	nucleus p. 42
chloroplast p. 44	organ p. 47
cytoplasm p. 40	organelle p. 42
endoplasmic reticulum p. 45	ribosome p. 44
Golgi body p. 45	tissue p. 47
	virus p. 54

Using the vocabulary words, give an example of each of the following.

1. found in every organ
2. smaller than one cell
3. a plant-cell organelle
4. part of every cell
5. powerhouse of a cell
6. used by biologists
7. contains hereditary material
8. a structure that surrounds the cell
9. can be damaged by a virus
10. made up of cells

Checking Concepts

Choose the word or phrase that best answers the question.

11. What structure allows only certain things to pass in and out of the cell?
    A) cytoplasm **C)** ribosomes
    B) cell membrane **D)** Golgi body

12. What is the organelle to the right?
    A) nucleus
    B) cytoplasm
    C) Golgi body
    D) endoplasmic reticulum

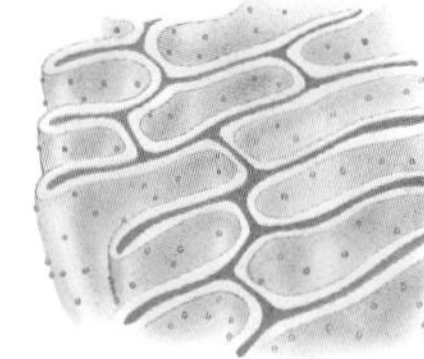

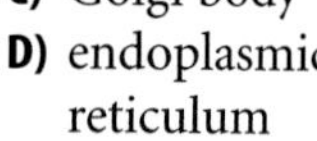

Use the illustration below to answer question 13.

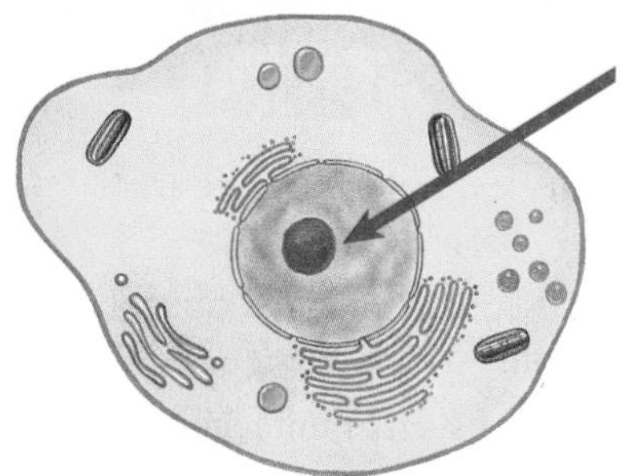

13. In the figure above, what is the function of the structure that the arrow is pointing to?
    A) recycles old cell parts
    B) controls cell activities
    C) protection
    D) releases energy

14. Which scientist gave the name *cells* to structures he viewed?
    A) Hooke **C)** Schleiden
    B) Schwann **D)** Virchow

15. Which of the following is a viral disease?
    A) tuberculosis **C)** smallpox
    B) anthrax **D)** tetanus

16. Which microscope can magnify up to a million times?
    A) compound light microscope
    B) stereomicroscope
    C) transmission electron microscope
    D) atomic force microscope

17. Which of the following is part of a bacterial cell?
    A) a cell wall **C)** mitochondria
    B) lysosomes **D)** a nucleus

18. Which of the following do groups of different tissues form?
    A) organ **C)** organ system
    B) organelle **D)** organism

booka.msscience.com/vocabulary_puzzlemaker

Use the ExamView® Pro Testmaker CD-ROM to:
- create multiple versions of tests
- create modified tests with one mouse click for inclusion students
- edit existing questions and add your own questions
- build tests aligned with state standards using built-in State Curriculum Tags
- change English tests to Spanish with one mouse click and vice versa

Thinking Critically

19. **Infer** why it is difficult to treat a viral disease.
20. **Explain** which type of microscope would be best to view a piece of moldy bread.
21. **Predict** what would happen to a plant cell that suddenly lost its chloroplasts.
22. **Predict** what would happen if the animal cell shown to the right didn't have ribosomes.

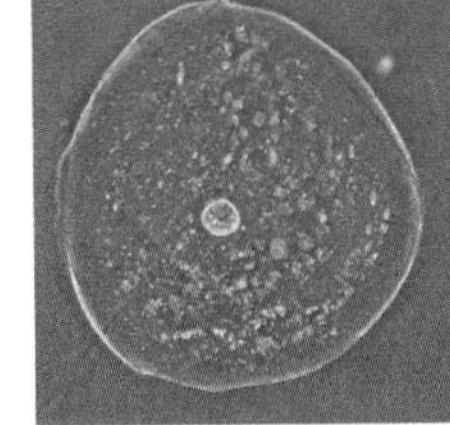

23. **Determine** how you would decide whether an unknown cell was an animal cell, a plant cell, or a bacterial cell.
24. **Concept Map** Make an events-chain concept map of the following from simple to complex: *small intestine, circular muscle cell, human,* and *digestive system.*
25. **Interpret Scientific Illustrations** Use the illustrations in **Figure 1** to describe how the shape of a cell is related to its function.

Use the table below to answer question 26.

Cell Structures

Structure	Prokaryotic Cell	Eukaryotic Cell
Cell membrane	Yes	Yes
Cytoplasm	Yes	Yes
Nucleus	No	Yes
Endoplasmic reticulum	No	Yes
Golgi bodies	No	Yes

26. **Compare and Contrast** Copy and complete the table above.

27. **Make a Model** Make and illustrate a time line about the development of the cell theory. Begin with the development of the microscope and end with Virchow. Include the contributions of Leeuwenhoek, Hooke, Schleiden, and Schwann.

Performance Activities

28. **Model** Use materials that resemble cell parts or represent their functions to make a model of a plant cell or an animal cell. Include a cell-parts key.
29. **Poster** Make a poster about the history of vaccinations. Contact your local Health Department for current information.

Applying Math

Use the illustration below to answer question 30.

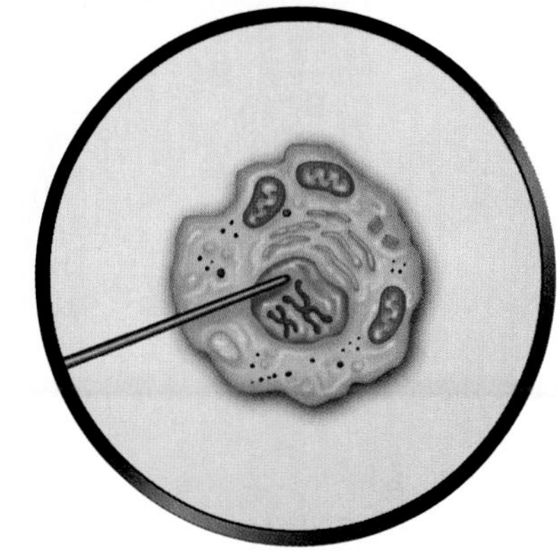

30. **Cell Width** If the pointer shown above with the cell is 10 micrometers (μm) in length, then about how wide is this cell?
    A) 20 μm
    B) 10 μm
    C) 5 μm
    D) 0.1 μm
31. **Magnification** Calculate the magnification of a microscope with a 20× eyepiece and a 40× objective.

Assessment Resources

Reproducible Masters

Chapter *Fast File* Resources
- Chapter Review, pp. 37–38
- Chapter Tests, pp. 39–42
- Assessment Transparency Activity, p. 49

Glencoe Science Web site
- Chapter Review Test
- Standardized Test Practice

Glencoe Technology
- Assessment Transparency
- Exam*View*® Pro Testmaker
- MindJogger Videoquiz
- Interactive Chalkboard

Thinking Critically

22. No proteins could be made, and the animal cell would die.
23. If there is a cell wall and chloroplasts, it is a plant cell. A cell with no chloroplasts or cell wall is an animal cell. If no membrane-bound organelles are present, it is a bacterial cell.
24. circular muscle cell, small intestine, digestive system, human
25. Answers will vary but should relate each shape to a function of the cell, such as the elongated shape of the nerve cell and its function in transmitting impulses.
26. See student page.
27. The time line should have equal divisions of time and cover from the late 1500s to the late 1800s. Include these dates: late 1500s, microscope invented; late 1600s, Leeuwenhoek improves microscope; 1665, Hooke uses the word *cell;* 1830s, Schleiden discovers plants are made of cells; mid 1800s, Schwann discovers animals are made of cells; mid 1800s, Virchow concludes that all cells come from cells.

Performance Activities

28. Model should include cell parts and a key to identify them. Use **PASC,** p. 123.
29. Posters should correctly show the history of vaccinations. Use **PASC,** p. 145.

Applying Math

National Math Standards

4, 9

30. B
31. the magnification would be 800×

chapter 2 Standardized Test Practice

Part 1 Multiple Choice

Record your answers on the answer sheet provided by your teacher or on a sheet of paper.

1. What do a bacterial cell, a plant cell, and a nerve cell have in common?
   A. cell wall and nucleus
   B. cytoplasm and cell membrane
   C. endoplasmic reticulum
   D. flagella

2. Which of the following is not a function of an organelle?
   A. tough outer coating
   B. energy producers
   C. chemical producers
   D. chemical storage

Use the images below to answer question 3.

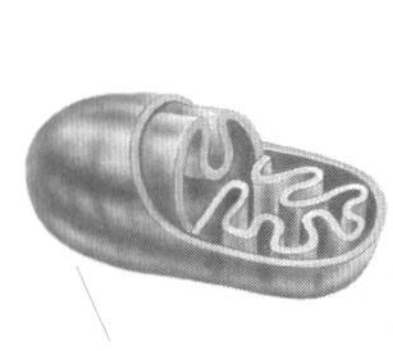

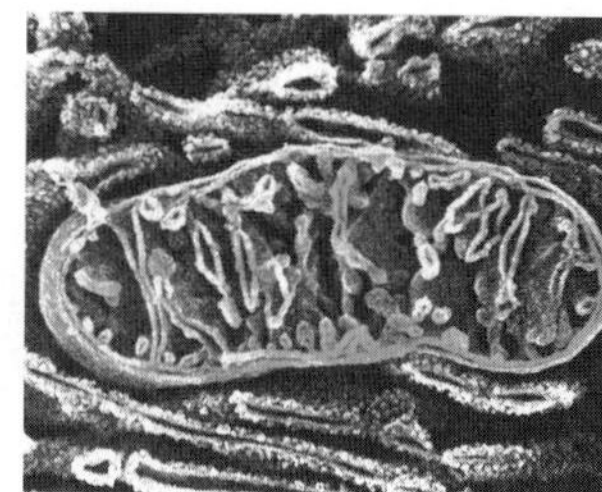

3. What is the primary function of this organelle?
   A. capturing light energy
   B. directing cell processes
   C. releasing energy stored in food
   D. making proteins

4. Which organelles receive the directions from the DNA in the nucleus about which proteins to make?
   A. ribosomes
   B. endoplasmic reticulum
   C. Golgi bodies
   D. cell wall

5. Why is a virus not considered a living cell?
   A. It has a cell wall.
   B. It has hereditary material.
   C. It has no organelles.
   D. It cannot multiply.

Use the illustration below to answer questions 6 and 7.

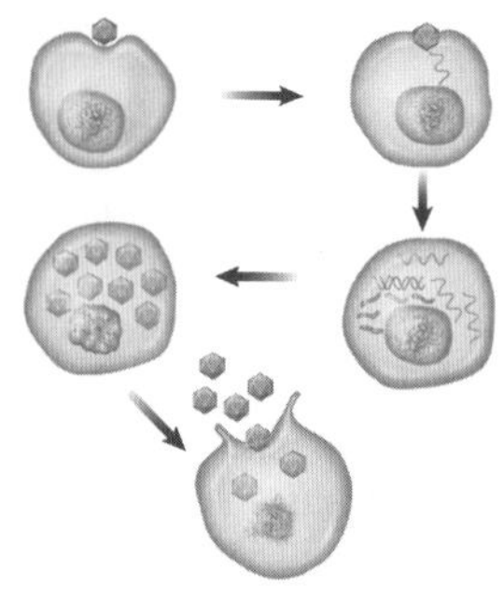

6. What does the diagram above represent?
   A. cell reproduction
   B. bacterial reproduction
   C. active virus multiplication
   D. vaccination

7. What does the largest circular structure represent?
   A. a host cell **C.** a vacuole
   B. a ribosome **D.** the nucleus

8. Where do most of a cell's life processes occur?
   A. nucleus **C.** organ
   B. cell wall **D.** cytoplasm

9. A group of similar cells that work together is a(n)
   A. tissue. **C.** organ system.
   B. organ. **D.** organism.

Test-Taking Tip

Read Carefully Read each question carefully for full understanding.

FAST FILE

Answer Sheet A practice answer sheet can be found at booka.msscience.com/answer_sheet.

Assessment Student Recording Sheet — Standardized Test Practice — SAMPLE

Part 1 Multiple Choice

1. B
2. A
3. C
4. A
5. D
6. C
7. D
8. D
9. A

Part 2 Short Response

10. Cell walls are outer coverings for the cell that are tough, rigid and provide cell shape found in plants, fungi and bacteria. The cell membrane is a protective layer around the cell that regulates the movement of water, food and other particles into and out of the cell.
11. by digesting it with the enzymes present in the lysosome or vacuole
12. The body produces interferons which is a protective protein, when it is infected by a virus. This protein is rapidly transported to neighboring cells to help protect them against infection. Other ways to protect against viral infection are anti-viral medication, vaccines, improved sanitary conditions (washing hands), isolating sick individuals and controlling animals that spread the disease.
13. in the cell wall; The fibers form a thick mesh to support the cell and let water and other materials pass through it.
14.

Organelle	Function
(nucleus)	directs all cellular activities
Mitochondria	(releases energy stored in food)
(chloroplasts)	captures light energy to make glucose
Ribosomes	(where proteins are made)

15. The Golgi bodies sort proteins and other substances and package them into vesicles to be delivered to other parts of the cell or released out of the cell just like how items are packaged and shipped in a plant.
16. Viruses need a host cell to make copies of themselves.
17. an example might be the cardiovascular system; heart, arteries, veins, and capillaries

Part 2 Short Response/Grid In

Record your answers on the answer sheet provided by your teacher or on a sheet of paper.

10. Compare and contrast the cell wall and the cell membrane.

11. How would a cell destroy or breakdown a harmful chemical which entered the cytoplasm?

12. How does your body stop viral infections? What are other ways of protection against viral infections?

13. Where is cellulose found in a cell and what is its function?

Use the following table to answer question 14.

Organelle	Function
	Directs all cellular activities
Mitochondria	
	Captures light energy to make glucose
Ribosomes	

14. Copy and complete the table above with the appropriate information.

15. How are Golgi bodies similar to a packaging plant?

16. Why does a virus need a host cell?

17. Give an example of an organ system and list the organs in it.

18. Compare and contrast the energy processing organelles.

19. Describe the structure of viruses.

20. How do ribosomes differ from other cell structures found in the cytoplasm?

21. What kind of microscope uses a series of lenses to magnify?

Part 3 Open Ended

Record your answers on a sheet of paper.

22. Name three different types of microscopes and give uses for each.

23. Some viruses, like the common cold, only make the host organism sick, but other viruses, like *Ebola*, are deadly to the host organism. Which of these strategies is more effective for replication and transmission of the virus to new host organisms? Which type of virus would be easier to study and develop a vaccine against?

24. Discuss the importance of the cytoplasm.

25. Explain how Hooke, Schleiden, and Schwann contributed to the cell theory.

Use the illustration below to answer question 26.

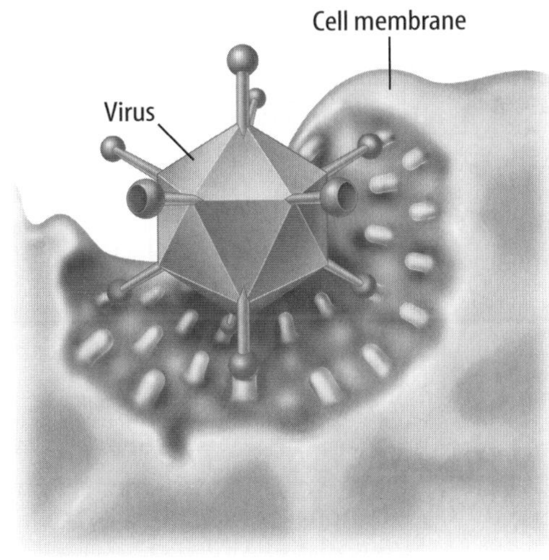

26. What interaction is taking place in the illustration above? What are two possible outcomes of this interaction?

27. Describe how the first vaccine was developed.

18. Chloroplasts and mitochondria are both energy-processing organelles. Chloroplasts use light energy to make sugar from carbon dioxide and water. Mitochondria release energy from the breakdown of food into carbon dioxide and water.

19. A strand of hereditary material is surrounded by a protein coating; there is no nucleus or other organelles; viruses lack a cell membrane.

20. They are not membrane bound; some float freely, and others are attached to the endoplasmic reticulum.

21. a compound microscope

Part 3 Open Ended

22. simple microscope has one lens—to view objects such as the surface of a leaf; compound microscope has two lenses to produce 3-D images—to view plant or animal cells; scanning or transmission electron microscope—to view specimens such as the organelles of a cell

23. The common cold is more effective for replication and transmission of the virus because the host is still alive to carry the virus around. *Ebola* kills the host before there is a lot of chance for replication and transmission to the next host. The common cold would be easier to study because there are many sources and it only makes the individual sick. However, there is no vaccine for the common cold because there are so many types of viruses.

24. Many important chemical reactions take place in the cytoplasm. The cytoplasm contains the framework cytoskeleton which supports the organelles and maintains the shape of the cell. Eukaryotic cells have organelles in the cytoplasm.

25. Hooke coined the term *cells* by observing cork cells. Schleiden observed plant cells and stated that all plants were made up of cells. Schwann observed animal cells and stated that animals were made up of cells.

26. A virus is attaching to a host cell at the cell surface. If the virus and the cell match, the virus will infect the cell and replicate. If the virus and the cell do not match, there will be no infection.

27. Edward Jenner notice people who got the disease cowpox did not get smallpox. Injecting cowpox protected people from getting smallpox.

Rubrics

For more help evaluating open-ended assessment questions, see the rubic on p. 10T.

chapter 3 Organizer

Section/Objectives	Standards		Labs/Features
	National	State/Local	
Chapter Opener	See pp. 16T–17T for a Key to Standards.		**Launch Lab:** Why does water enter and leave plant cells?, p. 67 **Foldables,** p. 67
Section 1 Chemistry of Life 2 sessions 1 block 1. **List** the differences among atoms, elements, molecules, and compounds. 2. **Explain** the relationship between chemistry and life science. 3. **Discuss** how organic compounds are different from inorganic compounds.	National Content Standards: UCP.1, UCP.2, UCP.3, UCP.5, A.1, A.2, B.1, C.1		**Science Online,** p. 72 **MiniLAB:** Observing How Enzymes Work, p. 73 **Applying Math:** Calculating the Importance of Water, p. 74
Section 2 Moving Cellular Materials 2 sessions 1 block 4. **Describe** the function of a selectively permeable membrane. 5. **Explain** how the processes of diffusion and osmosis move molecules in living cells. 6. **Explain** how passive transport and active transport differ	National Content Standards: UCP.1, UCP.2, UCP.3, UCP.5, A.1, A.2, C.1, C.3		**MiniLAB:** Observing Diffusion, p. 77 **Integrate Health,** p. 79 **Visualizing Cell Membrane Transport,** p. 81 **Lab:** Observing Osmosis, p. 82
Section 3 Energy for Life 3 sessions 1.5 blocks 7. **List** the differences between producers and consumers. 8. **Explain** how the processes of photosynthesis and respiration store and release energy. 9. **Describe** how cells get energy from glucose through fermentation.	National Content Standards: UCP.1, UCP.2, UCP.3, UCP.5, A.1, C.1, G.1, G.2, G.3		**Integrate Career,** p. 85 **Science Online,** p. 86 **Lab:** Photosynthesis and Respiration, p. 88 **Science and Language Arts:** from "Tulip," p. 90

Lab Materials	Reproducible Resources	Section Assessment	Technology
Launch Lab: bowl (2), label, water (500 mL), salt (15 g), carrot sticks (6), watch or clock, beaker (250mL), stirrer	**Chapter *Fast File* Resources** Foldables Worksheet, p. 15 Directed Reading Overview, p. 17 Note-taking Worksheets, pp. 31–33	Glencoe's Assessment Advantage	TeacherWorks includes: • Interactive Teacher Edition • Lesson Planner with calendar • Access to all program blacklines • Correlations to standards • Web links
MiniLAB: 2 small cups of prepared gelatin, fresh pineapple pieces *Need materials?* Contact Science Kit at 1-800-828-7777 or www.sciencekit.com on the Internet.	**Chapter *Fast File* Resources** Transparency Activity, p. 42 MiniLAB, p. 3 Enrichment, p. 28 Reinforcement, p. 25 Directed Reading, p. 18 Transparency Activity, pp. 45–46 **Cultural Diversity,** p. 65	Portfolio Science Journal, p. 72 Performance MiniLAB, p. 73 Applying Math, p. 74 Applying Skills, p. 75 Content Section Review, p. 75	Section Focus Transparency Teaching Transparency Virtual Labs CD-ROM Guided Reading Audio Program Interactive Chalkboard CD-ROM
MiniLAB: clean glasses (2 of equal size), labels, very warm water, cold water, food coloring, dropper, clock, marker or wax pencil **Lab:** unshelled egg, balance, spoon, distilled water (250 mL), light corn syrup (250 mL), 500-mL container	**Chapter *Fast File* Resources** Transparency Activity, p. 43 MiniLAB, p. 4 Enrichment, p. 29 Reinforcement, p. 26 Directed Reading, p. 18 Lab Activity, pp. 9–10 Lab Worksheet, pp. 5–6 **Home and Community Involvement,** p. 47	Portfolio Visual Learning, p. 81 Performance MiniLAB, p. 77 Applying Skills, p. 80 Content Section Review, p. 80	Section Focus Transparency Virtual Labs CD-ROM Guided Reading Audio Program Interactive Chalkboard CD-ROM Video Lab
Lab: 16-mm test tubes (3), 150-mm test tubes with stoppers (4), test-tube rack, stirring rod, scissors, carbonated water (5 mL), bromthymol blue solution in dropper bottle, aged tap water (20 mL), sprig of *Elodea*	**Chapter *Fast File* Resources** Transparency Activity, p. 44 Enrichment, p. 30 Reinforcement, p. 27 Directed Reading, pp. 19, 20 Lab Activity, pp. 11–14 Lab Worksheet, pp. 7–8 **Lab Management and Safety,** p. 63	Portfolio Visual Learning, p. 87 Performance Applying Math, p. 87 Content Section Review, p. 87	Section Focus Transparency Virtual Labs CD-ROM Guided Reading Audio Program Interactive Chalkboard CD-ROM

End of Chapter Assessment

Glencoe's Assessment Advantage

Blackline Masters	Technology	Professional Series
Chapter *Fast File* Resources Chapter Review, pp. 35–36 Chapter Tests, pp. 37–40 **Standardized Test Practice,** pp. 15–18	MindJogger Videoquiz Virtual Labs CD-ROM Exam*View*® Pro Testmaker TeacherWorks CD-ROM Interactive Chalkboard CD-ROM	**Performance Assessment in the Science Classroom (PASC)**

Transparencies

Section Focus

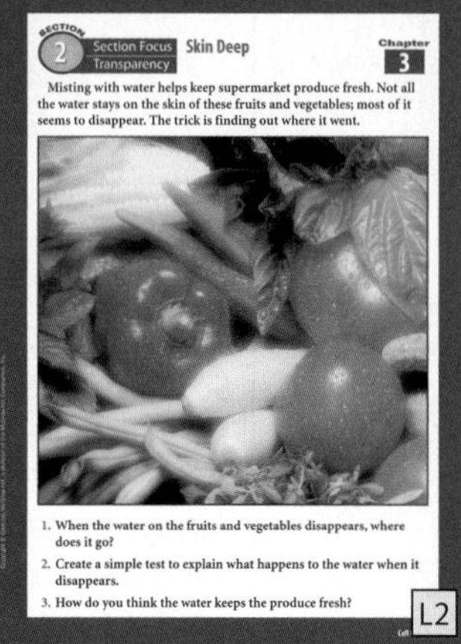

This is a representation of key blackline masters available in the Teacher Classroom Resources. See Resource Manager boxes within the chapter for additional information.

Assessment

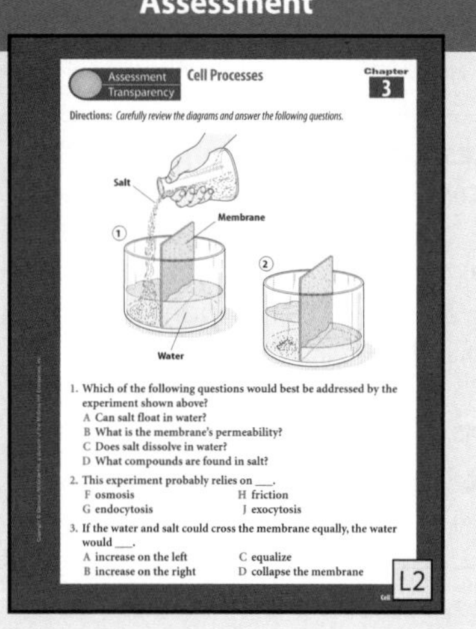

Teaching

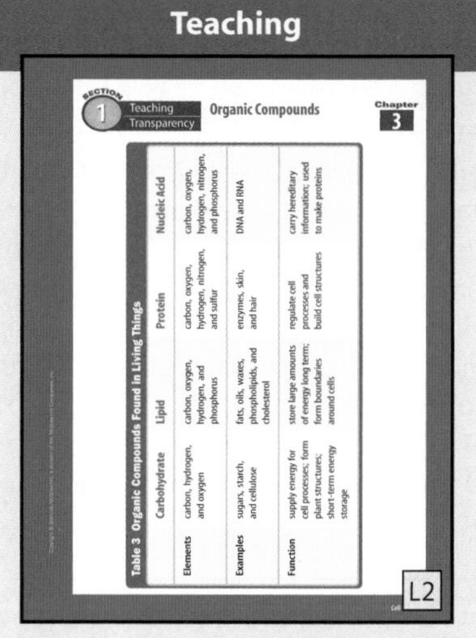

Key to Teaching Strategies

The following designations will help you decide which activities are appropriate for your students.

- L1 Level 1 activities should be appropriate for students with learning difficulties.
- L2 Level 2 activities should be within the ability range of all students.
- L3 Level 3 activities are designed for above-average students.
- ELL ELL activities should be within the ability range of English-Language Learners.
- COOP LEARN Cooperative Learning activities are designed for small group work.
- LS Multiple Learning Styles logos, as described on page 12T, are used throughout to indicate strategies that address different learning styles.
- P These strategies represent student products that can be placed into a best-work portfolio.
- PBL Problem-Based Learning activities apply real-world situations to learning.

Hands-on Activities

Student Text Lab Worksheet

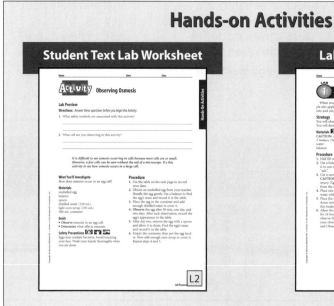

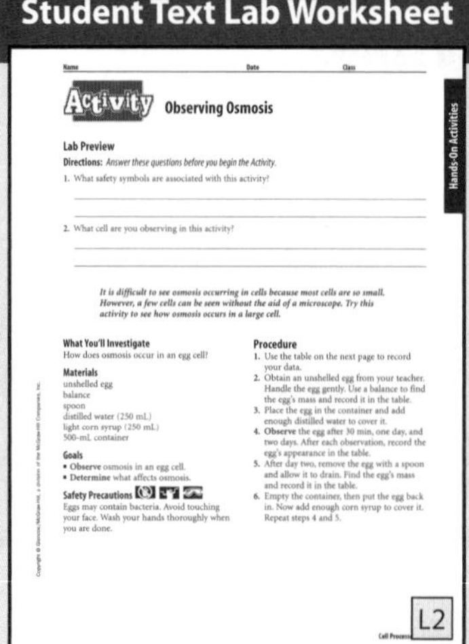

Laboratory Activities

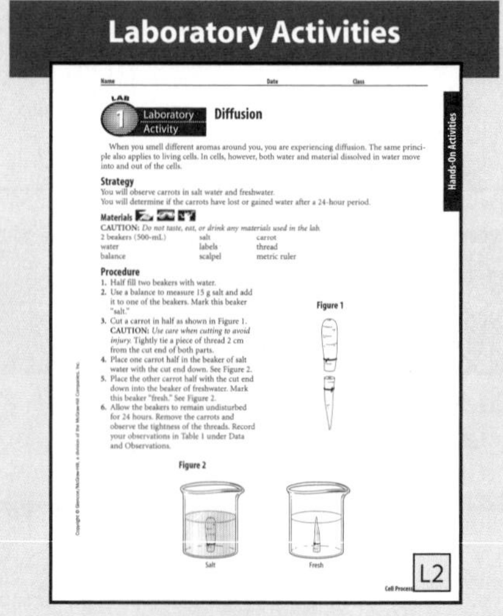

Resource Manager

Meeting Different Ability Levels

Content Outline

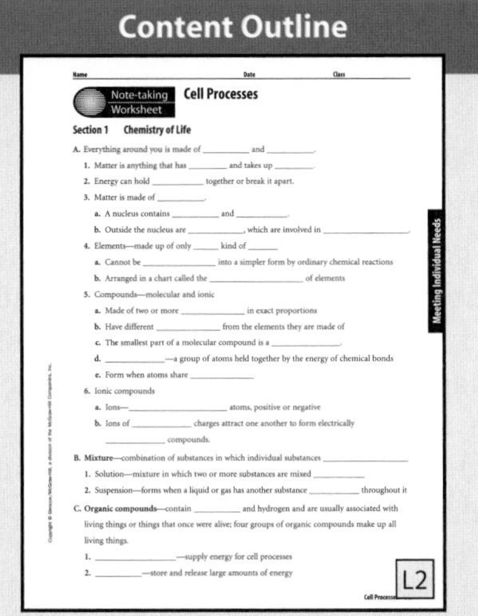

Name Date Class

Note-taking Worksheet — Cell Processes

Section 1 Chemistry of Life

A. Everything around you is made of ________ and ________.
1. Matter is anything that has ________ and takes up ________.
2. Energy can hold ________ together or break it apart.
3. Matter is made of ________.
a. A nucleus contains ________ and ________.
b. Outside the nucleus are ________, which are involved in ________.
4. Elements—made up of only ______ kind of ______
a. Cannot be ________ into a simpler form by ordinary chemical reactions
b. Arranged in a chart called the ________ of elements
5. Compounds—molecular and ionic
a. Made of two or more ________ in exact proportions
b. Have different ________ from the elements they are made of
c. The smallest part of a molecular compound is a ________
d. ________—a group of atoms held together by the energy of chemical bonds
e. Form when atoms share ________
6. Ionic compounds
a. Ions—________ atoms, positive or negative
b. Ions of ________ charges attract one another to form electrically ________ compounds.
B. Mixture—combination of substances in which individual substances ________
1. Solution—mixture in which two or more substances are mixed ________
2. Suspension—forms when a liquid or gas has another substance ________ throughout it
C. Organic compounds—contain ________ and hydrogen and are usually associated with living things or things that once were alive; four groups of organic compounds make up all living things.
1. ________—supply energy for cell processes
2. ________—store and release large amounts of energy

Meeting Individual Needs

L2

Reinforcement

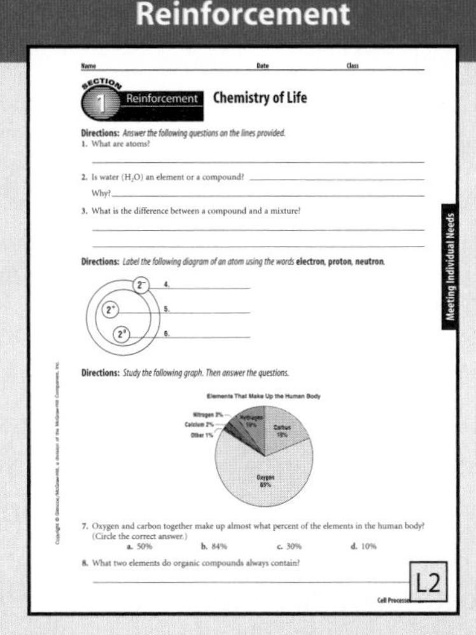

Name Date Class

Section 1 Reinforcement — Chemistry of Life

Directions: Answer the following questions on the lines provided.
1. What are atoms?
2. Is water (H_2O) an element or a compound? Why?
3. What is the difference between a compound and a mixture?

Directions: Label the following diagram of an atom using the words electron, proton, neutron.

Directions: Study the following graph. Then answer the questions.

Elements That Make Up the Human Body

7. Oxygen and carbon together make up almost what percent of the elements in the human body? (Circle the correct answer.)
a. 50% b. 84% c. 30% d. 10%
8. What two elements do organic compounds always contain?

Meeting Individual Needs

L2

Enrichment

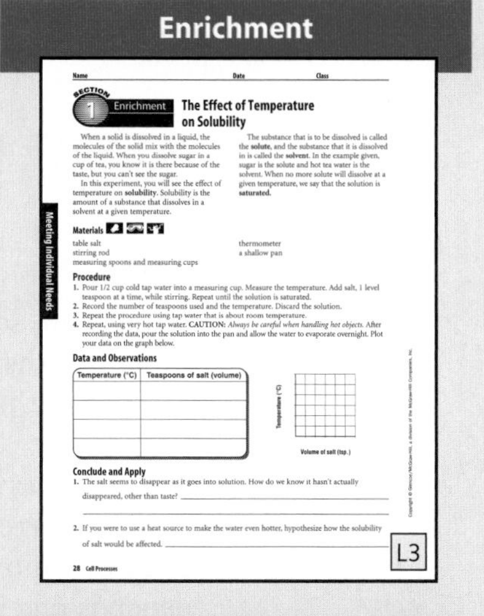

Name Date Class

Section 1 Enrichment — The Effect of Temperature on Solubility

When a solid is dissolved in a liquid, the molecules of the solid mix with the molecules of the liquid. When you dissolve sugar in a cup of tea, you know it is there because of the taste, but you can't see the sugar. In this experiment, you will see the effect of temperature on solubility. Solubility is the amount of a substance that dissolves in a solvent at a given temperature.

The substance that is to be dissolved is called the solute, and the substance that it is dissolved in is called the solvent. In the example given, sugar is the solute and hot tea water is the solvent. When no more solute will dissolve at a given temperature, we say that the solution is saturated.

Materials
table salt, stirring rod, measuring spoons and measuring cups, thermometer, a shallow pan

Procedure
1. Pour 1/2 cup cold tap water into a measuring cup. Measure the temperature. Add salt, 1 level teaspoon at a time, while stirring. Repeat until the solution is saturated.
2. Record the number of teaspoons used and the temperature. Discard the solution.
3. Repeat the procedure using tap water that is about room temperature.
4. Repeat, using very hot tap water. CAUTION: Always be careful when handling hot objects. After recording the data, pour the solution into the pan and allow the water to evaporate overnight. Plot your data on the graph below.

Data and Observations

Temperature (°C)	Teaspoons of salt (volume)

Conclude and Apply
1. The salt seems to disappear as it goes into solution. How do we know it hasn't actually disappeared, other than taste?
2. If you were to use a heat source to make the water even hotter, hypothesize how the solubility of salt would be affected.

28 Cell Processes

Meeting Individual Needs

L3

Directed Reading (English/Spanish)

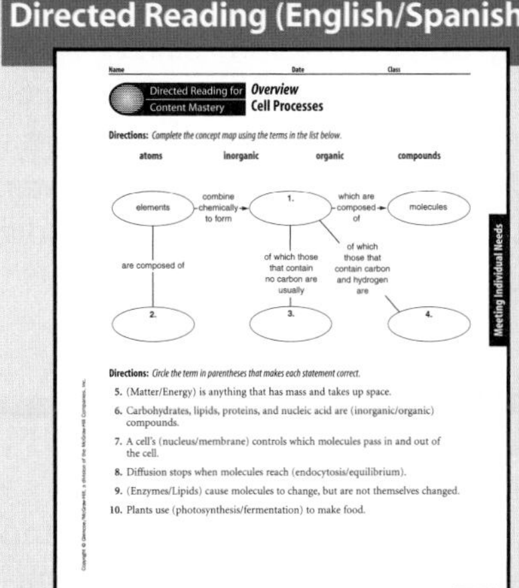

Name Date Class

Directed Reading for Content Mastery — Overview — Cell Processes

Directions: Complete the concept map using the terms in the list below.

atoms inorganic organic compounds

Directions: Circle the term in parentheses that makes each statement correct.
5. (Matter/Energy) is anything that has mass and takes up space.
6. Carbohydrates, lipids, proteins, and nucleic acid are (inorganic/organic) compounds.
7. A cell's (nucleus/membrane) controls which molecules pass in and out of the cell.
8. Diffusion stops when molecules reach (endocytosis/equilibrium).
9. (Enzymes/Lipids) cause molecules to change, but are not themselves changed.
10. Plants use (photosynthesis/fermentation) to make food.

Meeting Individual Needs

L1

Study Guide

Study Guide
Features
• Contains a study guide page for each section of the chapter
• Reviews key concepts
• Includes answer pages
L2

Reading Essentials

Reading Essentials for Glencoe Science
An Interactive Student Workbook
Features
• Condensed core content
• Actively involves students in reading
• Reinforces key vocabulary
L1

Assessment

Test Practice Workbook

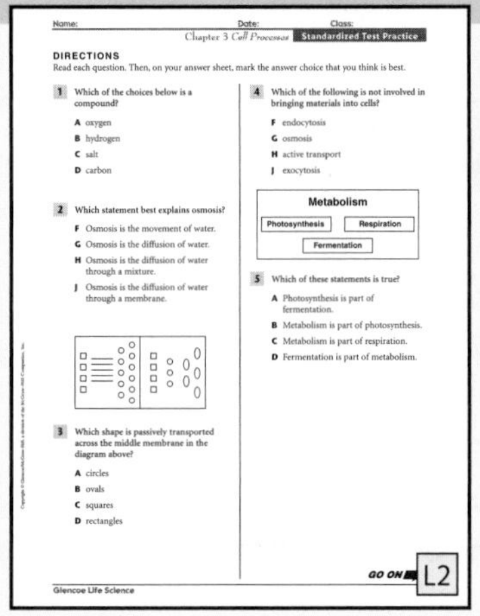

Name: Date: Class:

Chapter 3 Cell Processes — Standardized Test Practice

DIRECTIONS
Read each question. Then, on your answer sheet, mark the answer choice that you think is best.

1 Which of the choices below is a compound?
A oxygen
B hydrogen
C salt
D carbon

2 Which statement best explains osmosis?
F Osmosis is the movement of water.
G Osmosis is the diffusion of water.
H Osmosis is the diffusion of water through a mixture.
J Osmosis is the diffusion of water through a membrane.

3 Which shape is passively transported across the middle membrane in the diagram above?
A circles
B ovals
C squares
D rectangles

4 Which of the following is not involved in bringing materials into cells?
F endocytosis
G osmosis
H active transport
J exocytosis

Metabolism: Photosynthesis, Respiration, Fermentation

5 Which of these statements is true?
A Photosynthesis is part of fermentation.
B Metabolism is part of photosynthesis.
C Metabolism is part of respiration.
D Fermentation is part of metabolism.

GO ON

Glencoe Life Science

L2

Chapter Review

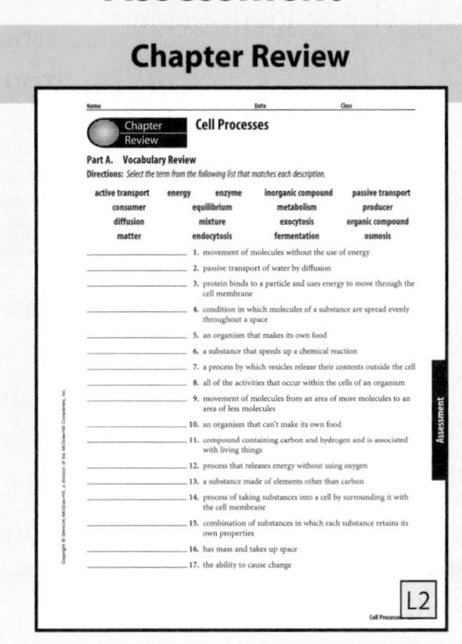

Name Date Class

Chapter Review — Cell Processes

Part A. Vocabulary Review

Directions: Select the term from the following list that matches each description.

active transport, energy, enzyme, inorganic compound, passive transport, consumer, equilibrium, metabolism, producer, diffusion, mixture, exocytosis, organic compound, matter, endocytosis, fermentation, osmosis

1. movement of molecules without the use of energy
2. passive transport of water by diffusion
3. protein binds to a particle and uses energy to move through the cell membrane
4. condition in which molecules of a substance are spread evenly throughout a space
5. an organism that makes its own food
6. a substance that speeds up a chemical reaction
7. a process by which vesicles release their contents outside the cell
8. all of the activities that occur within the cells of an organism
9. movement of molecules from an area of more molecules to an area of less molecules
10. an organism that can't make its own food
11. compound containing carbon and hydrogen and is associated with living things
12. process that releases energy without using oxygen
13. a substance made of elements other than carbon
14. process of taking substances into a cell by surrounding it with the cell membrane
15. combination of substances in which each substance retains its own properties
16. has mass and takes up space
17. the ability to cause change

Assessment

L2

Chapter Tests

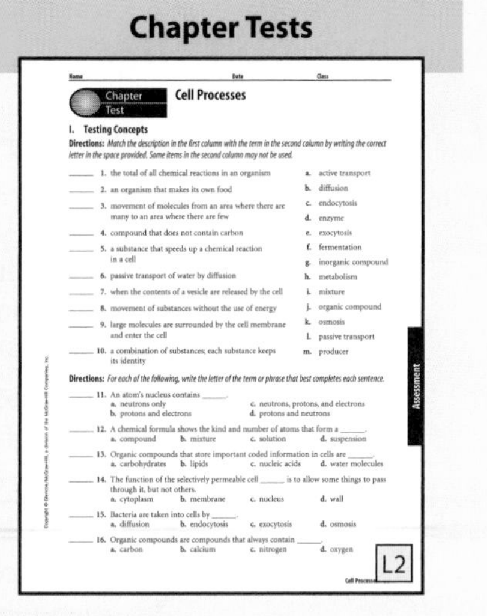

Name Date Class

Chapter Test — Cell Processes

I. Testing Concepts

Directions: Match the description in the first column with the term in the second column by writing the correct letter in the space provided. Some items in the second column may not be used.

1. the total of all chemical reactions in an organism
2. an organism that makes its own food
3. movement of molecules from an area where there are many to an area where there are few
4. compound that does not contain carbon
5. a substance that speeds up a chemical reaction in a cell
6. passive transport of water by diffusion
7. when the contents of a vesicle are released by the cell
8. movement of substances without the use of energy
9. large molecules are surrounded by the cell membrane and enter the cell
10. a combination of substances; each substance keeps its identity

a. active transport
b. diffusion
c. endocytosis
d. enzyme
e. exocytosis
f. fermentation
g. inorganic compound
h. metabolism
i. mixture
j. organic compound
k. osmosis
l. passive transport
m. producer

Directions: For each of the following, write the letter of the term or phrase that best completes each sentence.

11. An atom's nucleus contains ______.
a. neutrons only c. neutrons, protons, and electrons
b. protons and electrons d. protons and neutrons
12. A chemical formula shows the kind and number of atoms that form a ______.
a. compound b. mixture c. solution d. suspension
13. Organic compounds that store important coded information in cells are ______.
a. carbohydrates b. lipids c. nucleic acids d. water molecules
14. The function of the selectively permeable cell ______ is to allow some things to pass through it, but not others.
a. cytoplasm b. membrane c. nucleus d. wall
15. Bacteria are taken into cells by ______.
a. diffusion b. endocytosis c. exocytosis d. osmosis
16. Organic compounds are compounds that always contain ______.
a. carbon b. calcium c. nitrogen d. oxygen

Assessment

L2

Science Content Background

section 1 Chemistry of Life

The Nature of Matter

Democritus, an ancient Greek philosopher, proposed that atoms were small, solid spheres. Until recently, it was thought that negatively-charged electrons orbited the positively-charged nucleus in specific paths. Quantum mechanics provide us with the current model of a positively-charged nucleus surrounded by a region in which the electrons move. The location of the electrons depends on each electron's energy level.

Compounds and Mixtures

Compounds are formed when two or more elements combine by a chemical reaction. Molecular components form when atoms share electrons. Ionic compounds form when negative and positive ions join. Organic compounds all contain carbon atoms and most are produced within living organisms. However, organic compounds such as plastics and synthetic fibers are made from organic substances such as petroleum. Inorganic compounds usually are made from elements other than carbon. Water is the most important inorganic compound.

Most things in nature are mixtures of elements. Components of homogeneous mixtures, such as solutions, cannot be distinguished from one another. The components of a heterogeneous mixture are generally visibly identifiable.

section 2 Moving Cellular Materials

Maintaining Balance

The cell membrane regulates what enters and leaves a cell. The path taken through a membrane depends on the substance's size, shape, and electrical charge. A cell must maintain its internal concentrations of substances such as water, glucose, and other nutrients and eliminate waste products.

Transport

Passive transport—transport without the input of energy—depends on temperature. One form of passive transport, called diffusion, occurs when molecules move from an area where their concentration is greater into an area where they are less concentrated. Osmosis is the diffusion of water into or out of a cell. Active transport, transport with energy input, requires transport proteins.

section 3 Energy for Life

Photosynthesis, Respiration, and Fermentation

During photosynthesis, plants and other producers convert light energy to chemical energy and make carbohydrates (food). During respiration, the food is broken down and the released energy can be used by the producer, other producers, and consumers. When there is a shortage of oxygen, fermentation is a process some cells can use to release energy from glucose.

chapter content resources

Internet Resources

For additional content background, visit **booka.msscience.com** to:

- access your book online
- find references to related articles in popular science magazines
- access Web links with related content background
- access current events with science journal topics

Print Resources

Cells and Systems (Life Processes), by Holly Wallace and Anita Ganeri, Heinemann Library, 2001

Atoms and Molecules, by Phil Roxbee Cox, E D C Publications, 1993

Illustrated Dictionary of Science, by Corinne Stockley, Usborne Books, 2000

IDENTIFYING Misconceptions

Find Out What Students Think

Students may think that . . .

Plants do not use oxygen and do not release carbon dioxide.

Students may not understand the complementary nature of photosynthesis and respiration, especially with respect to exchange of gases.

Demonstration

Ask students to give the relationship among producers, consumers, oxygen, and carbon dioxide. Summarize students' responses on the board. If students do not respond that plants also give off carbon dioxide, let that understanding come from the activities below.

Promote Understanding

Activity 1

WARNING: *Remind students not to suck on the straw.*

Prepare a 0.1% solution of bromthymol blue.

- Have students blow through a straw into the bromthymol blue solution. The solution should turn yellow as the carbon dioxide dissolves forming carbonic acid.
- Have students add drops of dilute ammonium hydroxide so that the solution again turns blue. Explain that the bromthymol blue is an indicator that turns yellow in an acidic solution and blue in a neutral or alkaline solution.
- Ask students what gas is given off in the process of respiration. (carbon dioxide) Explain that the carbon dioxide blown into the solution dissolves and makes the solution slightly acidic. Point out that adding the ammonium hydroxide made the solution slightly basic. L2

Activity 2

Acidify a large test tube of bromthymol blue by adding carbonated water to the solution. Add a sprig of *Elodea* to the tube.

- Put the test tube in sunlight or under a bright light. The solution should begin to turn blue in 30 to 45 minutes. Have students record results.
- Also, have students put a sprig of *Elodea* in a test tube of bromthymol blue solution that is slightly alkaline and blue. Place the tube in a dark area. Within 24 hours the solution should change to a pale yellow as the plant respires and releases carbon dioxide. Again have students record their results. L2

Discussion

- Ask why the bromthymol blue solution turned blue in the light. Ask students what evidence supports their answer. Explicitly reinforce the fact the carbon dioxide was absorbed by the plant and used in the process of photosynthesis.
- Ask students whether they think carbon dioxide was given off by the *Elodea* kept in the dark. Light-independent photosynthesis and respiration occur in the dark, so less carbon dioxide is used and released. Stress that their results indicate that plants give off carbon dioxide during respiration. Point out that all living things must carry out some form of respiration.

Assess

After completing the chapter, see *Identifying Misconceptions* in the Study Guide at the end of the chapter.

chapter 3

Chapter Vocabulary

mixture, p. 71
organic compound, p. 72
enzyme, p. 73
inorganic compound, p. 73
passive transport, p. 76
diffusion, p. 77
equilibrium, p. 77
osmosis, p. 78
active transport, p. 79
endocytosis, p. 80
exocytosis, p. 80
metabolism, p. 83
photosynthesis, p. 84
respiration, p. 85
fermentation, p. 86

Science Journal Student responses will vary, but may include "from the Sun" and "from the ground."

PowerPoint® Presentations

This CD-ROM is an editable Microsoft® PowerPoint® presentation that includes:

- a pre-made presentation for every chapter
- interactive graphics
- animations
- audio clips
- image bank
- all new section and chapter questions
- Standardized Test Practice
- transparencies
- pre-lab questions for all labs
- Foldables directions
- links to booka.msscience.com

chapter 3

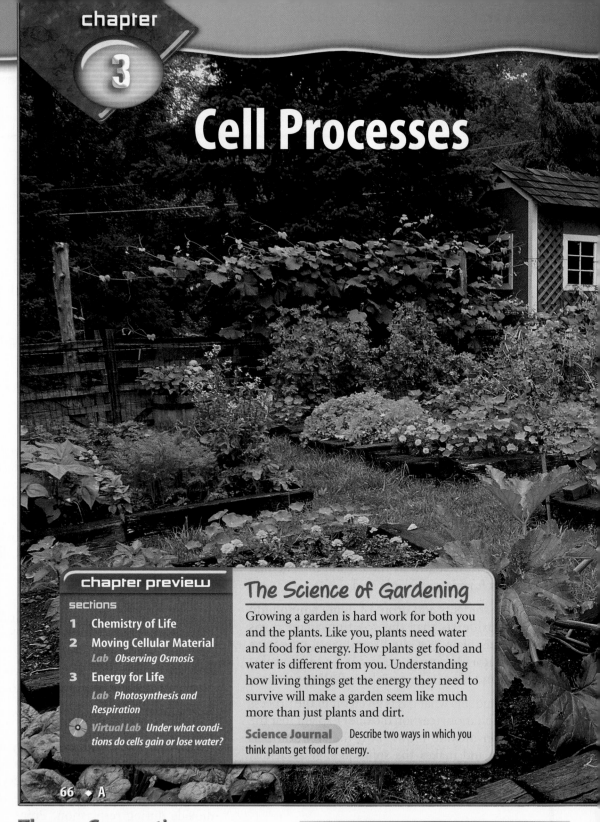

Cell Processes

chapter preview

sections

1 Chemistry of Life
2 Moving Cellular Material
Lab *Observing Osmosis*
3 Energy for Life
Lab *Photosynthesis and Respiration*
Virtual Lab *Under what conditions do cells gain or lose water?*

The Science of Gardening

Growing a garden is hard work for both you and the plants. Like you, plants need water and food for energy. How plants get food and water is different from you. Understanding how living things get the energy they need to survive will make a garden seem like much more than just plants and dirt.

Science Journal Describe two ways in which you think plants get food for energy.

66 ◆ A

Theme Connection

Stability and Change Living things function as a result of chemical reactions in cells. The equilibrium maintained by cells results from their selectively permeable membranes. This is critical to the life of cells and the organism as a whole.

About the Photo

A Growing Garden Growing a bountiful garden requires sunlight, soil, and lots of water. Each plant in a garden, however, has individual requirements. The amount of sunlight, nutrients required, and amount of water needed have to be considered for all the types of plants.

Start-Up Activities

Why does water enter and leave plant cells?

If you forget to water a plant, it will wilt. After you water the plant, it probably will straighten up and look healthier. In the following lab, find out how water causes a plant to wilt and straighten.

1. Label a small bowl *Salt Water.* Pour 250 mL of water into the bowl. Then add 15 g of salt to the water and stir.
2. Pour 250 mL of water into another small bowl.
3. Place two carrot sticks into each bowl. Also, place two carrot sticks on the lab table.
4. After 30 min, remove the carrot sticks from the bowls and keep them next to the bowl they came from. Examine all six carrot sticks, then describe them in your Science Journal.
5. **Think Critically** Write a paragraph in your Science Journal that describes what would happen if you moved the carrot sticks from the plain water to the lab table, the ones from the salt water into the plain water, and the ones from the lab table into the salt water for 30 min. Now move the carrot sticks as described and write the results in your Science Journal.

How Living Things Survive Make the following vocabulary Foldable to help you understand the chemistry of living things and how energy is obtained for life.

STEP 1 **Fold** a vertical sheet of notebook paper from side to side.

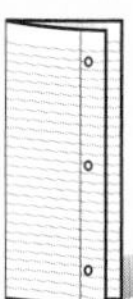

STEP 2 **Cut** along every third line of only the top layer to form tabs.

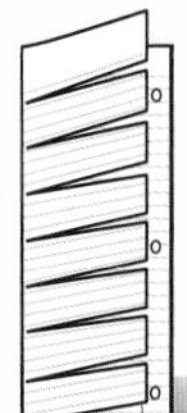

Build Vocabulary As you read this chapter, list the vocabulary words about cell processes on the tabs. As you learn the definitions, write them under the tab for each vocabulary word. Write a sentence about one of the cell processes using the vocabulary word on the tab.

Preview this chapter's content and activities at booka.msscience.com

Purpose Use the Launch Lab to show students that water moves into and out of carrot cells. Explain that the materials moving into and out of cells are atoms, molecules, and compounds. L1 **LS** **Visual-Spatial**

Preparation Purchase carrots for the lab. Peel and cut the carrots into sticks.

Materials salt, 250-mL beaker, 2 bowls, stirrer, 6 carrot sticks, water, label, watch or clock

Teaching Strategy Provide students with water at room temperature so the salt will dissolve more readily.

Think Critically

The carrot sticks in salt water and on the lab table were limp because water moved out of them. The carrot sticks in plain water were crisp because water moved into the cells that had less water. Students should predict that these conditions are reversible, depending on the relative amount of water inside and outside the carrot's cells. L1

Assessment

Oral Why does a wilted plant become rigid again after it has been watered? The water diffuses into the plant's cells.

Dinah Zike Study Fold

Student preparation materials for this Foldable are available in the **Chapter *Fast File* Resources.**

1 Motivate

Bellringer

Section Focus Transparencies also are available on the Interactive Chalkboard CD-ROM. L2 

SECTION 1 Section Focus Transparency — Chemicals for Life — Chapter 3

Every living thing is made of compounds containing carbon and hydrogen. We consume many of these compounds for energy. However, some compounds that we consume do not contain the elements carbon and hydrogen. These compounds are also necessary for life.

1. Of the objects above, which come from living things?
2. Which objects do not contain substances that were once alive?
3. Name three substances that your body needs to survive that do not come from living things.

Cell Processes

Tie to Prior Knowledge

Food Labels Bring in labels from foods and cleaning products. Have students use the periodic table at the back of the book to determine what elements are in the compounds contained in these products. L2

section 1 Chemistry of Life

as you read

What You'll Learn

- **List** the differences among atoms, elements, molecules, and compounds.
- **Explain** the relationship between chemistry and life science.
- **Discuss** how organic compounds are different from inorganic compounds.

Why It's Important

You grow because of chemical reactions in your body.

Review Vocabulary

cell: the smallest unit of a living thing that can perform the functions of life

New Vocabulary

- mixture
- organic compound
- enzyme
- inorganic compound

The Nature of Matter

Think about everything that surrounds you—chairs, books, clothing, other students, and air. What are all these things made up of? You're right if you answer "matter and energy." Matter is anything that has mass and takes up space. Energy is anything that brings about change. Everything in your environment, including you, is made of matter. Energy can hold matter together or break it apart. For example, the food you eat is matter that is held together by chemical energy. When food is cooked, energy in the form of heat can break some of the bonds holding the matter in food together.

Atoms Whether it is solid, liquid, or gas, matter is made of atoms. **Figure 1** shows a model of an oxygen atom. At the center of an atom is a nucleus that contains protons and neutrons. Although they have nearly equal masses, a proton has a positive charge and a neutron has no charge. Outside the nucleus are electrons, each of which has a negative charge. It takes about 1,837 electrons to equal the mass of one proton. Electrons are important because they are the part of the atom that is involved in chemical reactions. Look at **Figure 1** again and you will see that an atom is mostly empty space. Energy holds the parts of an atom together.

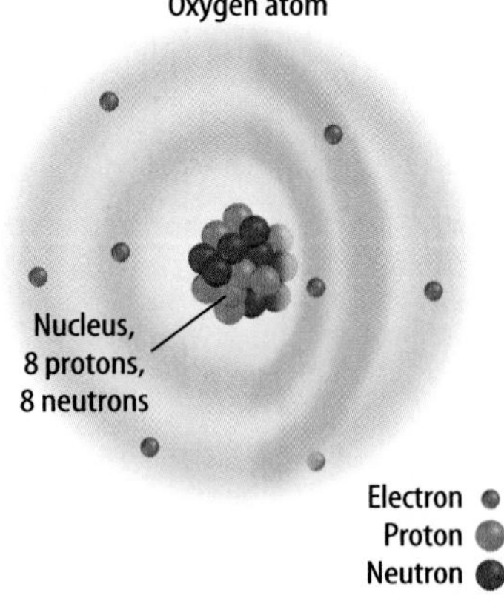

Figure 1 An oxygen atom model shows the placement of electrons, protons, and neutrons.

Section 1 Resource Manager

Chapter *FAST FILE* Resources

Transparency Activity, p. 42
Directed Reading for Content Mastery, pp. 17, 18
Note-taking Worksheets, pp. 31–33
Enrichment, p. 28
MiniLAB, p. 3
Reinforcement, p. 25

68 ◆ A CHAPTER 3 Cell Processes

Table 1 Elements in the Human Body		
Symbol	Element	Percent
O	Oxygen	65.0
C	Carbon	18.5
H	Hydrogen	9.5
N	Nitrogen	3.2
Ca	Calcium	1.5
P	Phosphorus	1.0
K	Potassium	0.4
S	Sulfur	0.3
Na	Sodium	0.2
Cl	Chlorine	0.2
Mg	Magnesium	0.1
	Other elements	0.1

Elements When something is made up of only one kind of atom, it is called an element. An element can't be broken down into a simpler form by chemical reactions. The element oxygen is made up of only oxygen atoms, and hydrogen is made up of only hydrogen atoms. Scientists have given each element its own one- or two-letter symbol.

All elements are arranged in a chart known as the periodic table of elements. You can find this table at the back of this book. The table provides information about each element including its mass, how many protons it has, and its symbol.

Everything is made up of elements. Most things, including all living things, are made up of a combination of elements. Few things exist as pure elements. **Table 1** lists elements that are in the human body. What two elements make up most of your body?

Six of the elements listed in the table are important because they make up about 99 percent of living matter. The symbols for these elements are S, P, O, N, C, and H. Use **Table 1** to find the names of these elements.

Reading Check *What types of things are made up of elements?*

2 Teach

Teacher FYI

Element Names Elements are often given names by their discoverers. An element's name may reflect a property of the element. For example, chlorine, a greenish gas, comes from the Greek word *chloros*, which means "green." Some elements, such as ytterbium—discovered in Ytterby, Sweden—are named for the place where they were discovered. Other elements are named to honor someone. Einsteinium is named in honor of Albert Einstein, fermium for Enrico Fermi, and curium for Marie and Pierre Curie.

Activity

Elements Song Play Tom Lehrer's *Elements Song*, which lists the elements. Have students listen to see how many elements they recognize. L2

Fun Fact

The symbols of many elements are derived from the first one or two letters of the Greek, Latin, or English name of the elements. Scientists worldwide use these symbols.

Text Question Answer

oxygen and carbon

Reading Check

Answer Everything is made up of elements or a combination of elements.

Differentiated Instruction

Visually Impaired To help visually impaired students understand the structure of an atom, make a model of an atom. Outline the nucleus and energy levels by gluing yarn to cardboard. Use marshmallows for protons, gumdrops for neutrons, and red hots for electrons. Have students feel the model to compare the sizes of the different parts. L1 LS **Kinesthetic**

Caption Answer

Figure 2 A molecule, the smallest part of a molecular compound, is a group of atoms held together by chemical bonds.

Quick Demo

Opposite Charges Attract

Materials comb

Estimated Time five minutes

Procedure Demonstrate the attraction between opposite charges. Run a comb through your hair. Then, bring the comb close to your hair without touching it. The hair is attracted to the comb because the negative charges on the comb are attracted to the positive charges of the hair.

Discussion

Ionic Bonding Have students predict what might happen when a negatively charged ion comes in contact with a positively charged ion. The two ions may bond to form an electrically neutral compound. L2

Figure 2 The words *atoms, molecules,* and *compounds* are used to describe substances.
Explain *how these terms are related to each other.*

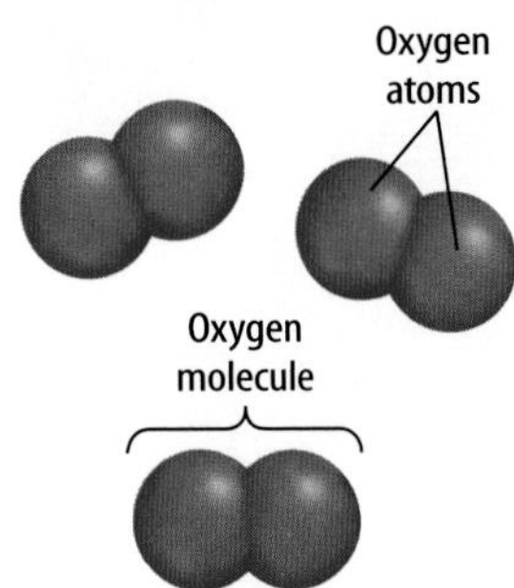

A Some elements, like oxygen, occur as molecules. These molecules contain atoms of the same element bonded together.

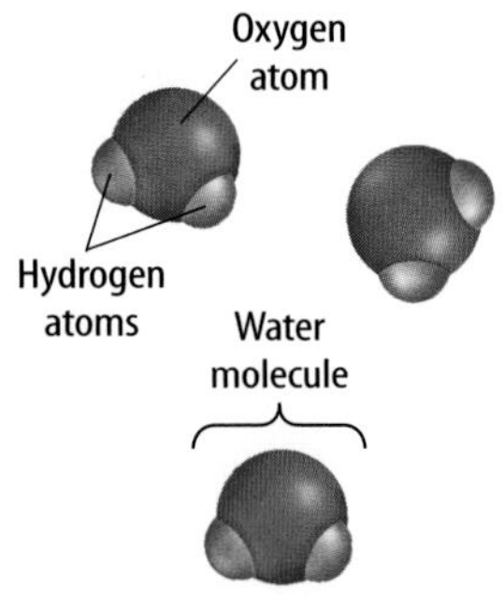

B Compounds also are composed of molecules. Molecules of compounds contain atoms of two or more different elements bonded together, as shown by these water molecules.

Compounds and Molecules

Suppose you make a pitcher of lemonade using a powdered mix and water. The water and the lemonade mix, which is mostly sugar, contain the elements oxygen and hydrogen. Yet, in one, they are part of a nearly tasteless liquid—water. In the other they are part of a sweet solid—sugar. How can the same elements be part of two materials that are so different? Water and sugar are compounds. Compounds are made up of two or more elements in exact proportions. For example, pure water, whether one milliliter of it or one million liters, is always made up of hydrogen atoms bonded to oxygen atoms in a ratio of two hydrogen atoms to one oxygen atom. Compounds have properties different from the elements they are made of. There are two types of compounds—molecular compounds and ionic compounds.

Molecular Compounds The smallest part of a molecular compound is a molecule. A molecule is a group of atoms held together by the energy of chemical bonds, as shown in **Figure 2.** When chemical reactions occur, chemical bonds break, atoms are rearranged, and new bonds form. The molecules produced are different from those that began the chemical reaction.

Molecular compounds form when different atoms share their outermost electrons. For example, two atoms of hydrogen each can share one electron on one atom of oxygen to form one molecule of water, as shown in **Figure 2B.** Water does not have the same properties as oxygen and hydrogen. Under normal conditions on Earth, oxygen and hydrogen are gases. Yet, water can be a liquid, a solid, or a gas. When hydrogen and oxygen combine, changes occur and a new substance forms.

Ions Atoms also combine because they've become positively or negatively charged. Atoms are usually neutral—they have no overall electric charge. When an atom loses an electron, it has more protons than electrons, so it becomes positively charged. When an atom gains an electron, it has more electrons than protons, so it becomes negatively charged. Electrically charged atoms—positive or negative—are called ions.

Differentiated Instruction

Hearing Impaired Provide discussion questions to hearing-impaired students before discussion. Assign another student to record the answers to the questions when they are discussed. Remind hearing students to face hearing-impaired students during the discussion if possible. L2

LS **Auditory-Musical**

Curriculum Connection

History Have students research alchemy. During the Middle Ages, alchemists searched for a way to turn common metals into gold. Though unsuccessful, they were precursors to modern chemists. Much of alchemy was based on Aristotle's idea that matter tries to reach perfection. Alchemists concluded that there must be a way to turn other metals into gold, since it was the "perfect" metal.

L3 LS **Linguistic**

Ionic Compounds Ions of opposite charges attract one another to form electrically neutral compounds called ionic compounds. Table salt is made of sodium (Na) and chlorine (Cl) ions, as shown in **Figure 3B.** When they combine, a chlorine atom gains an electron from a sodium atom. The chlorine atom becomes a negatively charged ion, and the sodium atom becomes a positively charged ion. These oppositely charged ions then are attracted to each other and form the ionic compound sodium chloride, NaCl.

Ions are important in many life processes that take place in your body and in other organisms. For example, messages are sent along your nerves as potassium and sodium ions move in and out of nerve cells. Calcium ions are important in causing your muscles to contract. Ions also are involved in the transport of oxygen by your blood. The movement of some substances into and out of a cell would not be possible without ions.

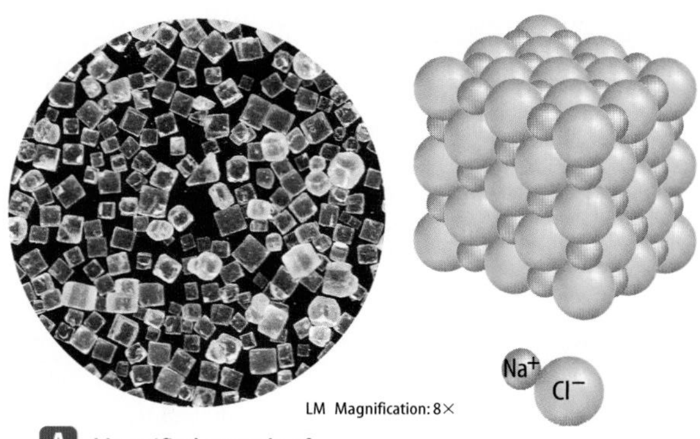

A Magnified crystals of salt look like this.

B A salt crystal is held together by the attractions between sodium ions and chlorine ions.

Figure 3 Table salt crystals are held together by ionic bonds.

Mixtures

Some substances, such as a combination of sugar and salt, can't change each other or combine chemically. A **mixture** is a combination of substances in which individual substances retain their own properties. Mixtures can be solids, liquids, gases, or any combination of them.

Reading Check ***Why is a combination of sugar and salt said to be a mixture?***

Most chemical reactions in living organisms take place in mixtures called solutions. You've probably noticed the taste of salt when you perspire. Sweat is a solution of salt and water. In a solution, two or more substances are mixed evenly. A cell's cytoplasm is a solution of dissolved molecules and ions.

Living things also contain mixtures called suspensions. A suspension is formed when a liquid or a gas has another substance evenly spread throughout it. Unlike solutions, the substances in a suspension eventually sink to the bottom. If blood, shown in **Figure 4,** is left undisturbed, the red blood cells and white blood cells will sink gradually to the bottom. However, the pumping action of your heart constantly moves your blood and the blood cells remain suspended.

Figure 4 When a test tube of whole blood is left standing, the blood cells sink in the watery plasma.

Teacher FYI

Common Bonds The two most common bonds in compounds are covalent and ionic. In covalent bonds, atoms share outermost electrons. In ionic bonds, oppositely charged ions are attracted to one another.

Quick Demo

Mixtures and Compounds

Materials baking soda, sand, vinegar, clear-plastic container

Estimated Time 10 minutes

Procedure Mix baking soda with darker sand. Point out the different, distinct parts of the mixture. Then, mix baking soda with vinegar in a clear-plastic container. The bubbles indicate that a new compound—carbon dioxide—has formed. *Note: Make sure students understand that formation of bubbles does not always indicate that a chemical reaction has taken place.*

Reading Check

Answer It is a combination of two substances, each of which retains its own properties when combined with the other.

Visual Learning

Figure 4 The transparent substance in the test tube is plasma. The substance at the bottom of the tube is red and white blood cells. Describe what would happen if the tube was shaken. The blood cells and plasma would mix forming a suspension. This suspension is blood. L2

Differentiated Instruction

Challenge Have students investigate the properties of solutions and suspensions. Students can dissolve one cup of sugar in one cup of warm water. Students then analyze the resulting solution: What is the volume of the resulting solution? Where is the sugar in the solution? Extend this by having students mix one cup of sand with one cup of water. What is the volume of the resulting suspension? Students can compare and contrast the mixtures. L3 LS **Logical Mathematical**

SECTION 1 Chemistry of Life **A** ◆ **71**

IDENTIFYING Misconceptions

Lipids Student awareness of the emphasis on maintaining a "low-fat" diet may lead them to believe that all lipids are harmful. Explain that fats and other lipids have many useful functions in living organisms, such as energy storage, and are a vital component of cell membranes.

Activity

Organic Compounds Display a Food Guide Pyramid and discuss the types of organic compounds represented by foods in each group. Ask students to use this information to create a bulletin board display of foods rich in carbohydrates, lipids, and proteins. Have students illustrate the display with pictures of the foods. L2

Fun Fact

A paste made of meat tenderizer and water is often used to treat bee and jellyfish stings. An enzyme in the meat tenderizer helps to break down the proteins in the venom, making the area less painful.

Answer fats, oils, and phospholipids

Table 2 Organic Compounds Found in Living Things

	Carbohydrates	Lipids	Proteins	Nucleic Acids
Elements	carbon, hydrogen, and oxygen	carbon, oxygen, hydrogen, and phosphorus	carbon, oxygen, hydrogen, nitrogen, and sulfur	carbon, oxygen, hydrogen, nitrogen, and phosphorus
Examples	sugars, starch, and cellulose	fats, oils, waxes, phospholipids, and cholesterol	enzymes, skin, and hair	DNA and RNA
Function	supply energy for cell processes; form plant structures; short-term energy storage	store large amounts of energy long term; form boundaries around cells	regulate cell processes and build cell structures	carry hereditary information; used to make proteins

Topic: Air Quality

Visit booka.msscience.com for Web links to information about air quality.

Activity Look up the air quality forecast for today. List three locations where the air quality forecast is good, and three locations where it is unhealthy.

Organic Compounds

You and all living things are made up of compounds that are classified as organic or inorganic. Rocks and other nonliving things contain inorganic compounds, but most do not contain large amounts of organic compounds. **Organic compounds** always contain carbon and hydrogen and usually are associated with living things. One exception would be nonliving things that are products of living things. For example, coal contains organic compounds because it was formed from dead and decaying plants. Organic molecules can contain hundreds or even thousands of atoms that can be arranged in many ways. **Table 2** compares the four groups of organic compounds that make up all living things—carbohydrates, lipids, proteins, and nucleic acids.

Carbohydrates Carbohydrates are organic molecules that supply energy for cell processes. Sugars and starches are carbohydrates that cells use for energy. Some carbohydrates also are important parts of cell structures. For example, a carbohydrate called cellulose is an important part of plant cells.

Lipids Another type of organic compound found in living things is a lipid. Lipids do not mix with water. Lipids such as fats and oils store and release even larger amounts of energy than carbohydrates do. One type of lipid, the phospholipid, is a major part of cell membranes.

Reading Check *What are three types of lipids?*

Science Journal

CFCs Have students research and summarize in their Science Journals the organic compounds known as chlorofluorocarbons (CFCs). Summaries should include a description of the composition of these compounds, their use as refrigerants, and a description of how the use of these substances has impacted the environment. L3 P

Proteins Organic compounds called proteins have many important functions in living organisms. They are made up of smaller molecules called amino acids. Proteins are the building blocks of many structures in organisms. Your muscles contain large amounts of protein. Proteins are scattered throughout cell membranes. Certain proteins called **enzymes** regulate nearly all chemical reactions in cells.

Nucleic Acids Large organic molecules that store important coded information in cells are called nucleic acids. One nucleic acid, deoxyribonucleic acid, or DNA—genetic material—is found in all cells at some point in their life. It carries information that directs each cell's activities. Another nucleic acid, ribonucleic acid, or RNA, is needed to make enzymes and other proteins.

Inorganic Compounds

Most **inorganic compounds** are made from elements other than carbon. Generally, inorganic molecules contain fewer atoms than organic molecules. Inorganic compounds are the source for many elements needed by living things. For example, plants take up inorganic compounds from the soil. These inorganic compounds can contain the elements nitrogen, phosphorus, and sulfur. Many foods that you eat contain inorganic compounds. **Table 3** shows some of the inorganic compounds that are important to you. One of the most important inorganic compounds for living things is water.

Table 3 Some Inorganic Compounds Important in Humans

Compound	Use in Body
Water	makes up most of the blood; most chemical reactions occur in water
Calcium phosphate	gives strength to bones
Hydrochloric acid	breaks down foods in the stomach
Sodium bicarbonate	helps the digestion of food to occur
Salts containing sodium, chlorine, and potassium	important in sending messages along nerves

Mini LAB

Observing How Enzymes Work

Procedure

1. Get two small cups of **prepared gelatin** from your teacher. Do not eat or drink anything in lab.
2. On the gelatin in one of the cups, place a piece of **fresh pineapple.**
3. Let both cups stand undisturbed overnight.
4. Observe what happens to the gelatin.

Analysis

1. What effect did the piece of fresh pineapple have on the gelatin?
2. What does fresh pineapple contain that caused it to have the effect on the gelatin you observed?
3. Why do the preparation directions on a box of gelatin dessert tell you not to mix it with fresh pineapple?

Mini LAB

Purpose to observe the effects of enzymes on gelatin L1 LS **Visual-Spatial**

Materials two small cups of prepared gelatin, one slice of fresh pineapple

Teaching Strategies

- To prepare gelatin, add only half the amount of water indicated on the gelatin package.
- After students add pineapple to one cup, allow both cups of gelatin to sit overnight.

Analysis

1. The gelatin under the fresh pineapple turned to a liquid.
2. an enzyme
3. The gelatin would not solidify if in contact with fresh pineapple.

Assessment

Performance Have students design an experiment to show conclusively that fresh pineapple contains enzymes that keep gelatin from becoming solid. They can repeat the experiment using canned pineapple. Use **Performance Assessment in the Science Classroom,** p. 95.

Teacher FYI

Water Life on Earth could not have evolved without water. Wherever life is found, water is found. Life is found in water at all temperatures. Bacteria can live under snow and in the near-boiling water of hot springs.

Curriculum Connection

Health Provide students with copies of the periodic table. Ask them to research which elements are important for good health. They can find this information on food labels, in reference books, and on the Internet. Ask students to shade each element they discover on the table and to share their results with the class. L2 LS **Interpersonal**

Teacher FYI

Water Temperatures Earth's distance from the Sun provides the right conditions for liquid water: temperatures between 0°C and 100°C (32°F and 212°F). Water has or would have evaporated from planets closer to the Sun.

Make a Model

Water Molecule Have students make a model of a water molecule. They may use foam balls or colored marshmallows to represent the atoms, and toothpicks to hold them together. L2 IS **Kinesthetic**

Applying Math

National Math Standards

Correlation to Mathematics Objectives

1, 9

Answers to Practice Problems

1. Calculate the infant's water weight and the adult's water weight, then subtract to find the difference.
   Infant: $78/100 = x \div 3.2$ kg
   $x = (78 \times 3.2) \div 100$
   $x = 2.496$ kg of water;
   Adult: $60 \div 100 = x \div 95$ kg
   $x = (60 \times 95) \div 100$
   $x = 57$ kg of water;
   Difference: 57 kg − 2.496 kg = 54.504 kg
2. Calculate the adult woman's water weight and the adult man's water weight, then subtract to find the difference, as in problem 1. The man has 19.5 kg more water than the woman.

Importance of Water Some scientists hypothesize that life began in the water of Earth's ancient oceans. Chemical reactions might have occurred that produced organic molecules. Similar chemical reactions can take place in cells in your body.

Living things are composed of more than 50 percent water and depend on water to survive. You can live for weeks without food but only for a few days without water. **Figure 5** shows where water is found in your body. Although seeds and spores of plants, fungi, and bacteria can exist without water, they must have water if they are to grow and reproduce. All the chemical reactions in living things take place in water solutions, and most organisms use water to transport materials through their bodies. For example, many animals have blood that is mostly water and moves materials. Plants use water to move minerals and sugars between the roots and leaves.

Applying Math — Solve an Equation

CALCULATE THE IMPORTANCE OF WATER All life on Earth depends on water for survival. Water is the most vital part of humans and other animals. It is required for all of the chemical processes that keep us alive. At least 60 percent of an adult human body consists of water. If an adult man weighs 90 kg, how many kilograms of water does his body contain?

Solution

1. *This is what you know:*
   - adult human body = 60% water
   - man = 90 kg
2. *This is what you need to find:* How many kilograms of water does the adult man have?
3. *This is the procedure you need to use:*
   - Set up the ratio: $60/100 = x/90$.
   - Solve the equation for x: $(60 \times 90)/100$.
   - The adult man has 54 kg of water.
4. *Check your answer:* Divide your answer by 90, then multiply by 100. You should get 60%.

Practice Problems

1. A human body at birth consists of 78 percent water. This gradually decreases to 60 percent in an adult. Assume a baby weighed 3.2 kg at birth and grew into an adult weighing 95 kg. Calculate the approximate number of kilograms of water the human gained.
2. Assume an adult woman weighs 65 kg and an adult man weighs 90 kg. Calculate how much more water, in kilograms, the man has compared to the woman.

For more practice, visit booka.msscience.com/math_practice

Curriculum Connection

Art Have students cut out pictures from magazines that illustrate water use by organisms, in industry, and in the environment. Then, have each student make a water collage using the pictures they chose. Display collages in the classroom. L1 IS **Visual-Spatial**

74 ◆ A CHAPTER 3 Cell Processes

INTEGRATE Physics

Characteristics of Water The atoms of a water molecule are arranged in such a way that the molecule has areas with different charges. Water molecules are like magnets. The negative part of a water molecule is attracted to the positive part of another water molecule just like the north pole of a magnet is attracted to the south pole of another magnet. This attraction, or force, between water molecules is why a film forms on the surface of water. The film is strong enough to support small insects because the forces between water molecules are stronger than the force of gravity on the insect.

When heat is added to any substance, its molecules begin to move faster. Because water molecules are so strongly attracted to each other, the temperature of water changes slowly. The large percentage of water in living things acts like an insulator. The water in a cell helps keep its temperature constant, which allows life-sustaining chemical reactions to take place.

You've seen ice floating on water. When water freezes, ice crystals form. In the crystals, each water molecule is spaced at a certain distance from all the others. Because this distance is greater in frozen water than in liquid water, ice floats on water. Bodies of water freeze from the top down. The floating ice provides insulation from extremely cold temperatures and allows living things to survive in the cold water under the ice.

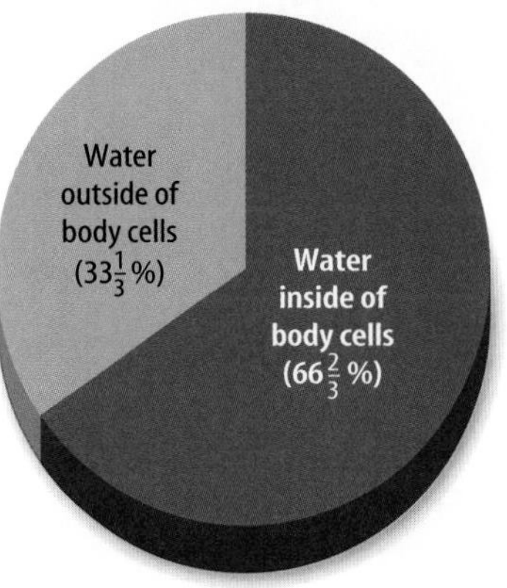

Figure 5 About two-thirds of your body's water is located within your body's cells. Water helps maintain the cells' shapes and sizes. One-third of your body's water is outside of your body's cells.

section 1 review

Summary

The Nature of Matter

- Atoms are made up of protons, neutrons, and electrons.
- Elements are made up of only one kind of atom.
- Compounds are made up of two or more elements.

Mixtures

- Solutions are made of two or more substances and are mixed evenly, whereas substances in suspension eventually will sink to the bottom.

Organic Compounds

- All living things contain organic compounds.

Inorganic Compounds

- Water is one of the most important inorganic compounds for living things.

Self Check

1. **Compare and contrast** atoms and molecules.
2. **Describe** the differences between an organic and an inorganic compound. Given an example of each type of compound.
3. **List** the four types of organic compounds found in all living things.
4. **Infer** why life as we know it depends on water.
5. **Think Critically** If you mix salt, sand, and sugar with water in a small jar, will the resulting mixture be a suspension, a solution, or both?

Applying Skills

6. **Interpret** Carefully observe **Figure 1** and determine how many protons, neutrons, and electrons an atom of oxygen has.

Science Online booka.msscience.com/self_check_quiz

3 Assess

DAILY INTERVENTION

Check for Understanding

Visual-Spatial Display different liquids, such as a glass of fruit juice, a jar of paint, a bottle of oil, and a glass of water. Discuss the uniqueness of water, in that it is mostly found in liquid form on Earth, that it expands when it freezes, and that it is the most common solvent in the world.

Reteach

Organic Compounds Display carbon compounds such as starch, soap, vinegar, and alcohol. Ask students to explain why these are considered to be organic compounds. They all contain carbon and hydrogen. L2 LS **Logical-Mathematical**

Assessment

Portfolio Have students write an essay to explain why water is important to them. Ask them to think about their family's use of water each day and what would happen if they were asked to cut their water usage. Use **Performance Assessment in the Science Classroom,** p. 157. L1

section 1 review

1. Possible answer: similarities—both are made of smaller units. Atoms consist of protons, neutrons, and electrons and molecules consist of two or more atoms; differences—molecules are larger than atoms. Molecules can be formed or broken down in a chemical reaction but atoms cannot.
2. Organic compounds, such as lipids, contain carbon; most inorganic compounds, such as water, do not.
3. lipids, carbohydrates, proteins, and nucleic acids
4. Most life processes can occur only in water solutions.
5. Salt and sugar dissolve in water forming a solution; if shaken, sand will spread throughout the solution and form a suspension.
6. 8 protons, 8 neutrons, and 8 electrons

section 2

Moving Cellular Materials

1 Motivate

Bellringer

Section Focus Transparencies also are available on the Interactive Chalkboard CD-ROM.

L2 ELL

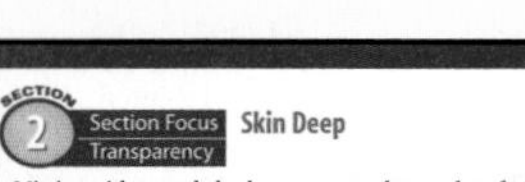

Section 2 Section Focus Transparency — Skin Deep — Chapter 3

Misting with water helps keep supermarket produce fresh. Not all the water stays on the skin of these fruits and vegetables; most of it seems to disappear. The trick is finding out where it went.

1. When the water on the fruits and vegetables disappears, where does it go?
2. Create a simple test to explain what happens to the water when it disappears.
3. How do you think the water keeps the produce fresh?

Cell Processes

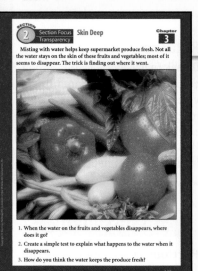

Tie to Prior Knowledge

Cell Parts Use an overhead transparency to review the parts of a cell. Point out that the cell membrane helps a cell maintain a balance between the cell and materials, such as water, salt, and sugars, in its environment.

Virtual Labs

Water Loss or Gain *Under what conditions do cells gain or lose water?*

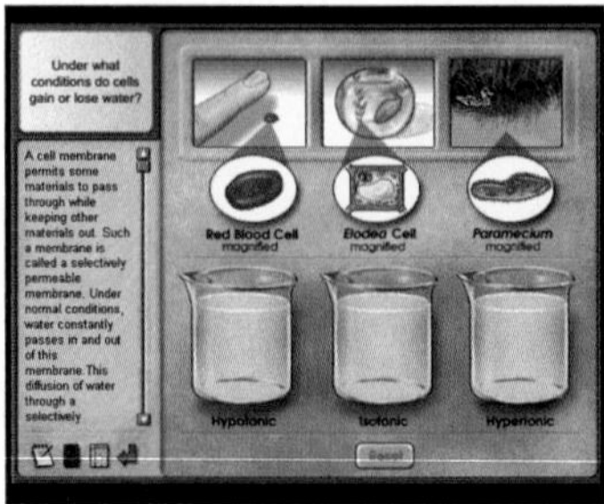

as you read

What You'll Learn

- **Describe** the function of a selectively permeable membrane.
- **Explain** how the processes of diffusion and osmosis move molecules in living cells.
- **Explain** how passive transport and active transport differ.

Why It's Important

Cell membranes control the substances that enter and leave the cells in your body.

Review Vocabulary
cytoplasm: constantly moving gel-like mixture inside the cell membrane that contains hereditary material and is the location of most of a cell's life process

New Vocabulary
- passive transport
- diffusion
- equilibrium
- osmosis
- active transport
- endocytosis
- exocytosis

Passive Transport

"Close that window. Do you want to let in all the bugs and leaves?" How do you prevent unwanted things from coming through the window? As seen in **Figure 6,** a window screen provides the protection needed to keep unwanted things outside. It also allows some things to pass into or out of the room like air, unpleasant odors, or smoke.

Cells take in food, oxygen, and other substances from their environments. They also release waste materials into their environments. A cell has a membrane around it that works for a cell like a window screen does for a room. A cell's membrane is selectively permeable (PUR mee uh bul). It allows some things to enter or leave the cell while keeping other things outside or inside the cell. The window screen also is selectively permeable based on the size of its openings.

Things can move through a cell membrane in several ways. Which way things move depends on the size of the molecules or particles, the path taken through the membrane, and whether or not energy is used. The movement of substances through the cell membrane without the input of energy is called **passive transport.** Three types of passive transport can occur. The type depends on what is moving through the cell membrane.

Figure 6 A cell membrane, like a screen, will let some things through more easily than others. Air gets through a screen, but insects are kept out.

Section 2 Resource Manager

Chapter FAST FILE Resources
- Transparency Activity, p. 43
- Directed Reading for Content Mastery, p. 18
- MiniLAB, p. 4
- Enrichment, p. 29
- Reinforcement, p. 26
- Lab Activity, pp. 9–10
- Lab Worksheet, pp. 5–6

Life Science Critical Thinking/Problem Solving, p. 15

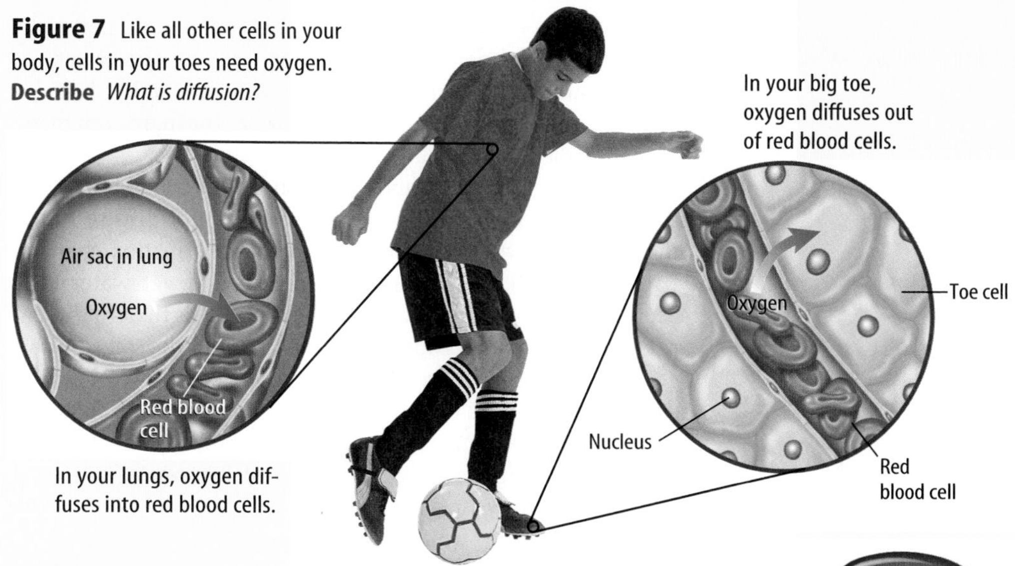

Figure 7 Like all other cells in your body, cells in your toes need oxygen.
Describe *What is diffusion?*

In your lungs, oxygen diffuses into red blood cells.

Diffusion Molecules in solids, liquids, and gases move constantly and randomly. You might smell perfume when you sit near or as you walk past someone who is wearing it. This is because perfume molecules randomly move throughout the air. This random movement of molecules from an area where there is relatively more of them into an area where there is relatively fewer of them is called **diffusion.** Diffusion is one type of cellular passive transport. Molecules of a substance will continue to move from one area into another until the relative number of these molecules is equal in the two areas. When this occurs, **equilibrium** is reached and diffusion stops. After equilibrium occurs, it is maintained because molecules continue to move.

Reading Check *What is equilibrium?*

Every cell in your body uses oxygen. When you breathe, how does oxygen get from your lungs to cells in your big toe? Oxygen is carried throughout your body in your blood by the red blood cells. When your blood is pumped from your heart to your lungs, your red blood cells do not contain much oxygen. However, your lungs have more oxygen molecules than your red blood cells do, so the oxygen molecules diffuse into your red blood cells from your lungs, as shown in **Figure 7.** When the blood reaches your big toe, there are more oxygen molecules in your red blood cells than in your big toe cells. The oxygen diffuses from your red blood cells and into your big toe cells, as shown also in **Figure 7.**

Observing Diffusion

Procedure
1. Use two clean glasses of equal size. Label one *Hot,* then fill it until half full with **very warm water.** Label the other *Cold,* then fill it until half full with **cold water. WARNING:** *Do not use boiling hot water.*
2. Add one drop of **food coloring** to each glass. Carefully release the drop just at the water's surface to avoid splashing the water.
3. Observe the water in the glasses. Record your observations immediately and again after 15 min.

Analysis
1. Describe what happens when food coloring is added to each glass.
2. How does temperature affect the rate of diffusion?

Try at Home

2 Teach

Caption Answer

Figure 7 the random movement of molecules from where there is more of them to where there is fewer of them

Purpose to investigate the effect of temperature on diffusion rate L1 ELL COOP LEARN IN **Logical-Mathematical**

Materials two clean glasses, very warm water, cold water, food coloring, dropper, marker or wax pencil, clock, labels

Teaching Strategies
- Have students record how long it takes the food coloring to diffuse evenly throughout each beaker.
- Caution students not to move the water-filled beakers.

Analysis
1. The food coloring spreads throughout the water; it spreads faster in the hot water.
2. Heat increases the rate of diffusion.

Assessment

Performance To further assess understanding of the effect of temperature on diffusion, have students repeat the activity using ice water instead of hot water. Use **Performance Assessment in the Science Classroom,** p. 105. L1

Reading Check

Answer when the relative number of molecules of a substance is equal in the two areas

Teacher FYI

Membranes A permeable membrane allows all molecules to pass through. An impermeable membrane doesn't allow any to pass. Only some molecules can pass through a semi-permeable membrane—usually only small molecules that can pass through quickly.

Quick Demo

Selectively Permeable Membrane

Materials sand, salt, marbles, water, kitchen strainer

Estimated Time five minutes

Procedure Pour different substances through the kitchen strainer. Select some substances that will pass through the strainer and some that will not.

Inquiry Lab

Observing the Effect of Salt on Plants

Purpose to design an experiment to grow plants treated with salt

Possible Materials container, soil, fast-growing plants or seeds such as grass or radishes, table salt or road salt

Estimated Time one month

Teaching Strategies

- Students can vary the amount of salt, and whether it is added to the soil or to leaves.
- Students can predict what the effect of the salt will be by testing rate of growth, plant height, plant color, and leaf number. L2

For additional inquiry activities, see *Science Inquiry Labs*.

Caption Answer

Figure 8 diffusion of water through a cell membrane

Reading Check

Answer Because there are fewer water molecules around the carrot cells than inside the carrot cells, water leaves the carrot and moves into the salt solution.

Osmosis—The Diffusion of Water Remember that water makes up a large part of living matter. Cells contain water and are surrounded by water. Water molecules move by diffusion into and out of cells. The diffusion of water through a cell membrane is called **osmosis.**

If cells weren't surrounded by water that contains few dissolved substances, water inside of cells would diffuse out of them. This is why water left the carrot cells in this chapter's Launch Lab. Because there were relatively fewer water molecules in the salt solution around the carrot cells than in the carrot cells, water moved out of the cells and into the salt solution.

Losing water from a plant cell causes its cell membrane to come away from its cell wall, as shown on the left in **Figure 8.** This reduces pressure against its cell wall, and a plant cell becomes limp. If the carrot sticks were taken out of salt water and put in pure water, the water around the cells would move into them and they would fill with water. Their cell membranes would press against their cell walls, as shown on the right in **Figure 8,** pressure would increase, and the cells would become firm. That is why the carrot sticks would be crisp again.

Reading Check *Why do carrots in salt water become limp?*

Osmosis also takes place in animal cells. If animal cells were placed in pure water, they too would swell up. However, animal cells are different from plant cells. Just like an overfilled water balloon, animal cells will burst if too much water enters the cell.

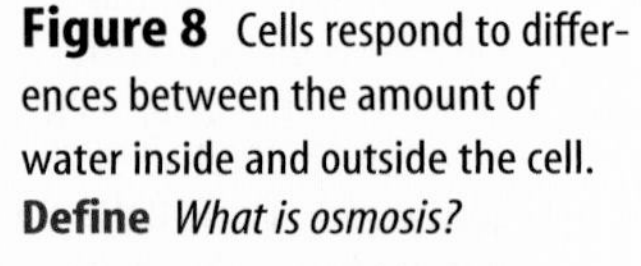

Figure 8 Cells respond to differences between the amount of water inside and outside the cell.
Define *What is osmosis?*

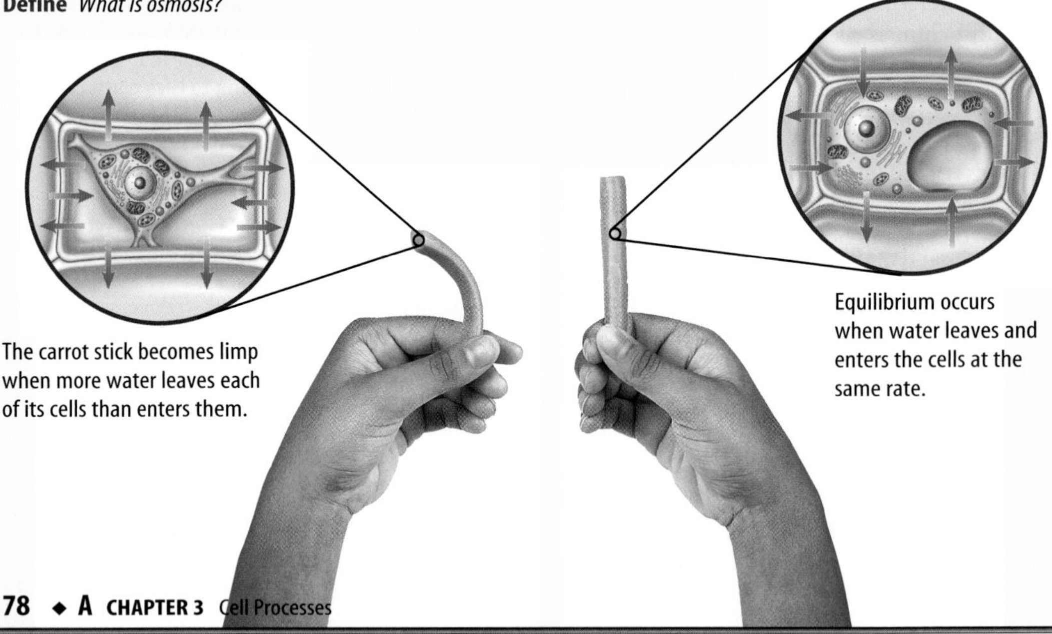

The carrot stick becomes limp when more water leaves each of its cells than enters them.
Equilibrium occurs when water leaves and enters the cells at the same rate.

LAB DEMONSTRATION

Purpose to observe diffusion

Materials self-sealing plastic sandwich bag, cooked rice, tincture of iodine, 8-oz clear plastic cups, tablespoon

Preparation Half-fill the plastic cups with water and add 6 drops of tincture of iodine. Cook rice before class.

Procedure Seal a sandwich bag containing 2 tbsp of rice, and place it into the water that contains iodine. Observe after 10 min.

Expected Outcome Iodine molecules will move through the plastic bag, turning the rice blue-black. Iodine turns blue-black in the presence of starch.

Assessment

What did you observe? The rice inside the plastic bag turned blue-black. Explain what occurred. Iodine molecules diffused from an area where there was a large number of iodine molecules (outside the bag) to an area where there were few iodine molecules (inside the bag).

Facilitated Diffusion Cells take in many substances. Some substances pass easily through the cell membrane by diffusion. Other substances, such as glucose molecules, are so large that they can enter the cell only with the help of molecules in the cell membrane called transport proteins. This process, a type of passive transport, is known as facilitated diffusion. Have you ever used the drive through at a fast-food restaurant to get your meal? The transport proteins in the cell membrane are like the drive-through window at the restaurant. The window lets you get food out of the restaurant and put money into the restaurant. Similarly, transport proteins are used to move substances into and out of the cell.

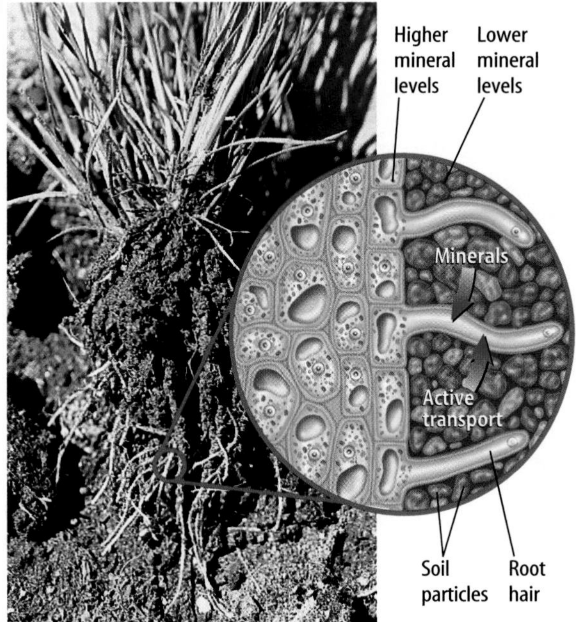

Figure 9 Some root cells have extensions called root hairs that may be 5 mm to 8 mm long. Minerals are taken in by active transport through the cell membranes of root hairs.

Active Transport

Imagine that a football game is over and you leave the stadium. As soon as you get outside of the stadium, you remember that you left your jacket on your seat. Now you have to move against the crowd coming out of the stadium to get back in to get your jacket. Which required more energy—leaving the stadium with the crowd or going back to get your jacket? Something similar to this happens in cells.

Sometimes, a substance is needed inside a cell even though the amount of that substance inside the cell is already greater than the amount outside the cell. For example, root cells require minerals from the soil. The roots of the plant in **Figure 9** already might contain more of those mineral molecules than the surrounding soil does. The tendency is for mineral molecules to move out of the root by diffusion or facilitated diffusion. But they need to move back across the cell membrane and into the cell just like you had to move back into the stadium. When an input of energy is required to move materials through a cell membrane, **active transport** takes place.

Active transport involves transport proteins, just as facilitated diffusion does. In active transport, a transport protein binds with the needed particle and cellular energy is used to move it through the cell membrane. When the particle is released, the transport protein can move another needed particle through the membrane.

Transport Proteins Your health depends on transport proteins. Sometimes transport proteins are missing or do not function correctly. What would happen if proteins that transport cholesterol across membranes were missing? Cholesterol is an important lipid used by your cells. Write your ideas in your Science Journal.

Discussion

Salt and Thirst Why do salty foods make you thirsty? The salt present in the food causes water to leave your cells; the lost water needs to be replaced by the body.

Caption Answer

Figure 8 The diffusion of water through a cell membrane.

Use an Analogy

Active and Passive Transport Have students compare active and passive transport with the energy they must exert to get a bicycle to the top of a hill and then ride it back down. Students must exert energy to get the bicycle up the hill. In the same way, the cell uses energy to move substances from areas of low concentration to areas of high concentration. Students do not need to exert energy to ride the bicycle down the hill. In passive transport, cells do not have to use energy to move substances from areas of high concentration to areas of low concentration. L2 LS **Logical-Mathematical**

Text Question Answer

going back for the jacket

Transport Proteins Cholesterol would not be transported to different areas of the body. Without cholesterol, the body could not synthesize bile acids, steroid hormones, or Vitamin D.

Research Have students research the "good" types and "bad" types of cholesterol. Why does the body need cholesterol? They should include why the body needs "good" cholesterol and why certain types of cholesterol are bad for people's health. Students can design a health pamphlet on the ways to lower health risks associated with high cholesterol. L2

Cultural Diversity

Preserving Foods A practical use of osmosis is the drying and salting of food. Have students report on the processes and uses of dried and salted foods in Native American and other cultures. For example, the French developed a vegetable dehydrator in 1795. Both processes remove water from cells in order to preserve the food. In drying, water evaporates. In salting, a salt solution is used to remove water from cells. L2

Teacher FYI

Membranes Cell membranes contain spaces through which some substances (water molecules, mineral ions, sugar molecules) can pass easily. The spaces are too small for large molecules to pass through. Some ions cannot pass through membranes due to their charge. These move into a cell via channels or active transport.

Use Science Words

Word Meaning Have students use a dictionary to find the meanings of the prefixes *endo-* and *exo-* ("taking in" and "turning out"). Ask them to find examples of other words that make use of these prefixes, and to explain how the meaning of the prefix relates to the meaning of the word. Possible answers: endoskeleton, a skeleton that is inside the body; exoskeleton, a skeleton that is outside the body L2

3 Assess

DAILY INTERVENTION

Checking for Understanding

Visual-Spatial Have students make a poster that diagrams the processes of endocytosis and exocytosis. Ask them to draw the processes in a stepwise manner with labels. Discuss how the processes are similar and how they differ. L2

Reteach

Diffusion Place two or three drops of vanilla extract inside a balloon. Blow up the balloon and tie it. Have students observe the balloon until they can smell the vanilla. Then have them explain why they smell the vanilla outside the balloon. Diffusion has taken place across the membrane. L2

Assessment

Oral Would a cell placed in syrup lose or gain water? Explain. It would lose water; water molecules move by diffusion from areas of high concentration to areas of low concentration.

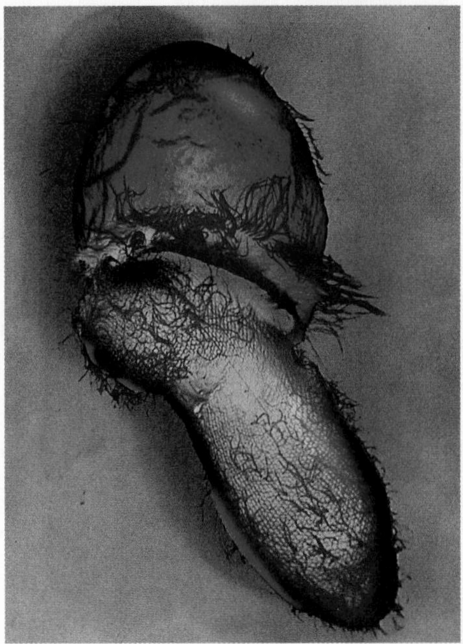

Color-enhanced TEM Magnification: 1,400×

Figure 10 One-celled organisms like this egg-shaped one can take in other one-celled organisms using endocytosis.

Endocytosis and Exocytosis

Some molecules and particles are too large to move by diffusion or to use the cell membrane's transport proteins. Large protein molecules and bacteria, for example, can enter a cell when they are surrounded by the cell membrane. The cell membrane folds in on itself, enclosing the item in a sphere called a vesicle. Vesicles are transport and storage structures in a cell's cytoplasm. The sphere pinches off, and the resulting vesicle enters the cytoplasm. A similar thing happens when you poke your finger into a partially inflated balloon. Your finger is surrounded by the balloon in much the same way that the protein molecule is surrounded by the cell membrane. This process of taking substances into a cell by surrounding it with the cell membrane is called **endocytosis** (en duh si TOH sus). Some one-celled organisms, as shown in **Figure 10,** take in food this way.

The contents of a vesicle can be released by a cell using the process called **exocytosis** (ek soh si TOH sus). Exocytosis occurs in the opposite way that endocytosis does. A vesicle's membrane fuses with a cell's membrane, and the vesicle's contents are released. Cells in your stomach use this process to release chemicals that help digest food. The ways that materials can enter or leave a cell are summarized in **Figure 11.**

section 2 review

Summary

Passive Transport

- Cells take in substances and release waste through their cell membranes.
- Facilitated diffusion and osmosis are types of passive transport.

Active Transport

- Transport proteins are involved in active transport.
- Transport proteins can be reused many times.

Endocytosis and Exocytosis

- Vesicles are formed when a cell takes in a substance by endocytosis.
- Contents of a vesicle are released to the outside of a cell by exocytosis.

Self Check

1. **Describe** how cell membranes are selectively permeable.
2. **Compare and contrast** the processes of osmosis and diffusion.
3. **Infer** why endocytosis and exocytosis are important processes to cells.
4. **Think Critically** Why are fresh fruits and vegetables sprinkled with water at produce markets?

Applying Skills

5. **Communicate** Seawater is saltier than tap water. Explain why drinking large amounts of seawater would be dangerous for humans.

Science Online booka.msscience.com/self_check_quiz

section 2 review

1. They allow some molecules to pass through, but not others.
2. In both, molecules move from areas with many molecules to areas with few molecules. Osmosis is the diffusion of water across a cell membrane; diffusion can apply to any form of matter.
3. Molecules and particles that are too large to move by diffusion or by the cell's transport proteins can move into and out of cells using endocytosis and exocytosis.
4. Water will diffuse into the fruits and vegetables and keep them crisp.
5. The high levels of salt in seawater would cause water to move out of the cells, resulting in dehydration.

Figure 11

A flexible yet strong layer, the cell membrane is built of two layers of lipids (gold) pierced by protein "passageways" (purple). Molecules can enter or exit the cell by slipping between the lipids or through the protein passageways. Substances that cannot enter or exit the cell in these ways may be surrounded by the membrane and drawn into or expelled from the cell.

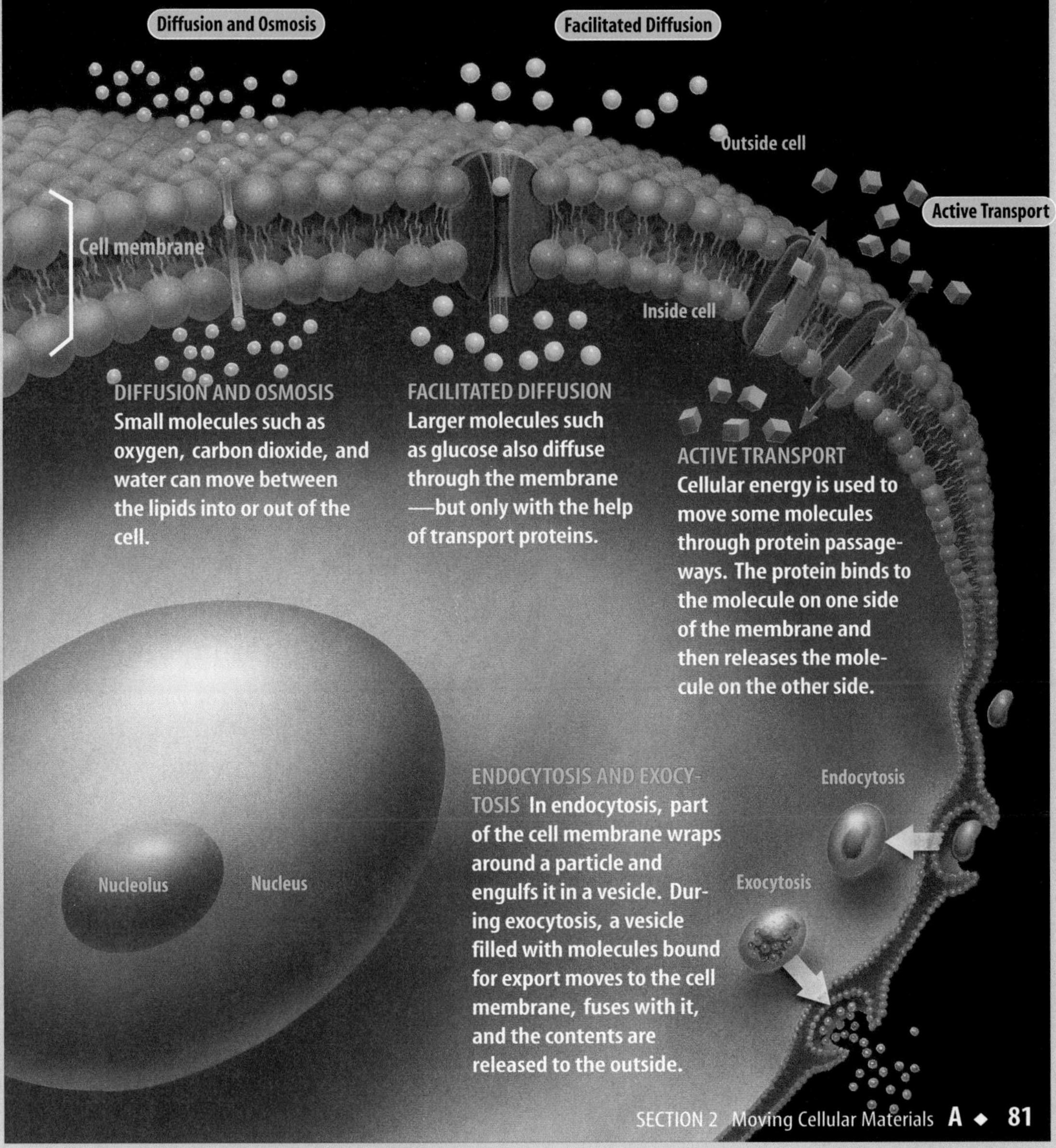

DIFFUSION AND OSMOSIS Small molecules such as oxygen, carbon dioxide, and water can move between the lipids into or out of the cell.

FACILITATED DIFFUSION Larger molecules such as glucose also diffuse through the membrane —but only with the help of transport proteins.

ACTIVE TRANSPORT Cellular energy is used to move some molecules through protein passageways. The protein binds to the molecule on one side of the membrane and then releases the molecule on the other side.

ENDOCYTOSIS AND EXOCYTOSIS In endocytosis, part of the cell membrane wraps around a particle and engulfs it in a vesicle. During exocytosis, a vesicle filled with molecules bound for export moves to the cell membrane, fuses with it, and the contents are released to the outside.

SECTION 2 Moving Cellular Materials A ◆ 81

Visualizing Cell Membrane Transport

Have students examine the pictures and read the captions. Then ask students the following questions.

Why do some substances move through the cell membrane through exocytosis and endocytosis instead of one of the other transport methods? These substances, which include proteins and nucleic acids, are too large to use the other methods. For example, cholesterol enters by endocytosis; neurotransmitters exit by exocytosis.

Which transport method(s) is like floating downstream? Which is like paddling upstream? Why? In diffusion (osmosis and facilitated diffusion), a substance moves from an area of higher concentration to an area of lower concentration. This does not require energy because it goes with the flow, like floating downstream. In active transport, the substance must go against the concentration gradient which, like paddling upstream, requires energy.

Activity

Cell Membrane Transport Have students make a model of a cell that illustrates one type of cell membrane transport. L2

LS **Kinesthetic**

Visual Learning

Figure 11 Transport of a molecule across a cell membrane can occur in several ways, such as diffusion and osmosis, facilitated diffusion, active transport, and endocytosis and exocytosis. Have students make an outline of the transport of a molecule across a membrane by using this figure. L2 P

Differentiated Instruction

English-Language Learners Pair students and on flashcards have them write key terms and definitions that deal with the movement of cellular materials. Students should include diffusion, osmosis, facilitated diffusion, active transport, exocytosis and endocytosis on their cards. L2

Challenge Have students investigate transport proteins and the substances each transports. Students can make a card game to teach other students what they learned. L3

Real-World Question

Purpose to observe and measure the amount of water diffusing through an egg membrane L2 IN **Logical-Mathematical**

Process Skills observe and infer, measure, communicate, recognize cause and effect, form operational definitions

Time Required 50 minutes to set up, 5 minutes each day to observe, 15 minutes to summarize

Procedure

Alternate Materials Food containers with lids may be used to hold the unshelled egg.

Teaching Strategy Cover raw eggs with vinegar. Leave undisturbed for two or three days until the shells dissolve.

Troubleshooting

- Remind students to handle unshelled eggs carefully.
- Thick syrup works better than thin syrup.
- Make sure students replace lids on containers.

Conclude and Apply

1. water— increased in size; corn syrup—decreased in size
2. about 30 mL of water entered; about 40 mL of water left
3. The eggshell is not permeable to water and syrup.
4. cell membrane

Observing Osmosis

It is difficult to observe osmosis in cells because most cells are so small. However, a few cells can be seen without the aid of a microscope. Try this lab to observe osmosis.

Real-World Question

How does osmosis occur in an egg cell?

Materials

unshelled egg*
balance
spoon
distilled water (250 mL)
light corn syrup (250 mL)
500-mL container

an egg whose shell has been dissolved by vinegar

Goals

- **Observe** osmosis in an egg cell.
- **Determine** what affects osmosis.

Safety Precautions

WARNING: *Eggs may contain bacteria. Avoid touching your face.*

Procedure

1. Copy the table below into your Science Journal and use it to record your data.

Egg Mass Data

	Beginning Egg Mass	Egg Mass After Two Days
Distilled water		
Corn syrup		

2. Obtain an unshelled egg from your teacher. Handle the egg gently. Use a balance to find the egg's mass and record it in the table.
3. Place the egg in the container and add enough distilled water to cover it.
4. **Observe** the egg after 30 min, one day, and two days. After each observation, record the egg's appearance in your Science Journal.
5. After day two, remove the egg with a spoon and allow it to drain. Find the egg's mass and record it in the table.
6. Empty the container, then put the egg back in. Now add enough corn syrup to cover it. Repeat steps 4 and 5.

Conclude and Apply

1. **Explain** the difference between what happened to the egg in water and in corn syrup.
2. **Calculate** the mass of water that moved into and out of the egg.
3. **Hypothesize** why you used an unshelled egg for this investigation.
4. **Infer** what part of the egg controlled water's movement into and out of the egg.

Communicating Your Data

Compare your conclusions with those of other students in your class. **For more help, refer to the** Science Skill Handbook.

Assessment

Performance Have students place ten dried beans in water overnight. Direct them to explain their observations. Use **Performance Assessment in the Science Classroom,** p. 97 L2

Students should discuss why their conclusions did or did not agree with those of other students.

Energy for Life

Trapping and Using Energy

Think of all the energy that players use in a basketball game. Where does the energy come from? The simplest answer is "from the food they eat." The chemical energy stored in food molecules is changed inside of cells into forms needed to perform all the activities necessary for life. In every cell, these changes involve chemical reactions. All of the activities of an organism involve chemical reactions in some way. The total of all chemical reactions in an organism is called **metabolism.**

The chemical reactions of metabolism need enzymes. What do enzymes do? Suppose you are hungry and decide to open a can of spaghetti. You use a can opener to open the can. Without a can opener, the spaghetti is unusable. The can of spaghetti changes because of the can opener, but the can opener does not change. The can opener can be used again later to open more cans of spaghetti. Enzymes in cells work something like can openers. The enzyme, like the can opener, causes a change, but the enzyme is not changed and can be used again, as shown in **Figure 12.** Unlike the can opener, which can only cause things to come apart, enzymes also can cause molecules to join. Without the right enzyme, a chemical reaction in a cell cannot take place. Each chemical reaction in a cell requires a specific enzyme.

as you read

***What* You'll Learn**

- **List** the differences between producers and consumers.
- **Explain** how the processes of photosynthesis and respiration store and release energy.
- **Describe** how cells get energy from glucose through fermentation.

***Why* It's Important**

Because of photosynthesis and respiration, you use the Sun's energy.

Review Vocabulary
mitochondrion: cell organelle that breaks down lipids and carbohydrates and releases energy

New Vocabulary
- metabolism
- photosynthesis
- respiration
- fermentation

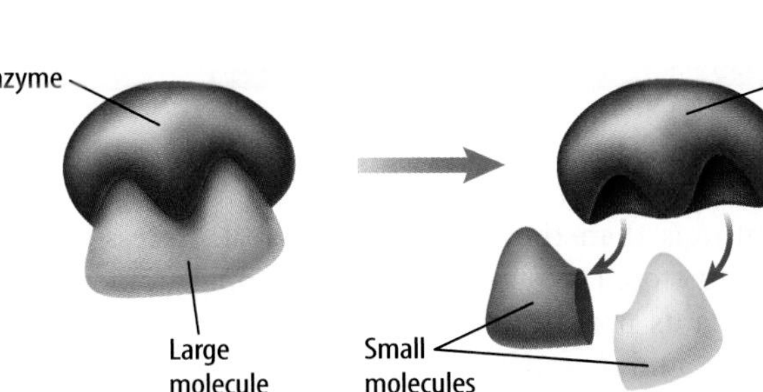

The enzyme attaches to the large molecule it will help change.

The enzyme causes the larger molecule to break down into two smaller molecules. Like a can opener, the enzyme is not changed and can be used again.

Figure 12 Enzymes are needed for most chemical reactions that take place in cells.
Determine *What is the sum of all chemical reactions in an organism called?*

1 Motivate

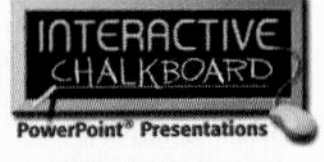

Bellringer

Section Focus Transparencies also are available on the Interactive Chalkboard CD-ROM. L2 

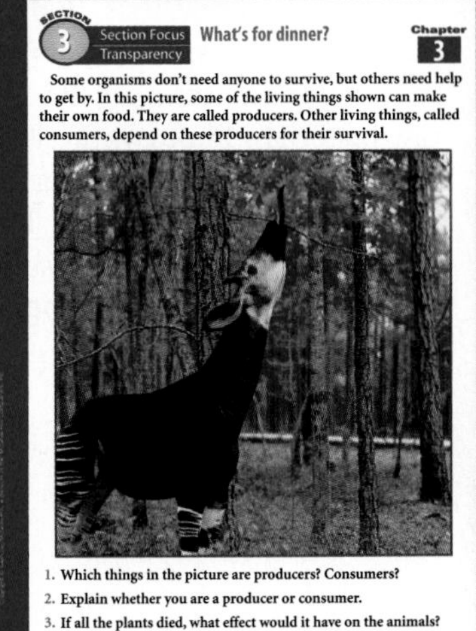
Section 3 Section Focus Transparency — What's for dinner? Chapter 3

Some organisms don't need anyone to survive, but others need help to get by. In this picture, some of the living things shown can make their own food. They are called producers. Other living things, called consumers, depend on these producers for their survival.

1. Which things in the picture are producers? Consumers?
2. Explain whether you are a producer or consumer.
3. If all the plants died, what effect would it have on the animals?

Tie to Prior Knowledge

Energy Sources Display pictures of people using energy—playing sports, gardening, working, and so on. Ask students to identify the source of this energy. chemical bonds in food Then ask where the energy in the food came from. It was derived from plants that captured the Sun's energy. L2

Caption Answer

Figure 12 metabolism

Section 3 Resource Manager

Chapter *FAST FILE* Resources
Transparency Activity, p. 44
Directed Reading for Content Mastery, pp. 19, 20
Lab Activity, pp. 11–14
Enrichment, p. 30
Reinforcement, p. 27
Lab Worksheet, pp. 7–8

Life Science Critical Thinking/Problem Solving, p. 15

Lab Management and Safety, p. 63

2 Teach

Activity

Bubbles Pick a leaf from a plant that has been exposed to sunlight for a few hours. Submerge it in water. Observe the surface of the leaf. What forms on the leaf? Why? Bubbles; the leaf is giving off oxygen. L2

Use an Analogy

Construction and Photosynthesis Compare the construction of a house to photosynthesis. Building a house is a physical process that requires the putting together of raw materials. Photosynthesis is a chemical process of putting raw materials together. They both require raw materials and result in a usable product. LS **Logical-Mathematical**

Caption Answer

Figure 13 carbon dioxide, water, light energy, and chlorophyll

IDENTIFYING Misconceptions

Plant Food Some students may think that plants obtain food from the soil. Plants take in a variety of minerals and other substances from the soil, but these are not used as food. They are dissolved in water and absorbed through the plant's roots. Once absorbed, they are transported to structures in the plant where they are needed. The food of plants—glucose—is produced by plants in the chloroplasts of their cells from carbon dioxide and water and using light energy.

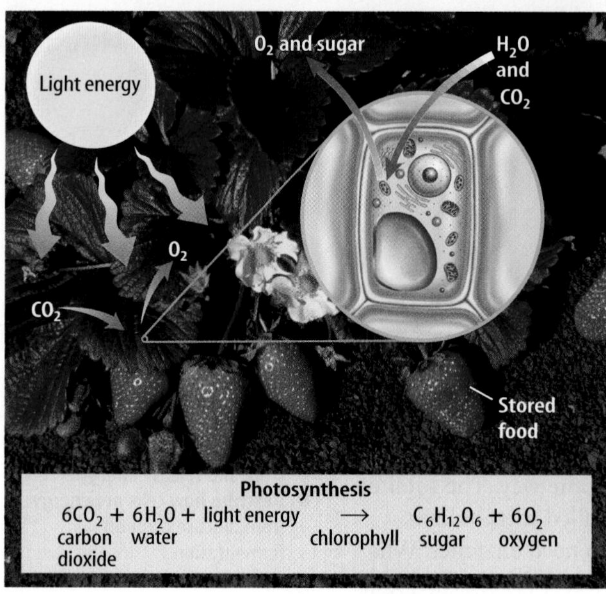

Figure 13 Plants use photosynthesis to make food.
Determine *According to the chemical equation, what raw materials would the plant pictured need for photosynthesis?*

Photosynthesis Living things are divided into two groups—producers and consumers—based on how they obtain their food. Organisms that make their own food, such as plants, are called producers. Organisms that cannot make their own food are called consumers.

If you have ever walked barefoot across a sidewalk on a sunny summer day, you probably moved quickly because the sidewalk was hot. Sunlight energy was converted into thermal energy and heated the sidewalk. Plants and many other producers can convert light energy into another kind of energy—chemical energy. The process they use is called photosynthesis. During **photosynthesis,** producers use light energy to make sugars, which can be used as food.

Producing Carbohydrates Producers that use photosynthesis are usually green because they contain a green pigment called chlorophyll (KLOR uh fihl). Chlorophyll and other pigments are used in photosynthesis to capture light energy. In plant cells, these pigments are found in chloroplasts.

The captured light energy is used to drive chemical reactions during which the raw materials, carbon dioxide and water, are used to produce sugar and oxygen. For plants, the raw materials come from air and soil. Some of the captured light energy is stored in the chemical bonds that hold the sugar molecules together. **Figure 13** shows what happens during photosynthesis in a plant. Enzymes also are needed before these reactions can occur.

Storing Carbohydrates Plants make more sugar during photosynthesis than they need for survival. Excess sugar is changed and stored as starches or used to make other carbohydrates. Plants use these carbohydrates as food for growth, maintenance, and reproduction.

Why is photosynthesis important to consumers? Do you eat apples? Apple trees use photosynthesis to produce apples. Do you like cheese? Some cheese comes from milk, which is produced by cows that eat plants. Consumers take in food by eating producers or other consumers. No matter what you eat, photosynthesis was involved directly or indirectly in its production.

Differentiated Instruction

Challenge There are certain plants, such as the Indian pipe *(Monotropa uniflora)* and dodder *(Cuscuta)*, that lack chlorophyll. Have students research these plants and write a report about how they obtain food to present to the class. L2

Science Journal

Energy and Photosynthesis In their Science Journals, have students list all the foods they eat in one day. Have them to divide the list into two groups: (1) foods formed directly by photosynthesis, (2) foods not formed directly by photosynthesis. Use the lists to help students see that all food energy comes from photosynthesis, whether directly or indirectly. L2

84 ◆ A CHAPTER 3 Cell Processes

Respiration Imagine that you get up late for school. You dress quickly, then run three blocks to school. When you get to school, you feel hot and are breathing fast. Why? Your muscle cells use a lot of energy when you run. To get this energy, muscle cells break down food. Some of the energy from the food is used when you move and some of it becomes thermal energy, which is why you feel warm or hot. Most cells also need oxygen to break down food. You were breathing fast because your body was working to get oxygen to your muscles. Your muscle cells were using the oxygen for the process of respiration. During **respiration,** chemical reactions occur that break down food molecules into simpler substances and release their stored energy. Just as in photosynthesis, enzymes are needed for the chemical reactions of respiration.

Reading Check *What must happen to food molecules for respiration to take place?*

Breaking Down Carbohydrates The type of food molecules most easily broken down by cells is carbohydrates. Respiration of carbohydrates begins in the cytoplasm of the cell. The carbohydrates are broken down into glucose molecules. Each glucose molecule is broken down further into two simpler molecules. As the glucose molecules are broken down, energy is released.

The two simpler molecules are broken down again. This breakdown occurs in the mitochondria of the cells of plants, animals, fungi, and many other organisms. This process uses oxygen, releases much more energy, and produces carbon dioxide and water as wastes. When you exhale, you breathe out carbon dioxide and some of the water.

Respiration occurs in the cells of all living things. **Figure 14** shows how respiration occurs in one consumer. As you are reading this section of the chapter, millions of cells in your body are breaking down glucose, releasing energy, and producing carbon dioxide and water.

Microbiologist Dr. Harold Amos is a microbiologist who has studied cell processes in bacteria and mammals. He has a medical degree and a doctorate in bacteriology and immunology. He has also received many awards for his scientific work and his contributions to the careers of other scientists. Research microbiology careers, and write what you find in your Science Journal.

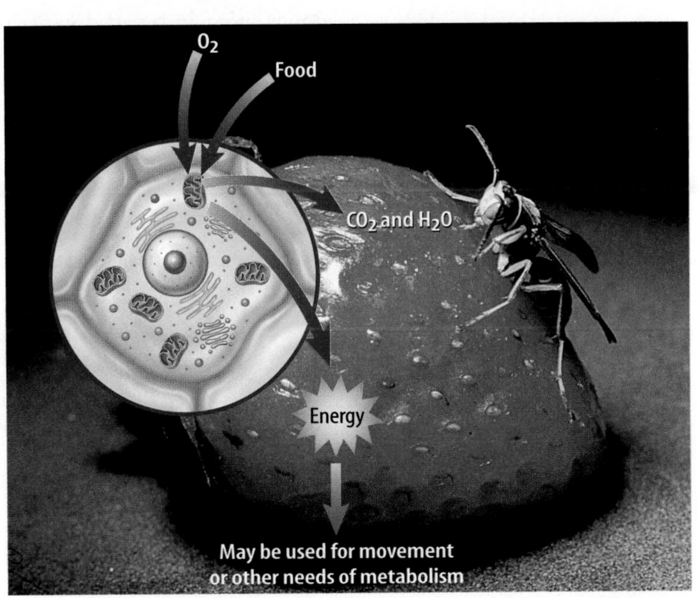

Figure 14 Producers and consumers carry on respiration that releases energy from foods.

Microbiologist Scientists in the field of microbiology study organisms of microscopic or submicroscopic size. A bachelor's degree is required to work in this field. Students interested in a career in microbiology should study sciences, math, and Latin.

Use Science Words

Word Origin Have students study the parts of the word *photosynthesis.* It comes from the Greek *photo, syn-,* and *thesis.* Have them find the meaning of these words and word parts and describe how the word is defined. photo: "light;" syn-: "together;" thesis: "to place;" Photosynthesis uses light to place compounds together. L2

Reading Check

Answer They must be broken down into simpler substances and their stored energy released.

IDENTIFYING Misconceptions

Plant Gases Students often think that plants do not use oxygen, only that they produce oxygen and use carbon dioxide during photosynthesis. See page F at the beginning of this chapter for teaching strategies that address this misconception.

Active Reading

Buddy Interviews This strategy helps students understand and clarify the reading. Have students interview one another to find out what helps them to understand what they are reading, how they find answers, and how they assimilate new vocabulary terms. Have students use Buddy Interviews to help them master photosynthesis and respiration. L2

Answer cytoplasm

Teacher FYI

Athletes' Oxygen The body of an average person running a 100-yard dash in 12 seconds would require 6 L (1.6 gal.) of air. The person's lungs could supply only about 1.2 L of air. As a result, oxygen debt would occur, and the muscles would produce lactic acid. Most athletes take in at least 10 percent more oxygen than the average person; trained marathon runners take in up to 45 percent more oxygen. They have more efficient respiratory and circulatory systems and can exert greater effort without incurring oxygen debt.

Discussion

Yeast Why do bakers use yeast for breadmaking? Yeast carry out processes that release energy in the absence of oxygen and produce carbon dioxide, which causes bread to rise.

Quick Demo

Fermentation

Materials sugar, water, jar, yeast

Estimated Time five minutes to prepare, several hours before class; 10 minutes to observe

Procedure Prepare a sugar solution by mixing 1 tablespoon of sugar with 1 cup of warm water. Add some yeast to the solution a few hours before class and cover it. Have students note the odor of alcohol and the bubbles of carbon dioxide. Point out that these products result from alcoholic fermentation.

Fermentation Remember imagining you were late and had to run to school? During your run, your muscle cells might not have received enough oxygen, even though you were breathing rapidly. When cells do not have enough oxygen for respiration, they use a process called **fermentation** to release some of the energy stored in glucose molecules.

Like respiration, fermentation begins in the cytoplasm. Again, as the glucose molecules are broken down, energy is released. But the simple molecules from the breakdown of glucose do not move into the mitochondria. Instead, more chemical reactions occur in the cytoplasm. These reactions release some energy and produce wastes. Depending on the type of cell, the wastes may be lactic acid, alcohol, and carbon dioxide, as shown in **Figure 15.** Your muscle cells can use fermentation to change the simple molecules into lactic acid while releasing energy. The presence of lactic acid is why your muscle cells might feel stiff and sore after you run to school.

Topic: Beneficial Microorganisms

Visit booka.msscience.com for Web links to information about how microorganisms are used to produce many useful products.

Activity Find three other ways that microorganisms are beneficial.

Reading Check *Where in a cell does fermentation take place?*

Some microscopic organisms, such as bacteria, carry out fermentation and make lactic acid. Some of these organisms are used to produce yogurt and some cheeses. These organisms break down a sugar in milk to release energy. The lactic acid produced causes the milk to become more solid and gives these foods some of their flavor.

Have you ever used yeast to make bread? Yeasts are one-celled living organisms. Yeast cells use fermentation to break down sugar in bread dough. They produce alcohol and carbon dioxide as wastes. The carbon dioxide waste is a gas that makes bread dough rise before it is baked. The alcohol is lost as the bread bakes.

Figure 15 Organisms that use fermentation produce several different wastes.

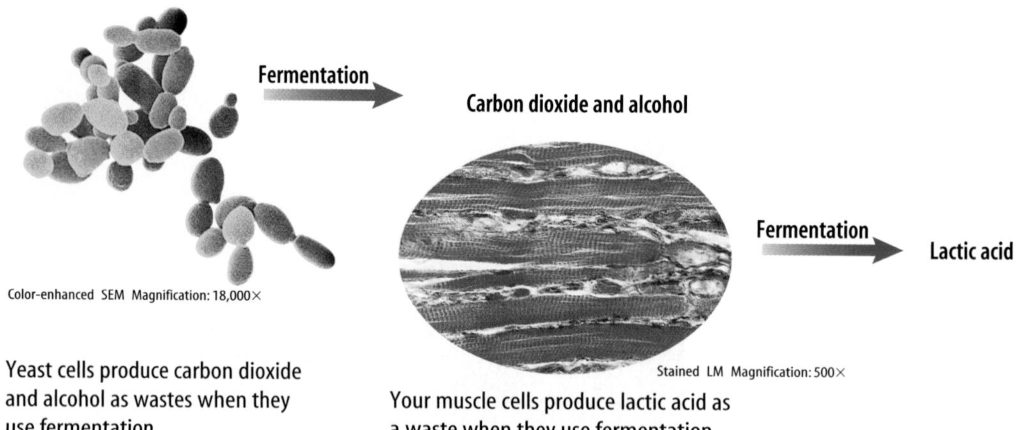

Yeast cells produce carbon dioxide and alcohol as wastes when they use fermentation.

Your muscle cells produce lactic acid as a waste when they use fermentation.

Cultural Diversity

Fermenting Food Lactic acid fermentation by bacteria is responsible for a number of foods from different cultures. Have students research these foods and report their findings to the class in oral reports. Possible topics: Hawaiian *poi*, Japanese soy sauce, Korean *kimchi*, German sauerkraut, yogurt. L3

CO_2, H_2O

Sugars, O_2

Figure 16 The chemical reactions of photosynthesis and respiration could not take place without each other.

Related Processes How are photosynthesis, respiration, and fermentation related? Some producers use photosynthesis to make food. All living things use respiration or fermentation to release energy stored in food. If you think carefully about what happens during photosynthesis and respiration, you will see that what is produced in one is used in the other, as shown in **Figure 16.** These two processes are almost the opposite of each other. Photosynthesis produces sugars and oxygen, and respiration uses these products. The carbon dioxide and water produced during respiration are used during photosynthesis. Most life would not be possible without these important chemical reactions.

section 3 review

Summary

Trapping and Using Energy

- Metabolism is the total of all chemical reactions in an organism.
- During photosynthesis, light energy is used to make sugars.
- Chlorophyll and other pigments capture light energy.
- Consumers take in energy by eating producers and other consumers.
- Living cells break down glucose and release energy. This is called respiration.
- Fermentation changes simple molecules and releases energy.
- Without photosynthesis and respiration, most life would not be possible.

Self Check

1. **Explain** the difference between producers and consumers and give three examples of each.
2. **Infer** how the energy used by many living things on Earth can be traced back to sunlight.
3. **Compare and contrast** respiration and fermentation.
4. **Think Critically** How can some indoor plants help to improve the quality of air in a room?

Applying Math

5. **Solve** Refer to the chemical equation for photosynthesis. Calculate then compare the number of carbon, hydrogen, and oxygen atoms before and after photosynthesis.

section 3 review

1. Producers make food. Consumers get energy by eating producers, food made by producers, or other consumers. Examples will vary.
2. Energy used by living things is released from food molecules during cellular respiration. Photosynthetic producers convert light energy–usually from the Sun–into the chemical energy in the sugar molecules that they produce. Consumers get this energy by eating producers or other consumers that eat producers.
3. The amount of energy released by fermentation is less than that released by respiration.
4. Plants remove carbon dioxide from the air, use it in photosynthesis, and produce oxygen.
5. The number of atoms is the same before and after photosynthesis; C = 6, H = 12, O = 18.

Visual Learning

Figure 16 The arrows in the figure illustrate the interdependence of photosynthesis and respiration. Producers take in carbon dioxide and water, undergo photosynthesis, and produce oxygen and sugars. Other living organisms take in oxygen and sugars, undergo respiration, and give off carbon dioxide and water. Have students create an events chain concept map to illustrate what is occurring in the pictures in this figure. L2 P

3 Assess

DAILY INTERVENTION

Checking for Understanding

Logical-Mathematical Using a three-column chart, have students brainstorm with the class about different organisms and whether they use photosynthesis, respiration, or fermentation. Discuss how these processes are related and under what circumstances an organism would use them. L2

Reteach

Using Energy Have students identify organisms that photosynthesize and those that respire. Only organisms with chlorophyll photosynthesize; all organisms respire. L1

Assessment

Content Have students make a table to compare and contrast photosynthesis and respiration. Use **Performance Assessment in the Science Classroom,** p. 109. L2

Real-World Question

Purpose Students observe photosynthesis and respiration in plants and infer whether the processes occur in light or darkness. L2 ELL COOP LEARN

LS **Visual-Spatial**

Process Skills measure, observe, infer, communicate, compare and contrast, recognize cause and effect, separate and control variables, interpret data

Time Required 50 minutes (leave overnight if using artificial light)

Safety Precautions Students should use care when working with chemicals.

Procedure

Tie to Prior Knowledge Most students are aware that plants use light energy to make food and that photosynthesis will occur in the tube placed near the light.

Troubleshooting *Elodea* should be kept in the dark for two days before the activity. Use sharp scissors to make a clean diagonal cut at the bottom of each stem.

LAB

Photosynthesis and Respiration

Goals

- **Observe** green water plants in the light and dark.
- **Determine** whether plants carry on photosynthesis and respiration.

Materials

16-mm test tubes (3)
150-mm test tubes with stoppers (4)
small, clear-glass baby food jars with lids (4)
test-tube rack
stirring rod
scissors
carbonated water (5 mL)
bromthymol blue solution in dropper bottle
aged tap water (20 mL)
distilled water (20 mL)
sprigs of *Elodea* (2)
other water plants
Alternate materials

Safety Precautions

WARNING: *Wear splashproof safety goggles to protect eyes from hazardous chemicals.*

Real-World Question

Every living cell carries on many chemical processes. Two important chemical processes are respiration and photosynthesis. All cells, including the ones in your body, carry on respiration. However, some plant cells can carry on both processes. In this experiment you will investigate when these processes occur in plant cells. How could you find out when plants were using these processes? Are the products of photosynthesis and respiration the same? When do plants carry on photosynthesis and respiration?

Procedure

1. In your Science Journal, copy and complete the test-tube data table as you perform this lab.

Test-Tube Data

Test Tube	Color at Start	Color After 30 Minutes
1	yellow	blue
2	yellow	yellow
3	blue	yellow
4	blue	blue

Alternative Inquiry Lab

Photosynthesis and Respiration To make this Lab an Inquiry Lab, have students relate the problem to nature. Explain to students that plants undergo some form of respiration. What happens to plants that survive during periods without light? Students can observe photosynthesis and respiration in plants. To determine if they both occur in plants, have students design an experiment to measure the outputs of photosynthesis and respiration. They can use *Elodea* or other water plants and the materials described above to set up the experiment. Unsafe or impractical questions should be eliminated.

2. Label each test tube using the numbers *1, 2, 3,* and *4.* Pour 5 mL of aged tap water into each test tube.
3. Add 10 drops of carbonated water to test tubes *1* and *2.*
4. Add 10 drops of bromthymol blue to all of the test tubes. Bromthymol blue turns green to yellow in the presence of an acid.
5. Cut two 10-cm sprigs of *Elodea.* Place one sprig in test tube *1* and one sprig in test tube *3.* Stopper all test tubes.
6. Place test tubes *1* and *2* in bright light. Place tubes *3* and *4* in the dark. Observe the test tubes for 30 min or until the color changes. Record the color of each of the four test tubes.

Analyze Your Data

1. **Identify** what is indicated by the color of the water in all four test tubes at the start of the activity.
2. **Infer** what process occurred in the test tube or tubes that changed color after 30 min.

Conclude and Apply

1. **Describe** the purpose of test tubes *2* and *4* in this experiment.
2. **Explain** whether or not the results of this experiment show that photosynthesis and respiration occur in plants.

Communicating Your Data

Choose one of the following activities to **communicate** your data. Prepare an oral presentation that explains how the experiment showed the differences between products of photosynthesis and respiration. Draw a cartoon strip to **explain** what you did in this experiment. Use each panel to show a different step. **For more help, refer to the** Science Skill Handbook.

Analyze Your Data

Expected Outcome Most results will reflect that plants used carbon dioxide in the light and gave off carbon dioxide in the dark.

Answers to Questions

1. Test tubes 1 and 2 contain carbon dioxide. Tubes 3 and 4 do not.
2. They underwent photosynthesis or respiration.

Error Analysis Have students compare their results and explain why any differences occurred. L2

Conclude and Apply

1. Tubes 2 and 4 were controls.
2. Yes, the experimental results showed that both processes happen in plant cells. In test tube 1, the green plant used carbon dioxide for photosynthesis. In test tube 3, the green plant gave off carbon dioxide as a result of respiration.

Assessment

Oral How are fermentation and respiration similar? Both processes release energy through the breakdown of other substances. Use **Performance Assessment in the Science Classroom,** p. 99. L2

Differentiated Instruction

Visually Impaired Pair students who are visually impaired with those who can describe to them the colors in the test tubes and other observations, both before and after the experiment. L2

Communicating Your Data

Students should use data from the experiment for the presentation or cartoon.

Understanding Literature

Personification When she states that the tulip inspires love.

Respond to the Reading

1. Possible answers: The tulip bulb is buried deep in the ground; the tulip is a hardy plant.
2. the yellow color at the base of each petal
3. **Linking Science and Writing** As they observe the plant, students should record the change in the plant's growth.

Plant Dormancy

Plant stems play a part in the transport of materials from roots to leaves. Stems vary greatly in size and shape from one plant species to another. Some grow entirely underground and other stems can store water and nutrients. Plants often store food in their stems during their growth period. When a plant's growth stops, this stored food enables them to survive dormancy. Dormancy occurs during a cold winter or a long dry period. The dormant plant uses the stored food to begin growing when conditions again become favorable.

Science and Language Arts

from "Tulip"

by Penny Harter

I watched its first green push
through bare dirt, where the builders
had dropped boards, shingles,
plaster—
killing everything.
I could not recall what grew there,
what returned each spring,
but the leaves looked tulip,
and one morning it arrived,
a scarlet slash against the aluminum siding.
Mornings, on the way to my car,
I bow to the still bell
of its closed petals; evenings,
it greets me, light ringing
at the end of my driveway.
Sometimes I kneel
to stare into the yellow throat . . . .
It opens and closes my days.
It has made me weak with love . . . .

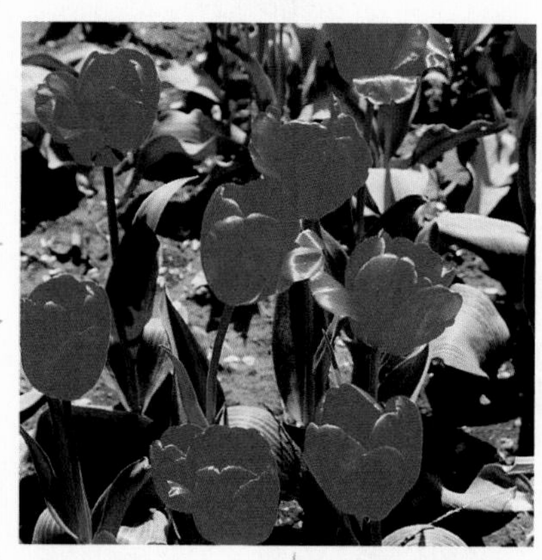

Understanding Literature

Personification Using human traits or emotions to describe an idea, animal, or inanimate object is called personification. When the poet writes that the tulip has a "yellow throat," she uses personification. Where else does the poet use personification?

Respond to the Reading

1. Why do you suppose the tulip survived the builders' abuse?
2. What is the yellow throat that the narrator is staring into?
3. **Linking Science and Writing** Keep a gardener's journal of a plant for a month, describing weekly the plant's condition, size, health, color, and other physical qualities.

Because most chemical reactions in plants take place in water, plants must have water in order to grow. The water carries nutrients and minerals from the soil into the plant. The process of active transport allows needed nutrients to enter the roots. The cell membranes of root cells contain proteins that bind with the needed nutrients. Cellular energy is used to move these nutrients through the cell membrane.

Resources for Teachers and Students

Tulipa: A Photographer's Botonical, by Christopher Baker (Photographer), Willem Lemmers, Emma Sweeny, and Michael Pollan, Artisan, 1999

Photosynthesis, by Krishna Rao and David O. Hall, Cambridge University Press, 1999

Plant Identification Terminology: An Illustrated Glossary, by James G. Harris and Melinda Woolf Harris, Spring Lake Publishers, 2001

American Society for Microbiology, Office of Education, 1325 Massachusetts Avenue, NW, Washington, DC 20005–4171

chapter 3 Study Guide

Reviewing Main Ideas

Section 1 Chemistry of Life

1. Matter is anything that has mass and takes up space.
2. Energy in matter is in the chemical bonds that hold matter together.
3. All organic compounds contain the elements hydrogen and carbon. The organic compounds in living things are carbohydrates, lipids, proteins, and nucleic acids.
4. Organic and inorganic compounds are important to living things.

Section 2 Moving Cellular Materials

1. The selectively permeable cell membrane controls which molecules can pass into and out of the cell.
2. In diffusion, molecules move from areas where there are relatively more of them to areas where there are relatively fewer of them.
3. Osmosis is the diffusion of water through a cell membrane.
4. Cells use energy to move molecules by active transport but do not use energy for passive transport.
5. Cells move large particles through cell membranes by endocytosis and exocytosis.

Section 3 Energy for Life

1. Photosynthesis is the process by which some producers change light energy into chemical energy.
2. Respiration that uses oxygen releases the energy in food molecules and produces waste carbon dioxide and water.
3. Some one-celled organisms and cells that lack oxygen use fermentation to release small amounts of energy from glucose. Wastes such as alcohol, carbon dioxide, and lactic acid are produced.

Visualizing Main Ideas

Copy and complete the following table on energy processes.

Energy Processes

	Photosynthesis	Respiration	Fermentation
Energy source	light	food (glucose)	food (glucose)
In plant and animal cells, occurs in	chloroplast	mitochondria	cytoplasm
Reactants are	water, carbon dioxide	glucose, oxygen	glucose, oxygen
Products are	glucose, oxygen	water, carbon dioxide	lactic acid, alcohol, carbon dioxide

Reviewing Main Ideas

Summary statements can be used by students to review the major concepts of the chapter.

Visualizing Main Ideas

See student page.

Visit booka.msscience.com
/self_check_quiz
/interactive_tutor
/vocabulary_puzzlemaker
/chapter_review
/standardized_test

Assessment Transparency

For additional assessment questions, use the *Assessment Transparency* located in the transparency book.

Assessment

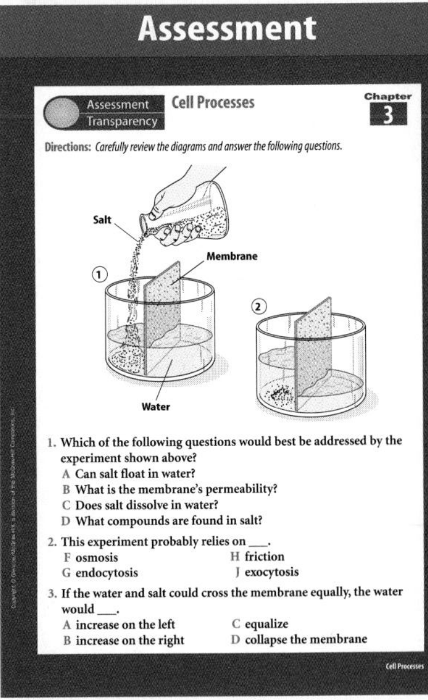

Assessment Transparency — Cell Processes — Chapter 3

Directions: *Carefully review the diagrams and answer the following questions.*

1. Which of the following questions would best be addressed by the experiment shown above?
   A Can salt float in water?
   B What is the membrane's permeability?
   C Does salt dissolve in water?
   D What compounds are found in salt?
2. This experiment probably relies on ___.
   F osmosis
   G endocytosis
   H friction
   J exocytosis
3. If the water and salt could cross the membrane equally, the water would ___.
   A increase on the left
   B increase on the right
   C equalize
   D collapse the membrane

Cell Processes

Identifying Misconceptions

Assess

Discussion Do animals ever give off oxygen as a product of their metabolic activities? No Explain Oxygen is given off as a product of photosynthesis, thus only organisms that can carry out photosynthesis produce this gas. Animals are not photosynthetic organisms. What products do plants release during their metabolic processes? both oxygen and carbon dioxide

Specifically reinforce the idea that plants carry out both photosynthesis and respiration.

Expected Outcome At this point students should understand and be able to explain the complementary processes of photosynthesis and respiration in plants and animals.

Using Vocabulary

1. osmosis
2. enzymes
3. by endocytosis
4. inorganic compound
5. photosynthesis
6. organic compounds
7. respiration
8. metabolism

Checking Concepts

9. C	13. D
10. B	14. C
11. A	15. A
12. B	16. C

chapter 3 Review

Using Vocabulary

active transport p. 79	metabolism p. 83
diffusion p. 77	mixture p. 71
endocytosis p. 80	organic compound p. 72
enzyme p. 73	osmosis p. 78
equilibrium p. 77	passive transport p. 76
exocytosis p. 80	photosynthesis p. 84
fermentation p. 86	respiration p. 85
inorganic compound p. 73	

Use what you know about the vocabulary words to answer the following questions.

1. What is the diffusion of water called?
2. What type of protein regulates nearly all chemical reactions in cells?
3. How do large food particles enter an amoeba?
4. What type of compound is water?
5. What process is used by some producers to convert light energy into chemical energy?
6. What type of compounds always contain carbon and hydrogen?
7. What process uses oxygen to break down glucose?
8. What is the total of all chemical reactions in an organism called?

Checking Concepts

Choose the word or phrase that best answers the question.

9. What is it called when cells use energy to move molecules?
   A) diffusion **C)** active transport
   B) osmosis **D)** passive transport

Use the photo below to answer question 10.

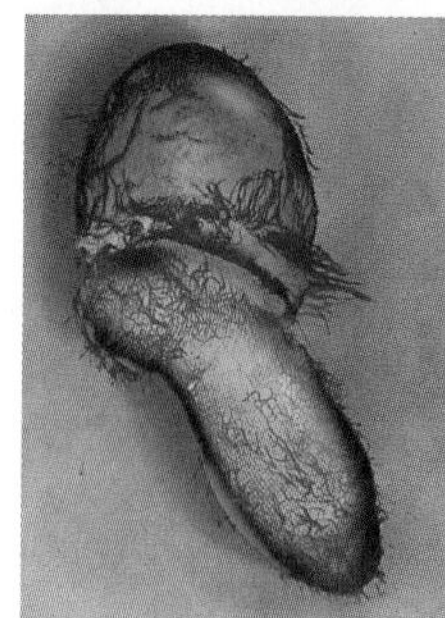

10. What cell process is occurring in the photo?
    A) osmosis **C)** exocytosis
    B) endocytosis **D)** diffusion
11. What occurs when the number of molecules of a substance is equal in two areas?
    A) equilibrium **C)** fermentation
    B) metabolism **D)** cellular respiration
12. Which of the following substances is an example of a carbohydrate?
    A) enzymes **C)** waxes
    B) sugars **D)** proteins
13. What is RNA an example of?
    A) carbon dioxide **C)** lipid
    B) water **D)** nucleic acid
14. What organic molecule stores the greatest amount of energy?
    A) carbohydrate **C)** lipid
    B) water **D)** nucleic acid
15. Which of these formulas is an example of an organic compound?
    A) $C_6H_{12}O_6$ **C)** H_2O
    B) NO_2 **D)** O_2
16. What are organisms that cannot make their own food called?
    A) biodegradables **C)** consumers
    B) producers **D)** enzymes

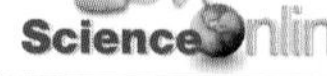
booka.msscience.com/vocabulary_puzzlemaker

Use the Exam*View*® Pro Testmaker CD-ROM to:

- create multiple versions of tests
- create modified tests with one mouse click for inclusion students
- edit existing questions and add your own questions
- build tests aligned with state standards using built-in State Curriculum Tags
- change English tests to Spanish with one mouse click and vice versa

Thinking Critically

17. **Concept Map** Copy and complete the events-chain concept map to sequence the following parts of matter from smallest to largest: *atom, electron,* and *compound.*

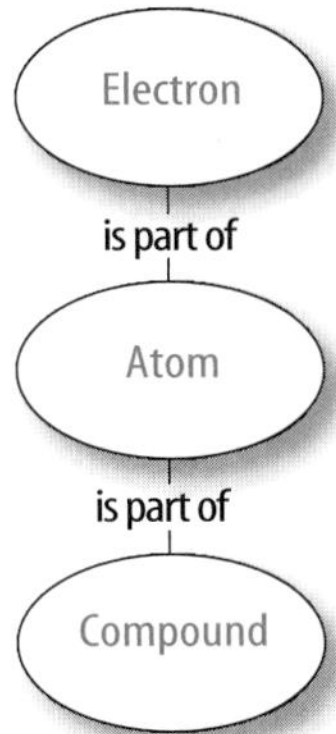

Use the table below to answer question 18.

Photosynthesis in Water Plants

Beaker Number	Distance from Light (cm)	Bubbles per Minute
1	10	45
2	30	30
3	50	19
4	70	6
5	100	1

18. **Interpret Data** Water plants were placed at different distances from a light source. Bubbles coming from the plants were counted to measure the rate of photosynthesis. What can you say about how the distance from the light affected the rate?

19. **Infer** why, in snowy places, salt is used to melt ice on the roads. Explain what could happen to many roadside plants as a result.

20. **Draw a conclusion** about why sugar dissolves faster in hot tea than in iced tea.

21. **Predict** what would happen to the consumers in a lake if all the producers died.

22. **Explain** how meat tenderizers affect meat.

23. **Form a hypothesis** about what will happen to wilted celery when placed in a glass of plain water.

Performance Activities

24. **Puzzle** Make a crossword puzzle with words describing ways substances are transported across cell membranes. Use the following words in your puzzle: *diffusion, osmosis, facilitated diffusion, active transport, endocytosis,* and *exocytosis.* Make sure your clues give good descriptions of each transport method.

Applying Math

25. **Light and Photosynthesis** Using the data from question 18, make a line graph that shows the relationship between the rate of photosynthesis and the distance from light.

26. **Importance of Water** Assume the brain is 70% water. If the average adult human brain weighs 1.4 kg, how many kilograms of water does it contain?

Use the equation below to answer question 27.

$$6CO_2 + 6H_2O + \text{light energy} \xrightarrow[\text{chlorophyll}]{\text{Photosynthesis}} C_6H_{12}O_6 + 6O_2$$

carbon dioxide, water, sugar, oxygen

27. **Photosynthesis** Refer to the chemical equation above. If 18 CO_2 molecules and 18 H_2O molecules are used with light energy to make sugar, how many sugar molecules will be produced? How many oxygen molecules will be produced?

✓ Assessment Resources

Reproducible Masters

Chapter *Fast File* Resources
- Chapter Review, pp. 35–36
- Chapter Tests, pp. 37–40
- Assessment Transparency Activity, p. 47

Glencoe Science Web site
- Chapter Review Test
- Standardized Test Practice

Glencoe Technology
- Assessment Transparency
- Exam*View*® Pro Testmaker
- MindJogger Videoquiz
- Interactive Chalkboard
- Virtual Labs CD-ROM

chapter 3 Review

Thinking Critically

17. See student page.
18. The closer a plant is to light, the faster its rate of photosynthesis.
19. Plants die as water molecules move out of the cells into the salty soil.
20. The molecules in hot water move faster than those in cold. These faster-moving molecules bump into the sugar molecules more often and more vigorously, dissolving the sugar faster.
21. Consumers would also die; they depend on producers for food.
22. The enzymes increase the rate at which protein bonds are broken; this makes the meat more tender.
23. Wilted celery will become crisp as water molecules move by osmosis into its cells to reach equilibrium.

Performance Activities

24. Definitions in the chapter for these terms can be used. Use **PASC,** p. 91.

Applying Math

National Math Standards

1, 2, 5, 6, 9

25.

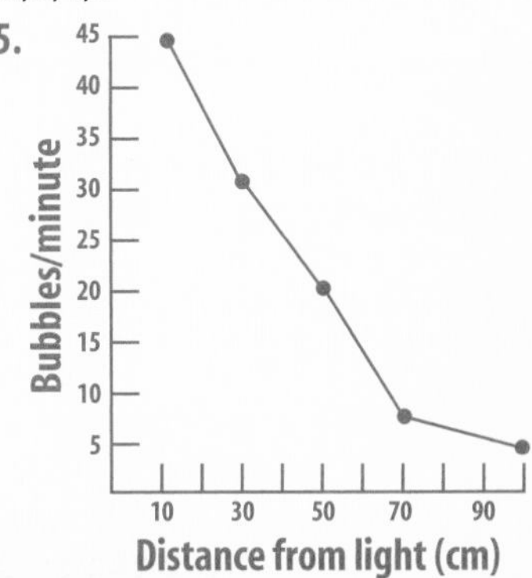

26. 0.98 kg
27. 3 sugar molecules and 18 oxygen molecules will be produced.

FAST FILE

Answer Sheet A practice answer sheet can be found at booka.msscience.com/answer_sheet.

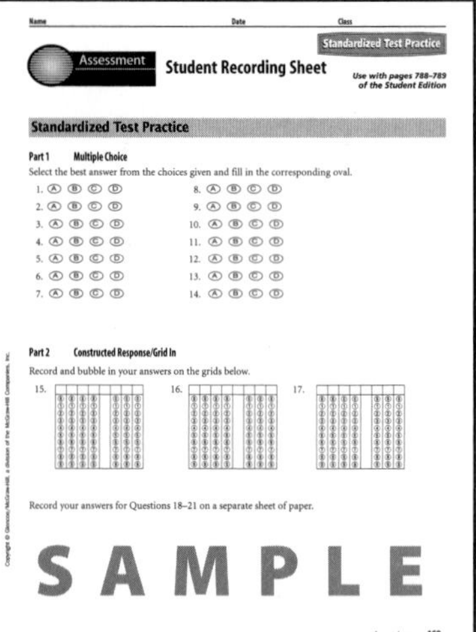

Part 1 Multiple Choice

1. C
2. B
3. D
4. A
5. B
6. B
7. A
8. D
9. C
10. C

Part 2 Short Response

11. An atom has a nucleus that contains the protons and neutrons. Protons are positively charged particles and neutrons have no charge. Electrons are negatively charged particles that are found outside the nucleus and participate in chemical reactions.
12. It helps to break down the food for digestion so that the body is better able to release the chemical energy stored in the food.
13. Ice floats because the space between water molecules is greater in ice than in liquid. Fish are able to live in the water under the ice.
14. Photosynthesis produces more sugar than the plant needs for survival. This extra sugar is stored in the potato as starch.
15. Respiration releases more energy for an athlete's muscles. Fermentation; a product of fermentation is lactic acid and the buildup of lactic acid will make muscles sore.
16. salt—inorganic; fat—organic, lipid; skin—organic, protein; DNA—organic, nucleic acid; sugar—organic, carbohydrate; water—inorganic; potassium salt—inorganic
17. Selectively permeable means that only certain molecules are allowed to pass across the membrane. For proper cell function, what enters and leaves a cell needs to be controlled.
18. Source—the Sun; they take place in the chloroplast of a plant cell.

chapter 3 Standardized Test Practice

Part 1 Multiple Choice

Record your answers on the answer sheet provided by your teacher or on a sheet of paper.

1. An element cannot be broken down by chemical reactions and is made up of only one kind of
   A. electron. **C.** atom.
   B. carbohydrate. **D.** molecule.

Use the illustration below to answer questions 2 and 3.

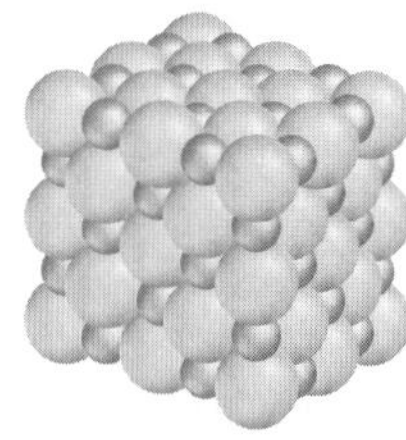

2. What kind of chemical compound do salt and water form?
   A. covalent
   B. ionic
   C. solution
   D. lipid
3. Salt is very important in the human body. What kind of compound is salt?
   A. organic
   B. carbohydrate
   C. protein
   D. inorganic
4. A cell that contains 40% water is placed in a solution that is 20% water. The cell and the solution will reach equilibrium when they both contain how much water?
   A. 30% **C.** 60%
   B. 40% **D.** 20%
5. All chemical reactions in living things take place in what kind of a solution?
   A. protein **C.** gas
   B. water **D.** solid
6. The sum of all the chemical reactions in an organism is
   A. respiration. **C.** fermentation.
   B. metabolism. **D.** endocytosis.
7. What is needed for all chemical reactions in cells?
   A. enzymes **C.** DNA
   B. lipids **D.** cell membrane
8. The carbon dioxide that you exhale is a product of
   A. osmosis.
   B. DNA synthesis.
   C. photosynthesis.
   D. respiration.
9. Matter cannot be held together or broken apart without
   A. gas.
   B. liquid.
   C. energy.
   D. temperature.

Use the table below to answer question 10.

Cell Substances		
Organic Compound	**Flexibility**	**Found in**
Keratin	Not very flexible	Hair and skin of mammals
Collagen	Not very flexible	Skin, bones, and tendons of mammals
Chitin	Very rigid	Tough outer shell of insects and crabs
Cellulose	Very flexible	Plant cell walls

10. According to this information, which organic compound is the least flexible?
   A. keratin
   B. collagen
   C. chitin
   D. cellulose

Part 2 Short Response/Grid In

Record your answers on the answer sheet provided by your teacher or on a sheet of paper.

11. Explain the structure of an atom.
12. How does chewing food affect your body's ability to release the chemical energy of the food?
13. Ice fishing is a popular sport in the winter. What properties of water is this sport based on?
14. Explain where the starch in a potato comes from.
15. Does fermentation or respiration release more energy for an athlete's muscles? Which process would be responsible for making muscles sore?

Use the table below to answer question 16.

Classification of Compounds			
Compound	Organic	Inorganic	Type of organic compound
Salt			
Fat			
Skin			
DNA			
Sugar			
Water			
Potassium			

16. Copy and complete the table above. Identify each item as inorganic or organic. If the item is an organic compound further classify it as a protein, carbohydrate, lipid or nucleic acid.
17. Define selectively permeable and discuss why it is important for the cell membrane.
18. What is the source of energy for the photosynthesis reactions and where do they take place in a cell?

Part 3 Open Ended

Record your answers on a sheet of paper.

19. Give examples of each of the four types of organic molecules and why they are needed in a plant cell.
20. Trace the path of how oxygen molecules are produced in a plant cell to how they are used in human cells.
21. Describe four ways a large or small molecule can cross the cell membrane.
22. Discuss how water is bonded together and the unique properties that result from the bonds.

Use the illustration below to answer question 23.

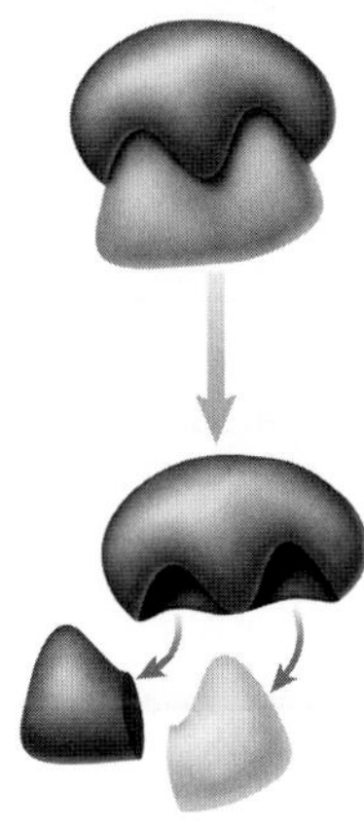

23. Describe in detail what process is taking place in this diagram and its significance for a cell.
24. How do plants use carbon dioxide? Why would plants need oxygen?

Test-Taking Tip

Diagrams Study a diagram carefully, being sure to read all labels and captions.

Part 3 Open Ended

19. Carbohydrates found in a plant cell are sugars, starch and cellulose. These molecules can be used for energy and cell structure. Lipids are fats, oils waxes, phospholipids and cholesterol. These molecules are sources of long term energy storage and are a component of cell boundaries. Enzymes are proteins and they regulate all chemical reactions in a cell. Nucleic acids carry the hereditary information and carry the code to make proteins.
20. Plants make sugar from carbon dioxide and water. The product of this process is oxygen. This oxygen is released into the air and inhaled by humans. The oxygen diffuses into the bloodstream in the lungs. It is then carried to the cells where it diffuses into the cells and is used in the mitochondria for respiration.
21. Molecules can move from areas of high concentration to areas of low concentration by diffusing across the cell membrane. Facilitated diffusion use transport proteins to help larger molecules cross the cell membrane. Water moves across the cell membrane by osmosis. Osmosis is the movement of water from areas of high concentration to areas of low concentration. Active transport of molecules across the cell membrane requires cellular energy. The cell membrane engulfs a particle for endocytosis and a vesicle fuses with the cell membrane to release particles from the cell in exocytosis.
22. A water molecule has an area of negative charge and an area of positive charge. The opposite charges attract water molecules to one another. This makes water a good insulator. In ice, the molecules are spaced further apart. This allows ice to float on water providing a layer of insulation for organisms living below the ice.
23. In this diagram an enzyme is being used for a chemical reaction. The enzyme causes the larger molecule to breakdown into smaller molecules. The enzyme is needed for this reaction and is reusable. This reaction is significant for a cell because enzymes are needed for most of the chemical reactions that take place in a cell.
24. Carbon dioxide is used in the process of photosynthesis. Carbon dioxide and water are converted to sugar molecules in the chloroplast. Energy from the Sun is used to drive this reaction. Oxygen is a product of this reaction and is used in plant cells for respiration.

Rubrics

For more help evaluating open-ended assessment questions, see the rubric on p. 10T.

chapter 4 Organizer

Section/Objectives	Standards		Labs/Features
	National	State/Local	
Chapter Opener	See pp. 16T–17T for a Key to Standards.		**Launch Lab:** Infer About Seed Growth, p. 97 **Foldables,** p. 97 A data-collection lab using Probeware technology can be found in **Probeware Labs,** pp. 1–4
Section 1 **Cell Division and Mitosis** 2 sessions 1 block 1. **Explain** why mitosis is important. 2. **Examine** the steps of mitosis. 3. **Compare** mitosis in plant and animal cells. 4. **List** two examples of asexual reproduction.	National Content Standards: UCP.1, UCP.2, UCP.3, A.1, A.2, C.1, C.2, C.3		**Integrate Career,** p. 99 **MiniLAB:** Modeling Mitosis, p. 103 **Lab:** Mitosis in Plant Cells, p. 105
Section 2 **Sexual Reproduction and Meiosis** 2 sessions 1 block 5. **Describe** the stages of meiosis and how sex cells are produced. 6. **Explain** why meiosis is needed for sexual reproduction. 7. **Name** the cells that are involved in fertilization. 8. **Explain** how fertilization occurs in sexual reproduction.	National Content Standards: UCP.1, UCP.2, A.1, C.1, C.2, C.3, C.5		**Integrate Chemistry,** p. 107 **Applying Science:** How can chromosome numbers be predicted? p. 109 **Visualizing Polyploidy in Plants,** p. 110
Section 3 **DNA** 3 sessions 1.5 blocks 9. **Identify** the parts of a DNA molecule and its structure. 10. **Explain** how DNA copies itself. 11. **Describe** the structure and function of each kind of RNA.	National Content Standards: UCP.1–UCP.5, A.1, A.2, C.1, C.2, C.3		**MiniLAB:** Modeling DNA Replication, p. 113 **Science Online,** p. 115 **Science Online,** p. 117 **Lab:** Mutations, p. 118 **Oops! Accidents in Science:** A Tangled Tale, p. 120

Lab Materials	Reproducible Resources	Section Assessment	Technology
Launch Lab: soaked bean seeds, water, paper towels, self-sealing plastic bags, magnifying lens	**Chapter *Fast File* Resources** Foldables Worksheet, p. 15 Directed Reading Overview, p. 17 Note-taking Worksheets, pp. 31–33	Glencoe's Assessment Advantage	TeacherWorks includes: • Interactive Teacher Edition • Lesson Planner with calendar • Access to all program blacklines • Correlations to standards • Web links Video Lab
MiniLAB: colored paper, poster board, markers, toothpicks, yarn, thread, glue, scissors **Lab:** prepared slide of onion root tip, microscope	**Chapter *Fast File* Resources** Transparency Activity, p. 42 MiniLAB, p. 3 Enrichment, p. 28 Reinforcement, p. 25 Transparency Activity, pp. 45–46 Lab Worksheet, pp. 5–6 Directed Reading, p. 18 Lab Activity, pp. 9–10	Portfolio Visual Learning, p. 99 Performance MiniLAB, p. 103 Applying Math, p. 104 Content Challenge, p. 101 Section Review, p. 104	Section Focus Transparency Teaching Transparency Virtual Labs CD-ROM Guided Reading Audio Program Interactive Chalkboard CD-ROM
Need materials? Contact Science Kit at 1-800-828-7777 or www.sciencekit.com on the Internet.	**Chapter *Fast File* Resources** Transparency Activity, p. 43 Enrichment, p. 29 Reinforcement, p. 26 Directed Reading, p. 18 **Life Science Critical Thinking/ Problem Solving,** p. 19 **Mathematics Skill Activities,** p. 3 **Performance Assessment in the Science Classroom,** p. 57	Portfolio Make a Model, p. 109 Performance Applying Science, p. 109 Applying Skills, p. 111 Content Challenge, p. 108 Section Review, p. 111	Section Focus Transparency Virtual Labs CD-ROM Guided Reading Audio Program Interactive Chalkboard CD-ROM
MiniLAB: pencil, paper **Lab:** Web sites and other resources on mutations	**Chapter *Fast File* Resources** Transparency Activity, p. 44 MiniLAB, p. 4 Enrichment, p. 30 Reinforcement, p. 27 Directed Reading, pp. 19, 20 Lab Worksheet, pp. 7–8 Lab Activity, pp. 11–13 **Home and Community Involvement,** p. 36	Portfolio Extension, p. 115 Performance MiniLAB, p. 113 Applying Skills, p. 117 Content Challenge, p. 116 Section Review, p. 117	Section Focus Transparency Virtual Labs CD-ROM Guided Reading Audio Program Interactive Chalkboard CD-ROM Probeware Lab

End of Chapter Assessment

Glencoe's Assessment Advantage

Blackline Masters	Technology	Professional Series
Chapter *Fast File* Resources Chapter Review, pp. 35–36 Chapter Tests, pp. 37–40 **Standardized Test Practice,** pp. 19–22	MindJogger Videoquiz Virtual Labs CD-ROM Exam*View*® Pro Testmaker TeacherWorks CD-ROM Interactive Chalkboard CD-ROM	**Performance Assessment in the Science Classroom (PASC)**

chapter  Cell Reproduction

Transparencies

Section Focus

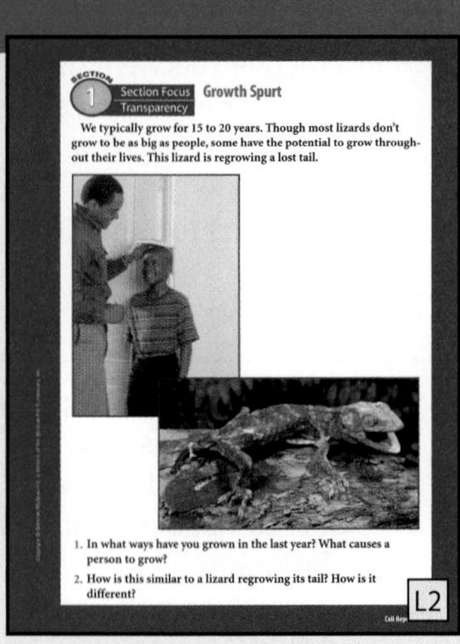
Section 1 Section Focus Transparency — Growth Spurt

We typically grow for 15 to 20 years. Though most lizards don't grow to be as big as people, some have the potential to grow throughout their lives. This lizard is regrowing a lost tail.

1. In what ways have you grown in the last year? What causes a person to grow?
2. How is this similar to a lizard regrowing its tail? How is it different?

L2

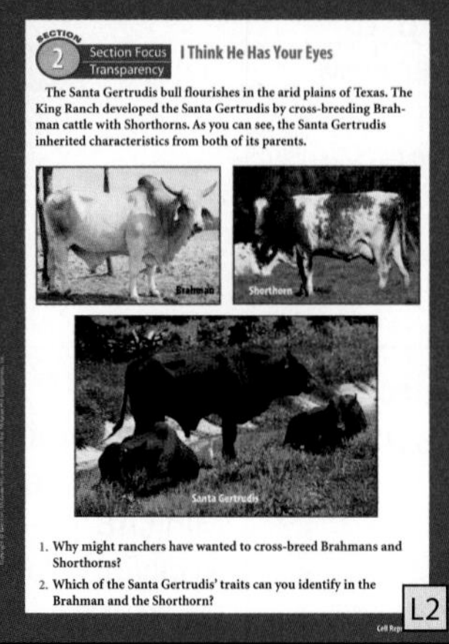
Section 2 Section Focus Transparency — I Think He Has Your Eyes

The Santa Gertrudis bull flourishes in the arid plains of Texas. The King Ranch developed the Santa Gertrudis by cross-breeding Brahman cattle with Shorthorns. As you can see, the Santa Gertrudis inherited characteristics from both of its parents.

1. Why might ranchers have wanted to cross-breed Brahmans and Shorthorns?
2. Which of the Santa Gertrudis' traits can you identify in the Brahman and the Shorthorn?

L2

Section 3 Section Focus Transparency — Curly Cat

This unusual cat is a Devon Rex. It appeared in Devonshire, England in 1960 when a genetic change occurred among British barn cats. The Devon Rex has a small head and a curly coat.

1. Based on the picture and the description above, what do you think a genetic change is?
2. How can cat breeders attempt to continue the characteristics of the Devon Rex?

L2

This is a representation of key blackline masters available in the Teacher Classroom Resources. See Resource Manager boxes within the chapter for additional information.

Assessment

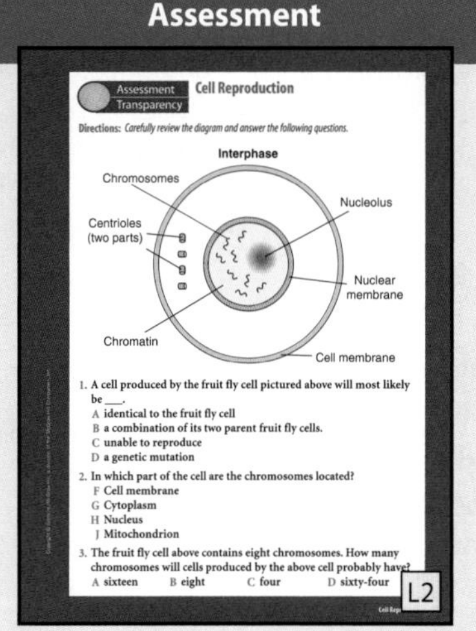
Assessment Transparency — Cell Reproduction

Directions: *Carefully review the diagram and answer the following questions.*

1. A cell produced by the fruit fly cell pictured above will most likely be ___.
   A identical to the fruit fly cell
   B a combination of its two parent fruit fly cells.
   C unable to reproduce
   D a genetic mutation
2. In which part of the cell are the chromosomes located?
   F Cell membrane
   G Cytoplasm
   H Nucleus
   J Mitochondrion
3. The fruit fly cell above contains eight chromosomes. How many chromosomes will cells produced by the above cell probably have?
   A sixteen B eight C four D sixty-four

L2

Teaching

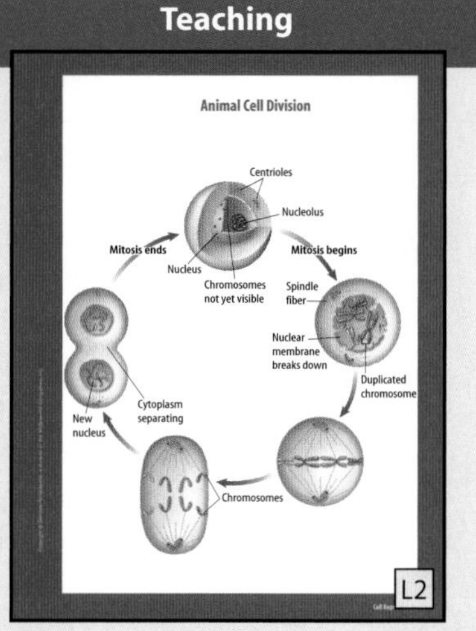

L2

Key to Teaching Strategies

The following designations will help you decide which activities are appropriate for your students.

L1 Level 1 activities should be appropriate for students with learning difficulties.

L2 Level 2 activities should be within the ability range of all students.

L3 Level 3 activities are designed for above-average students.

ELL ELL activities should be within the ability range of English-Language Learners.

COOP LEARN Cooperative Learning activities are designed for small group work.

LS Multiple Learning Styles logos, as described on page 12T, are used throughout to indicate strategies that address different learning styles.

P These strategies represent student products that can be placed into a best-work portfolio.

PBL Problem-Based Learning activities apply real-world situations to learning.

Hands-on Activities

Student Text Lab Worksheet

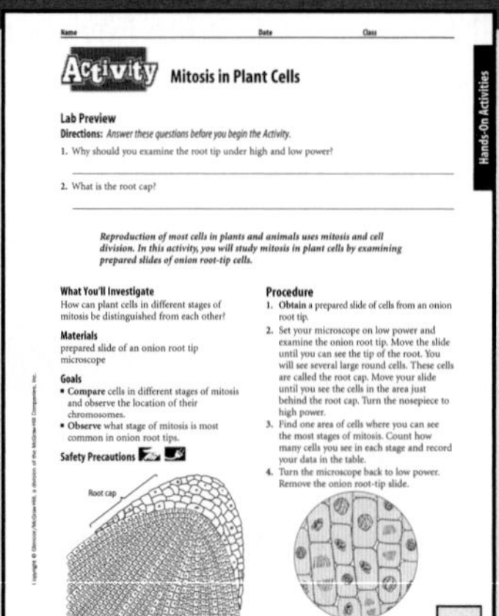
Name Date Class

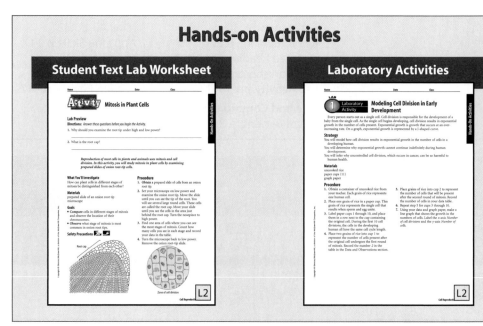

Activity — Mitosis in Plant Cells

Hands-On Activities

Lab Preview

Directions: *Answer these questions before you begin the Activity.*

1. Why should you examine the root tip under high and low power?
2. What is the root cap?

Reproduction of most cells in plants and animals uses mitosis and cell division. In this activity, you will study mitosis in plant cells by examining prepared slides of onion root-tip cells.

What You'll Investigate

How can plant cells in different stages of mitosis be distinguished from each other?

Materials

prepared slide of an onion root tip
microscope

Goals

- **Compare** cells in different stages of mitosis and observe the location of their chromosomes.
- **Observe** what stage of mitosis is most common in onion root tips.

Safety Precautions

Procedure

1. **Obtain** a prepared slide of cells from an onion root tip.
2. Set your microscope on low power and examine the onion root tip. Move the slide until you can see the tip of the root. You will see several large round cells. These cells are called the root cap. Move your slide until you see the cells in the area just behind the root cap. Turn the nosepiece to high power.
3. Find one area of cells where you can see the most stages of mitosis. Count how many cells you see in each stage and record your data in the table.
4. Turn the microscope back to low power. Remove the onion root-tip slide.

L2

Laboratory Activities

Name Date Class

LAB 1 Laboratory Activity — Modeling Cell Division in Early Development

Hands-On Activities

Every person starts out as a single cell. Cell division is responsible for the development of a baby from the single cell. As the single cell begins developing, cell division results in exponential growth in the number of cells present. Exponential growth is growth that occurs at an ever-increasing rate. On a graph, exponential growth is represented by a J-shaped curve.

Strategy

You will model how cell division results in exponential growth in the number of cells in a developing human.
You will determine why exponential growth cannot continue indefinitely during human development.
You will infer why uncontrolled cell division, which occurs in cancer, can be so harmful to human health.

Materials

uncooked rice
paper cups (11)
graph paper

Procedure

1. Obtain a container of uncooked rice from your teacher. Each grain of rice represents one human cell.
2. Place one grain of rice in a paper cup. This grain of rice represents the single cell that results when sperm and egg unite.
3. Label paper cups 1 through 10, and place them in a row next to the cup containing the original cell. During the first 10 cell divisions, the cells in the developing human all have the same cell cycle length.
4. Place two grains of rice into cup 1 to represent the number of cells present after the original cell undergoes the first round of mitosis. Record the number *2* in the table in the Data and Observations section.
5. Place grains of rice into cup 2 to represent the number of cells that will be present after the second round of mitosis. Record the number of cells in your data table.
6. Repeat step 5 for cups 3 through 10.
7. Using your data and graph paper, make a line graph that shows the growth in the numbers of cells. Label the x-axis *Number of cell divisions* and the y-axis *Number of cells.*

L2

Meeting Different Ability Levels

Content Outline

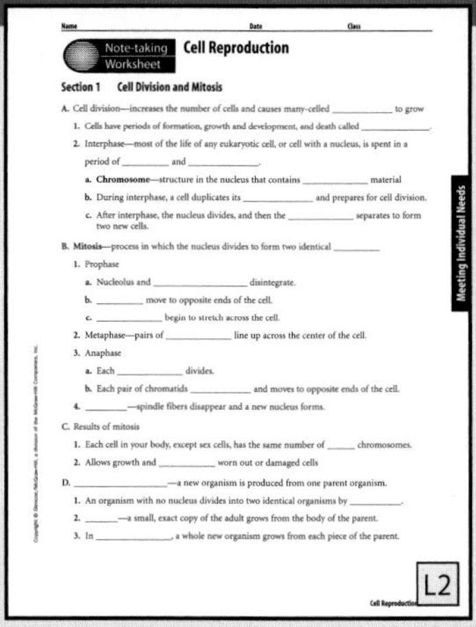

Name Date Class

Note-taking Worksheet **Cell Reproduction**

Section 1 Cell Division and Mitosis

A. Cell division—increases the number of cells and causes many-celled __________ to grow
1. Cells have periods of formation, growth and development, and death called __________.
2. Interphase—most of the life of any eukaryotic cell, or cell with a nucleus, is spent in a period of __________ and __________.
   a. **Chromosome**—structure in the nucleus that contains __________ material
   b. During interphase, a cell duplicates its __________ and prepares for cell division.
   c. After interphase, the nucleus divides, and then the __________ separates to form two new cells.

B. **Mitosis**—process in which the nucleus divides to form two identical __________
1. Prophase
   a. Nucleolus and __________ disintegrate.
   b. __________ move to opposite ends of the cell.
   c. __________ begin to stretch across the cell.
2. Metaphase—pairs of __________ line up across the center of the cell.
3. Anaphase
   a. Each __________ divides.
   b. Each pair of chromatids __________ and moves to opposite ends of the cell.
4. __________—spindle fibers disappear and a new nucleus forms.

C. Results of mitosis
1. Each cell in your body, except sex cells, has the same number of __________ chromosomes.
2. Allows growth and __________ worn out or damaged cells

D. __________—a new organism is produced from one parent organism.
1. An organism with no nucleus divides into two identical organisms by __________.
2. __________—a small, exact copy of the adult grows from the body of the parent.
3. In __________, a whole new organism grows from each piece of the parent.

Meeting Individual Needs

Cell Reproduction

L2

Reinforcement

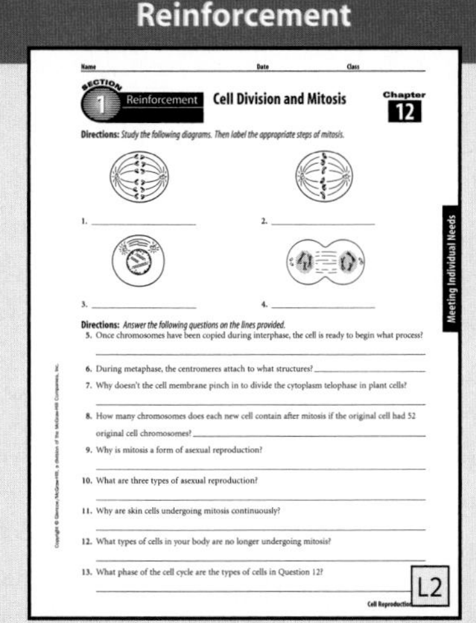

Name Date Class

Section 1 Reinforcement **Cell Division and Mitosis** Chapter 12

Directions: *Study the following diagrams. Then label the appropriate steps of mitosis.*

1. __________ 2. __________

3. __________ 4. __________

Directions: *Answer the following questions on the lines provided.*

5. Once chromosomes have been copied during interphase, the cell is ready to begin what process?
6. During metaphase, the centromeres attach to what structures?
7. Why doesn't the cell membrane pinch in to divide the cytoplasm telophase in plant cells?
8. How many chromosomes does each new cell contain after mitosis if the original cell had 52 original cell chromosomes?
9. Why is mitosis a form of asexual reproduction?
10. What are three types of asexual reproduction?
11. Why are skin cells undergoing mitosis continuously?
12. What types of cells in your body are no longer undergoing mitosis?
13. What phase of the cell cycle are the types of cells in Question 12?

Meeting Individual Needs

Cell Reproduction

L2

Enrichment

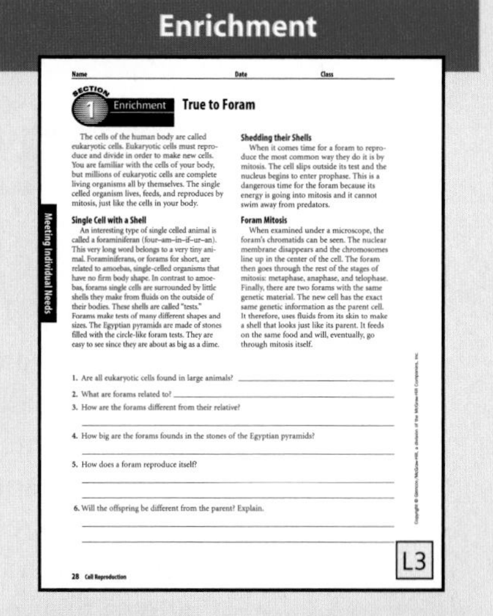

Name Date Class

Section 1 Enrichment **True to Foram**

Meeting Individual Needs

1. Are all eukaryotic cells found in large animals?
2. What are forams related to?
3. How are the forams different from their relative?
4. How big are the forams founds in the stones of the Egyptian pyramids?
5. How does a foram reproduce itself?
6. Will the offspring be different from the parent? Explain.

28 Cell Reproduction

L3

Directed Reading (English/Spanish)

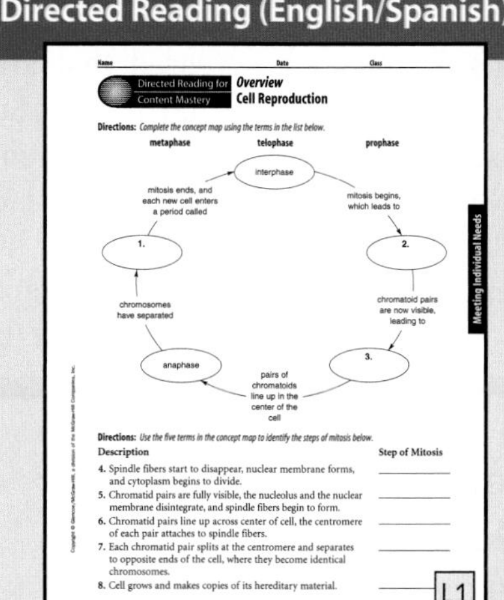

Name Date Class

Directed Reading for Content Mastery **Overview Cell Reproduction**

Directions: *Complete the concept map using the terms in the list below.*

metaphase telophase prophase

interphase
mitosis ends, and each new cell enters a period called
1.
mitosis begins, which leads to
2.
chromatoid pairs are now visible, leading to
3.
pairs of chromatoids line up in the center of the cell
anaphase
chromosomes have separated

Directions: *Use the five terms in the concept map to identify the steps of mitosis below.*

Description	Step of Mitosis
4. Spindle fibers start to disappear, nuclear membrane forms, and cytoplasm begins to divide.	
5. Chromatid pairs are fully visible, the nucleolus and the nuclear membrane disintegrate, and spindle fibers begin to form.	
6. Chromatid pairs line up across center of cell, the centromere of each pair attaches to spindle fibers.	
7. Each chromatid pair splits at the centromere and separates to opposite ends of the cell, where they become identical chromosomes.	
8. Cell grows and makes copies of its hereditary material.	

Meeting Individual Needs

Cell Reproduction

L1

Study Guide

Study Guide
Features
• Contains a study guide page for each section of the chapter
• Reviews key concepts
• Includes answer pages
L2

Reading Essentials

Reading Essentials for Glencoe Science
An Interactive Student Workbook
Features
• Condensed core content
• Actively involves students in reading
• Reinforces key vocabulary
L1

Assessment

Test Practice Workbook

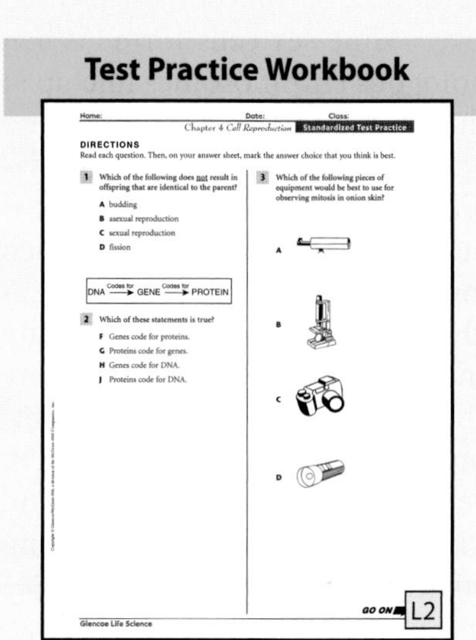

Name: Date: Class:

Chapter 4 Cell Reproduction Standardized Test Practice

DIRECTIONS

Read each question. Then, on your answer sheet, mark the answer choice that you think is best.

1 Which of the following does not result in offspring that are identical to the parent?
A budding
B asexual reproduction
C sexual reproduction
D fission

DNA —codes for→ GENE —codes for→ PROTEIN

2 Which of these statements is true?
F Genes code for proteins.
G Proteins code for genes.
H Genes code for DNA.
J Proteins code for DNA.

3 Which of the following pieces of equipment would be best to use for observing mitosis in onion skin?
A
B
C
D

GO ON

Glencoe Life Science

L2

Chapter Review

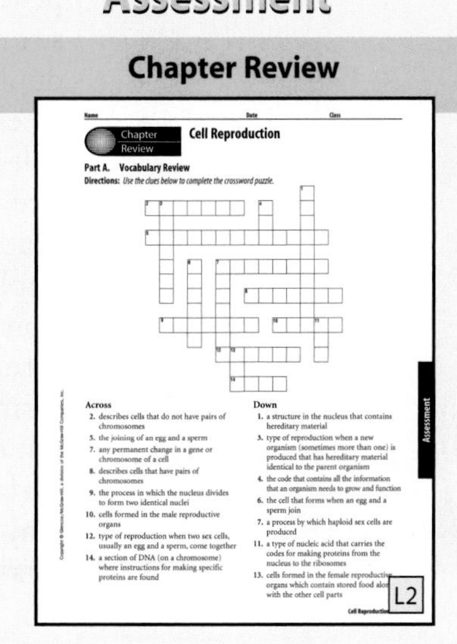

Name Date Class

Chapter Review **Cell Reproduction**

Part A. Vocabulary Review

Directions: *Use the clues below to complete the crossword puzzle.*

Across
2. describes cells that do not have pairs of chromosomes
5. the joining of an egg and a sperm
7. any permanent change in a gene or chromosome of a cell
8. describes cells that have pairs of chromosomes
9. the process in which the nucleus divides to form two identical nuclei
10. cells formed in the male reproductive organs
12. type of reproduction when two sex cells, usually an egg and a sperm, come together
14. a section of DNA (on a chromosome) where instructions for making specific proteins are found

Down
1. a structure in the nucleus that contains hereditary material
3. type of reproduction when a new organism (sometimes more than one) is produced that has hereditary material identical to the parent organism
4. the code that contains all the information that an organism needs to grow and function
6. the cell that forms when an egg and a sperm join
7. a process by which haploid sex cells are produced
11. a type of nucleic acid that carries the codes for making proteins from the nucleus to the ribosomes
13. cells formed in the female reproductive organs which contain stored food along with the other cell parts

Assessment

Cell Reproduction

L2

Chapter Tests

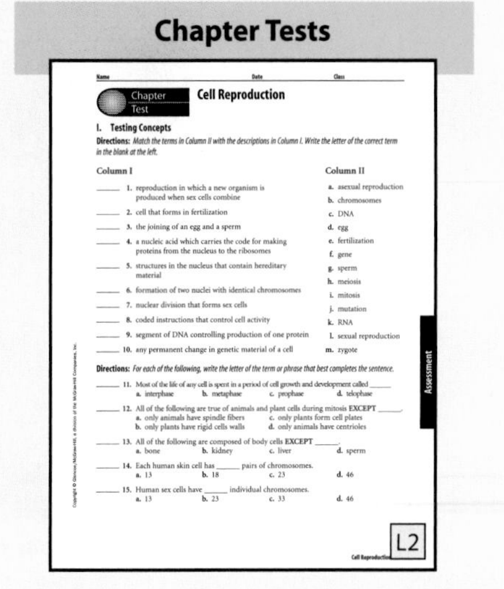

Name Date Class

Chapter Test **Cell Reproduction**

I. Testing Concepts

Directions: *Match the terms in Column II with the descriptions in Column I. Write the letter of the correct term in the blank at the left.*

Column I	Column II
1. reproduction in which a new organism is produced when sex cells combine	a. asexual reproduction
2. cell that forms in fertilization	b. chromosomes
3. the joining of an egg and a sperm	c. DNA
4. a nucleic acid which carries the code for making proteins from the nucleus to the ribosomes	d. egg
5. structures in the nucleus that contain hereditary material	e. fertilization
6. formation of two nuclei with identical chromosomes	f. gene
7. nuclear division that forms sex cells	g. sperm
8. coded instructions that control cell activity	h. meiosis
9. segment of DNA controlling production of one protein	i. mitosis
10. any permanent change in genetic material of a cell	j. mutation
	k. RNA
	l. sexual reproduction
	m. zygote

Directions: *For each of the following, write the letter of the term or phrase that best completes the sentence.*

11. Most of the life of any cell is spent in a period of cell growth and development called ______.
a. interphase b. metaphase c. prophase d. telophase

12. All of the following are true of animals and plant cells during mitosis EXCEPT ______.
a. only animals have spindle fibers c. only plants form cell plates
b. only plants have rigid cells walls d. only animals have centrioles

13. All of the following are composed of body cells EXCEPT ______.
a. bone b. kidney c. liver d. sperm

14. Each human skin cell has ______ pairs of chromosomes.
a. 13 b. 18 c. 23 d. 46

15. Human sex cells have ______ individual chromosomes.
a. 13 b. 23 c. 33 d. 46

Assessment

Cell Reproduction

L2

Science Content Background

section 1 Cell Division and Mitosis

Results of Mitosis

Every species has a characteristic number of chromosomes in each cell. A cat has 38 chromosomes, whereas a potato and a chimpanzee each have 48 chromosomes. In all sexually reproducing organisms, chromosomes occur in homologous pairs. Except for some sex chromosomes, homologous chromosomes are of equal length and have the same genes at the same relative locations. The alleles may or may not be identical. For example, the gene for hair color would be at the same location on homologous chromosomes but may code for brunette on one chromosome and blonde on the other.

Teacher to Teacher
Patricia M. Horton, Mentor Teacher
Summit Intermediate School
Etiwanda, California

"To demonstrate osmosis, I put liquid starch in a plastic sandwich bag and close it with a twist tie. I then place the plastic bag into a beaker filled with a mixture of water and iodine. As the iodine moves through the plastic bag membrane, the starch begins to turn purple."

Patricia M. Horton

Reuters New Media Inc./Corbis

Animals and some plants have one pair of sex chromosomes. In most animals, including humans, the sex chromosomes of the female are truly homologous, whereas the male sex chromosomes are of unequal lengths and have many different genes. This is reversed in birds and butterflies, with males having the truly homologous sex chromosomes.

Asexual Reproduction

Eukaryotes, which include many protists, some fungi, and plants, reproduce asexually by mitosis. Prokaryotes, like bacteria, reproduce by fission. Depending on the organism, one or several new organisms can be created that are genetically identical to, or clones of, the original organism. Most animals do not use asexual reproduction. Recently scientists have been able to stimulate cells from adult animals to divide by mitosis and reproduce new animals that are clones of the organism from which the cells were taken.

section 2 Sexual Reproduction and Meiosis

Sexual Reproduction

Sex cells, or gametes, are the result of meiosis. Because of a process that happens at metaphase I called independent assortment, the possible combination of chromosomes for each sex cell varies every time sex cells form. When duplicated homologous chromosomes line up at a cell's center during metaphase I, there are no rules about how a particular pair is aligned relative to any other pair. The only requirement is that the alignment results in one half of each duplicated chromosome moving in one direction and the other half moving in the opposite direction during anaphase I. The offspring formed by fertilization has its own unique combination of genetic material. This produces variation between parents and offspring and may give offspring a better chance of surviving in a changing environment.

Meiosis and Sex Cells

This process is often called reduction division since the number of chromosomes in the cells produced is half that of the original cell. Meiosis provides for great diversity within a species because of the many ways the chromosomes can align during metaphase I. There are more than 8 million possible gametes that can be produced from the 23 pairs of human chromosomes.

In animals, meiosis results in haploid egg and sperm cells. In plants, meiosis results in haploid spores that later produce egg and sperm cells.

DNA

What is DNA?

The information in DNA that determines what an organism will be is contained in a code dictated by the order of subunits called nucleotides. A nucleotide consists of the sugar deoxyribose, a phosphate molecule, and one of the four possible nitrogen bases. A DNA molecule is two chains of nucleotides. These two chains are antiparallel and run in opposite directions. One chain ends with a phosphate, and the other chain ends with deoxyribose. Just as the order of letters on this page determines what words you are reading, the order of nucleotides determines the message on the DNA. Because DNA is copied from one generation to the next, any change, or mutation, in a gene is also preserved. If the change occurs in cells that become gametes, it is passed on to future generations in a process called heredity.

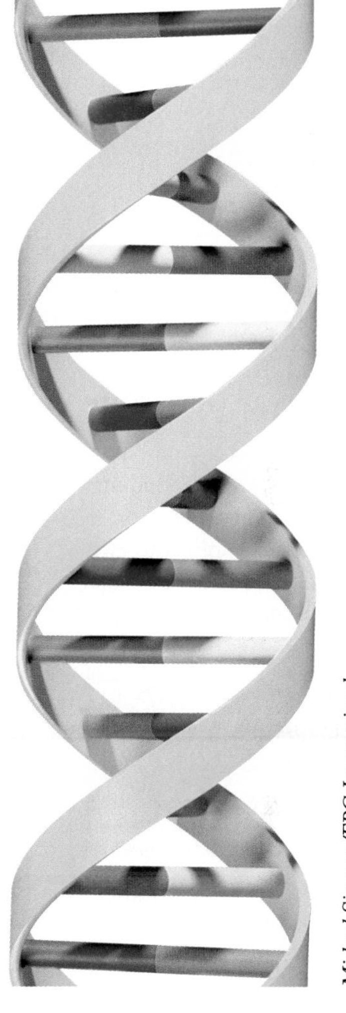

Michael Simpson/FPG International

A DNA Model

The process of DNA replication is directed by the enzyme called DNA polymerase. It moves along the separated DNA molecule and inserts the correct, complementary nucleotides onto the exposed nitrogen bases. This happens at many locations along the length of the DNA molecule simultaneously. Otherwise the time it would take to match up the millions of nitrogen bases would be astronomical.

Mutations

A change in a cell's genetic message is called a mutation. Some mutations affect the message itself, altering the sequence of DNA nucleotides. Other classes of mutations involve sequences of DNA that can move from place to place and are often called jumping genes. When a particular gene is mutated, its function is often destroyed.

chapter content resources

Internet Resources

For additional content background, visit **booka.msscience.com** to:

- access your book online
- find references to related articles in popular science magazines
- access Web links with related content background
- access current events with science journal topics

Print Resources

James Watson & Francis Crick: Discovery of the Double Helix and Beyond (Makers of Modern Science), by David E. Newton and David B. Newton, Facts on File, Inc., 1992

DNA (Science Concepts), by Alvin Silverstein, Virginia B. Silverstein, Laura Silverstein Nunn, Twenty-First Century Books (E), 2002

My Name Is Gene, Second Edition, N.L. Eskeland, N.C. Bailey, Science2Discover, 2002

Chapter Vocabulary

mitosis, p. 100
chromosome, p. 100
asexual reproduction, p. 103
sexual reproduction, p. 106
sperm, p. 106
egg, p. 106
fertilization, p. 106
zygote, p. 106
diploid, p. 106
haploid, p. 107
meiosis, p. 107
DNA, p. 112
gene, p. 114
RNA, p. 114
mutation, p. 116

Science Journal Student responses will vary, but may include that cells split into two and that they reproduce so that an organism can grow.

PowerPoint® Presentations

This CD-ROM is an editable Microsoft® PowerPoint® presentation that includes:

- a pre-made presentation for every chapter
- interactive graphics
- animations
- audio clips
- image bank
- all new section and chapter questions
- Standardized Test Practice
- transparencies
- pre-lab questions for all labs
- Foldables directions
- links to booka.msscience.com

chapter 4

Cell Reproduction

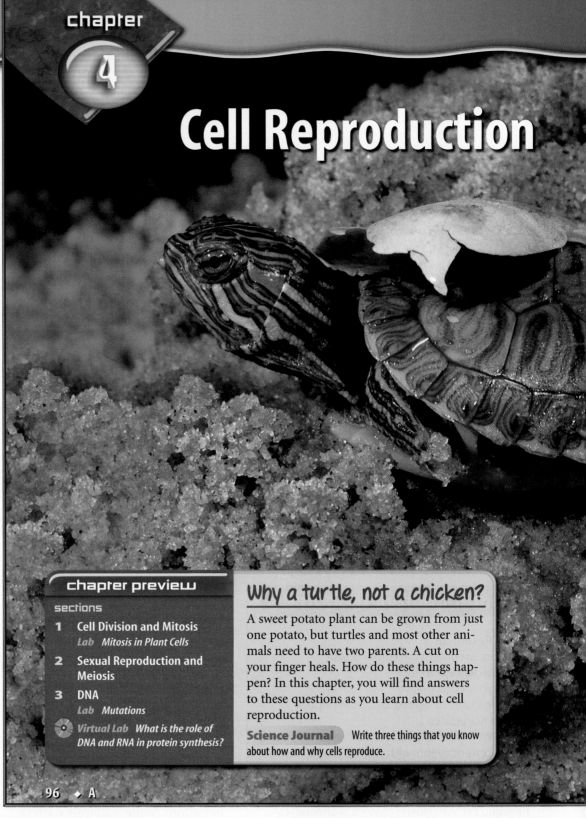

chapter preview

sections

1 Cell Division and Mitosis
Lab *Mitosis in Plant Cells*
2 Sexual Reproduction and Meiosis
3 DNA
Lab *Mutations*
Virtual Lab *What is the role of DNA and RNA in protein synthesis?*

Why a turtle, not a chicken?

A sweet potato plant can be grown from just one potato, but turtles and most other animals need to have two parents. A cut on your finger heals. How do these things happen? In this chapter, you will find answers to these questions as you learn about cell reproduction.

Science Journal Write three things that you know about how and why cells reproduce.

96 ◆ A

Theme Connection

Stability and Change DNA controls all cell activities by directing the production of proteins in living organisms. Changes in DNA can result in evolutionary changes that are inherited.

About the Photo

Hatchlings Turtles reproduce on land. Female turtles lay eggs, usually at night, and then bury them to protect them from predators, to keep the eggs moist, and to help maintain the proper temperature for development. Eggs usually hatch in 60–140 days. Hatchling turtles use an "egg tooth" to break their way out of the egg. Hatchlings usually emerge in early evening.

Start-Up Activities

Infer About Seed Growth

Most flower and vegetable seeds sprout and grow into entire plants in just a few weeks. Although all of the cells in a seed have information and instructions to produce a new plant, only some of the cells in the seed use the information. Where are these cells in seeds? Do the following lab to find out.

1. Carefully split open two bean seeds that have soaked in water overnight.
2. Observe both halves and record your observations.
3. Wrap all four halves in a moist paper towel. Then put them into a self-sealing, plastic bag and seal the bag.
4. Make observations every day for a few days.
5. **Think Critically** Write a paragraph that describes what you observe. Hypothesize which cells in seeds use information about how plants grow.

Preview this chapter's content and activities at booka.msscience.com

How and Why Cells Divide Make the following Foldable to help you organize information from the chapter about cell reproduction.

STEP 1 **Draw** a mark at the midpoint of a vertical sheet of paper along the side edge.

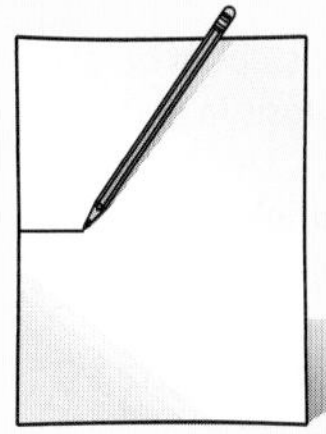

STEP 2 **Turn** the paper horizontally and **fold** the outside edges in to touch at the midpoint mark.

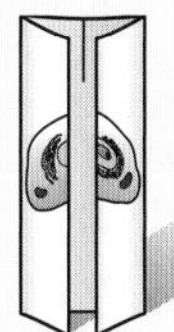

STEP 3 **Use** a pencil to draw a cell on the front of your Foldable as shown.

Analyze As you read the chapter, write under the flaps how cells divide. In the middle section, list why cells divide.

A ◆ 97

Purpose Use the Launch Lab to introduce students to growth; as they read the chapter, they will understand that growth is the result of mitosis. L2 LS **Kinesthetic**

Preparation Soak pinto beans or other large seeds for 24 hours.

Materials 2 soaked seeds, paper towels, self-sealing plastic bag, magnifying lens, water

Teaching Strategy After soaking, the seeds should split easily. If students have difficulty, forceps can be used to separate the seeds.

Think Critically

Students should observe and record the growth of a new plant from one-half of each seed. They should predict that the cells of the seed embryo are able to use the information needed to grow into a plant.

Assessment

Performance Have students repeat the experiment using corn seeds and observe the new plant that grows from each seed. Use **Performance Assessment in the Science Classroom,** p. 89. L2

Dinah Zike Study Fold

Student preparation materials for this Foldable are available in the **Chapter *Fast File* Resources.**

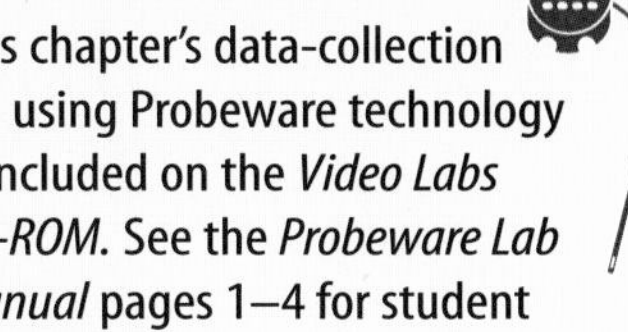

Probeware Labs

This chapter's data-collection lab using Probeware technology is included on the *Video Labs CD-ROM.* See the *Probeware Lab Manual* pages 1–4 for student worksheets.

section 1

Cell Division and Mitosis

1 Motivate

Bellringer

Section Focus Transparencies also are available on the Interactive Chalkboard CD-ROM.

Section 1 Section Focus Transparency Growth Spurt

We typically grow for 15 to 20 years. Though most lizards don't grow to be as big as people, some have the potential to grow throughout their lives. This lizard is regrowing a lost tail.

1. In what ways have you grown in the last year? What causes a person to grow?
2. How is this similar to a lizard regrowing its tail? How is it different?

Tie to Prior Knowledge

Cell Functions Use a diagram or transparency to review the parts of a cell and their functions. Explain that mitosis involves only the nucleus.

---

as you read

What You'll Learn

- **Explain** why mitosis is important.
- **Examine** the steps of mitosis.
- **Compare** mitosis in plant and animal cells.
- **List** two examples of asexual reproduction.

Why It's Important

Your growth, like that of many organisms, depends on cell division.

Review Vocabulary
nucleus: organelle that controls all the activities of a cell and contains hereditary material made of proteins and DNA

New Vocabulary
- mitosis
- chromosome
- asexual reproduction

Why is cell division important?

What do you, an octopus, and an oak tree have in common? You share many characteristics, but an important one is that you are all made of cells—trillions of cells. Where did all of those cells come from? As amazing as it might seem, many organisms start as just one cell. That cell divides and becomes two, two become four, four become eight, and so on. Many-celled organisms, including you, grow because cell division increases the total number of cells in an organism. Even after growth stops, cell division is still important. Every day, billions of red blood cells in your body wear out and are replaced. During the few seconds it takes you to read this sentence, your bone marrow produced about six million red blood cells. Cell division is important to one-celled organisms, too—it's how they reproduce themselves, as shown in **Figure 1.** Cell division isn't as simple as just cutting the cell in half, so how do cells divide?

The Cell Cycle

A living organism has a life cycle. A life cycle begins with the organism's formation, is followed by growth and development, and finally ends in death. Right now, you are in a stage of your life cycle called adolescence, which is a period of active growth and development. Individual cells also have life cycles.

Figure 1 All organisms use cell division. Many-celled organisms, such as this octopus, grow by increasing the numbers of their cells.

Like this dividing amoeba, a one-celled organism reaches a certain size and then reproduces.

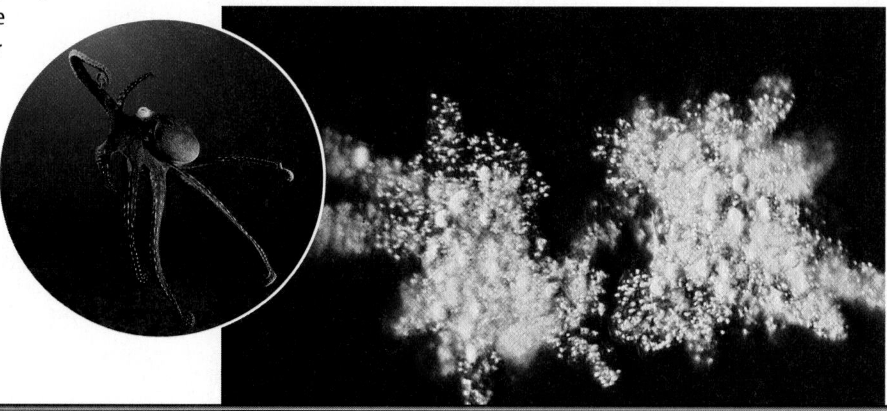

Section 1 Resource Manager

Chapter *FAST FILE* Resources

Transparency Activity, pp. 42, 45–46
Directed Reading for Content Mastery, pp. 17, 18
Note-taking Worksheets, pp. 31–33
Enrichment, p. 28
MiniLAB, p. 3
Lab Activity, pp. 9–10
Reinforcement, p. 25
Lab Worksheet, pp. 5–6

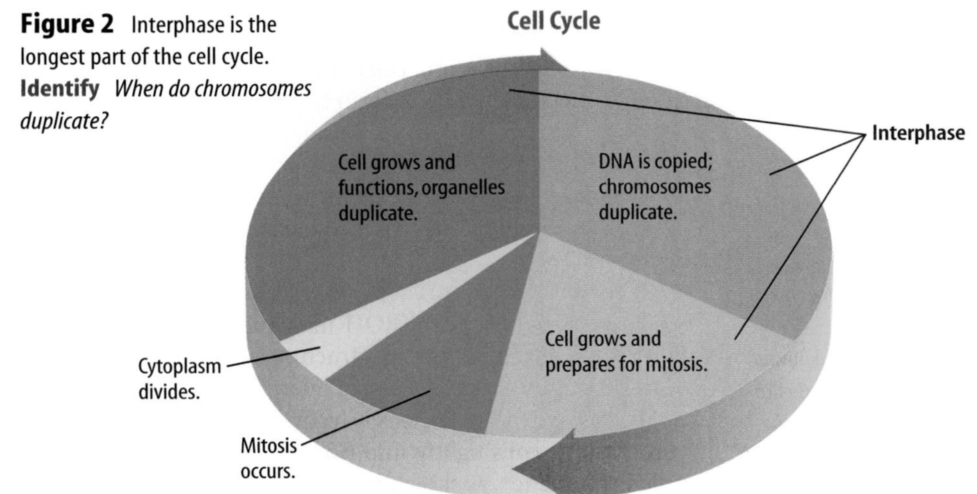

Cell Cycle
Interphase
Cell grows and functions, organelles duplicate.
DNA is copied; chromosomes duplicate.
Cell grows and prepares for mitosis.
Cytoplasm divides.
Mitosis occurs.

Figure 2 Interphase is the longest part of the cell cycle.
Identify *When do chromosomes duplicate?*

Length of Cycle The cell cycle, as shown in **Figure 2,** is a series of events that takes place from one cell division to the next. The time it takes to complete a cell cycle is not the same in all cells. For example, the cycle for cells in some bean plants takes about 19 h to complete. Cells in animal embryos divide rapidly and can complete their cycles in less than 20 min. In some human cells, the cell cycle takes about 16 h. Cells in humans that are needed for repair, growth, or replacement, like skin and bone cells, constantly repeat the cycle.

Interphase Most of the life of any eukaryotic cell—a cell with a nucleus—is spent in a period of growth and development called interphase. Cells in your body that no longer divide, such as nerve and muscle cells, are always in interphase. An actively dividing cell, such as a skin cell, copies its hereditary material and prepares for cell division during interphase.

Why is it important for a cell to copy its hereditary information before dividing? Imagine that you have a part in a play and the director has one complete copy of the script. If the director gave only one page to each person in the play, no one would have the entire script. Instead the director makes a complete, separate copy of the script for each member of the cast so that each one can learn his or her part. Before a cell divides, a copy of the hereditary material must be made so that each of the two new cells will get a complete copy. Just as the actors in the play need the entire script, each cell needs a complete set of hereditary material to carry out life functions.

After interphase, cell division begins. The nucleus divides, and then the cytoplasm separates to form two new cells.

Oncologist In most cells, the cell cycle is well controlled. Cancer cells, however, have uncontrolled cell division. Doctors who diagnose, study, and treat cancer are called oncologists. Someone wanting to become an oncologist must first complete medical school before training in oncology. Research the subspecialities of oncology. List and describe them in your Science Journal.

2 Teach

Caption Answer

Figure 2 during interphase

Visual Learning

Figure 2 Have students make an events chain concept map that outlines the steps of the cell cycle as illustrated in **Figure 2.** L2 LS **Visual-Spatial** P

Oncologist There are many oncology specialties, including medical oncology, pediatric oncology, radiation oncology, and surgical oncology. After completion of medical school and training in a specialty, physicians must pass a certifying exam.

Research Have students research ways that help prevent cancerous cells from forming. Some preventive measures include using sunscreen, not smoking, and eating certain foods. Can cancer be prevented completely? Are there vaccinations against cancer? Students can write a health pamphlet that encourages a healthy lifestyle to minimize cancer risks. L2

Science Journal

Life of a Cell Have students write creative stories about the life cycle of a cell from its beginning to its end. Have them use section vocabulary words as they describe what happens in the cell. L2 LS **Linguistic**

Nondividing Cells Students may assume that all cells divide. However, some cells do not divide at all. Red blood cells circulating in the blood vessels do not have a nucleus and do not divide; they live for 90 days before they are replaced by new cells.

Use an Analogy

Telephone Cord Compare chromosome thickening to a coiled telephone cord. When stretched out, the cord is long and thin, like chromosomes during interphase. When the cord returns to its usual position, it shortens and thickens, like chromosomes preparing to divide. L1 LS **Visual-Spatial**

Reading Check

Answer A duplicated chromosome is made up of two chromatids.

Fun Fact

Most cells are not actively engaged in mitosis. Skin cells spend 15–20 days in interphase. After infancy, nerve cells stay in interphase.

Caption Answer

Figure 4 interphase

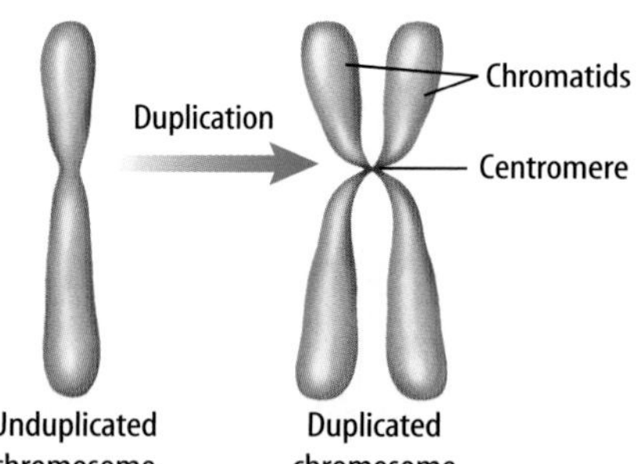

Figure 3 DNA is copied during interphase. An unduplicated chromosome has one strand of DNA. A duplicated chromosome has two identical DNA strands, called chromatids, that are held together at a region called the centromere.

Mitosis

Mitosis (mi TOH sus) is the process in which the nucleus divides to form two identical nuclei. Each new nucleus also is identical to the original nucleus. Mitosis is described as a series of phases, or steps. The steps of mitosis in order are named prophase, metaphase, anaphase, and telophase.

Steps of Mitosis When any nucleus divides, the chromosomes (KROH muh sohmz) play the important part. A **chromosome** is a structure in the nucleus that contains hereditary material. During interphase, each chromosome duplicates. When the nucleus is ready to divide, each duplicated chromosome coils tightly into two thickened, identical strands called chromatids, as shown in **Figure 3.**

Reading Check *How are chromosomes and chromatids related?*

During prophase, the pairs of chromatids are fully visible when viewed under a microscope. The nucleolus and the nuclear membrane disintegrate. Two small structures called centrioles (SEN tree olz) move to opposite ends of the cell. Between the centrioles, threadlike spindle fibers begin to stretch across the cell. Plant cells also form spindle fibers during mitosis but do not have centrioles.

In metaphase, the pairs of chromatids line up across the center of the cell. The centromere of each pair usually becomes attached to two spindle fibers—one from each side of the cell.

In anaphase, each centromere divides and the spindle fibers shorten. Each pair of chromatids separates, and chromatids begin to move to opposite ends of the cell. The separated chromatids are now called chromosomes. In the final step, telophase, spindle fibers start to disappear, the chromosomes start to uncoil, and a new nucleus forms.

Figure 4 The cell plate shown in this plant cell appears when the cytoplasm is being divided. **Identify** *what phase of mitosis will be next.*

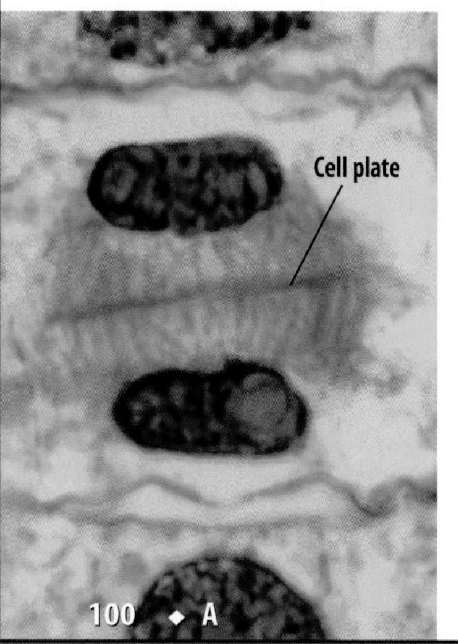

Division of the Cytoplasm For most cells, after the nucleus has divided, the cytoplasm separates and two new cells are formed. In animal cells, the cell membrane pinches in the middle, like a balloon with a string tightened around it, and the cytoplasm divides. In plant cells, the appearance of a cell plate, as shown in **Figure 4,** tells you that the cytoplasm is being divided. New cell walls form along the cell plate, and new cell membranes develop inside the cell walls. Following division of the cytoplasm, most new cells begin the period of growth, or interphase, again. Review cell division for an animal cell using the illustrations in **Figure 5.**

Differentiated Instruction

Visually Impaired Have selected students make three-dimensional models of mitosis on poster board. Display the posters in the classroom for visually impaired students to feel. L2 LS **Visual-Spatial**

Cultural Diversity

Historic Contributions In 1887, Edouard-Joseph-Marie van Beneden, a Belgian scientist, discovered that each species has a fixed number of chromosomes. He also observed the formation of a haploid cell. In 1956, J. Hin Tjio and Albert Levan showed that each human cell has 46 chromosomes.

Figure 5 Cell division for an animal cell is shown here. Each micrograph shown in this figure is magnified 600 times.

Mitosis begins
Centrioles
Nucleus
Nucleolus
Interphase
During interphase, the cell's chromosomes duplicate. The nucleolus is clearly visible in the nucleus.
Spindle fibers
Prophase
The chromatid pairs are now visible and the spindle is beginning to form.
Duplicated chromosome (2 chromatids)
Metaphase
Chromatid pairs are lined up in the center of the cell.
Anaphase
The chromosomes have separeted.
Chromosomes
Telophase
In the final step, the cytoplasm is beginning to separate.
Cytoplasm separating
New nucleus
Mitosis ends
The two new cells enter interphase and cell division usually begins again.

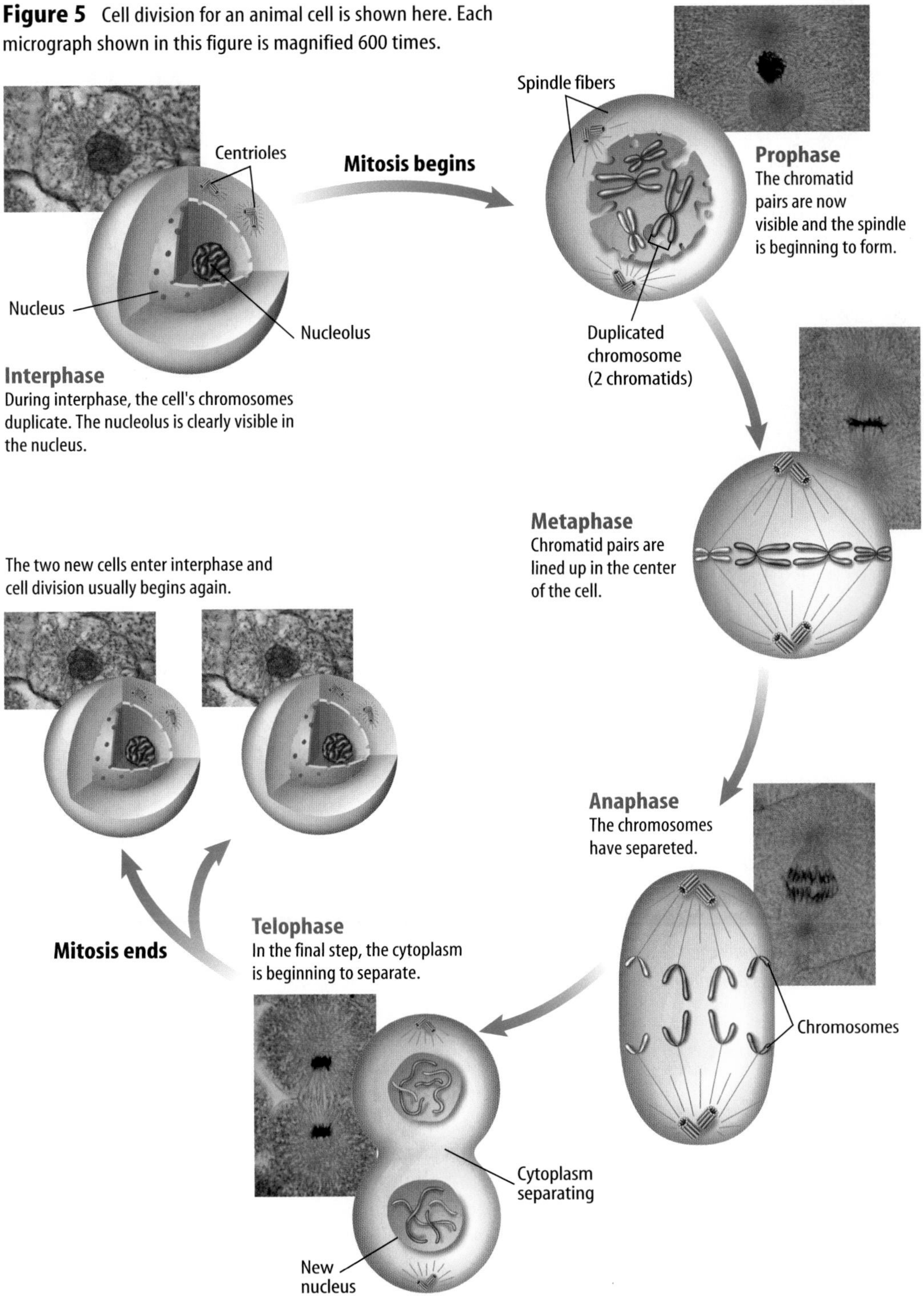

Quick Demo

Mitosis

Materials microprojector, fertilized frog eggs

Estimated Time 10 minutes

Procedure Demonstrate mitotic cell divisions in the growth of fertilized frog eggs. The increasing numbers of cells can be seen readily during the early stages of tadpole development.

Teacher FYI

Interphase Duplication The fact that chromosomes are duplicated in the nucleus during interphase has been hypothesized for more than a hundred years, but evidence for the hypothesis did not appear until 1981.

Use Science Words

Word Meaning Explain that the word *mitosis* derives from the Greek word for "thread." Have students explain the derivation. During mitosis, the replicated chromosomes—threadlike structures—separate. Then point out that *phase* is another word for "stage." Have students use a dictionary to find the meanings of the prefixes *inter-* (between), *pro-* (before), *meta-* (after), *ana-* (up), and *telo-* (end). L2

Differentiated Instruction

Challenge Have students make a paper-and-string model of mitosis. The stages of mitosis can be connected using string, and colored string can be used to represent duplicated chromosomes. Students should include labels and descriptions of what occurs at each stage. The models can then be displayed in the classroom. L3

Curriculum Connection

Math It takes 15 minutes for certain embryo cells to divide. Have students calculate how many cells would be produced from one embryo cell after four hours. 240 minutes divided by 15 minutes = 16 cell divisions; $2^{16} = 65,536$ cells L2 LS **Logical-Mathematical**

Discussion

Spinal Cord Damage Have students use their knowledge of the cell cycle to infer why even slight injuries to the brain and spinal cord can be serious and permanent. Because nerve cells do not undergo mitosis, damaged cells are not replaced, although some repair does occur. L2

Discussion

Nonliving Growth Many nonliving things such as icicles, stalagmites, crystals, and sand dunes appear to grow. Ask students to give examples of other nonliving things that appear to grow. Possible answers: highway systems, buildings, developments, shopping malls Have students distinguish between the processes involved in the growth of living things and the growth of nonliving things. In nonliving things, growth is caused by the surrounding environment. In living things, growth is caused by processes within the organism. L1

Caption Answer

Figure 6 the sex of the organism

Activity

Cancer Have students research and report on cancer. The report should include how cancer relates to mitosis and some of the technology used to diagnose and treat cancer. Display written reports.

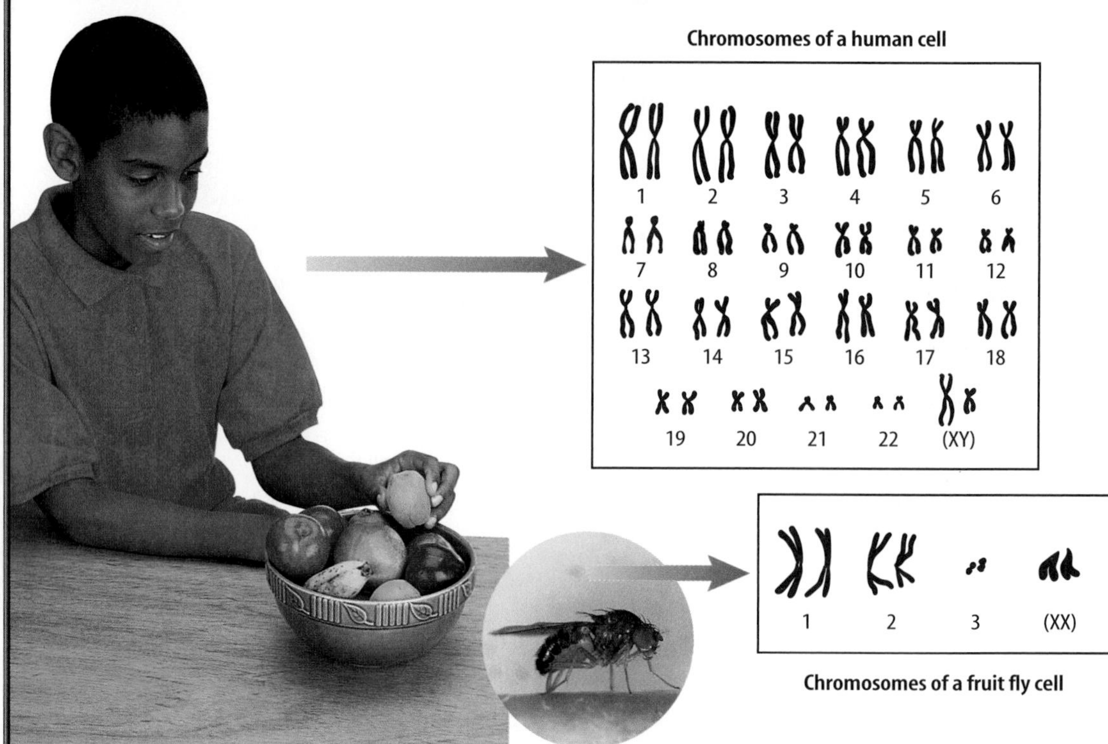

Figure 6 Pairs of chromosomes are found in the nucleus of most cells. All chromosomes shown here are in their duplicated form. Most human cells have 23 pairs of chromosomes including one pair of chromosomes that help determine sex such as the XY pair above. Most fruit fly cells have four pairs of chromosomes.
Infer *What do you think the XX pair in fruit flies helps determine?*

Results of Mitosis You should remember two important things about mitosis. First, it is the division of a nucleus. Second, it produces two new nuclei that are identical to each other and the original nucleus. Each new nucleus has the same number and type of chromosomes. Every cell in your body, except sex cells, has a nucleus with 46 chromosomes—23 pairs. This is because you began as one cell with 46 chromosomes in its nucleus. Skin cells, produced to replace or repair your skin, have the same 46 chromosomes as the original single cell you developed from. Each cell in a fruit fly has eight chromosomes, so each new cell produced by mitosis has a copy of those eight chromosomes. **Figure 6** shows the chromosomes found in most human cells and those found in most fruit fly cells.

Each of the trillions of cells in your body, except sex cells, has a copy of the same hereditary material. Even though all actors in a play have copies of the same script, they do not learn the same lines. Likewise, all of your cells use different parts of the same hereditary material to become different types of cells.

Cell division allows growth and replaces worn out or damaged cells. You are much larger and have more cells than a baby mainly because of cell division. If you cut yourself, the wound heals because cell division replaces damaged cells. Another way some organisms use cell division is to produce new organisms.

LAB DEMONSTRATION

Purpose to observe asexual reproduction in a sweet potato

Materials sweet potato with leaf buds, water, widemouthed glass jar, 4 toothpicks

Preparation Obtain a sweet potato that has purple leaf buds growing at its scarred end.

Procedure Fill a jar almost full of water, and place sweet potato with buds or scarred end up so at least half of the potato is in water. Toothpicks can hold the potato in place. Keep the water level constant and observe for three weeks.

Expected Outcome Students should observe the formation of roots and leaf growth.

Assessment

Ask students what part of the sweet potato produced leaves and roots. Leaves developed from the buds; roots grew from the bottom half of the sweet potato. Is this an example of sexual or asexual reproduction? Explain. Asexual; a new organism is produced from one parent. L2

Asexual Reproduction

Reproduction is the process by which an organism produces others of its same kind. Among living organisms, there are two types of reproduction—sexual and asexual. Sexual reproduction usually requires two organisms. In **asexual reproduction,** a new organism (sometimes more than one) is produced from one organism. The new organism will have hereditary material identical to the hereditary material of the parent organism.

Reading Check *How many organisms are needed for asexual reproduction?*

Cellular Asexual Reproduction Organisms with eukaryotic cells asexually reproduce by cell division. A sweet potato growing in a jar of water is an example of asexual reproduction. All the stems, leaves, and roots that grow from the sweet potato have been produced by cell division and have the same hereditary material. New strawberry plants can be reproduced asexually from horizontal stems called runners. **Figure 7** shows asexual reproduction in a potato and a strawberry plant.

Recall that mitosis is the division of a nucleus. However, bacteria do not have a nucleus so they can't use mitosis. Instead, bacteria reproduce asexually by fission. During fission, an organism whose cells do not contain a nucleus copies its genetic material and then divides into two identical organisms.

Mini LAB

Modeling Mitosis

Procedure

1. Make models of cell division using **materials supplied by your teacher.**
2. Use four chromosomes in your model.
3. When finished, arrange the models in the order in which mitosis occurs.

Analysis

1. In which steps is the nucleus visible?
2. How many cells does a dividing cell form?

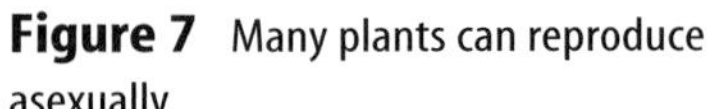

Figure 7 Many plants can reproduce asexually.

A new potato plant can grow from each sprout on this potato.

Infer *how the genetic material in the small strawberry plant above compares to the genetic material in the large strawberry plant.*

Reading Check

Answer one

Purpose Students will construct a model of mitosis. L2 ELL IN **Kinesthetic and Visual-Spatial**

Materials colored paper, poster board, markers, toothpicks, yarn, thread, glue, scissors

Teaching Strategy Student models should resemble mitosis as shown in **Figure 4.**

Analysis

1. prophase and telophase
2. two new cells

Assessment

Performance Assess students' understanding of mitosis by making flash cards of the stages and having students arrange them in the proper order. Use **Performance Assessment in the Science Classroom,** p. 163.

Caption Answer

Figure 7 They are identical.

Visual Learning

Figure 6 Have students name the stage of mitosis that the human cell was in when the chromosomes were extracted from it. The cell was in either prophase or metaphase. Chromosomes are not visible during interphase even though they are duplicated. They are visible when they become coiled tightly at the beginning of prophase and throughout metaphase. Pairs separate during anaphase and telophase. L2

Science Journal

Cloning Have students use science reference books, newspapers, and the Internet to research cloning, a process that artificially reproduces an exact duplicate of a single parent. Have students write reports in their Science Journals on the medical uses as well as the negative ethical implications of cloning technology. L2 IN **Linguistic**

SECTION 1 Cell Division and Mitosis A ◆ 103

Inquiry Lab

Observing Budding

Purpose to design an experiment to demonstrate yeast budding L2

Possible Materials package of yeast, sugar, warm water, microscope, microscope slides

Estimated Time one day

Teaching Strategies

- Mix a package of yeast, 1 tsp of sugar, and 0.5 L warm water. After a few hours in a warm place, budding yeast can be seen under a microscope.
- Students can infer why the water and sugar are necessary for yeast to undergo budding.

For additional inquiry activities, see *Science Inquiry Labs.*

Text Question Answer

Sea star numbers would increase.

3 Assess

DAILY INTERVENTION

Check for Understanding

Kinesthetic, Logical-Mathematical Using marbles as cells, have students demonstrate five cell divisions, beginning with one cell, two cells, and three cells. Record results in a table. L2

Reteach

Cell Cycle Have students draw the nucleus or chromosomes on cell cycle outlines and describe what is occurring at each stage. L1

ELL IN **Visual-Spatial**

Figure 8 Some organisms use cell division for budding and regeneration.

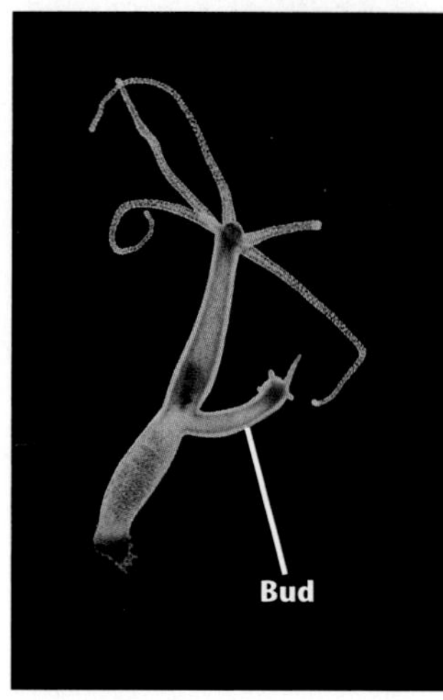

A Hydra, a freshwater animal, can reproduce asexually by budding. The bud is a small exact copy of the adult.

B This sea star is regenerating four new arms.

Budding and Regeneration Look at **Figure 8A.** A new organism is growing from the body of the parent organism. This organism, called a hydra, is reproducing by budding. Budding is a type of asexual reproduction made possible because of cell division. When the bud on the adult becomes large enough, it breaks away to live on its own.

Could you grow a new finger? Some organisms can regrow damaged or lost body parts, as shown in **Figure 8B.** Regeneration is the process that uses cell division to regrow body parts. Sponges, planaria, sea stars, and some other organisms can use regeneration for asexual reproduction. If these organisms break into pieces, a whole new organism will grow from each piece. Because sea stars eat oysters, oyster farmers dislike them. What would happen if an oyster farmer collected sea stars, cut them into pieces, and threw them back into the ocean?

section 1 review

Summary

The Cell Cycle

- The cell cycle is a series of events from one cell division to the next.
- Most of a eukaryotic cell's life is interphase.

Mitosis

- Mitosis is a series of four phases or steps.
- Each new nucleus formed by mitosis has the same number and type of chromosomes.

Asexual Reproduction

- In asexual reproduction, a new organism is produced from one organism.
- Cellular, budding, and regeneration are forms of asexual reproduction.

Self Check

1. **Define** mitosis. How does it differ in plants and animals?
2. **Identify** two examples of asexual reproduction in many-celled organisms.
3. **Describe** what happens to chromosomes before mitosis.
4. **Compare and contrast** the two new cells formed after mitosis and cell division.
5. **Think Critically** Why is it important for the nuclear membrane to disintegrate during mitosis?

Applying Math

6. **Solve One-Step Equations** If a cell undergoes cell division every 5 min, how many cells will there be after 1 h?

Science Online booka.msscience.com/self_check_quiz

Assessment

Oral How is mitosis different from cell division? Mitosis is the division of the nucleus. Cell division includes mitosis and the division of the cytoplasm and its contents. Use **PASC**, p. 89. L2

section 1 review

1. a process in which a cell nucleus divides into two nuclei, each of which has the same genetic information; in animal cells, the cytoplasm divides as the cell membrane pinches in the middle of the cell; in plant cells, the appearance of the cell plate indicates that the cytoplasm is being divided.
2. Possible answers: budding and regeneration
3. The chromosomes duplicate.
4. They both have the same genetic information.
5. Otherwise, the chromosomes would not be able to move to opposite ends of the cell.
6. 60 minutes divided by 5 minutes = 12 cell divisions; $2^{12} = 4,096$ cells

Mitosis in Plant Cells

Reproduction of most cells in plants and animals uses mitosis and cell division. In this lab, you will study mitosis in plant cells by examining prepared slides of onion root-tip cells.

Real-World Question

How can plant cells in different stages of mitosis be distinguished from each other?

Goals

- **Compare** cells in different stages of mitosis and observe the location of their chromosomes.
- **Observe** what stage of mitosis is most common in onion root tips.

Materials

prepared slide of an onion root tip
microscope

Safety Precautions

Procedure

1. Copy the data table in your Science Journal.

Number of Root-Tip Cells Observed

Stage of Mitosis	Number of Cells Observed	Percent of Cells Observed
Prophase	78	65
Metaphase	23	19
Anaphase	12	10
Telophase	7	6
Total	120	100

2. **Obtain** a prepared slide of cells from an onion root tip.

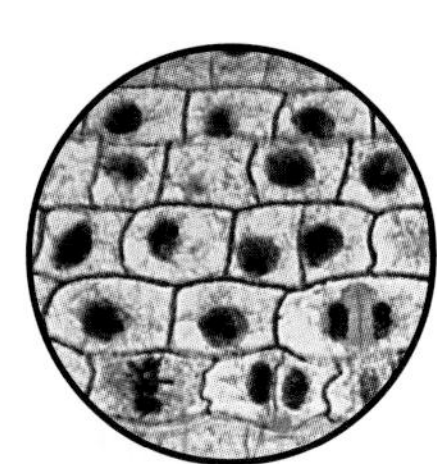

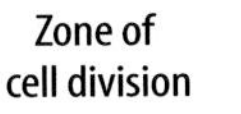

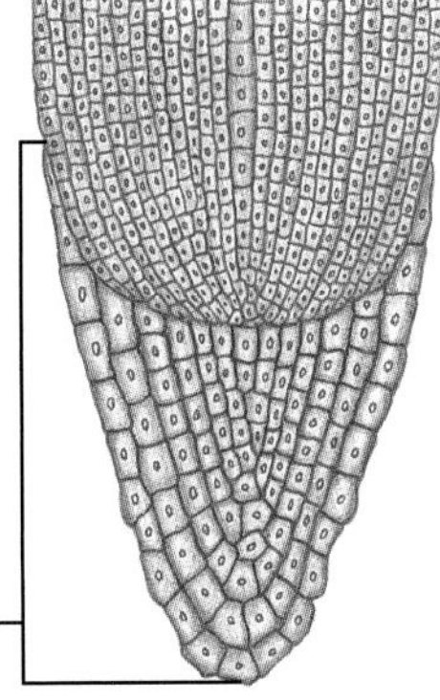

3. Set your microscope on low power and examine the slide. The large, round cells at the root tip are called the root cap. Move the slide until you see the cells just behind the root cap. Turn to the high-power objective.
4. Find an area where you can see the most stages of mitosis. Count and record how many cells you see in each stage.
5. Return the nosepiece to low power. Remove the onion root-tip slide.

Conclude and Apply

1. **Compare** the cells in the region behind the root cap to those in the root cap.
2. **Calculate** the percent of cells found in each stage of mitosis. Infer which stage of mitosis takes the longest period of time.

Communicating Your Data

Write and illustrate a story as if you were a cell undergoing mitosis. Share your story with your class. **For more help, refer to the** Science Skill Handbook.

Communicating Your Data

The story and drawings should include the stages in mitosis.

Real-World Question

Purpose Students observe the stages of mitosis. L2 ELL IS **Visual-Spatial**

Process Skills observe, infer, compare and contrast

Time Required 40 minutes

Procedure

Teaching Strategy Review the stages of mitosis before beginning the activity.

Troubleshooting Students may have difficulty locating all the phases. You may want to place an onion root tip slide on the microprojector and point out the phases.

Conclude and Apply

1. The cells behind the root cap are smaller than those in the root cap. Mitosis occurs at a faster rate in cells behind the root cap.
2. See student page; prophase takes the longest.

Assessment

Performance To further assess students' understanding of mitosis, give each one a sheet of paper listing a stage and have them describe what comes before and after that stage. Use **Performance Assessment in the Science Classroom,** p. 163. L2

1 Motivate

Bellringer

Section Focus Transparencies also are available on the Interactive Chalkboard CD-ROM.

Section Focus Transparency 2 — I Think He Has Your Eyes

The Santa Gertrudis bull flourishes in the arid plains of Texas. The King Ranch developed the Santa Gertrudis by cross-breeding Brahman cattle with Shorthorns. As you can see, the Santa Gertrudis inherited characteristics from both of its parents.

Brahman — Shorthorn — Santa Gertrudis

1. Why might ranchers have wanted to cross-breed Brahmans and Shorthorns?
2. Which of the Santa Gertrudis' traits can you identify in the Brahman and the Shorthorn?

Cell Reproduction

Tie to Prior Knowledge

Mitosis Stages As a review, ask students to describe the stages in mitosis. Then tell the students that for certain cells, the nucleus divides twice. They will learn why in this section.

section 2

Sexual Reproduction and Meiosis

as you read

What You'll Learn

- **Describe** the stages of meiosis and how sex cells are produced.
- **Explain** why meiosis is needed for sexual reproduction.
- **Name** the cells that are involved in fertilization.
- **Explain** how fertilization occurs in sexual reproduction.

Why It's Important

Meiosis and sexual reproduction are the reasons why no one else is exactly like you.

Review Vocabulary
organism: any living thing; uses energy, is made of cells, reproduces, responds, grows, and develops

New Vocabulary
- sexual reproduction
- sperm
- egg
- fertilization
- zygote
- diploid
- haploid
- meiosis

Sexual Reproduction

Sexual reproduction is another way that a new organism can be produced. During **sexual reproduction,** two sex cells, sometimes called an egg and a sperm, come together. Sex cells, like those in **Figure 9,** are formed from cells in reproductive organs. **Sperm** are formed in the male reproductive organs. **Eggs** are formed in the female reproductive organs. The joining of an egg and a sperm is called **fertilization,** and the cell that forms is called a **zygote** (ZI goht). Generally, the egg and the sperm come from two different organisms of the same species. Following fertilization, cell division begins. A new organism with a unique identity develops.

Diploid Cells Your body forms two types of cells—body cells and sex cells. Body cells far outnumber sex cells. Your brain, skin, bones, and other tissues and organs are formed from body cells. A typical human body cell has 46 chromosomes. Each chromosome has a mate that is similar to it in size and shape and has similar DNA. Human body cells have 23 pairs of chromosomes. When cells have pairs of similar chromosomes, they are said to be **diploid** (DIH ployd).

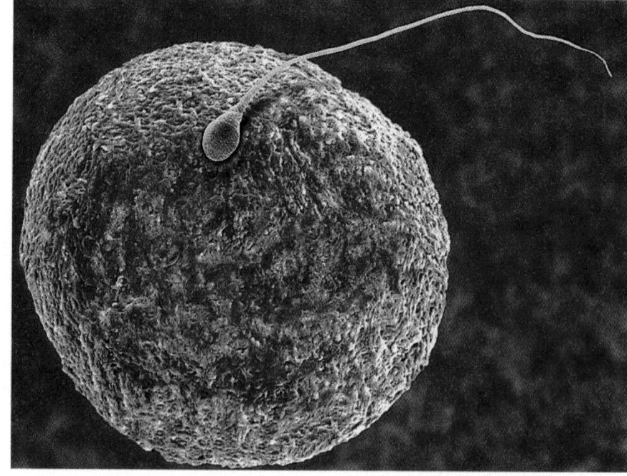

Figure 9 A human egg and a human sperm at fertilization.

Section 2 Resource Manager

Chapter *FAST FILE* Resources
- Transparency Activity, p. 43
- Directed Reading for Content Mastery, p. 18
- Enrichment, p. 29
- Reinforcement, p. 26

Life Science Critical Thinking/Problem Solving, p. 19

Mathematics Skill Activities, p. 3

Performance Assessment in the Science Classroom, p. 57

106 ◆ A CHAPTER 4 Cell Reproduction

Haploid Cells Because sex cells do not have pairs of chromosomes, they are said to be **haploid** (HA ployd). They have only half the number of chromosomes as body cells. *Haploid* means "single form." Human sex cells have only 23 chromosomes—one from each of the 23 pairs of similar chromosomes. Compare the chromosomes found in a sex cell, as shown in **Figure 9,** to the full set of human chromosomes seen in **Figure 6.**

How many chromosomes are usually in each human sperm?

Meiosis and Sex Cells

A process called **meiosis** (mi OH sus) produces haploid sex cells. What would happen in sexual reproduction if two diploid cells combined? The offspring would have twice as many chromosomes as its parent. Although plants with twice the number of chromosomes as the parent plants are often produced, most animals do not survive with a double number of chromosomes. Meiosis ensures that the offspring will have the same diploid number as its parent, as shown in **Figure 10.** After two haploid sex cells combine, a diploid zygote is produced that develops into a new diploid organism.

During meiosis, two divisions of the nucleus occur. These divisions are called meiosis I and meiosis II. The steps of each division have names like those in mitosis and are numbered for the division in which they occur.

Diploid Zygote The human egg releases a chemical into the surrounding fluid that attracts sperm. Usually, only one sperm fertilizes the egg. After the sperm nucleus enters the egg, the cell membrane of the egg changes in a way that prevents other sperm from entering. What adaptation in this process guarantees that the zygote will be diploid? Write a paragraph describing your ideas in your Science Journal.

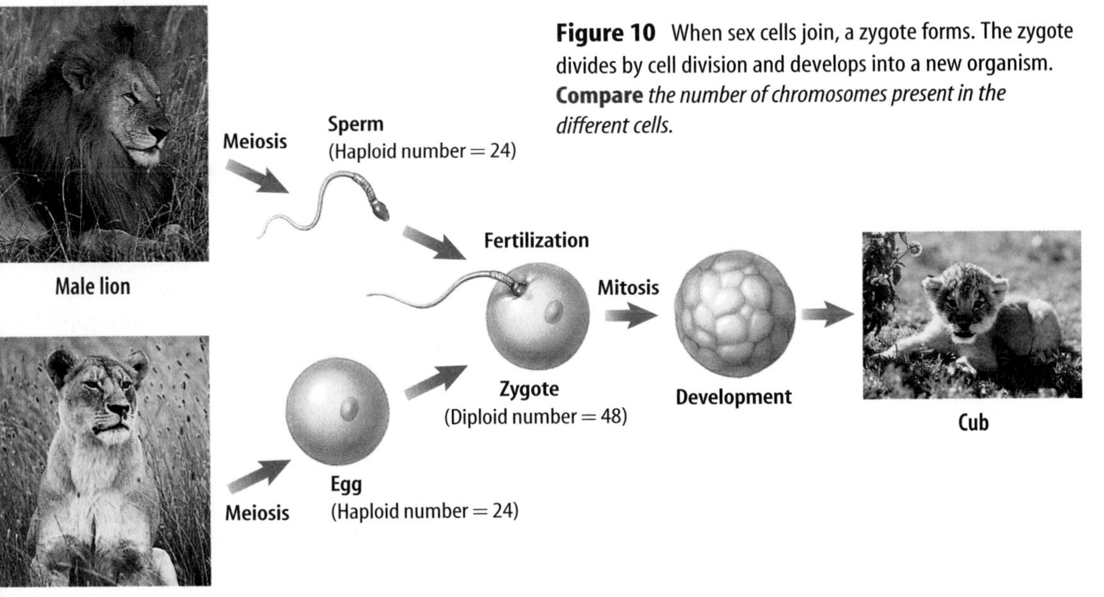

Figure 10 When sex cells join, a zygote forms. The zygote divides by cell division and develops into a new organism. **Compare** *the number of chromosomes present in the different cells.*

2 Teach

Reading Check

Answer 23 chromosomes

Diploid Zygote The changes in the egg prevent fertilization by more than one sperm.

Use Science Words

Word Origin The term *meiosis* comes from a Greek word for "diminution" or becoming less. Ask students what diminishes or becomes less in meiosis. The chromosome number in each cell is diminished. L2

Fun Fact

With 23 pairs of chromosomes in the human body, there are more than 8 million different combinations of chromosomes possible for every human cell formed by meiosis.

Caption Answer

Figure 10 Fertilized cells have twice the number of chromosomes found in sex cells.

Curriculum Connection

Math Have students use library references to find the number of chromosomes in the body cells of various plants and animals. Then have them determine the number of chromosomes in the sex cells of each one. The number of chromosomes in sex cells should be half the number of chromosomes in body cells. L3

LS **Logical-Mathematical**

Caption Answer

Figure 11 four

Teacher FYI

In-Vitro Fertilization is a procedure that joins sperm and eggs outside the body. Fertilized eggs (actually two-day-old embryos) are then implanted into the female.

Answer The duplicated chromosomes of each similar pair are pulled to opposite ends of the cell.

Use Science Words

Word Meaning Have students use a dictionary to find out what *triploid* and *tetraploid* mean. Have them write an explanation of how this condition occurs. *Triploid*—each cell in the organism contains three sets of chromosomes; plant endosperm is triploid and normal. *Tetraploid* organisms have four sets of chromosomes in each cell; these conditions arise from total nondisjunction during mitosis or meiosis. L2 LS **Linguistic**

Discussion

Controlled Traits In areas throughout the world, people have similar genetically controlled traits including skin color, height, and face shape. Cultures of people were unable to travel long distances for thousands of years and, therefore, reproduced mainly among themselves. As a result, genetic instructions for such traits remained within given cultures.

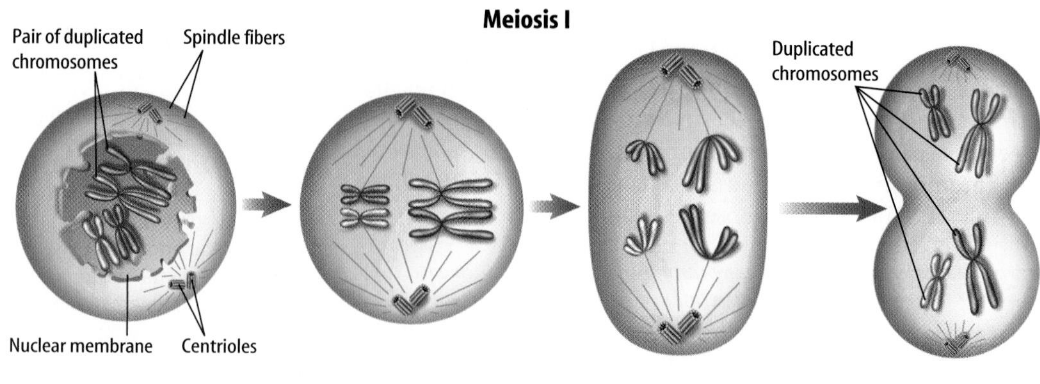

Figure 11 Meiosis has two divisions of the nucleus—meiosis I and meiosis II.
Determine *how many sex cells are finally formed after both divisions are completed.*

Meiosis I Before meiosis begins, each chromosome is duplicated, just as in mitosis. When the cell is ready for meiosis, each duplicated chromosome is visible under the microscope as two chromatids. As shown in **Figure 11,** the events of prophase I are similar to those of prophase in mitosis. In meiosis, each duplicated chromosome comes near its similar duplicated mate. In mitosis they do not come near each other.

In metaphase I, the pairs of duplicated chromosomes line up in the center of the cell. The centromere of each chromatid pair becomes attached to one spindle fiber, so the chromatids do not separate in anaphase I. The two pairs of chromatids of each similar pair move away from each other to opposite ends of the cell. Each duplicated chromosome still has two chromatids. Then, in telophase I, the cytoplasm divides, and two new cells form. Each new cell has one duplicated chromosome from each similar pair.

Reading Check *What happens to duplicated chromosomes during anaphase I?*

Meiosis II The two cells formed during meiosis I now begin meiosis II. The chromatids of each duplicated chromosome will be separated during this division. In prophase II, the duplicated chromosomes and spindle fibers reappear in each new cell. Then in metaphase II, the duplicated chromosomes move to the center of the cell. Unlike what occurs in metaphase I, each centromere now attaches to two spindle fibers instead of one. The centromere divides during anaphase II, and the chromatids separate and move to opposite ends of the cell. Each chromatid now is an individual chromosome. As telophase II begins, the spindle fibers disappear, and a nuclear membrane forms around the chromosomes at each end of the cell. When meiosis II is finished, the cytoplasm divides.

Differentiated Instruction

Challenge To encourage students to understand all of the stages of meiosis, have them create an eight-stage puzzle that demonstrates each phase of meiosis. Pieces of the puzzle can include cells, chromosomes, and centrioles. Students can work in pairs to test their ability to use the puzzle pieces to represent any stage of meiosis or the entire eight-stage process. L3

Learning Disabled Students who are dyslexic may have trouble distinguishing between the first and second parts of meiosis. Instead of Roman numbers, as in prophase I and prophase II, use Arabic numbers for easier identification (prophase 1 and prophase 2). L2

108 ◆ A CHAPTER 4 Cell Reproduction

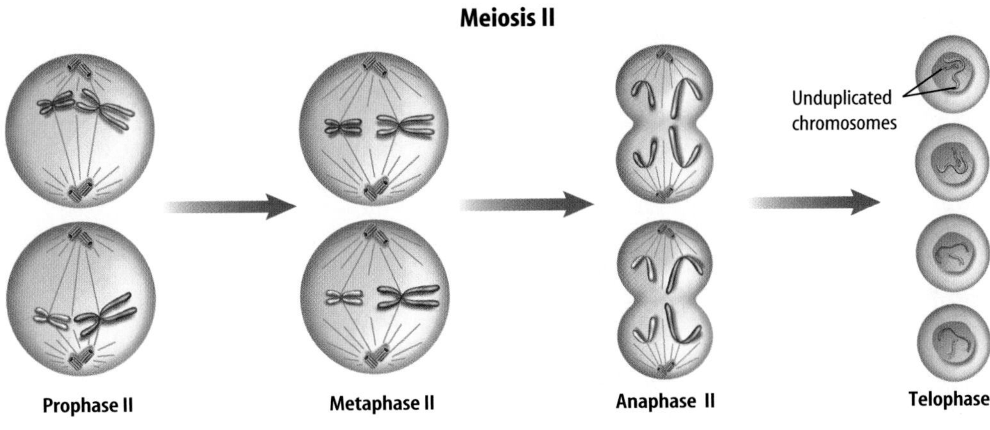

Summary of Meiosis Two cells form during meiosis I. In meiosis II, both of these cells form two cells. The two divisions of the nucleus result in four sex cells. Each has one-half the number of chromosomes in its nucleus that was in the original nucleus. From a human cell with 46 paired chromosomes, meiosis produces four sex cells each with 23 unpaired chromosomes.

Applying Science

How can chromosome numbers be predicted?

Offspring get half of their chromosomes from one parent and half from the other. What happens if each parent has a different diploid number of chromosomes?

Identifying the Problem

A zebra and a donkey can mate to produce a zonkey. Zebras have a diploid number of 46. Donkeys have a diploid number of 62.

Solving the Problem

1. How many chromosomes would the zonkey receive from each parent?
2. What is the chromosome number of the zonkey?
3. What would happen when meiosis occurs in the zonkey's reproductive organs?
4. Predict why zonkeys are usually sterile.

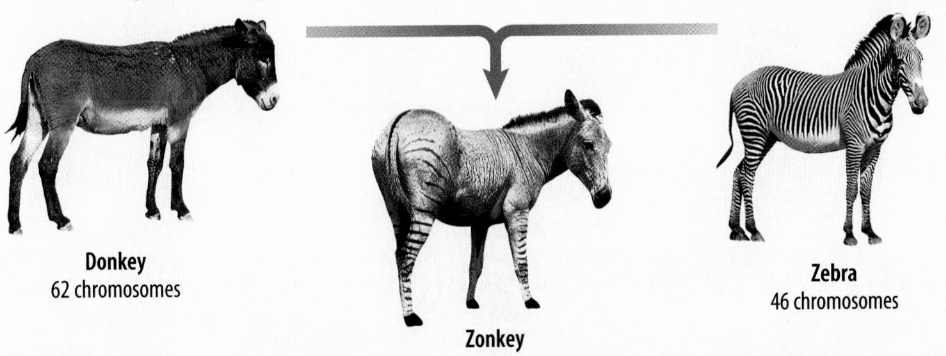

Make a Model

Stages of Meiosis Have students make a model of the stages of meiosis in an organism with three pairs of chromosomes. Have them use shapes to distinguish the chromosomes. L2 LS **Kinesthetic** P

Activity

Meiosis Lyrics Using one of their favorite songs, have students write substitute lyrics about what happens in meiosis. L2 LS **Auditory-Musical**

Applying Science

Answers

1. 23 from the zebra and 31 from the donkey
2. 54
3. Normal sex cells would not form because there are 8 unpaired chromosomes from the donkey.
4. Each sex cell could not have one-half the chromosomes of the original cell.

Quick Demo

Meiosis

Materials projecting microscope, prepared slides of lily anthers undergoing meiosis

Estimated Time 10 minutes

Procedure Demonstrate meiotic cell division in the lily anthers. Display the various stages of meiosis and have students draw what they see.

Active Reading

Flow Chart A flow chart helps students logically sequence events. Students will write major stages of the sequence in large ovals and write substages in smaller ovals under the larger ovals. Have students design a flow chart for a concept in this section. Sample flow chart: L2

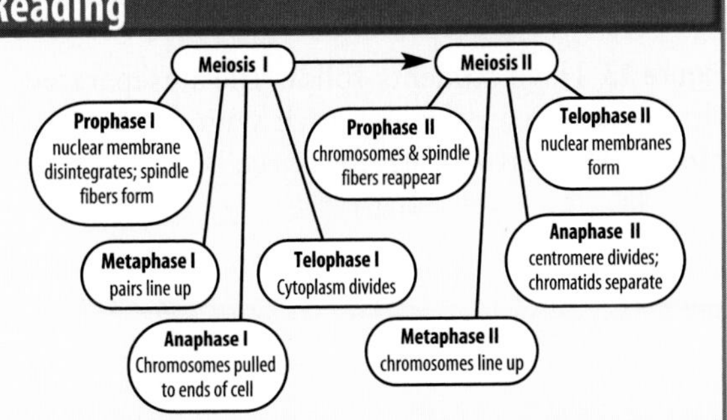

Visualizing Polyploidy in Plants

Have students examine the pictures and read the captions. Then ask the following questions.

What kinds of mistakes in meiosis or mitosis could result in a polyploid plant? A mistake that caused chromosome sets not to separate, allowing more than one full set to be present in a cell after division to form sex cells.

What is the main advantage of bananas being triploid? Triploid plants have very small seeds, so people can eat bananas without removing seeds.

Why wouldn't you find triploid peanuts in the grocery store? The part of a peanut plant you eat is a seed, but triploid plants have little or no seeds.

Activity

Plant Chromosomes Have students use pipe cleaners to model the chromosomes of one of the plants featured here. For example, a banana with 3 sets of 11 chromosomes, a strawberry with 8 sets of 7 chromosomes, or a peanut with 4 sets of 10 chromosomes. L2

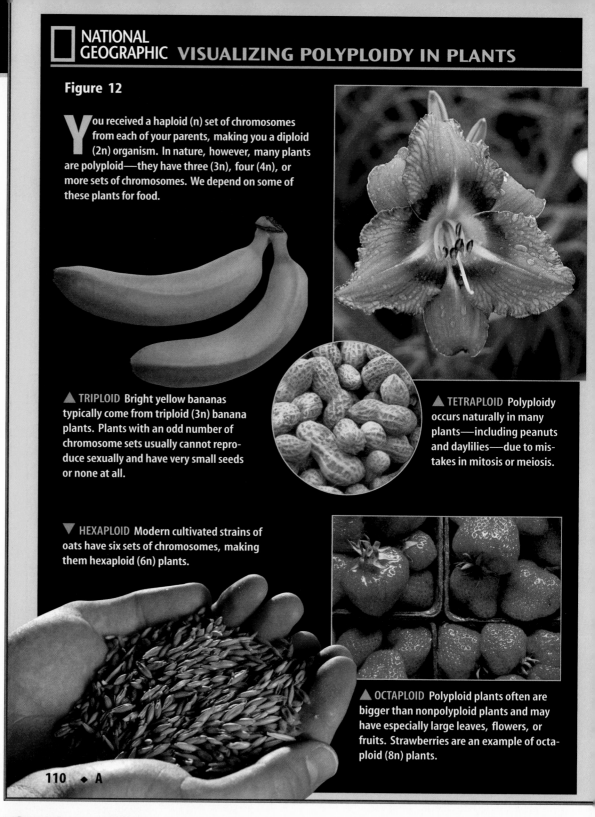

NATIONAL GEOGRAPHIC **VISUALIZING POLYPLOIDY IN PLANTS**

Figure 12

You received a haploid (n) set of chromosomes from each of your parents, making you a diploid (2n) organism. In nature, however, many plants are polyploid—they have three (3n), four (4n), or more sets of chromosomes. We depend on some of these plants for food.

▲ TRIPLOID Bright yellow bananas typically come from triploid (3n) banana plants. Plants with an odd number of chromosome sets usually cannot reproduce sexually and have very small seeds or none at all.

▲ TETRAPLOID Polyploidy occurs naturally in many plants—including peanuts and daylilies—due to mistakes in mitosis or meiosis.

▼ HEXAPLOID Modern cultivated strains of oats have six sets of chromosomes, making them hexaploid (6n) plants.

▲ OCTAPLOID Polyploid plants often are bigger than nonpolyploid plants and may have especially large leaves, flowers, or fruits. Strawberries are an example of octaploid (8n) plants.

Visual Learning

Figure 13 Have students follow the unseparated chromosome pair through each stage of meiosis. How did this error affect the sex cells? Some had too many chromosomes; others not enough. L2

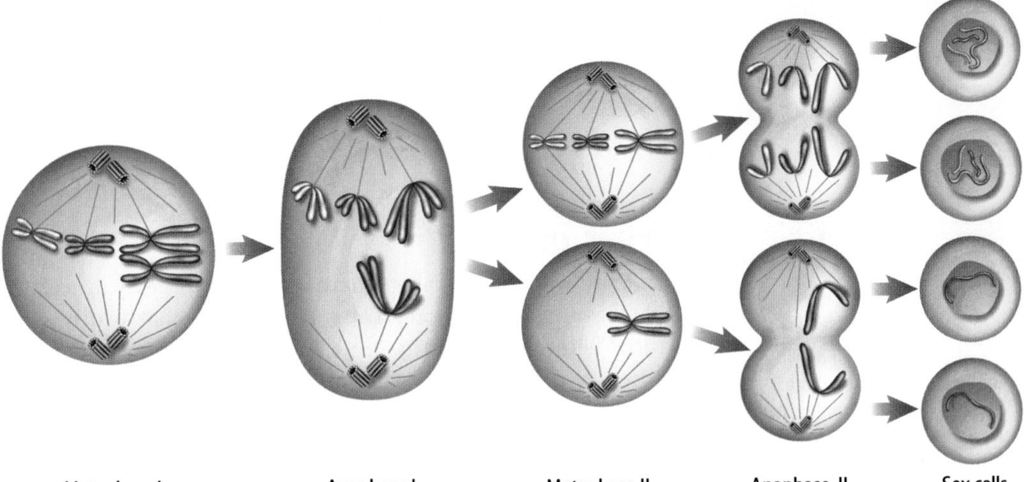

Figure 13 This diploid cell has four chromosomes. During anaphase I, one pair of duplicated chromosomes did not separate. **Infer** *how many chromosomes each sex cell usually has.*

Mistakes in Meiosis Meiosis occurs many times in reproductive organs. Although mistakes in plants, as shown in **Figure 12,** are common, mistakes are less common in animals. These mistakes can produce sex cells with too many or too few chromosomes, as shown in **Figure 13.** Sometimes, zygotes produced from these sex cells die. If the zygote lives, every cell in the organism that grows from that zygote usually will have the wrong number of chromosomes. Organisms with the wrong number of chromosomes may not grow normally.

section 2 review

Summary

Sexual Reproduction

- During sexual reproduction, two sex cells come together.
- Cell division begins after fertilization.
- A typical human body cell has 46 chromosomes, and a human sex cell has 23 chromosomes.

Meiosis and Sex Cells

- Each chromosome is duplicated before meiosis, then two divisions of the nucleus occur.
- During meiosis I, duplicated chromosomes are separated into new cells.
- Chromatids separate during meiosis II.
- Meiosis I and meiosis II result in four sex cells.

Self Check

1. **Describe** a zygote and how it is formed.
2. **Explain** where sex cells form.
3. **Compare** what happens to chromosomes during anaphase I and anaphase II.
4. **Think Critically** Plants grown from runners and leaf cuttings have the same traits as the parent plant. Plants grown from seeds can vary from the parent plants in many ways. Why can this happen?

Applying Skills

5. **Make and use a table** to compare mitosis and meiosis in humans. Vertical headings should include: *What Type of Cell (Body or Sex), Beginning Cell (Haploid or Diploid), Number of Cells Produced, End-Product Cell (Haploid or Diploid),* and *Number of Chromosomes in New Cells.*

Science Online booka.msscience.com/self_check_quiz

Caption Answer
Figure 13 two

3 Assess

DAILY INTERVENTION

Check for Understanding

Visual-Spatial Have students use colored pipe cleaners as chromosomes to demonstrate the process of meiosis. Pipe cleaners of the same color can be paired as duplicated chromosomes. Students should repeat the process with varying numbers of chromosomes. Students should also demonstrate the result when a pair of duplicated chromosomes does not separate properly. L2

Reteach

Meiosis Show the phases of meiosis out of sequence. Have students identify each phase and place the phases in order. L2 ELL IN **Visual-Spatial**

Assessment

Content Write these chromosome numbers on the board: *horse—66; cat—38; potato—48.* How many chromosomes would be in a cell of each organism produced by mitosis and meiosis? horse—66, 33; cat—38, 19; potato—48, 24 Use **PASC,** p. 101.

section 2 review

1. A zygote is the cell that forms when a sperm fertilizes an egg.
2. Sperm cells form in male reproductive organs; egg cells form in female reproductive organs.
3. Anaphase I—duplicated chromosome pairs separate and move to opposite ends of the cell; anaphase II—chromatids separate and move to opposite ends of the cell.
4. Plants produced by asexual reproduction are the result of mitosis. Plants grown from seeds vary from their parents, because seeds are produced by sexual reproduction.
5. See table.

Feature	Mitosis	Meiosis
Type of cell	Body cell	Sex cell
Beginning cell	Diploid	Diploid
Number of cells produced	Two	Four
End product	Diploid	Haploid
Number of chromosomes	Same as original cell	Half the original cell

section 3

DNA

1 Motivate

Bellringer

Section Focus Transparencies also are available on the Interactive Chalkboard CD-ROM.

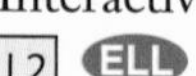

L2 ELL

Section Focus Transparency 3 Curly Cat

This unusual cat is a Devon Rex. It appeared in Devonshire, England in 1960 when a genetic change occurred among British barn cats. The Devon Rex has a small head and a curly coat.

1. Based on the picture and the description above, what do you think a genetic change is?
2. How can cat breeders attempt to continue the characteristics of the Devon Rex?

Tie to Prior Knowledge

Template Games Students should be familiar with template systems, such as keys and locks and peg-and-hole games. Ask for other examples. Use this knowledge to explain that DNA in the nucleus serves as a template for RNA.

Virtual Labs

Protein Synthesis *What is the role of DNA and RNA in protein synthesis?*

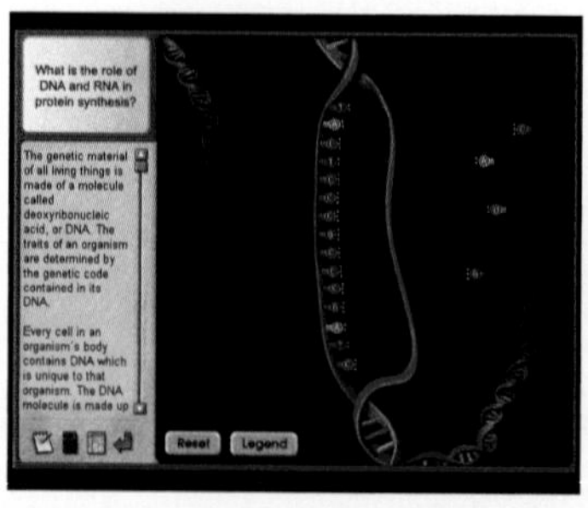

as you read

***What* You'll Learn**

- **Identify** the parts of a DNA molecule and its structure.
- **Explain** how DNA copies itself.
- **Describe** the structure and function of each kind of RNA.

***Why* It's Important**

DNA helps determine nearly everything your body is and does.

Review Vocabulary
heredity: the passing of traits from parents to offspring

New Vocabulary
- DNA
- gene
- RNA
- mutation

What is DNA?

Why was the alphabet one of the first things you learned when you started school? Letters are a code that you need to know before you learn to read. A cell also uses a code that is stored in its hereditary material. The code is a chemical called deoxyribonucleic (dee AHK sih ri boh noo klay ihk) acid, or **DNA.** It contains information for an organism's growth and function. **Figure 14** shows how DNA is stored in cells that have a nucleus. When a cell divides, the DNA code is copied and passed to the new cells. In this way, new cells receive the same coded information that was in the original cell. Every cell that has ever been formed in your body or in any other organism contains DNA.

INTEGRATE Chemistry

Discovering DNA Since the mid-1800s, scientists have known that the nuclei of cells contain large molecules called nucleic acids. By 1950, chemists had learned what the nucleic acid DNA was made of, but they didn't understand how the parts of DNA were arranged.

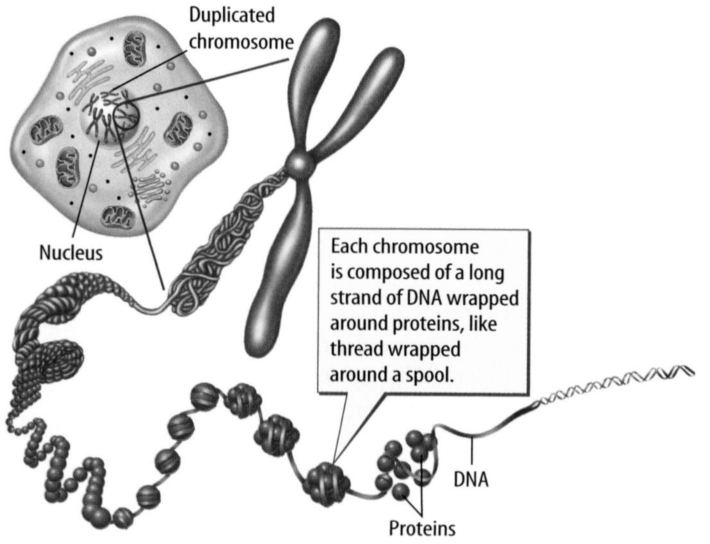

Duplicated chromosome
Nucleus
Each chromosome is composed of a long strand of DNA wrapped around proteins, like thread wrapped around a spool.
DNA
Proteins

Figure 14 DNA is part of the chromosomes found in a cell's nucleus.

Section 3 Resource Manager

Chapter *Fast File* Resources
- Transparency Activity, p. 44
- Directed Reading for Content Mastery, pp. 19, 20
- MiniLAB, p. 4
- Enrichment, p. 30
- Reinforcement, p. 27
- Lab Activity, pp. 11–13
- Lab Worksheet, pp. 7–8

Home and Community Involvement, p. 36
Cultural Diversity, p. 19
Lab Management and Safety, p. 58

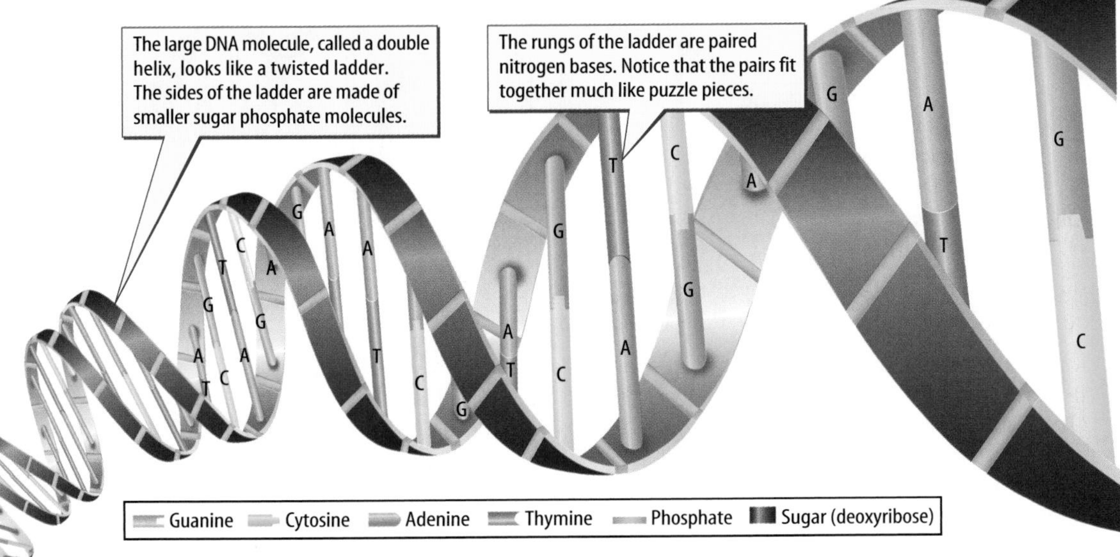

The large DNA molecule, called a double helix, looks like a twisted ladder. The sides of the ladder are made of smaller sugar phosphate molecules.
The rungs of the ladder are paired nitrogen bases. Notice that the pairs fit together much like puzzle pieces.
Guanine
Cytosine
Adenine
Thymine
Phosphate
Sugar (deoxyribose)

DNA's Structure In 1952, scientist Rosalind Franklin discovered that DNA is two chains of molecules in a spiral form. By using an X-ray technique, Dr. Franklin showed that the large spiral was probably made up of two spirals. As it turned out, the structure of DNA is similar to a twisted ladder. In 1953, using the work of Franklin and others, scientists James Watson and Francis Crick made a model of a DNA molecule.

A DNA Model What does DNA look like? According to the Watson and Crick DNA model, each side of the ladder is made up of sugar-phosphate molecules. Each molecule consists of the sugar called deoxyribose (dee AHK sih ri bohs) and a phosphate group. The rungs of the ladder are made up of other molecules called nitrogen bases. Four kinds of nitrogen bases are found in DNA—adenine (A duh neen), guanine (GWAH neen), cytosine (SI tuh seen), and thymine (THI meen). The bases are represented by the letters A, G, C, and T. The amount of cytosine in cells always equals the amount of guanine, and the amount of adenine always equals the amount of thymine. This led to the hypothesis that these bases occur as pairs in DNA. **Figure 14** shows that adenine always pairs with thymine, and guanine always pairs with cytosine. Like interlocking pieces of a puzzle, each base bonds only with its correct partner.

Reading Check *What are the nitrogen base pairs in a DNA molecule?*

Mini LAB

Modeling DNA Replication

Procedure

1. Suppose you have a segment of DNA that is six nitrogen base pairs in length. On **paper,** using the letters A, T, C, and G, write a combination of six pairs, remembering that A and T are always a pair and C and G are always a pair.
2. Duplicate your segment of DNA. On paper, diagram how this happens and show the new DNA segments.

Analysis

Compare the order of bases of the original DNA to the new DNA molecules.

Try at Home

Mini LAB

Purpose Students will model DNA replication. L2 LS **Visual-Spatial**

Materials pencil and paper

Teaching Strategy Make sure students understand that they are to make up a sample strand of DNA, then make the complementary strand, then split the two strands and make those complementary strands, so they can see that the new strands are identical to the original.

Analysis

Answers will vary with the bases chosen, but bases should be in the same order as the original DNA.

Assessment

Performance Draw and label one strand of DNA. Have students draw the complementary strand. Use **Performance Assessment in the Science Classroom,** p. 127. L2

Reading Check

Answer Adenine pairs with thymine, and guanine with cytosine.

Differentiated Instruction

English-Language Learners Use unifix cubes to demonstrate the various bases. Have students make their own models of base pairs, using a different color for each base. L2 ELL LS **Kinesthetic**

Use an Analogy

Morse Code Students are probably familiar with Morse code. Morse code uses only two symbols—the dot and the dash—in combinations to represent numbers and letters of the alphabet. DNA has four symbols. The order of nitrogen bases, rather than the sequence of dots and dashes, expresses the information needed for life processes.

Discussion

DNA Sequence How can you predict the base sequence of a second strand of DNA? by knowing the base-pairing rules and the sequence of the original DNA strand

Fun Fact

When students hear about the "code of life," they are hearing about the order of nitrogen bases in DNA.

Teacher FYI

Human Genome An individual's complete set of genetic material is its genome. In early 2001, it was announced that a working draft of the human genome had been mapped. The knowledge gained from the project will be a basis for studying human diseases and accelerating biomedical research.

Text Question Answer

It could cause serious health problems.

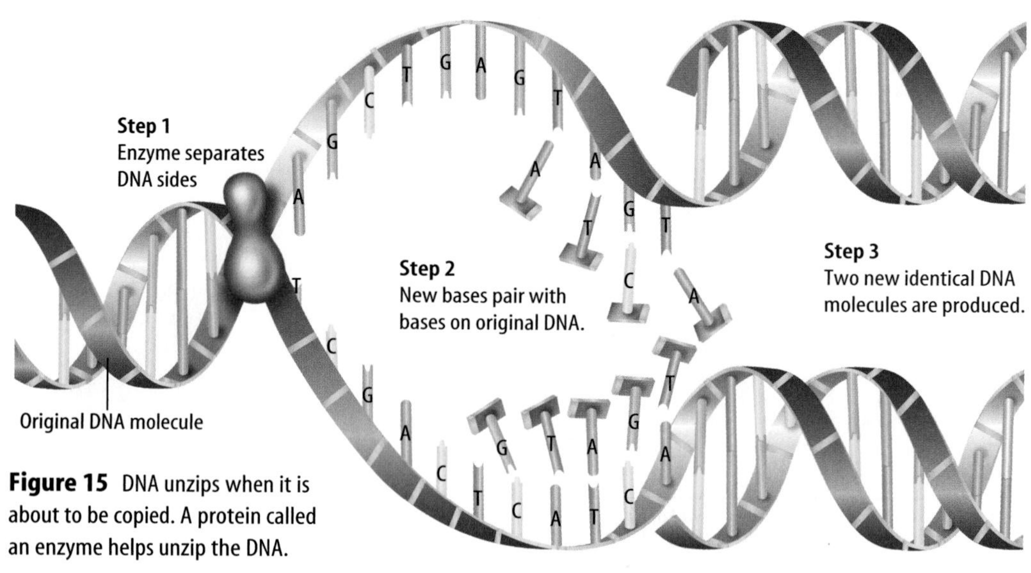

Figure 15 DNA unzips when it is about to be copied. A protein called an enzyme helps unzip the DNA.

Copying DNA When chromosomes are duplicated before mitosis or meiosis, the amount of DNA in the nucleus is doubled. The Watson and Crick model shows how this takes place. The two sides of DNA unwind and separate. Each side then becomes a pattern on which a new side forms, as shown in **Figure 15.** The new DNA has bases that are identical to those of the original DNA and are in the same order.

Figure 16 This diagram shows just a few of the genes that have been identified on human chromosome 7. The bold print is the name that has been given to each gene.

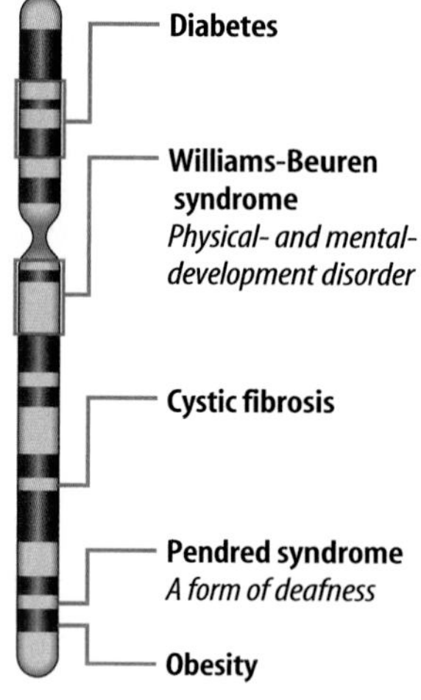

Genes

Most of your characteristics, such as the color of your hair, your height, and even how things taste to you, depend on the kinds of proteins your cells make. DNA in your cells stores the instructions for making these proteins.

Proteins build cells and tissues or work as enzymes. The instructions for making a specific protein are found in a **gene** which is a section of DNA on a chromosome. As shown in **Figure 16,** each chromosome contains hundreds of genes. Proteins are made of chains of hundreds or thousands of amino acids. The gene determines the order of amino acids in a protein. Changing the order of the amino acids makes a different protein. What might occur if an important protein couldn't be made or if the wrong protein was made in your cells?

Making Proteins Genes are found in the nucleus, but proteins are made on ribosomes in cytoplasm. The codes for making proteins are carried from the nucleus to the ribosomes by another type of nucleic acid called ribonucleic acid, or **RNA.**

Science Journal

DNA as Evidence Have students research the use of DNA technology in law enforcement and write a report in their Science Journals. Have them use the Internet, news magazines, reference books, and interview forensic scientists. L2 IN **Linguistic**

Curriculum Connection

Math The DNA code is written in four "letters" and the cell "reads" the code in groups of three. Have students determine how many different ways the four "letters" (A, T, G, and C) can be arranged in groups of three. There are 64 possible combinations. L2 IN **Logical-Mathematical**

Ribonucleic Acid RNA is made in the nucleus on a DNA pattern. However, RNA is different from DNA. If DNA is like a ladder, RNA is like a ladder that has all its rungs sawed in half. Compare the DNA molecule in **Figure 14** to the RNA molecule in **Figure 17.** RNA has the bases A, G, and C like DNA but has the base uracil (U) instead of thymine (T). The sugar-phosphate molecules in RNA contain the sugar ribose, not deoxyribose.

The three main kinds of RNA made from DNA in a cell's nucleus are messenger RNA (mRNA), ribosomal RNA (rRNA), and transfer RNA (tRNA). Protein production begins when mRNA moves into the cytoplasm. There, ribosomes attach to it. Ribosomes are made of rRNA. Transfer RNA molecules in the cytoplasm bring amino acids to these ribosomes. Inside the ribosomes, three nitrogen bases on the mRNA temporarily match with three nitrogen bases on the tRNA. The same thing happens for the mRNA and another tRNA molecule, as shown in **Figure 17.** The amino acids that are attached to the two tRNA molecules bond. This is the beginning of a protein.

The code carried on the mRNA directs the order in which the amino acids bond. After a tRNA molecule has lost its amino acid, it can move about the cytoplasm and pick up another amino acid just like the first one. The ribosome moves along the mRNA. New tRNA molecules with amino acids match up and add amino acids to the protein molecule.

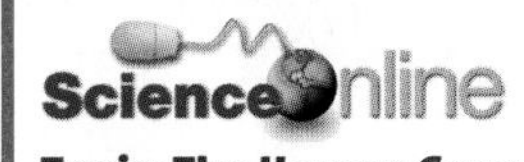

Topic: The Human Genome Project

Visit booka.msscience.com for Web links to information about the Human Genome Project.

Activity Find out when chromosomes 5, 16, 29, 21, and 22 were completely sequenced. Write about what scientists learned about each of these chromosomes.

Figure 17 Cells need DNA, RNA, and amino acids to make proteins.

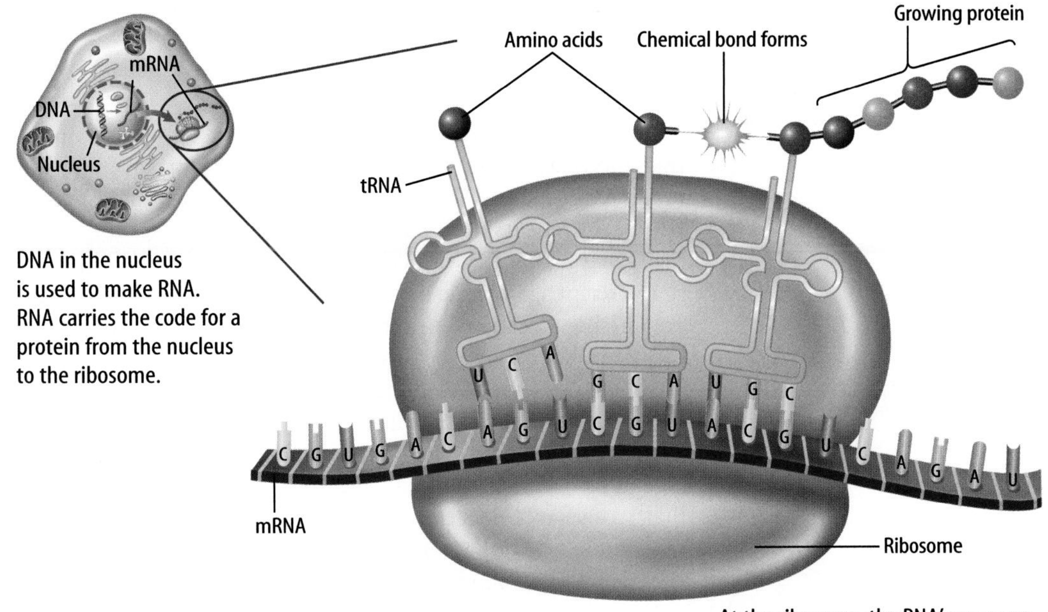

DNA in the nucleus is used to make RNA. RNA carries the code for a protein from the nucleus to the ribosome.

At the ribosome, the RNA's message is translated into a specific protein.

Make a Model

Protein Synthesis Have students draw a cell on a poster board and make a model demonstrating protein synthesis using materials such as craft sticks, beads, yarn, and so on. L2 LS **Visual-Spatial**

Activity

Corresponding Sequence On the board or an overhead transparency, write the sequence for one strand of DNA. Have students copy the sequence and write the corresponding sequence for mRNA and tRNA. L2 LS **Visual-Spatial**

Quick Demo

DNA Replication

Materials pipe cleaners in multiple colors

Estimated Time 5 minutes

Procedure Demonstrate the replication of DNA. Begin with two pipe cleaners of different colors, wrapped around one another as in a double helix. Unwind the strands and separate them. Wrap a new pipe cleaner around each strand, using the opposite color to demonstrate the complimentary strands.

Visual Learning

Figure 17 Have students make an events-chain concept map to outline the stages of protein synthesis. L2 LS **Visual-Spatial**

Curriculum Connection

History Have students study the history of DNA research. Then using poster board, students should draw and label a timeline showing the events of DNA research since DNA was first removed from a cell nucleus in 1869. L3 LS **Visual-Spatial and Kinesthetic** P

SECTION 3 DNA A ◆ 115

Teacher FYI

Mutagens Any agent that can cause a change in DNA is a mutagen. Mutagens can be radiation, chemicals, or even high temperatures. Asbestos, cyanide, and formaldehyde are highly reactive compounds found in buildings and the environment that can interact with DNA and cause changes.

IDENTIFYING Misconceptions

Beneficial Mutation Students may think that any mutation that might occur during duplication is harmful. More often than not, mutations have no effect on the characteristics of the organism. Some mutations, in fact, are adaptive, providing the organism with traits that make it better suited to its environment; these mutations play a major role in evolution. An example of a beneficial mutation in bacteria is antibiotic resistance.

Answer when DNA is being copied

Cells in the iris of the eye produce proteins needed for eye color.
Muscle cells produce proteins that help make muscles move.
Cells in the stomach produce proteins necessary to digest food.

Figure 18 Each cell in the body produces only the proteins that are necessary to do its job.

Controlling Genes You might think that because most cells in an organism have exactly the same chromosomes and the same genes, they would make the same proteins, but they don't. In many-celled organisms like you, each cell uses only some of the thousands of genes that it has to make proteins. Just as each actor uses only the lines from the script for his or her role, each cell uses only the genes that direct the making of proteins that it needs. For example, muscle proteins are made in muscle cells, as represented in **Figure 18,** but not in nerve cells.

Cells must be able to control genes by turning some genes off and turning other genes on. They do this in many different ways. Sometimes the DNA is twisted so tightly that no RNA can be made. Other times, chemicals bind to the DNA so that it cannot be used. If the incorrect proteins are produced, the organism cannot function properly.

Mutations

Sometimes mistakes happen when DNA is being copied. Imagine that the copy of the script the director gave you was missing three pages. You use your copy to learn your lines. When you begin rehearsing for the play, everyone is ready for one of the scenes except for you. What happened? You check your copy of the script against the original and find that three of the pages are missing. Because your script is different from the others, you cannot perform your part correctly.

If DNA is not copied exactly, the proteins made from the instructions might not be made correctly. These mistakes, called **mutations,** are any permanent change in the DNA sequence of a gene or chromosome of a cell. Some mutations include cells that receive an entire extra chromosome or are missing a chromosome. Outside factors such as X rays, sunlight, and some chemicals have been known to cause mutations.

Reading Check *When are mutations likely to occur?*

Science Journal

Effects of Mutation Have students research and write a report on mutations. Have them give examples of mutations, indicate whether the mutation is harmful, benign, or beneficial, and include the cause of the mutation. L2 LS **Linguistic**

Differentiated Instruction

Challenge Have students research the history of the discovery of DNA. Using historical facts, students can include information on DNA pioneers such as Francis Crick, James Watson, Rosalind Franklin, Barbara McClintock, and so on. Other information may include key experiments and how early discoveries helped to pave the way for current genetic technology. L3

Figure 19 Because of a defect on chromosome 2, the mutant fruit fly has short wings and cannot fly.
Predict *Could this defect be transferred to the mutant's offspring? Explain.*

Results of a Mutation Genes control the traits you inherit. Without correctly coded proteins, an organism can't grow, repair, or maintain itself. A change in a gene or chromosome can change the traits of an organism, as illustrated in **Figure 19.**

If the mutation occurs in a body cell, it might or might not be life threatening to the organism. However, if a mutation occurs in a sex cell, then all the cells that are formed from that sex cell will have that mutation. Mutations add variety to a species when the organism reproduces. Many mutations are harmful to organisms, often causing their death. Some mutations do not appear to have any effect on the organism, and some can even be beneficial. For example, a mutation to a plant might cause it to produce a chemical that certain insects avoid. If these insects normally eat the plant, the mutation will help the plant survive.

Science Online

Topic: Fruit Fly Genes

Visit booka.msscience.com for Web links to information about what genes are present on the chromosomes of a fruit fly.

Activity Draw a picture of one of the chromosomes of a fruit fly and label some of its genes.

section 3 review

Summary

What is DNA?

- Each side of the DNA ladder is made up of sugar-phosphate molecules, and the rungs of the ladder are made up of nitrogenous bases.
- When DNA is copied, the new DNA has bases that are identical to those of the original DNA.

Genes

- The instructions for making a specific protein are found in genes in the cell nucleus. Proteins are made on ribosomes in the cytoplasm.
- There are three main kinds of RNA—mRNA, rRNA, and tRNA.

Mutations

- If DNA is not copied exactly, the resulting mutations may cause proteins to be made incorrectly.

Self Check

1. **Describe** how DNA makes a copy of itself.
2. **Explain** how the codes for proteins are carried from the nucleus to the ribosomes.
3. **Apply** A strand of DNA has the bases AGTAAC. Using letters, show a matching DNA strand.
4. **Determine** how tRNA is used when cells build proteins.
5. **Think Critically** You begin as one cell. Compare the DNA in your brain cells to the DNA in your heart cells.

Applying Skills

6. **Concept Map** Using a Venn diagram, compare and contrast DNA and RNA.
7. **Use a word processor** to make an outline of the events that led up to the discovery of DNA. Use library resources to find this information.

Science Online booka.msscience.com/self_check_quiz

Caption Answer

Figure 19 yes, if the defect is in its reproductive cells

3 Assess

DAILY INTERVENTION

Check for Understanding

Visual-Spatial Have students make puzzle pieces that represent the key elements in protein synthesis—three types of RNA, ribosome, amino acids, chemical bond, and protein. Working in pairs, the students can put the puzzle together to demonstrate the process of protein synthesis and students can test each other's ability to identify what each puzzle piece represents. L2

Reteach

DNA and Protein Have students make a drawing of DNA replication and protein synthesis. L2 IN **Visual-Spatial**

Oral What are the three kinds of RNA and their functions? Messenger RNA, transfer RNA, and ribosomal RNA; mRNA is copied from DNA and moves from the nucleus to a ribosome; tRNA carries amino acids to ribosomes; rRNA makes up ribosomes. Use **Performance Assessment in the Science Classroom,** p. 89. L2

section 3 review

1. The two sides unwind and separate; a complementary strand is formed for each, and the resulting double-stranded DNA has one original strand and one new strand.
2. The codes are carried by mRNA from the nucleus to the ribosome.
3. TCATTG
4. The tRNA in the cytoplasm brings amino acids to the ribosomes. There, three nitrogen bases on the mRNA template match with three bases on the tRNA. The amino acids bond, and protein synthesis begins.
5. The DNA is identical.
6. Answers should be similar to the table for question 23 in the Chapter Review.
7. Students should be sure to include the contributions of Miescher, Griffith, Avery, Hershey, Chase, Chargraff, Wilkins, Franklin, Crick, and Watson.

Real-World Question

Purpose

Internet Students use Internet sites that can be accessed through booka.msscience.com/internet_lab.

They will observe genetic traits and mutations in animals. L2

Process Skills collect data, observe, research, communicate, make and use tables, form a hypothesis, compare, describe, record

Time Required about three days

Make a Plan

Preparation

Internet To run through the steps that the students will follow, visit booka.msscience.com/internet_lab.

Non-Internet Have students use books to select an animal and one of its traits to investigate.

LAB Use the Internet

Mutations

Fantail pigeon

Real-World Question

Mutations can result in dominant or recessive genes. A recessive characteristic can appear only if an organism has two recessive genes for that characteristic. However, a dominant characteristic can appear if an organism has one or two dominant genes for that characteristic. Why do some mutations result in more common traits while others do not? Form a hypothesis about how a mutation can become a common trait.

Make a Plan

1. **Observe** common traits in various animals, such as household pets or animals you might see in a zoo.
2. **Learn** what genes carry these traits in each animal.
3. **Research** the traits to discover which ones are results of mutations. Are all mutations dominant? Are any of these mutations beneficial?

Goals

- **Observe** traits of various animals.
- **Research** how mutations become traits.
- Gather data about mutations.
- Make a frequency table of your findings and communicate them to other students.

Data Source

Science Online

Visit booka.msscience.com/internet_lab for more information on common genetic traits in different animals, recessive and dominant genes, and data from other students.

White tiger

Alternative Inquiry Lab

Real-World Connection To observe genetic traits and mutations in animals, give students a more personal investment into the Real-World Question by telling them that they are animal professionals at the zoo trying to maintain variety in the animals that are kept there. They can explore the Web sites of zoos on the Internet. To track what they learn, students can make a table of the different species that are found at the zoos that they investigate. What species are found at only a few zoos? For species that are found at many zoos, what unique traits do species have at the different zoos? Encourage students to research what zoos do to keep variety in the species of animals. Also, have them collect information on species that are becoming extinct.

Using Scientific Methods

Follow Your Plan

1. Make sure your teacher approves your plan before you start.
2. Visit the link shown below to access different Web sites for information about mutations and genetics.
3. **Decide** if a mutation is beneficial, harmful, or neither. Record your data in your Science Journal.

Analyze Your Data

1. **Record** in your Science Journal a list of traits that are results of mutations.
2. **Describe** an animal, such as a pet or an animal you've seen in the zoo. Point out which traits are known to be the result of a mutation.
3. **Make** a chart that compares recessive mutations to dominant mutations. Which are more common?
4. **Share** your data with other students by posting it at the link shown below.

Siberian Husky's eyes

Conclude and Apply

1. **Compare** your findings to those of your classmates and other data at the link shown below. What were some of the traits your classmates found that you did not? Which were the most common?
2. Look at your chart of mutations. Are all mutations beneficial? When might a mutation be harmful to an organism?
3. **Predict** how your data would be affected if you had performed this lab when one of these common mutations first appeared. Do you think you would see more or less animals with this trait?
4. Mutations occur every day but we only see a few of them. Infer how many mutations over millions of years can lead to a new species.

Communicating Your Data

Find this lab using the link below. **Post** your data in the table provided. Combine your data with that of other students and make a chart that shows all of the data.

Science Online
booka.msscience.com/internet_lab

Follow Your Plan

Teaching Strategy Have students use animal population data to see how often that mutation is found. L2

Analyze Your Data

1. Answers will vary. Color can result from a mutation.
2. Answers will depend upon animals chosen.
3. Answers will vary, but dominant genes are not necessarily more common.
4. Students may need help posting data.

Conclude and Apply

1. Answers will vary. Remind students that the most common traits may be the result of mutations.
2. Answers will vary. Have students think about the mutation they are investigating and how helpful or harmful it is to the animal.
3. If you had investigated the mutation when it first appeared, you may have seen fewer animals with the trait. With the passage of time, you can determine if the mutation is beneficial.
4. Organisms with mutations may be better suited to a particular environment. These traits would be passed on to their offspring. Many mutations may lead to a new species.

Communicating Your Data

Have students use the Internet resources to collect pictures of the animal they are investigating. Have them find pictures that show the mutation.

Assessment

Oral Students describe mutations they researched and discuss how helpful they are to animals. Show pictures of animals with the mutation. Use **Performance Assessment in the Science Classroom,** p. 143. L2

Oops! Accidents in SCIENCE

SOMETIMES GREAT DISCOVERIES HAPPEN BY ACCIDENT!

Content Background

Cytogenetics is the branch of science that studies heredity both through genetics and studies of the cell. In 1956, modern human cytogenetics began, thanks to the discovery of the number of human chromosomes present in each cell of the body. As early as 1905, scientists had determined that chromosomes are found in pairs, and in 1915 Thomas Hunt Morgan discovered that genes were found on chromosomes. It was not until 1952 that Dr. Hsu's work occurred, and 1953 when Watson and Crick used Rosalind Franklin's work to determine the structure of DNA. Studies of human chromosomes and genes have progressed at an astounding rate since that time. Scientists have determined the particular chromosome that carries the gene for many human diseases and other traits.

Discussion

Explain What type of mistake could the lab technician in Dr. Hsu's lab have made while mixing the solution to cause mysterious behavior of the chromosomes? Possible answer: The technician either added too little of the solute to a set amount of water, or too much water to a set amount of solute, causing the solution to have a higher water content than the cells.

Activity

Genetics Have students work in teams to research the major discoveries in the field of genetics. Have each team display their results on a time line made on a long piece of paper. Students should be encouraged to include discoveries from early research until present times and to include the names of the scientists who made the discoveries. L2

A Tangled Tale

How did a scientist get chromosomes to separate?

Thanks to chromosomes, each of us is unique!

Viewed under the microscope, chromosomes in cells sometimes look a lot like spaghetti. That's why scientists had such a hard time figuring out how many chromosomes are in each human cell. Imagine, then, how Dr. Tao-Chiuh Hsu (dow shew•SEW) must have felt when he looked into a microscope and saw "beautifully scattered chromosomes." The problem was, Hsu didn't know what he had done to separate the chromosomes into countable strands.

"I tried to study those slides and set up some more cultures to repeat the miracle," Hsu explained. "But nothing happened."

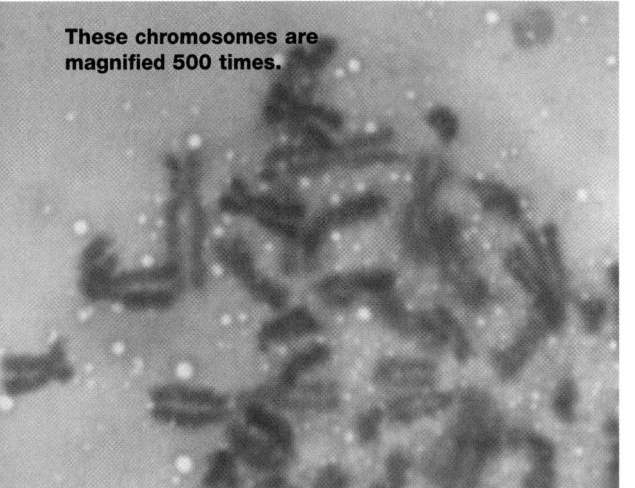

These chromosomes are magnified 500 times.

For three months Hsu tried changing every variable he could think of to make the chromosomes separate again. In April 1952, his efforts were finally rewarded. Hsu quickly realized that the chromosomes separated because of osmosis.

Osmosis is the movement of water molecules through cell membranes. This movement occurs in predictable ways. The water molecules move from areas with higher concentrations of water to areas with lower concentrations of water. In Hsu's case, the solution he used to prepare the cells had a higher concentration of water then the cell did. So water moved from the solution into the cell and the cell swelled until it finally exploded. The chromosomes suddenly were visible as separate strands.

What made the cells swell the first time? Apparently a technician had mixed the solution incorrectly. "Since nearly four months had elapsed, there was no way to trace who actually had prepared that particular [solution]," Hsu noted. "Therefore, this heroine must remain anonymous."

Research What developments led scientists to conclude that the human cell has 46 chromosomes? Visit the link shown to the right to get started.

For more information, visit booka.msscience.com/oops

Research As students research the history of research on human chromosomes, have them consider the rate at which discoveries occurred then and now. Point out that the Human Genome Project has increased the knowledge of genetics at an amazing rate. L2

Resources for Teachers and Students

DNA and Genetic Engineering (Cells & Life), by Robert Snedden, Heinemann Library, 2003

The Big Idea, by Paul Strathern. New York: Doubleday, 1999

Reviewing Main Ideas

Section 1 Cell Division and Mitosis

1. The life cycle of a cell has two parts—growth and development, and cell division.
2. In mitosis, the nucleus divides to form two identical nuclei. Mitosis occurs in four continuous steps, or phases—prophase, metaphase, anaphase, and telophase.
3. Cell division in animal cells and plant cells is similar, but plant cells do not have centrioles and animal cells do not form cell walls.
4. Organisms use cell division to grow, to replace cells, and for asexual reproduction. Asexual reproduction produces organisms with DNA identical to the parent's DNA. Fission, budding, and regeneration can be used for asexual reproduction.

Section 2 Sexual Reproduction and Meiosis

1. Sexual reproduction results when an egg and sperm join. This event is called fertilization, and the cell that forms is called the zygote.
2. Meiosis occurs in the reproductive organs, producing four haploid sex cells.
3. During meiosis, two divisions of the nucleus occur.
4. Meiosis ensures that offspring produced by fertilization have the same number of chromosomes as their parents.

Section 3 DNA

1. DNA is a large molecule made up of two twisted strands of sugar-phosphate molecules and nitrogen bases.
2. All cells contain DNA. The section of DNA on a chromosome that directs the making of a specific protein is a gene.
3. DNA can copy itself and is the pattern from which RNA is made. Messenger RNA, ribosomal RNA, and transfer RNA are used to make proteins.
4. Permanent changes in DNA are called mutations.

Visualizing Main Ideas

Think of four ways that organisms can use mitosis. Copy and complete the spider diagram below.

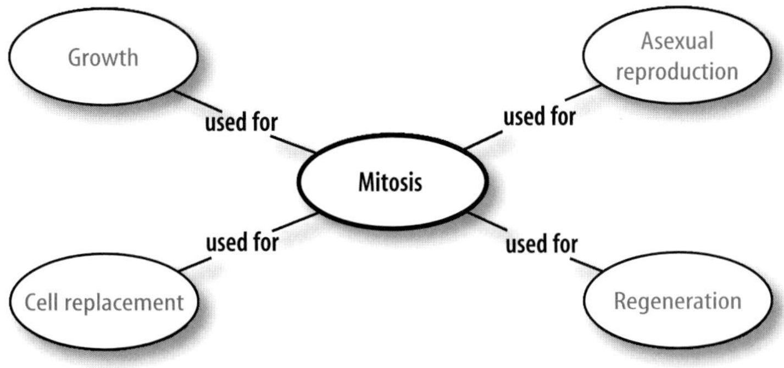

chapter 4 Study Guide

Reviewing Main Ideas

Summary statements can be used by students to review the major concepts of the chapter.

Visualizing Main Ideas

See student page.

Visit booka.msscience.com
/self_check_quiz
/interactive_tutor
/vocabulary_puzzlemaker
/chapter_review
/standardized_test

Assessment Transparency

For additional assessment questions, use the *Assessment Transparency* located in the transparency book.

Assessment

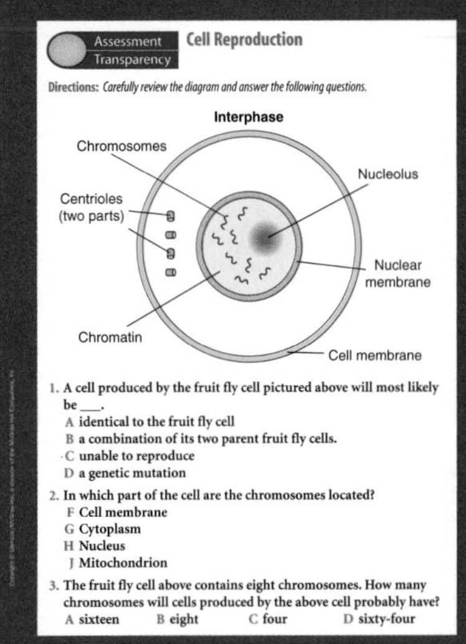

Assessment Transparency — Cell Reproduction

Directions: Carefully review the diagram and answer the following questions.

Interphase

1. A cell produced by the fruit fly cell pictured above will most likely be ___.
   A identical to the fruit fly cell
   B a combination of its two parent fruit fly cells.
   C unable to reproduce
   D a genetic mutation
2. In which part of the cell are the chromosomes located?
   F Cell membrane
   G Cytoplasm
   H Nucleus
   J Mitochondrion
3. The fruit fly cell above contains eight chromosomes. How many chromosomes will cells produced by the above cell probably have?
   A sixteen B eight C four D sixty-four

Using Vocabulary

1. Egg, sperm
2. Mitosis
3. DNA or RNA
4. gene
5. haploid
6. asexual reproduction
7. chromosome
8. Meiosis
9. Fertilization, meiosis, or sexual reproduction
10. mutation

Checking Concepts

11. D
12. D
13. B
14. C
15. A
16. A
17. D
18. C
19. B

chapter 4 Review

Using Vocabulary

asexual reproduction p. 103	haploid p. 107
chromosome p. 100	meiosis p. 107
diploid p. 106	mitosis p. 100
DNA p. 112	mutation p. 116
egg p. 106	RNA p. 114
fertilization p. 106	sexual reproduction p. 106
gene p. 114	sperm p. 106
	zygote p. 106

Fill in the blanks with the correct vocabulary word or words.

1. _________ and _________ cells are sex cells.
2. _________ produces two identical cells.
3. An example of a nucleic acid is _________.
4. A(n) _________ is the code for a protein.
5. A(n) _________ sperm is formed during meiosis.
6. Budding is a type of _________.
7. A(n) _________ is a structure in the nucleus that contains hereditary material.
8. _________ produces four sex cells.
9. As a result of _________, a new organism develops that has its own unique identity.
10. An error made during the copying of DNA is called a(n) _________.

Checking Concepts

Choose the word or phrase that best answers the question.

11. Which of the following is a double spiral molecule with pairs of nitrogen bases?
    A) RNA **C)** protein
    B) amino acid **D)** DNA

12. What is in RNA but not in DNA?
    A) thymine **C)** adenine
    B) thyroid **D)** uracil

13. If a diploid tomato cell has 24 chromosomes, how many chromosomes will the tomato's sex cells have?
    A) 6 **C)** 24
    B) 12 **D)** 48

14. During a cell's life cycle, when do chromosomes duplicate?
    A) anaphase **C)** interphase
    B) metaphase **D)** telophase

15. When do chromatids separate during mitosis?
    A) anaphase **C)** metaphase
    B) prophase **D)** telophase

16. How is the hydra shown in the picture reproducing?
    A) asexually, by budding
    B) sexually, by budding
    C) asexually, by fission
    D) sexually, by fission

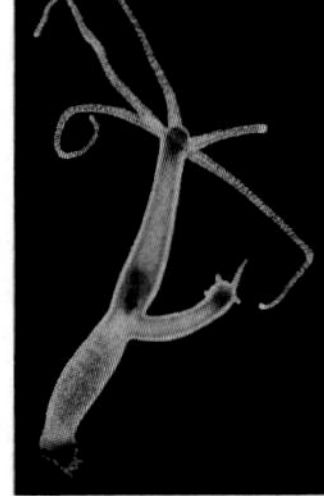

17. What is any permanent change in a gene or a chromosome called?
    A) fission **C)** replication
    B) reproduction **D)** mutation

18. What does meiosis produce?
    A) cells with the diploid chromosome number
    B) cells with identical chromosomes
    C) sex cells
    D) a zygote

19. What type of nucleic acid carries the codes for making proteins from the nucleus to the ribosome?
    A) DNA **C)** protein
    B) RNA **D)** genes

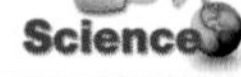

booka.msscience.com/vocabulary_puzzlemaker

Use the Exam*View*® Pro Testmaker CD-ROM to:

- create multiple versions of tests
- create modified tests with one mouse click for inclusion students
- edit existing questions and add your own questions
- build tests aligned with state standards using built-in State Curriculum Tags
- change English tests to Spanish with one mouse click and vice versa

Thinking Critically

20. **List** the base sequence of a strand of RNA made using the DNA pattern ATCCGTC. Look at **Figure 14** for a hint.

21. **Predict** whether a mutation in a human skin cell can be passed on to the person's offspring. Explain.

22. **Explain** how a zygote could end up with an extra chromosome.

23. **Classify** Copy and complete this table about DNA and RNA.

DNA and RNA

	DNA	RNA
Number of strands	2	1
Type of sugar	deoxyribose	ribose
Letter names of bases	G, A, C, T	G, A, C, U
Where found	nucleus	nucleus & cytoplasm

24. **Concept Map** Make an events-chain concept map of what occurs from interphase in the parent cell to the formation of the zygote. Tell whether the chromosome's number at each stage is haploid or diploid.

25. **Concept Map** Copy and complete the events-chain concept map of DNA synthesis.

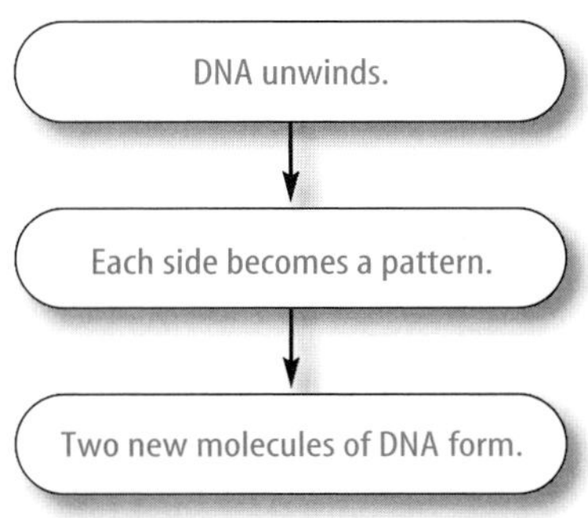
DNA unwinds.
Each side becomes a pattern.
Two new molecules of DNA form.

26. **Compare and Contrast** Meiosis is two divisions of a reproductive cell's nucleus. It occurs in a continuous series of steps. Compare and contrast the steps of meiosis I to the steps of meiosis II.

27. **Describe** what occurs in mitosis that gives the new cells identical DNA.

28. **Form a hypothesis** about the effect of an incorrect mitotic division on the new cells produced.

29. **Determine** how many chromosomes are in the original cell compared to those in the new cells formed by cell division. Explain.

Performance Activities

30. **Flash Cards** Make a set of 11 flash cards with drawings of a cell that show the different stages of meiosis. Shuffle your cards and then put them in the correct order. Give them to another student in the class to try.

Applying Math

31. **Cell Cycle** Assume an average human cell has a cell cycle of 20 hours. Calculate how many cells there would be after 80 hours.

Use the diagram below to answer question 32.

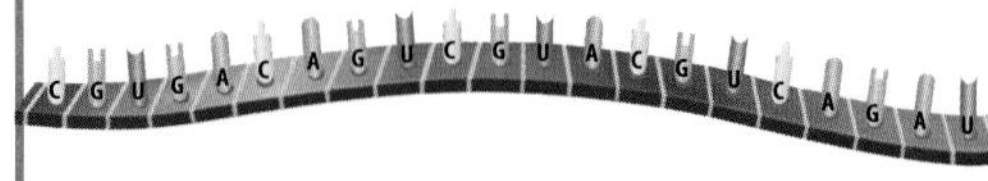
C G U G A C A G U C G U A C G U C A G A U

32. **Amino Acids** Sets of three nitrogen bases code for an amino acid. How many amino acids will make up the protein molecule that is coded for by the mRNA molecule above?

Science Online booka.msscience.com/chapter_review

✓ Assessment Resources

Reproducible Masters

Chapter *Fast File* Resources
- Chapter Review, pp. 35–36
- Chapter Tests, pp. 37–40
- Assessment Transparency Activity, p. 47

Glencoe Science Web site
- Chapter Review Test
- Standardized Test Practice

Glencoe Technology
- Assessment Transparency
- Exam*View*® Pro Testmaker
- MindJogger Videoquiz
- Interactive Chalkboard

Thinking Critically

20. UAGGCAG
21. No; in order for a mutation to be passed to offspring, the mutation must take place in a sex cell.
22. This could happen if nondisjunction (failure of like chromosomes or chromatids to separate) occurs during anaphase I or II.
23. See student page.
24. The order of events given for meiosis should reflect **Figure 11** and formation of the zygote, **Figure 10.** The cell at the beginning of meiosis is diploid. The four cells at the end of meiosis are all haploid.
25. See student page.
26. Student answers should reflect the information in Section 2 and **Figure 11.**
27. the copying of chromosomes in interphase; the separation of the copies at anaphase; the separation of two new cells at telophase
28. Incorrect division can result in an incorrect number of chromosomes, often leading to abnormal offspring.
29. The number of chromosomes in the new cell are the same as in the original cell; DNA is copied before mitosis so new cells retained the correct number of chromosomes.

Performance Activities

30. Cards should be sequenced as shown in **Figure 11.** If interphase is included, it should come before prophase I. **Use Performance Assessment in the Science Classroom,** p. 163.

Applying Math

National Math Standards

1, 6, 9

31. 80 hours divided by 20 hours = 4 cycles; $2^4 = 16$ cells
32. 7

FAST FILE

Answer Sheet A practice answer sheet can be found at booka.msscience.com/answer_sheet.

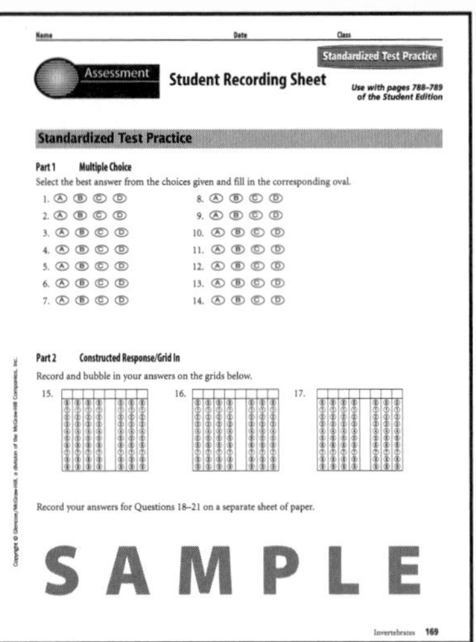
Name Date Class

Standardized Test Practice

Assessment **Student Recording Sheet**

Use with pages 788–789 of the Student Edition

Standardized Test Practice

Part 1 Multiple Choice

Select the best answer from the choices given and fill in the corresponding oval.

1. Ⓐ Ⓑ Ⓒ Ⓓ
2. Ⓐ Ⓑ Ⓒ Ⓓ
3. Ⓐ Ⓑ Ⓒ Ⓓ
4. Ⓐ Ⓑ Ⓒ Ⓓ
5. Ⓐ Ⓑ Ⓒ Ⓓ
6. Ⓐ Ⓑ Ⓒ Ⓓ
7. Ⓐ Ⓑ Ⓒ Ⓓ
8. Ⓐ Ⓑ Ⓒ Ⓓ
9. Ⓐ Ⓑ Ⓒ Ⓓ
10. Ⓐ Ⓑ Ⓒ Ⓓ
11. Ⓐ Ⓑ Ⓒ Ⓓ
12. Ⓐ Ⓑ Ⓒ Ⓓ
13. Ⓐ Ⓑ Ⓒ Ⓓ
14. Ⓐ Ⓑ Ⓒ Ⓓ

Part 2 Constructed Response/Grid In

Record and bubble in your answers on the grids below.

15. 16. 17.

Record your answers for Questions 18–21 on a separate sheet of paper.

SAMPLE

Invertebrates 169

Part 1 Multiple Choice

1. B	**4.** A	**7.** A
2. C	**5.** D	**8.** C
3. B	**6.** B	**9.** C

Part 2 Short Response

10. Non-circulating red blood cells and skin cells are constantly dividing to replace old cells and allow for growth. If cells divide too much, cancer may result.

11. meiosis, sex cells, fertilization, zygote, mitosis

12. messenger RNA (mRNA), carries the DNA code to the ribosomes; ribosomal RNA (rRNA), makes up part of the ribosome; and transfer RNA (tRNA), brings amino acids to the ribosomes

13. The instructions for making a specific protein are found in a gene which is a section of DNA on a chromosome.

chapter 4 Standardized Test Practice

Part 1 Multiple Choice

Record your answers on the answer sheet provided by your teacher or on a sheet of paper.

1. What stage of the cell cycle involves growth and function?
A. prophase **C.** mitosis
B. interphase **D.** cytoplasmic division

2. During interphase, which structure of a cell is duplicated?
A. cell plate
B. mitochondrion
C. chromosome
D. chloroplast

Use the figure below to answer questions 3 and 4.

3. What form of asexual reproduction is shown here?
A. regeneration **C.** sprouting
B. cell division **D.** meiosis

4. How does the genetic material of the new organism above compare to that of the parent organism?
A. It is exactly the same.
B. It is a little different.
C. It is completely different.
D. It is haploid.

5. Organisms with three or more sets of chromosomes are called
A. monoploid. **C.** haploid.
B. diploid. **D.** polyploid.

6. If a sex cell has eight chromosomes, how many chromosomes will there be after fertilization?
A. 8 **C.** 32
B. 16 **D.** 64

Use the diagram below to answer questions 7 and 8.

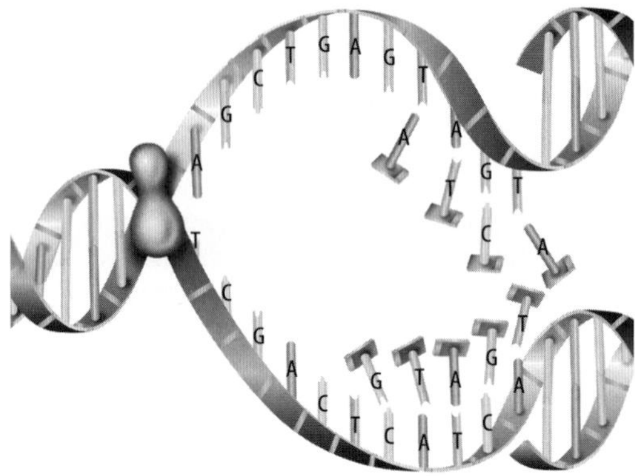

7. What does this diagram illustrate?
A. DNA duplication
B. RNA
C. cell reproduction
D. RNA synthesis

8. When does the process shown occur in the cell cycle?
A. prophase **C.** interphase
B. metaphase **D.** anaphase

9. Proteins are made of
A. genes **C.** amino acids
B. bases **D.** chromosomes

Test-Taking Tip

Prepare Avoid rushing on test day. Prepare your clothes and test supplies the night before. Wake up early and arrive at school on time on test day.

14. See student page.

15. Cells that are no longer dividing would remain constantly in interphase. Brain cells are an example of cells constantly in interphase.

16. Regeneration allows some organisms to grow back injured or removed body parts.

17. Plants are the most common types of polyploidy organisms and we use many of them as food.

18. In meiosis I each duplicated chromosome pairs with its duplicated mate and then they separate. In meiosis II the chromatids of each chromosome separate, resulting in four cells with half the original number of chromosomes.

19. A new organism can be produced via asexual reproduction. The resulting organism from budding or regeneration will be an exact copy of the parent organism. New organisms can also be produced by sexual reproduction where two sex cells come together during fertilization to create a unique new individual.

Part 2 Short Response/Grid In

Record your answers on the answer sheet provided by your teacher or on a sheet of paper.

10. In the human body, which cells are constantly dividing? Why is this important? How can this be potentially harmful?
11. Arrange the following terms in the correct order: *fertilization, sex cells, meiosis, zygote, mitosis.*
12. What are the three types of RNA used during protein synthesis? What is the function of each type of RNA?
13. Describe the relationship between gene, protein, DNA and chromosome.

Use the table below to answer question 14.

Phase of Cell Division	Action within the Cell
	Chromosomes duplicate
Prophase	
Metaphase	
	Chromosomes have separated
Telophase	

14. Fill in the blanks in the table with the appropriate term or definition.
15. What types of cells would constantly be in interphase?
16. Why is regeneration important for some organisms? In what way could regeneration of nerve cells be beneficial for humans?
17. What types of organisms are polyploidy? Why are they important?
18. What happens to chromosomes in meiosis I and meiosis II?
19. Describe several different ways that organisms can reproduce.

Part 3 Open Ended

Record your answers on a sheet of paper.

Use the photo below to answer question 20.

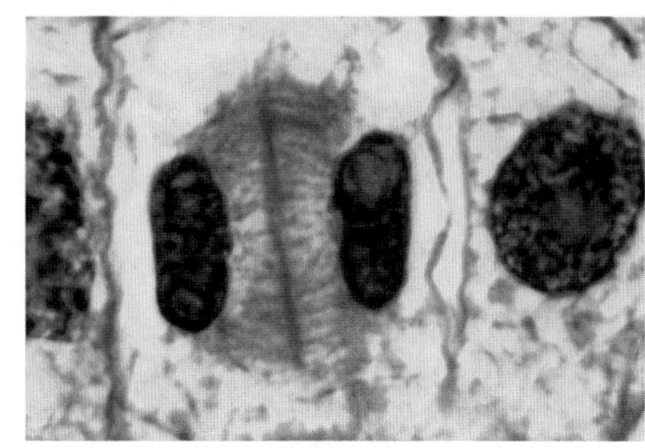

20. Is this a plant or an animal cell? Compare and contrast animal and plant cell division.
21. Describe in detail the structure of DNA.

Use the diagram below to answer question 22.

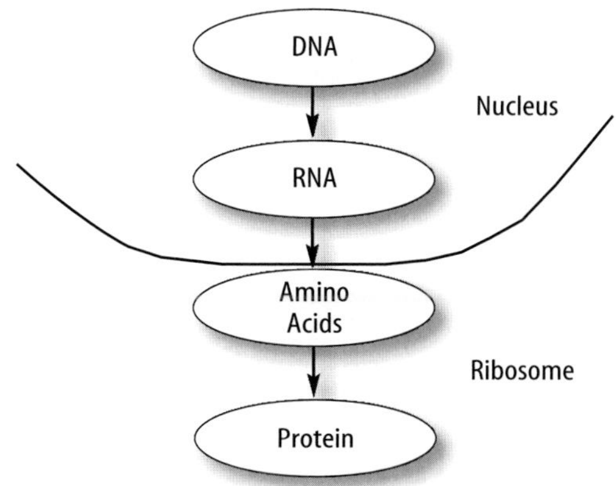

22. Discuss in detail what is taking place at each step of protein synthesis diagrammed above.
23. If a skin cell and a stomach cell have the same DNA then why are they so different?
24. What is mutation? Give examples where mutations could be harmful, beneficial or neutral.

Part 3 Open Ended

20. A plant cell appears in the picture. Cell division in a plant and animal cell are very similar. They both have interphase, mitosis and cytoplasmic division. The phases of mitosis are prophase, metaphase, anaphase and telophase. In prophase animal cells have centrioles and plant cells do not. In telophase, plant cells form a cell plate and animal cells do not.
21. DNA has a structure similar to a twisted ladder. The sides of the ladder are sugar-phosphate molecules and the rungs of the ladder are nitrogenous bases. RNA has only one side of the ladder with rungs of the nitrogenous bases. DNA and RNA both have the nitrogenous bases adenine, cytosine and guanine. RNA has uracil and DNA has thymine which pair with adenine.
22. In this diagram, DNA in the nucleus is used to make RNA. RNA carries the code for a protein from the nucleus to a ribosome. At the ribosome, the message is translated to assemble amino acids into proteins.
23. A skin cell and stomach cell are so different because cells can turn genes on and off. Different genes in the skin cell are turned on so that it can carry out different functions than the stomach cell.
24. A mutation is a change in the sequence of DNA that codes for a gene or a change in the number chromosomes. There are many examples of harmful mutations; some could just cause the organism to not thrive in the environment and some may cause death. Beneficial mutations are those which benefit the organism's chance of survival. Neutral mutations do not benefit or harm the organism.

Rubrics

For more help evaluating open-ended assessment questions, see the rubric on p. 10T.

chapter 5 Organizer

Section/Objectives	Standards		Labs/Features
	National	**State/Local**	
Chapter Opener	See pp. 16T–17T for a Key to Standards.		**Launch Lab:** Who around you has dimples?, p. 127 **Foldables,** p. 127
Section 1 Genetics 2 sessions 1 block 1. **Explain** how traits are inherited. 2. **Identify** Mendel's role in the history of genetics. 3. **Use** a Punnett square to predict the results of crosses. 4. **Compare and contrast** the difference between an individual's genotype and phenotype.	National Content Standards: UCP.1–UCP.3, UCP.5, A.1, A.2, C.1, C.2, G.2, G.3		**Science Online,** p. 129 **MiniLAB:** Comparing Common Traits, p. 130 **Visualizing Mendel's Experiments,** p. 131 **Applying Math:** Punnett Square, p. 133 **Lab:** Predicting Results, p. 135
Section 2 Genetics Since Mendel 2 sessions 1 block 5. **Explain** how traits are inherited by incomplete dominance. 6. **Compare** multiple alleles and polygenic inheritance, and give examples of each. 7. **Describe** two human genetic disorders and how they are inherited. 8. **Explain** how sex-linked traits are passed to offspring.	National Content Standards: UCP.1–UCP.5, A.1, A.2, C.1, C.2, F.1, G.1		**Science Online,** p. 137 **MiniLAB:** Interpreting Polygenic Inheritance, p. 138 **Integrate Career,** p. 139
Section 3 Advances in Genetics 3 sessions 1.5 blocks 9. **Evaluate** the importance of advances in genetics. 10. **Sequence** the steps in making genetically engineered organisms.	National Content Standards: UCP.1–UCP.5, A.1, A.2, C.1, C.2, F.3, F.5		**Integrate Environment,** p. 144 **Lab:** Tests for Color Blindness, p. 146 **Science Stats:** The Human Genome, p. 148

Lab Materials	Reproducible Resources	Section Assessment	Technology
Launch Lab: Science Journal	**Chapter *Fast File* Resources** Foldables Worksheets, p. 13 Directed Reading Overview, p. 15 Note-taking Worksheets, pp. 29–31	Glencoe's Assessment Advantage	TeacherWorks includes: • Interactive Teacher Edition • Lesson Planner with calendar • Access to all program blacklines • Correlations to standards • Web links
MiniLAB: pencil, paper **Lab:** paper bags (2), red beans (100), white beans (100)	**Chapter *Fast File* Resources** Transparency Activity, p. 40 MiniLAB, p. 3 Directed Reading, p. 16 Enrichment, p. 26 Reinforcement, p. 23 Lab Worksheet, pp. 5–6 Lab Activity, pp. 9–10, 11–12 **Mathematics Skill Activities,** p. 23	Portfolio Differentiated Instruction, p. 132 Performance MiniLAB, p. 130 Applying Math, p. 133 Applying Math, p. 134 Content Section Review, p. 134	Section Focus Transparency Virtual Labs CD-ROM Guided Reading Audio Program Interactive Chalkboard CD-ROM Video Lab
MiniLAB: paper, pencil, ruler *Need materials?* Contact Science Kit at 1-800-828-7777 or www.sciencekit.com on the Internet.	**Chapter *Fast File* Resources** Transparency Activity, p. 41 MiniLAB, p. 4 Enrichment, p. 27 Reinforcement, p. 24 Directed Reading, p. 16 Transparency Activity, pp. 43–44 **Life Science Critical Thinking/ Problem Solving,** p. 19	Portfolio Science Journal, p. 137 Performance MiniLAB, p. 138 Applying Skills, p. 142 Content Section Review, p. 142	Section Focus Transparency Teaching Transparency Virtual Labs CD-ROM Guided Reading Audio Program Interactive Chalkboard CD-ROM
Lab: white paper or poster board, colored markers	**Chapter *Fast File* Resources** Transparency Activity, p. 42 Enrichment, p. 28 Reinforcement, p. 25 Directed Reading, pp. 17, 18 Lab Worksheet, pp. 7–8 **Lab Management and Safety,** p. 74	Portfolio Assessment, p. 145 Performance Applying Skills, p. 145 Content Section Review, p. 145	Section Focus Transparency Virtual Labs CD-ROM Guided Reading Audio Program Interactive Chalkboard CD-ROM

End of Chapter Assessment

Glencoe's Assessment Advantage

Blackline Masters	Technology	Professional Series
Chapter *Fast File* Resources Chapter Review, pp. 33–34 Chapter Tests, pp. 35–38 **Standardized Test Practice,** pp. 23–26	MindJogger Videoquiz Virtual Labs CD-ROM Exam*View*® Pro Testmaker TeacherWorks CD-ROM Interactive Chalkboard CD-ROM	**Performance Assessment in the Science Classroom (PASC)**

Transparencies

Section Focus

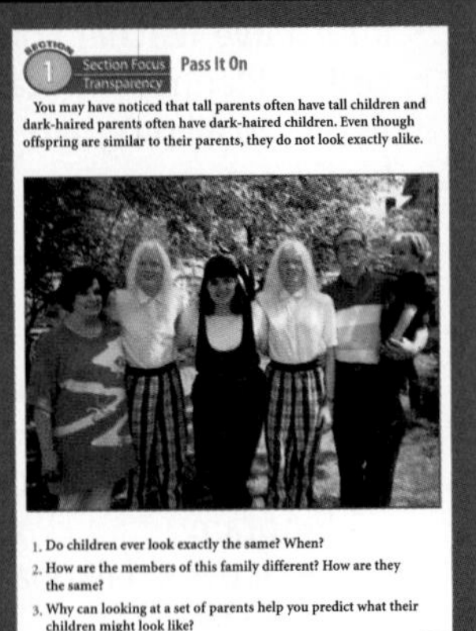

Section 1 Section Focus Transparency — Pass It On

You may have noticed that tall parents often have tall children and dark-haired parents often have dark-haired children. Even though offspring are similar to their parents, they do not look exactly alike.

1. Do children ever look exactly the same? When?
2. How are the members of this family different? How are they the same?
3. Why can looking at a set of parents help you predict what their children might look like?

L2

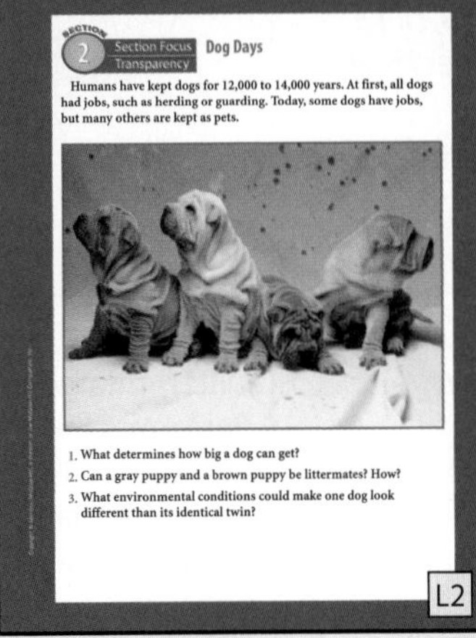

Section 2 Section Focus Transparency — Dog Days

Humans have kept dogs for 12,000 to 14,000 years. At first, all dogs had jobs, such as herding or guarding. Today, some dogs have jobs, but many others are kept as pets.

1. What determines how big a dog can get?
2. Can a gray puppy and a brown puppy be littermates? How?
3. What environmental conditions could make one dog look different than its identical twin?

L2

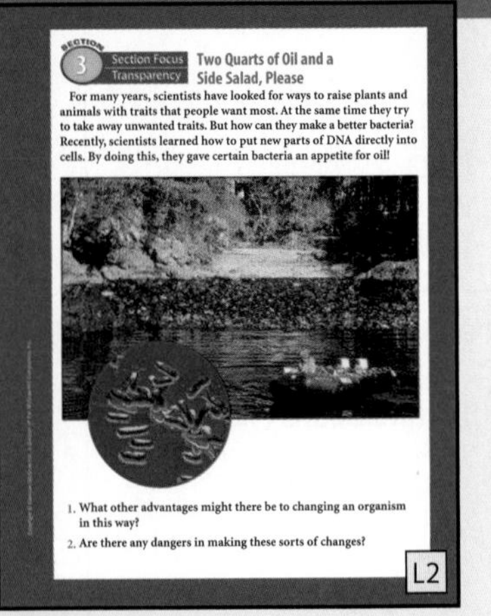

Section 3 Section Focus Transparency — Two Quarts of Oil and a Side Salad, Please

For many years, scientists have looked for ways to raise plants and animals with traits that people want most. At the same time they try to take away unwanted traits. But how can they make a better bacteria? Recently, scientists learned how to put new parts of DNA directly into cells. By doing this, they gave certain bacteria an appetite for oil!

1. What other advantages might there be to changing an organism in this way?
2. Are there any dangers in making these sorts of changes?

L2

This is a representation of key blackline masters available in the Teacher Classroom Resources. See Resource Manager boxes within the chapter for additional information.

Assessment

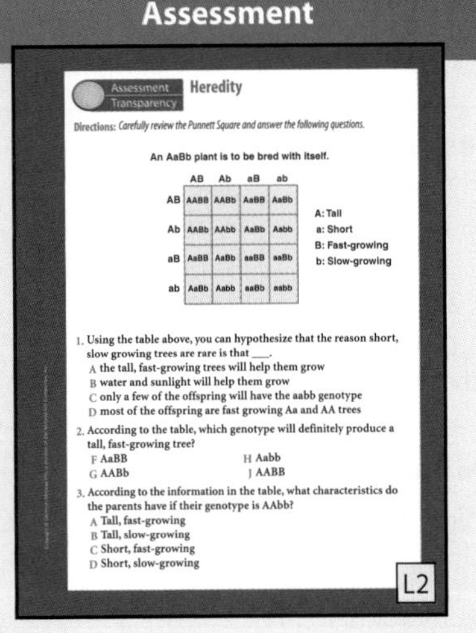

Assessment Transparency — Heredity

Directions: *Carefully review the Punnett Square and answer the following questions.*

An AaBb plant is to be bred with itself.

	AB	Ab	aB	ab
AB	AABB	AABb	AaBB	AaBb
Ab	AABb	AAbb	AaBb	Aabb
aB	AaBB	AaBb	aaBB	aaBb
ab	AaBb	Aabb	aaBb	aabb

A: Tall
a: Short
B: Fast-growing
b: Slow-growing

1. Using the table above, you can hypothesize that the reason short, slow growing trees are rare is that ___.
   A the tall, fast-growing trees will help them grow
   B water and sunlight will help them grow
   C only a few of the offspring will have the aabb genotype
   D most of the offspring are fast growing Aa and AA trees
2. According to the table, which genotype will definitely produce a tall, fast-growing tree?
   F AaBB
   G AABb
   H Aabb
   J AABB
3. According to the information in the table, what characteristics do the parents have if their genotype is AAbb?
   A Tall, fast-growing
   B Tall, slow-growing
   C Short, fast-growing
   D Short, slow-growing

L2

Teaching

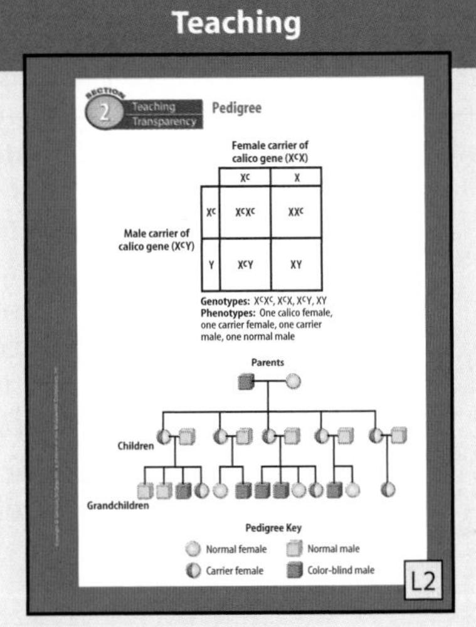

Section 2 Teaching Transparency — Pedigree

Female carrier of calico gene (X^cX)

Male carrier of calico gene (X^cY)

	X^c	X
X^c	X^cX^c	XX^c
Y	X^cY	XY

Genotypes: X^cX^c, X^cX, X^cY, XY
Phenotypes: One calico female, one carrier female, one carrier male, one normal male

L2

Key to Teaching Strategies

The following designations will help you decide which activities are appropriate for your students.

- **L1** Level 1 activities should be appropriate for students with learning difficulties.
- **L2** Level 2 activities should be within the ability range of all students.
- **L3** Level 3 activities are designed for above-average students.
- **ELL** ELL activities should be within the ability range of English-Language Learners.
- **COOP LEARN** Cooperative Learning activities are designed for small group work.
- **LS** Multiple Learning Styles logos, as described on page 12T, are used throughout to indicate strategies that address different learning styles.
- **P** These strategies represent student products that can be placed into a best-work portfolio.
- **PBL** Problem-Based Learning activities apply real-world situations to learning.

Hands-on Activities

Student Text Lab Worksheet

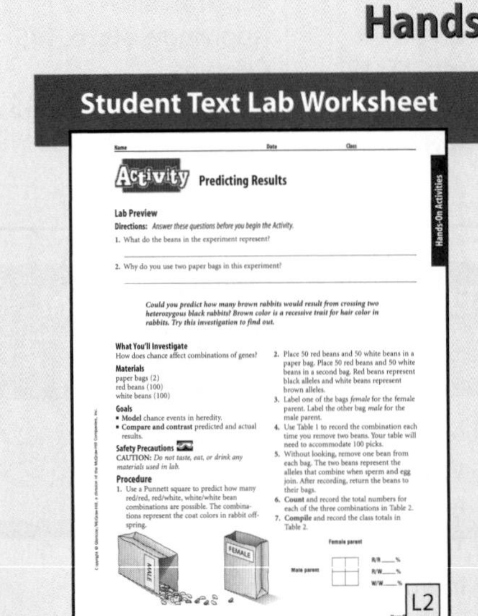

Name Date Class

Activity — Predicting Results

Lab Preview

Directions: *Answer these questions before you begin the Activity.*

1. What do the beans in the experiment represent?
2. Why do you use two paper bags in this experiment?

Could you predict how many brown rabbits would result from crossing two heterozygous black rabbits? Brown color is a recessive trait for hair color in rabbits. Try this investigation to find out.

What You'll Investigate
How does chance affect combinations of genes?

Materials
paper bags (2)
red beans (100)
white beans (100)

Goals
- **Model** chance events in heredity.
- **Compare and contrast** predicted and actual results.

Safety Precautions
CAUTION: *Do not taste, eat, or drink any materials used in lab.*

Procedure
1. Use a Punnett square to predict how many red/red, red/white, white/white bean combinations are possible. The combinations represent the coat colors in rabbit offspring.
2. Place 50 red beans and 50 white beans in a paper bag. Place 50 red beans and 50 white beans in a second bag. Red beans represent black alleles and white beans represent brown alleles.
3. Label one of the bags *female* for the female parent. Label the other bag *male* for the male parent.
4. Use Table 1 to record the combination each time you remove two beans. Your table will need to accommodate 100 picks.
5. Without looking, remove one bean from each bag. The two beans represent the alleles that combine when sperm and egg join. After recording, return the beans to their bags.
6. **Count** and record the total numbers for each of the three combinations in Table 2.
7. **Compile** and record the class totals in Table 2.

L2

Laboratory Activities

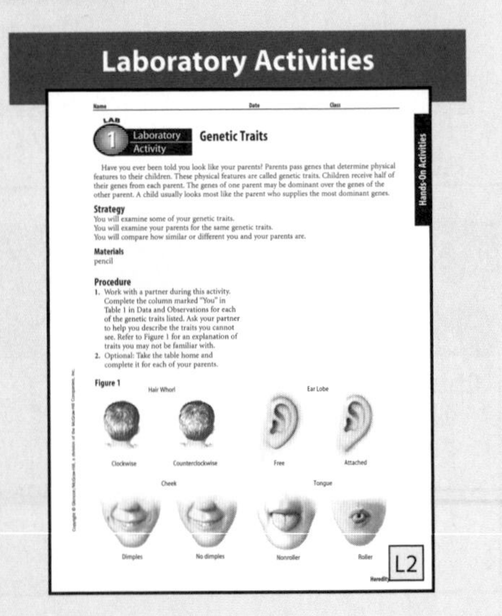

Name Date Class

Lab 1 Laboratory Activity — Genetic Traits

Have you ever been told you look like your parents? Parents pass genes that determine physical features to their children. These physical features are called genetic traits. Children receive half of their genes from each parent. The genes of one parent may be dominant over the genes of the other parent. A child usually looks most like the parent who supplies the most dominant genes.

Strategy
You will examine some of your genetic traits.
You will examine your parents for the same genetic traits.
You will compare how similar or different you and your parents are.

Materials
pencil

Procedure
1. Work with a partner during this activity. Complete the column marked "You" in Table 1 in Data and Observations for each of the genetic traits listed. Ask your partner to help you describe the traits you cannot see. Refer to Figure 1 for an explanation of traits you may not be familiar with.
2. Optional: Take the table home and complete it for each of your parents.

Figure 1

L2

Meeting Different Ability Levels

Content Outline

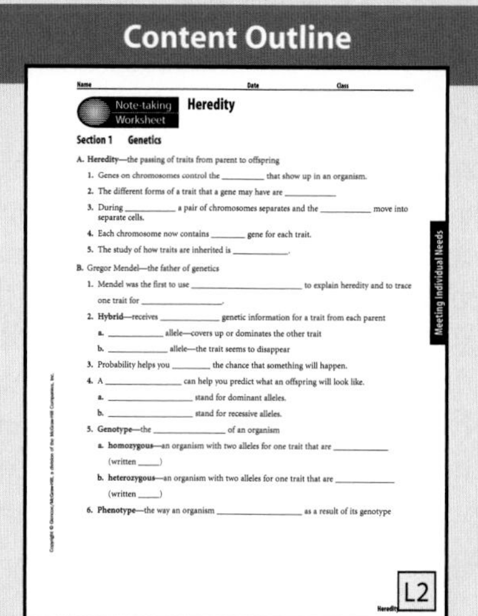

Reinforcement

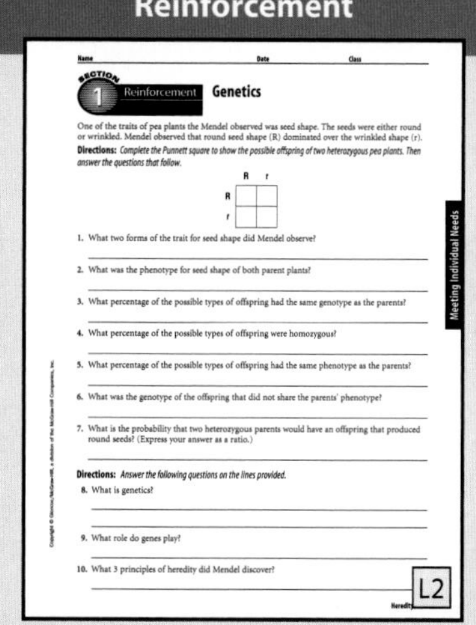

Enrichment

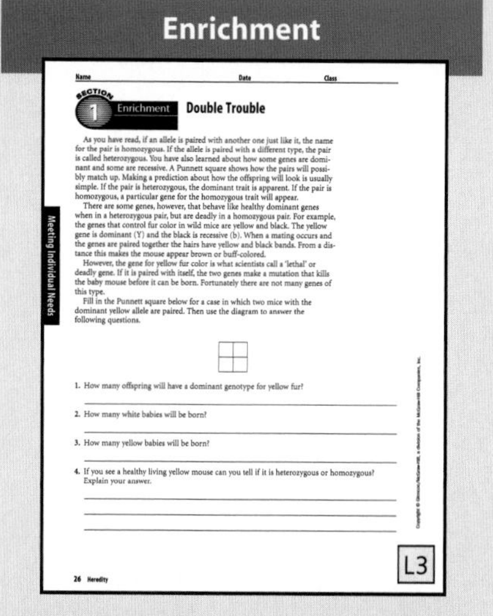

Directed Reading (English/Spanish)

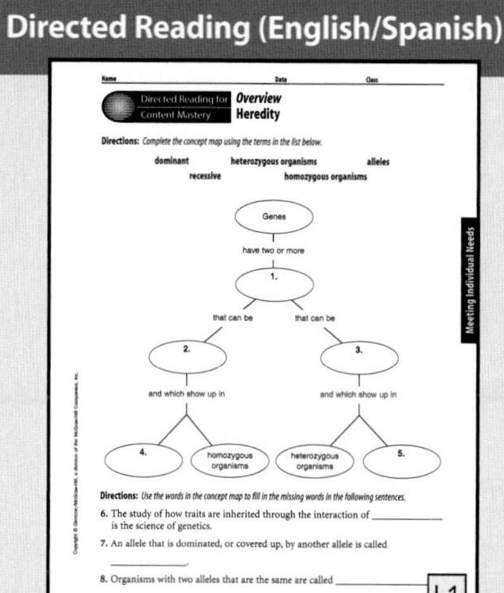

Study Guide

Reading Essentials

Assessment

Test Practice Workbook

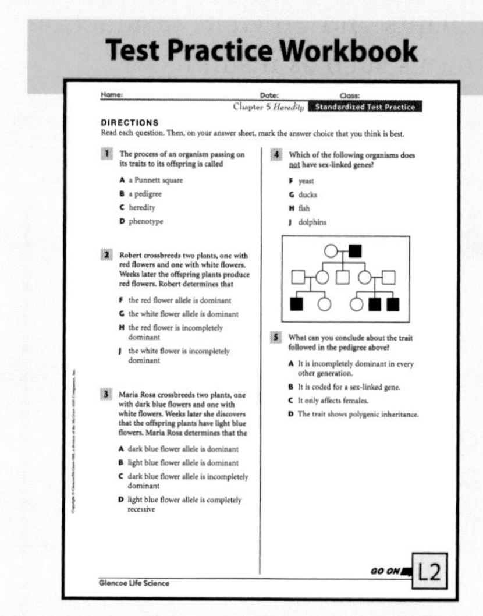

Chapter Review

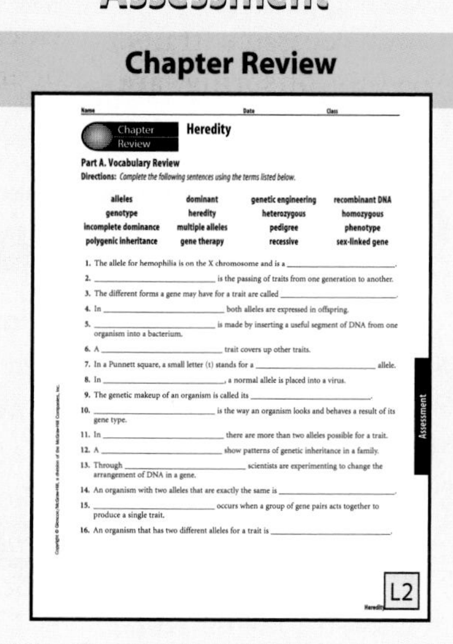

Chapter Tests

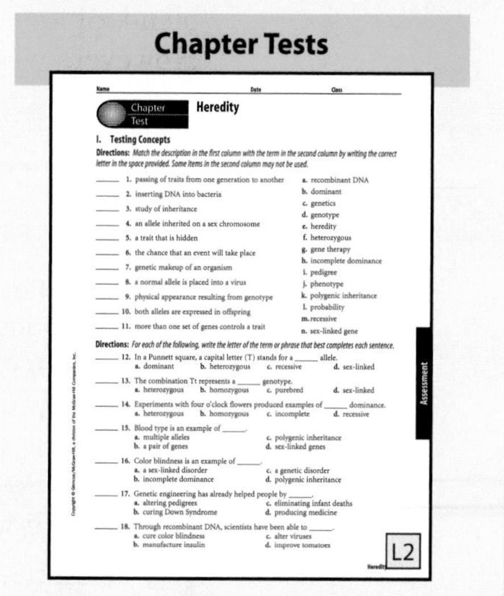

Science Content Background

section 1 Genetics

Mendelian Inheritance

Gregor Mendel, an Austrian monk, was the first scientist to bring an experimental and quantitative approach to genetics, the study of heredity. Mendelian inheritance reflects the mathematical rules of probability.

Dominant and Recessive Factors

In Mendel's experiments, the inheritance patterns of traits each possessed two alleles. The law of dominance explains that one trait, the dominant trait, is expressed in homozygous and heterozygous conditions. The recessive trait is expressed only in the homozygous condition.

Using a Punnett Square

Mendel developed the law of segregation, which shows that recessive alleles are not lost during meiosis. In Mendel's experiments with pea hybridization, the recessive trait reappeared in approximately one-fourth of the offspring produced by crossing two heterozygous pea plants.

section 2 Genetics Since Mendel

Other Modes of Inheritance

In incomplete dominance, the heterozygous condition results in an intermediate phenotype that appears to be a blend of the dominant and recessive traits. However, when heterozygous offspring are crossed, the next generation expresses the dominant, recessive, and intermediate phenotypes. In codominance, the heterozygous condition results in a phenotype that is a mixture of both dominant alleles. Sometimes there are multiple alleles for a trait, though each individual only carries two. Polygenic inheritance occurs when a trait is produced as a result of a group of genes. Mutations and chromosome disorders are caused by changes in genes.

Genetic Disorders

Many human disorders follow Mendelian inheritance patterns. Huntington's disease is carried on a dominant allele and causes lethal degeneration of the nervous system. Tay-Sachs is caused by a recessive allele and occurs most often in people of Jewish descent. Sickle-cell anemia is a recessive disorder that occurs most often in people of African descent. The red blood cells are malformed and cannot effectively transport oxygen.

Advances in Genetics

Benefits of Genetic Research

Advances made in the search for the molecular basis of inheritance are phenomenal. Technology is providing new tools to aid in research, genetic testing, and genetic counseling. Genetic engineering provides improved plants and efficient production of artificial chemicals such as insulin.

chapter content resources

Internet Resources

For additional content background, visit booka.msscience.com to:

- access your book online
- find references to related articles in popular science magazines
- access Web links with related content background
- access current events with science journal topics

Print Resources

Heredity Diseases, by Fern G. Brown, Franklin Watts, 1987

The Story of Science: The Treasure of Inheritance, by Roy A. Gallant, Benchmark Books, 2002

Genetics: The Study of Heredity (Investigating Science), by Ian Graham, Gareth Stevens, 2002

IDENTIFYING Misconceptions

Find Out What Students Think

Students may think that . . .

Dominant traits are the strongest, most superior, or most common traits in a population.

Genes coding for eye color in humans comes in two alleles. The dominant allele causes brown pigment to be produced in the iris, and the recessive allele does not produce a functional protein or pigment. Each person receives two alleles of each gene, one from each parent. If a person inherits at least one "brown" allele, the person's eyes will produce pigment. If a person has only recessive alleles, no pigment is made and the eyes appear blue. Human eye color is actually somewhat more complex than this, as it is controlled by several genes (not a single pair) as opposed to simple Mendelian inheritance. The greater the number of dominant alleles a person has, the darker the eyes appear.

Discussion

Ask the class, "If brown eyes are dominant over blue eyes, does this mean that someday all people will be brown-eyed?" Let students form small discussion groups. After a set time limit, let students present their answers and supporting evidence. Their answers will reveal their preconceived notions and their reasoning.

Promote Understanding

Activity

Group students in pairs, and give each pair an envelope containing five brown and five blue squares.

- Have each student draw one brown and one blue square. These squares represent the eye color alleles of an imaginary person. Ask what color of eyes the person has (brown).
- Tell students that their two imaginary people will have a child, so each must contribute one allele. Students should randomly draw a square from the envelope. Have students lay their contributed squares side by side and determine the eye color of the child.
- Count the number of blue-eyed and brown-eyed offspring produced in the class. Ask students why some of the brown-eyed parents had a child with blue eyes.
- Poll the class to see how many students have a widow's peak hairline (dominant) versus a straight hairline (recessive), and how many have a dimple in the chin (dominant) versus no dimple in the chin (recessive). These two traits have dominant forms that are usually infrequent in a population. L2

Assess

After completing the chapter, see *Identifying Misconceptions* in the Study Guide at the end of the chapter.

chapter 5

Chapter Vocabulary

heredity, p. 128
alleles, p. 128
genetics, p. 128
hybrid, p. 130
dominant, p. 130
recessive, p. 130
Punnett square, p. 132
genotype, p. 132
phenotype, p. 132
homozygous, p. 132
heterozygous, p. 132
incomplete dominance, p. 136
polygenic inheritance, p. 138
sex-linked gene, p. 141
genetic engineering, p. 143

Science Journal Student responses will vary, but traits may include eye color, hair color, or shape of face. Students may respond that they can determine how traits were passed on to them by looking at their family history of those traits.

INTERACTIVE CHALKBOARD with Image Bank

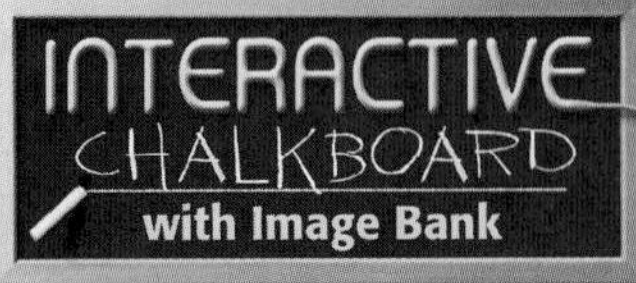

PowerPoint® Presentations

This CD-ROM is an editable Microsoft® PowerPoint® presentation that includes:

- a pre-made presentation for every chapter
- interactive graphics
- animations
- audio clips
- image bank
- all new section and chapter questions
- Standardized Test Practice
- transparencies
- pre-lab questions for all labs
- Foldables directions
- links to booka.msscience.com

chapter 5

Heredity

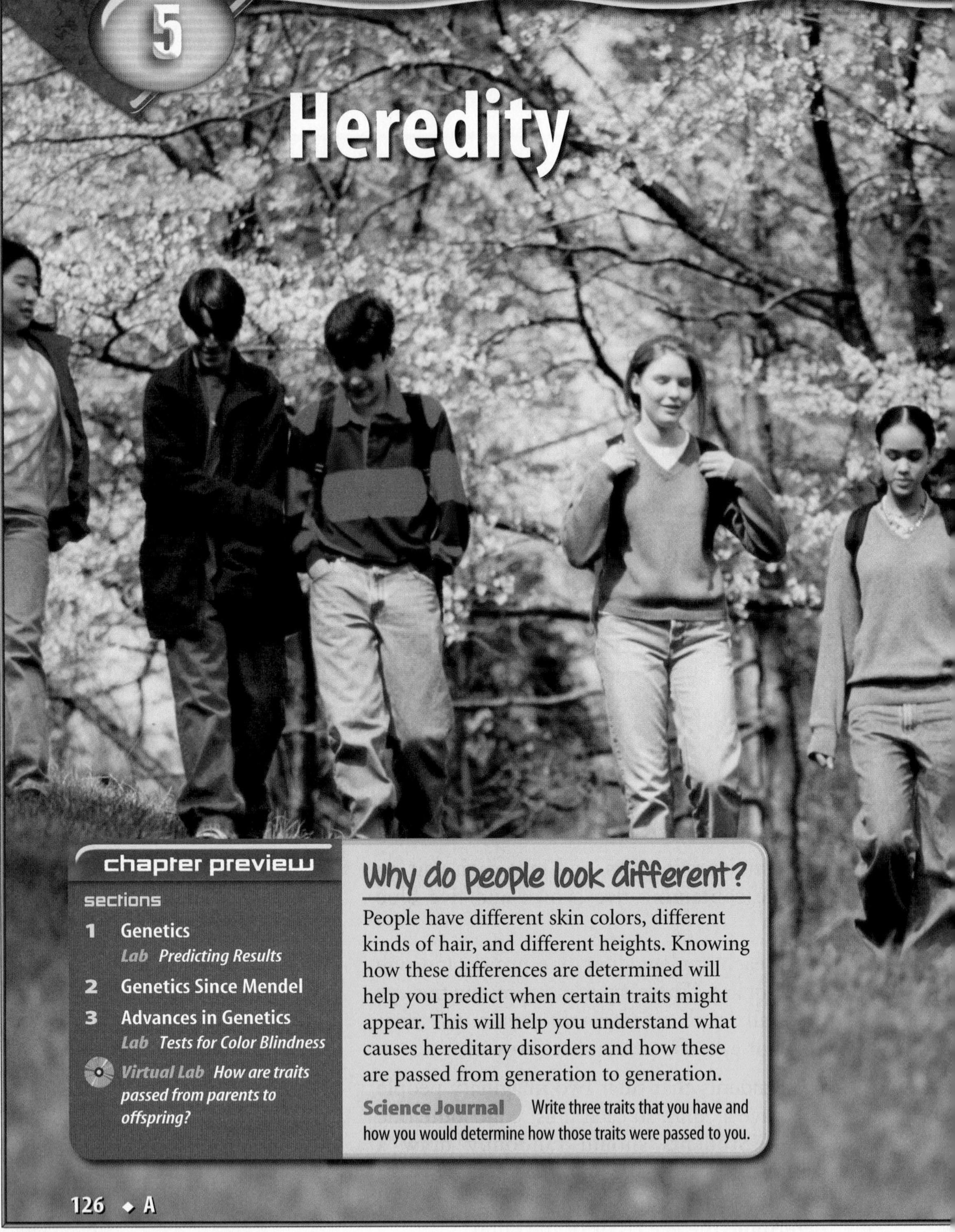

chapter preview

sections

1 Genetics
Lab Predicting Results
2 Genetics Since Mendel
3 Advances in Genetics
Lab Tests for Color Blindness
Virtual Lab How are traits passed from parents to offspring?

Why do people look different?

People have different skin colors, different kinds of hair, and different heights. Knowing how these differences are determined will help you predict when certain traits might appear. This will help you understand what causes hereditary disorders and how these are passed from generation to generation.

Science Journal Write three traits that you have and how you would determine how those traits were passed to you.

126 ◆ A

Theme Connection

Stability and Change Genes control stability through homeostasis at the organism level. Genetics provides background for understanding the changes involved in evolution.

About the Photo

Human Genome In 2001, the first draft of the human genome was published. The human genome contains approximately 30,000 genes. It is 25 times larger than any other genome sequenced so far. Despite the size of the human genome and the noticeable differences in human traits, any two humans differ in only about one or two nucleotide base pairs in every 1000 in their DNA sequence.

Start-Up Activities

Who around you has dimples?

You and your best friend enjoy the same sports, like the same food, and even have similar haircuts. But, there are noticeable differences between your appearances. Most of these differences are controlled by the genes you inherited from your parents. In the following lab, you will observe one of these differences.

1. Notice the two students in the photographs. One student has dimples when she smiles, and the other student doesn't have dimples.
2. Ask your classmates to smile naturally. In your Science Journal, record the name of each classmate and whether each one has dimples.
3. **Think Critically** In your Science Journal, calculate the percentage of students who have dimples. Are facial dimples a common feature among your classmates?

Classify Characteristics As you read this chapter about heredity, you can use the following Foldable to help you classify characteristics as inherited or not inherited.

STEP 1 **Fold** the top of a vertical piece of paper down and the bottom up to divide the paper into thirds.

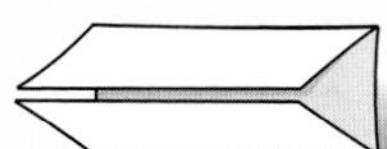

STEP 2 **Turn** the paper horizontally; **unfold and label** the three columns as shown.

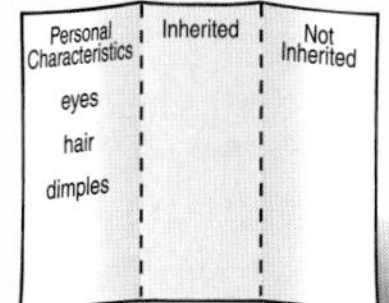

Read for Main Ideas Before you read the chapter, list personal characteristics and predict which are inherited or not inherited. As you read the chapter, check and change your list.

Preview this chapter's content and activities at booka.msscience.com

Purpose Use the Launch Lab to introduce students to inheritance. Inform students that they will be learning about inheritance and genetics as they read the chapter. L2 ELL COOP LEARN IN **Logical-Mathematical**

Preparation Discuss the photograph as a class to ensure that students recognize what dimples are.

Teaching Strategy Record data for each class and have students compare their results with those of other classes.

Think Critically

Percentages will vary depending upon how many students in the class have and do not have dimples. Generally, the percentage of students having dimples falls between 10 and 40 percent.

Assessment

Oral Have students suggest other features that are inherited. Possible answers: hair color and texture, skin and eye color, height, shape of facial features. Use **Performance Assessment in the Science Classroom**, p. 89.

Dinah Zike Study Fold

Student preparation materials for this Foldable are available in the **Chapter *Fast File* Resources.**

1 Motivate

Bellringer

Section Focus Transparencies also are available on the Interactive Chalkboard CD-ROM.  

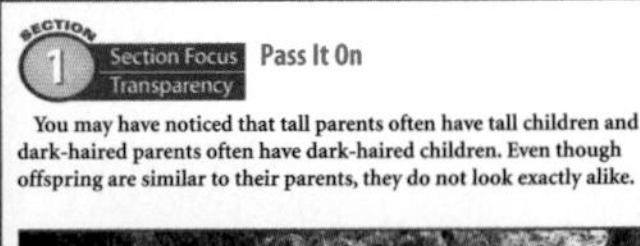
Section 1 Section Focus Transparency Pass It On

You may have noticed that tall parents often have tall children and dark-haired parents often have dark-haired children. Even though offspring are similar to their parents, they do not look exactly alike.

1. Do children ever look exactly the same? When?
2. How are the members of this family different? How are they the same?
3. Why can looking at a set of parents help you predict what their children might look like?

Tie to Prior Knowledge

Inherited Traits Show a picture of a mother dog and her puppies (or a cat and her kittens). Have students list characteristics of the offspring they think are inherited from the parents. Lead students to understand that all of the general physical traits, such as number of legs, length and shape of ears, eye color and shape, and so on, are inherited. L1

section 1 Genetics

as you read

***What* You'll Learn**

- **Explain** how traits are inherited.
- **Identify** Mendel's role in the history of genetics.
- **Use** a Punnett square to predict the results of crosses.
- **Compare and contrast** the difference between an individual's genotype and phenotype.

***Why* It's Important**

Heredity and genetics help explain why people are different.

Review Vocabulary
meiosis: reproductive process that produces four haploid sex cells from one diploid cell

New Vocabulary
- heredity
- allele
- genetics
- hybrid
- dominant
- recessive
- Punnett square
- genotype
- phenotype
- homozygous
- heterozygous

Inheriting Traits

Do you look more like one parent or grandparent? Do you have your father's eyes? What about Aunt Isabella's cheekbones? Eye color, nose shape, and many other physical features are some of the traits that are inherited from parents, as **Figure 1** shows. An organism is a collection of traits, all inherited from its parents. **Heredity** (huh REH duh tee) is the passing of traits from parent to offspring. What controls these traits?

What is genetics? Generally, genes on chromosomes control an organism's form and function. The different forms of a trait that a gene may have are called **alleles** (uh LEELZ). When a pair of chromosomes separates during meiosis (mi OH sus), alleles for each trait also separate into different sex cells. As a result, every sex cell has one allele for each trait, as shown in **Figure 2.** The allele in one sex cell may control one form of the trait, such as having facial dimples. The allele in the other sex cell may control a different form of the trait—not having dimples. The study of how traits are inherited through the interactions of alleles is the science of **genetics** (juh NE tihks).

Figure 1 Note the strong family resemblance among these four generations.

Section 1 Resource Manager 

Chapter *FAST FILE* Resources
- Transparency Activity, p. 40
- Directed Reading for Content Mastery, pp. 15, 16
- Note-taking Worksheets, pp. 29–31
- MiniLAB, p. 3
- Enrichment, p. 26
- Lab Activity, pp. 9–10, 11–12
- Lab Worksheet, pp. 5–6
- Reinforcement, p. 23

Home and Community Involvement, p. 36
Performance Assessment in the Science Classroom, p. 57
Mathematics Skill Activities, p. 23

Figure 2 An allele is one form of a gene. Alleles separate into separate sex cells during meiosis. In this example, the alleles that control the trait for dimples include *D*, the presence of dimples, and *d*, the absence of dimples.

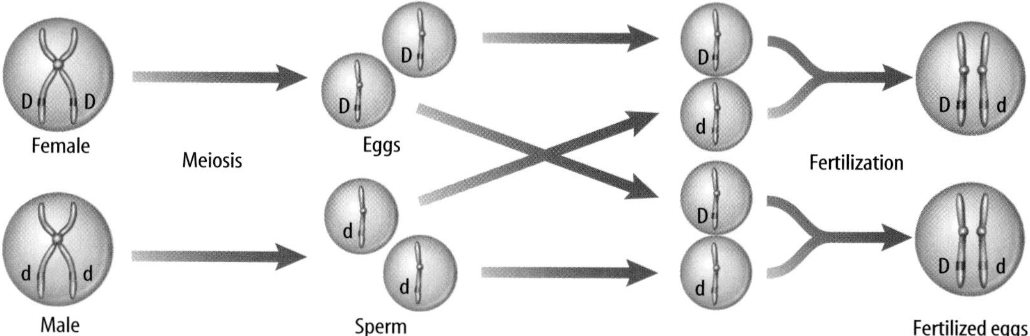

The alleles that control a trait are located on each duplicated chromosome.

During meiosis, duplicated chromosomes separate.

During fertilization, each parent donates one chromosome. This results in two alleles for the trait of dimples in the new individual formed.

Mendel—The Father of Genetics

Did you know that an experiment with pea plants helped scientists understand why your eyes are the color that they are? Gregor Mendel was an Austrian monk who studied mathematics and science but became a gardener in a monastery. His interest in plants began as a boy in his father's orchard where he could predict the possible types of flowers and fruits that would result from crossbreeding two plants. Curiosity about the connection between the color of a pea flower and the type of seed that same plant produced inspired him to begin experimenting with garden peas in 1856. Mendel made careful use of scientific methods, which resulted in the first recorded study of how traits pass from one generation to the next. After eight years, Mendel presented his results with pea plants to scientists.

Before Mendel, scientists mostly relied on observation and description, and often studied many traits at one time. Mendel was the first to trace one trait through several generations. He was also the first to use the mathematics of probability to explain heredity. The use of math in plant science was a new concept and not widely accepted then. Mendel's work was forgotten for a long time. In 1900, three plant scientists, working separately, reached the same conclusions as Mendel. Each plant scientist had discovered Mendel's writings while doing his own research. Since then, Mendel has been known as the father of genetics.

Topic: Genetics
Visit booka.msscience.com for Web links to information about early genetics experiments.

Activity List two other scientists who studied genetics, and what organism they used in their research.

2 Teach

Inquiry Lab

Observing Mendelian Genetics

Purpose to understand and observe the outcome of a cross between corn seedlings that are heterozygous for green pigment (*Cc*)

Possible Materials a flat of germinated albino corn

Estimated Time one class period

Teaching Strategies

- The dominant allele in corn is green pigment, so students can observe that most of the seedlings are green and they can predict why.
- Students can predict the genotypes of the green and albino seedlings.
- Students can count the number of green seedlings and the number of albino seedlings. They can predict what the ratio of green seedlings to albino seedlings should be and then calculate the actual ratio. Students can explain why the actual ratio may be different than the predicted ratio.
- Allow students to explore other questions that arise. L2

For additional inquiry activities, see *Science Inquiry Labs.*

Teacher FYI

Scientific Method Mendel's experiments illustrate the scientific method. Mendel worked with a single trait at a time, conducted carefully controlled experiments, collected and analyzed data, recorded his experiments so they could be repeated, worked with large samples, and shared results with his contemporaries.

Visual Learning

Figure 2 The arrows show how eggs and sperm, produced by meiosis, combine during fertilization. In this example, each parent was homozygous for a trait. What would the genotype of the fertilized eggs be if the female parent was heterozygous for the dimple trait (*Dd*)? One fertilized egg would be Dd and one would be dd.

Purpose to observe and calculate the occurrence of various traits in dogs L2 ELL LS **Logical-Mathematical**

Teaching Strategies Make sure students understand that variations make each dog unique.

Safety Precautions Caution students not to touch or approach dogs they do not know.

Analysis

1. Answers will vary depending on dogs observed.
2. There are many variations. Each dog looks different.

Assessment

Performance To further assess students' understanding of inherited traits, have volunteers observe and tabulate several traits among children, parents, and grandparents. Use **Performance Assessment in the Science Classroom,** p. 109.

Reading Check

Answer They can be relied upon to produce the same traits generation after generation.

Dominant Traits Some students think that dominant traits are those that will "take over" in a population. Refer to page F at the beginning of this chapter for teaching strategies that address this misconception.

Table 1 Traits Compared by Mendel

Traits	Shape of Seeds	Color of Seeds	Color of Pods	Shape of Pods	Plant Height	Position of Flowers	Flower Color
Dominant trait	Round	Yellow	Green	Full	Tall	At leaf junctions	Purple
Recessive trait	Wrinkled	Green	Yellow	Flat, constricted	short	At tips of branches	White

Genetics in a Garden

Each time Mendel studied a trait, he crossed two plants with different expressions of the trait and found that the new plants all looked like one of the two parents. He called these new plants **hybrids** (HI brudz) because they received different genetic information, or different alleles, for a trait from each parent. The results of these studies made Mendel even more curious about how traits are inherited.

Garden peas are easy to breed for pure traits. An organism that always produces the same traits generation after generation is called a purebred. For example, tall plants that always produce seeds that produce tall plants are purebred for the trait of tall height. **Table 1** shows other pea plant traits that Mendel studied.

Reading Check *Why might farmers plant purebred crop seeds?*

Comparing Common Traits

Procedure

1. Safely survey as many **dogs** in your neighborhood as you can for the presence of a solid color or spotted coat, short or long hair, and floppy or upright ears.
2. Make a data table that lists each of the traits. Record your data in the data table.

Analysis

1. Compare the number of dogs that have one form of a trait with those that have the other form.
2. What can you conclude about the variations you noticed in the dogs?

Try at Home

Dominant and Recessive Factors In nature, insects randomly pollinate plants as they move from flower to flower. In his experiments, Mendel used pollen from the flowers of purebred tall plants to pollinate by hand the flowers of purebred short plants. This process is called cross-pollination. He found that tall plants crossed with short plants produced seeds that produced all tall plants. Whatever caused the plants to be short had disappeared. Mendel called the tall form the **dominant** (DAH muh nunt) factor because it dominated, or covered up, the short form. He called the form that seemed to disappear the **recessive** (rih SE sihv) factor. Today, these are called dominant alleles and recessive alleles. What happened to the recessive form? **Figure 3** answers this question.

NATIONAL GEOGRAPHIC VISUALIZING MENDEL'S EXPERIMENTS

Figure 3

Gregor Mendel discovered that the experiments he carried out on garden plants provided an understanding of heredity. For eight years he crossed plants that had different characteristics and recorded how those characteristics were passed from generation to generation. One such characteristic, or trait, was the color of pea pods. The results of Mendel's experiment on pea pod color are shown below.

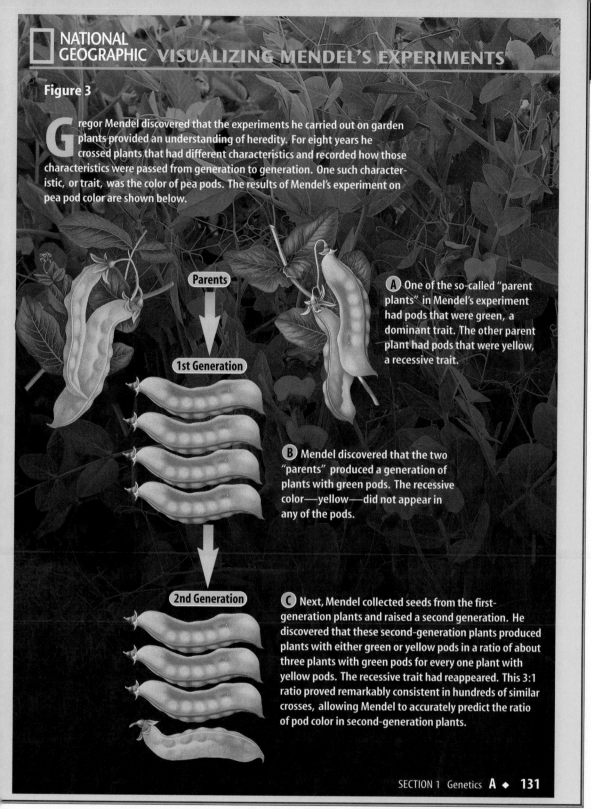

A One of the so-called "parent plants" in Mendel's experiment had pods that were green, a dominant trait. The other parent plant had pods that were yellow, a recessive trait.

B Mendel discovered that the two "parents" produced a generation of plants with green pods. The recessive color—yellow—did not appear in any of the pods.

C Next, Mendel collected seeds from the first-generation plants and raised a second generation. He discovered that these second-generation plants produced plants with either green or yellow pods in a ratio of about three plants with green pods for every one plant with yellow pods. The recessive trait had reappeared. This 3:1 ratio proved remarkably consistent in hundreds of similar crosses, allowing Mendel to accurately predict the ratio of pod color in second-generation plants.

Visualizing Mendel's Experiments

Have students examine the pictures and read the captions. Then ask the following questions:

Why is it important that Mendel based his conclusions on the results of hundreds of pea plant crosses? It's important to have as much data as possible before drawing conclusions about any experiment, and in general, the larger the sample size, the more accurate the results will be.

Would the allele for the recessive trait of yellow pea pod color be present in the first generation of pea plants? Yes, the allele would be present, but it would not be expressed because none of the plants are homozygous recessive.

Activity

Mendel's Ratios Have students work in small groups. Using the example shown in the Visualizing, have the students use Mendel's ratios to determine the number of yellow pea plants in the second generation if the second generation of plants contained the following: 100 total plants (25), 300 total plants (75). L2

Use an Analogy

Games of Chance The probability of genetic events is analogous to rolling a die and other games of chance.

Make a Model

Crossing Pea Plants Provide students with blocks of two different colors. Have them use the blocks to model the cross involving pea plant flowers described in the text. Help them use these tools to distinguish between genotype and phenotype, and homozygous and heterozygous. L2

Caption Answer

Figure 4 No; if red is recessive, then the genotype is homozygous recessive (rr), but if red is dominant, then the flower could be either homozygous (RR) or heterozygous (Rr).

Discussion

Allele Combinations Have students predict the possible allele combinations for a pea plant that is heterozygous for plant height, tall (Tt), and homozygous for seed shape, wrinkled (rr). The possible combinations are Tr and tr.

Reading Check

Answer Homozygous organisms carry the same two alleles for a trait. Heterozygous organisms carry two different alleles for a trait.

Figure 4 This snapdragon's phenotype is red.
Determine *Can you tell what the flower's genotype for color is? Explain your answer.*

Using Probability to Make Predictions If you and your sister can't agree on what movie to see, you could solve the problem by tossing a coin. When you toss a coin, you're dealing with probabilities. Probability is a branch of mathematics that helps you predict the chance that something will happen. If your sister chooses tails while the coin is in the air, what is the probability that the coin will land tail-side up? Because a coin has two sides, there are two possible outcomes, heads or tails. One outcome is tails. Therefore, the probability of one side of a coin showing is one out of two, or 50 percent.

Mendel also dealt with probabilities. One of the things that made his predictions accurate was that he worked with large numbers of plants. He studied almost 30,000 pea plants over a period of eight years. By doing so, Mendel increased his chances of seeing a repeatable pattern. Valid scientific conclusions need to be based on results that can be duplicated.

Punnett Squares Suppose you wanted to know what colors of pea plant flowers you would get if you pollinated white flowers on one pea plant with pollen from purple flowers on a different plant. How could you predict what the offspring would look like without making the cross? A handy tool used to predict results in Mendelian genetics is the **Punnett** (PUH nut) **square.** In a Punnett square, letters represent dominant and recessive alleles. An uppercase letter stands for a dominant allele. A lowercase letter stands for a recessive allele. The letters are a form of code. They show the **genotype** (JEE nuh tipe), or genetic makeup, of an organism. Once you understand what the letters mean, you can tell a lot about the inheritance of a trait in an organism.

The way an organism looks and behaves as a result of its genotype is its **phenotype** (FEE nuh tipe), as shown in **Figure 4.** If you have brown hair, then the phenotype for your hair color is brown.

Alleles Determine Traits Most cells in your body have two alleles for every trait. These alleles are located on chromosomes within the nucleus of cells. An organism with two alleles that are the same is called **homozygous** (hoh muh ZI gus). For Mendel's peas, this would be written as *TT* (homozygous for the tall-dominant trait) or *tt* (homozygous for the short-recessive trait). An organism that has two different alleles for a trait is called **heterozygous** (he tuh roh ZI gus). The hybrid plants Mendel produced were all heterozygous for height, *Tt.*

Reading Check *What is the difference between homozygous and heterozygous organisms?*

Differentiated Instruction

Challenge Have students form Punnett squares that show the results of first- and second-generation crosses between organisms that are pure bred for two traits. What is the genotype of all of the first generation offspring? They are all heterozygous. Students should then cross the heterozygous offspring to determine the second-generation genotype. What is the ratio obtained in the second generation? 9:3:3:1 ratio L3 ELL COOP LEARN P

Making a Punnett Square In a Punnett square for predicting one trait, the letters representing the two alleles from one parent are written along the top of the grid, one letter per section. Those of the second parent are placed down the side of the grid, one letter per section. Each square of the grid is filled in with one allele donated by each parent. The letters that you use to fill in each of the squares represent the genotypes of possible offspring that the parents could produce.

Applying Math — Calculate Percentages

PUNNET SQUARE One dog carries heterozygous, black-fur traits (*Bb*), and its mate carries homogeneous, blond-fur traits (*bb*). Use a Punnett square to determine the probability of one of their puppies having black fur.

Solution

1. *This is what you know:*
   - dominant allele is represented by *B*
   - recessive allele is represented by *b*
2. *This is what you need to find out:* What is the probability of a puppy's fur color being black?
3. *This is the procedure you need to use:*
   - Complete the Punnett square.
   - There are two *Bb* genotypes and four possible outcomes.
   - $\%(\text{black fur}) = \dfrac{\text{number of ways to get black fur}}{\text{number of possible outcomes}} = \dfrac{2}{4} = \dfrac{1}{2} = 50\%$

Black dog

Blond dog	B	b
b	Bb	bb
b	Bb	bb

Genotypes of offspring: 2Bb, 2bb
Phenotypes of offspring: 2 black, 2 blond

4. *Check your answer:* $\frac{1}{2}$ of 4 is 2, which is the number of black dogs.

Practice Problems

1. In peas, the color yellow (*Y*) is dominant to the color green (*y*). According to the Punnett square, what is the probability of an offspring being yellow?
2. What is the probability of an offspring having the *yy* genotype?

Parent (Yy)

Parent (Yy)	Y	y
Y	YY	Yy
y	Yy	yy

For more practice, visit booka.msscience.com/math_practice

Quick Demo

Beads as Traits

Materials string, colored beads

Estimated Time five minutes

Procedure Demonstrate alleles along a chromosome by stringing colored beads on a string. The colored beads represent genes for different traits along the chromosome. Create two strings of beads and bring the strands together to demonstrate the homozygous and heterozygous conditions.

Applying Math

National Math Standards

Correlation to Mathematics Objectives

1, 5, 9, 10

Answers to Practice Problems

1. 75% yellow
2. Genotype yy = 25%

Differentiated Instruction

Learning Disabled Have students choose one or two inherited traits (eye color, left- or right-handedness, and so on) and survey classmates to see how many of them display the characteristics. Results can be graphed. Other classrooms can be surveyed. Students can determine whether larger populations have the same ratio of the traits as subgroups. L1 COOP LEARN IN **Interpersonal**

Visual Learning

Table 2 Have students relate the principles of heredity to genetic examples they have studied in this section.

3 Assess

DAILY INTERVENTION

Check for Understanding

Visual-Spatial Have students fill in a Punnett square on a large poster that shows the results of a trihybrid cross between individuals who are heterozygous for all three traits. L2

Reteach

Human Alleles Take the class to a paved portion of the school yard and have students role-play the alleles in a cross. Use masking tape to mark out a large Punnett square on the pavement. Assign students to be certain alleles and allow them to arrange themselves and announce the phenotypes and genotypes produced. L2 ELL IN **Visual-Spatial**

Assessment

Performance Have students use a Punnett square to demonstrate their answer to Question 6. Use **Performance Assessment in the Science Classroom,** p. 97.

Principles of Heredity Even though Gregor Mendel didn't know anything about DNA, genes, or chromosomes, he succeeded in beginning to describe and mathematically represent how inherited traits are passed from parents to offspring. He realized that some factor in the pea plant produced certain traits. Mendel also concluded that these factors separated when the pea plant reproduced. Mendel arrived at his conclusions after years of detailed observation, careful analysis, and repeated experimentation. **Table 2** summarizes Mendel's principles of heredity.

Table 2 Principles of Heredity

1	Traits are controlled by alleles on chromosomes.
2	An allele's effect is dominant or recessive.
3	When a pair of chromosomes separates during meiosis, the different alleles for a trait move into separate sex cells.

section 1 review

Summary

Inheriting Traits

- Heredity is the passing of traits from parent to offspring.
- Genetics is the study of how traits are inherited through the interactions of alleles.

Mendel—The Father of Genetics

- In 1856, Mendel began experimenting with garden peas, using careful scientific methods.
- Mendel was the first to trace one trait through several generations.
- In 1900, three plant scientists separately reached the same conclusions as Mendel.

Genetics in a Garden

- Hybrids receive different genetic information for a trait from each parent.
- Genetics involves dominant and recessive factors.
- Punnett squares can be used to predict the results of a cross.
- Mendel's conclusions led to the principles of heredity.

Self Check

1. **Contrast** Alleles are described as being dominant or recessive. What is the difference between a dominant and a recessive allele?
2. **Describe** how dominant and recessive alleles are represented in a Punnett square.
3. **Explain** the difference between genotype and phenotype. Give examples.
4. **Infer** Gregor Mendel, an Austrian monk who lived in the 1800s, is known as the father of genetics. Explain why Mendel has been given this title.
5. **Think Critically** If an organism expresses a recessive phenotype, can you tell the genotype? Explain your answer by giving an example.

Applying Math

6. **Use Percentages** One fruit fly is heterozygous for long wings, and another fruit fly is homozygous for short wings. Long wings are dominant to short wings. Use a Punnett square to find the expected percent of offspring with short wings.

Science Online booka.msscience.com/self_check_quiz

section 1 review

1. A dominant allele is expressed if an allele pair is homozygous dominant or heterozygous. A recessive allele is expressed only when an allele pair is homozygous recessive.
2. Dominant alleles are represented with an uppercase letter, recessive alleles with a lowercase letter.
3. Genotype is the combination of alleles an organism contains; phenotype is the expression of the alleles in an organism. For example, a genotype might be Tt (heterozygous dominant), and the phenotype might be tall.
4. He was the first person to explain the mechanisms of heredity.
5. Yes, because two copies of the recessive allele must be present for the recessive phenotype to show up.
6. 50%

Predicting Results

Could you predict how many brown rabbits would result from crossing two heterozygous black rabbits? Try this investigation to find out. Brown color is a recessive trait for hair color in rabbits.

Real-World Question

How does chance affect combinations of genes?

Goals

- **Model** chance events in heredity.
- **Compare and contrast** predicted and actual results.

Materials

paper bags (2)
red beans (100)
white beans (100)

Safety Precautions

WARNING: *Do not taste, eat, or drink any materials used in the lab.*

Procedure

1. Use a Punnett square to predict how many red/red, red/white, and white/white bean combinations are possible. The combinations represent the coat colors in rabbit offspring.
2. Place 50 red beans and 50 white beans in a paper bag. Place 50 red beans and 50 white beans in a second bag. Red beans represent black alleles and white beans represent brown alleles.
3. Label one of the bags *Female* for the female parent. Label the other bag *Male* for the male parent.
4. Use a data table to record the combination each time you remove two beans. Your table will need to accommodate 100 picks.
5. Without looking, remove one bean from each bag. The two beans represent the alleles that combine when sperm and egg join. After recording, return the beans to their bags.
6. **Count** and record the total numbers for each of the three combinations in your data table.
7. **Compile and record** the class totals.

Conclude and Apply

1. **Name** the combination that occurred most often.
2. **Calculate** the ratio of red/red to red/white to white/white. What hair color in rabbits do these combinations represent?
3. **Compare** your predicted (expected) results with your observed (actual) results.
4. **Hypothesize** how you could get predicted results to be closer to actual results.

Gene Combinations

Rabbits	Red/ Red	Red/ White	White/ White
Your total			
Class total			

Communicating Your Data

Write a paragraph that clearly describes your results. Have another student read your paragraph. Ask if he or she could understand what happened. If not, rewrite your paragraph and have the other student read it again. **For more help, refer to the** **Science Skill Handbook.**

Real-World Question

Purpose Students use a model to investigate how the principles of heredity are related to chance. L2 ELL LS **Logical-Mathematical**

Process Skills predict, observe, record data, interpret data, use numbers, make and use tables

Time Required one class period

Procedure

Safety Precautions Remind students not to eat or throw the beans.

Teaching Strategies

- All the beans should be approximately the same size.
- Emphasize the importance of completing all 100 trials.

Troubleshooting Explain to students that beans must be returned to the bag after each draw so that the probability of choosing the different color combinations remains the same throughout the lab.

Conclude and Apply

1. red/white
2. Results should be close to 1:2:1; red/red represents a black rabbit, red/white represents a black rabbit, and white/white represents a brown rabbit.
3. Answers will vary, but should follow expected results closely.
4. A larger sample could be used or more trials done.

Assessment

Performance To further assess students' knowledge of probability, have them repeat the lab using three different kinds of beans. Use the **Performance Assessment in the Science Classroom,** p. 97. L2

Communicating Your Data

Students' paragraphs should indicate methods and results, as well as how the model relates to actual heredity principles.

section 2

Genetics Since Mendel

as you read

What **You'll Learn**

- **Explain** how traits are inherited by incomplete dominance.
- **Compare** multiple alleles and polygenic inheritance, and give examples of each.
- **Describe** two human genetic disorders and how they are inherited.
- **Explain** how sex-linked traits are passed to offspring.

Why **It's Important**

Most of your inherited traits involve more complex patterns of inheritance than Mendel discovered.

Review Vocabulary

gene: section of DNA on a chromosome that contains instructions for making specific proteins

New Vocabulary

- incomplete dominance
- polygenic inheritance
- sex-linked gene

Incomplete Dominance

Not even in science do things remain the same. After Mendel's work was rediscovered in 1900, scientists repeated his experiments. For some plants, such as peas, Mendel's results proved true. However, when different plants were crossed, the results were sometimes different. One scientist crossed purebred red four-o'clock plants with purebred white four-o'clock plants. He expected to get all red flowers, but they were pink. Neither allele for flower color seemed dominant. Had the colors become blended like paint colors? He crossed the pink-flowered plants with each other, and red, pink, and white flowers were produced. The red and white alleles had not become blended. Instead, when the allele for white flowers and the allele for red flowers combined, the result was an intermediate phenotype—a pink flower.

When the offspring of two homozygous parents show an intermediate phenotype, this inheritance is called **incomplete dominance.** Other examples of incomplete dominance include the flower color of some plant breeds and the coat color of some horse breeds, as shown in **Figure 5.**

Chestnut horse

Cremello horse

Figure 5 When a chestnut horse is bred with a cremello horse, all offspring will be palomino. The Punnett square shown on the opposite page can be used to predict this result. **Explain** *how the color of the palomino horse shows that the coat color of horses may be inherited by incomplete dominance.*

1 Motivate

Bellringer

Section Focus Transparencies also are available on the Interactive Chalkboard CD-ROM.

Section 2 Section Focus Transparency **Dog Days**

Humans have kept dogs for 12,000 to 14,000 years. At first, all dogs had jobs, such as herding or guarding. Today, some dogs have jobs, but many others are kept as pets.

1. What determines how big a dog can get?
2. Can a gray puppy and a brown puppy be littermates? How?
3. What environmental conditions could make one dog look different than its identical twin?

Heredity

Tie to Prior Knowledge

Complex Inheritance Ask students if any of them have eye color different from either parent. Explain that some inherited traits involve more complex patterns of inheritance, and students will learn about them in this section.

Caption Answer

Figure 5 The palomino's coat color is intermediate between its parents' coat colors.

Section 2 Resource Manager

Chapter *FAST FILE* Resources

Transparency Activity, pp. 41, 43–44

Directed Reading for Content Mastery, p. 16

MiniLAB, p. 4

Enrichment, p. 27

Reinforcement, p. 24

Life Science Critical Thinking/Problem Solving, p. 19

136 ◆ A CHAPTER 5 Heredity

Multiple Alleles Mendel studied traits in peas that were controlled by just two alleles. However, many traits are controlled by more than two alleles. A trait that is controlled by more than two alleles is said to be controlled by multiple alleles. Traits controlled by multiple alleles produce more than three phenotypes of that trait.

Imagine that only three types of coins are made—nickels, dimes, and quarters. If every person can have only two coins, six different combinations are possible. In this problem, the coins represent alleles of a trait. The sum of each two-coin combination represents the phenotype. Can you name the six different phenotypes possible with two coins?

Blood type in humans is an example of multiple alleles that produce only four phenotypes. The alleles for blood types are called A, B, and O. The O allele is recessive to both the A and B alleles. When a person inherits one A allele and one B allele for blood type, both are expressed—phenotype AB. A person with phenotype A blood has the genetic makeup, or genotype—AA or AO. Someone with phenotype B blood has the genotype BB or BO. Finally, a person with phenotype O blood has the genotype OO.

Reading Check *What are the six different blood type genotypes?*

Topic: Blood Types
Visit booka.msscience.com for Web links to information about the importance of blood types in blood transfusions.

Activity Make a chart showing which blood types can be used for transfusions into people with A, B, AB, or O blood phenotypes.

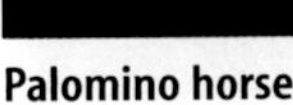

Palomino horse

Punnett square

Chestnut horse (CC) across top; Cremello horse (C'C') down side

	C	C
C'	CC'	CC'
C'	CC'	CC'

Genotypes: All CC'
Phenotypes: All palomino horses

2 Teach

Discussion

Predicting Traits Discuss why traits governed by incomplete dominance or multiple alleles might be more difficult to study. Help students see that these patterns do not conform to Mendel's prediction of a simple 3:1 ratio.

Text Question Answer

Possible combinations: nickel, dime; nickel, quarter; dime, quarter; nickel, nickel; dime, dime; quarter, quarter

Fun Fact

Blood types are important to the health profession. Matching blood types—both AB, A, B, or O and Rh—is important in transfusions. The recessive blood type, O, occurs in more than 30 percent of Americans.

Reading Check

Answer AA, AO, AB, BB, BO, OO

Science Journal

Genetics of Flower Color Explain that in hibiscus flowers, red is dominant to white. Have students explain why they can tell the genotype of a red four-o'clock, but not of a red hibiscus. Four-o'clocks inherit color by incomplete dominance. A red four-o'clock must be homozygous. If it were heterozygous, it would be pink. A red hibiscus might be heterozygous or homozygous. L2 P

Use Science Words

Word Origin Polygenic inheritance involves many genes. The prefix *poly-* means "many." Have students use a dictionary to find other words with this prefix and explain their meanings. Possible answers: polygon—many-sided figure; polychromatic—made of many colors L2

Purpose to determine the inheritance pattern that controls hand span L2 ELL
LS Logical-Mathematical

Materials paper, pencil, ruler

Teaching Strategy It may be easier for students to have each subject place his or her hand on a piece of paper and mark the width of the hand span before measuring it.

Analysis

1. Answers will vary. Spans may range from 12.5 cm to 24 cm or more.
2. Hand spans are determined by polygenic inheritance, not by a simple Mendelian pattern.

Assessment

Oral Ask students to determine if identical twins have identical hand spans. The spans are usually very close, but not identical because of environmental factors that affect growth. Use **Performance Assessment in the Science Classroom,** p. 89.

Reading Check

Answer amount of water or sunlight available, presence or absence of chemicals in soil

Interpreting Polygenic Inheritance

Procedure

1. Measure the hand spans of your classmates.
2. Using a **ruler,** measure from the tip of the thumb to the tip of the little finger when the hand is stretched out. Read the measurement to the nearest centimeter.
3. Record the name and hand-span measurement of each person in a data table.

Analysis

1. What range of hand spans did you find?
2. Are hand spans inherited as a simple Mendelian pattern or as a polygenic or incomplete dominance pattern? Explain.

Polygenic Inheritance

Eye color is an example of a trait that is produced by a combination of many genes. **Polygenic** (pah lih JEH nihk) **inheritance** occurs when a group of gene pairs acts together to produce a trait. The effects of many alleles produces a wide variety of phenotypes. For this reason, it may be hard to classify all the different shades of eye color.

Your height and the color of your eyes and skin are just some of the many human traits controlled by polygenic inheritance. It is estimated that three to six gene pairs control your skin color. Even more gene pairs might control the color of your hair and eyes. The environment also plays an important role in the expression of traits controlled by polygenic inheritance. Polygenic inheritance is common and includes such traits as grain color in wheat and milk production in cows. Egg production in chickens is also a polygenic trait.

Impact of the Environment Your environment plays a role in how some of your genes are expressed or whether they are expressed at all, as shown in **Figure 6.** Environmental influences can be internal or external. For example, most male birds are more brightly colored than females. Chemicals in their bodies determine whether the gene for brightly colored feathers is expressed.

Although genes determine many of your traits, you might be able to influence their expression by the decisions you make. Some people have genes that make them at risk for developing certain cancers. Whether they get cancer might depend on external environmental factors. For instance, if some people at risk for skin cancer limit their exposure to the Sun and take care of their skin, they might never develop cancer.

Reading Check *What environmental factors might affect the size of leaves on a tree?*

Figure 6 Himalayan rabbits have alleles for dark-colored fur. However, this allele is able to express itself only at lower temperatures. Only the areas located farthest from the rabbit's main body heat (ears, nose, feet, tail) have dark-colored fur.

Active Reading

Reflective Journal In this strategy, students identify activities and what they learned and record responses to the activities. Have students divide pieces of paper into several columns. Have them record their thoughts under headings such as *What I did, What I learned, What questions do I have, What surprises did I experience,* and *Overall response.* Have students write a Reflective Journal entry for the MiniLAB. L2

Human Genes and Mutations

Sometimes a gene undergoes a change that results in a trait that is expressed differently. Occasionally errors occur in the DNA when it is copied inside of a cell. Such changes and errors are called mutations. Not all mutations are harmful. They might be helpful or have no effect on an organism.

Certain chemicals are known to produce mutations in plants or animals, including humans. X rays and radioactive substances are other causes of some mutations. Mutations are changes in genes.

Chromosome Disorders In addition to individual mutations, problems can occur if the incorrect number of chromosomes is inherited. Every organism has a specific number of chromosomes. However, mistakes in the process of meiosis can result in a new organism with more or fewer chromosomes than normal. A change in the total number of human chromosomes is usually fatal to the unborn embryo or fetus, or the baby may die soon after birth.

Look at the human chromosomes in **Figure 7.** If three copies of chromosome 21 are produced in the fertilized human egg, Down's syndrome results. Individuals with Down's syndrome can be short, exhibit learning disabilities, and have heart problems. Such individuals can lead normal lives if they have no severe health complications.

Genetic Counselor Testing for genetic disorders may allow many affected individuals to seek treatment and cope with their diseases. Genetic counselors are trained to analyze a family's history to determine a person's health risk. Research what a genetic counselor does and how to become a genetic counselor. Record what you learn in your Science Journal.

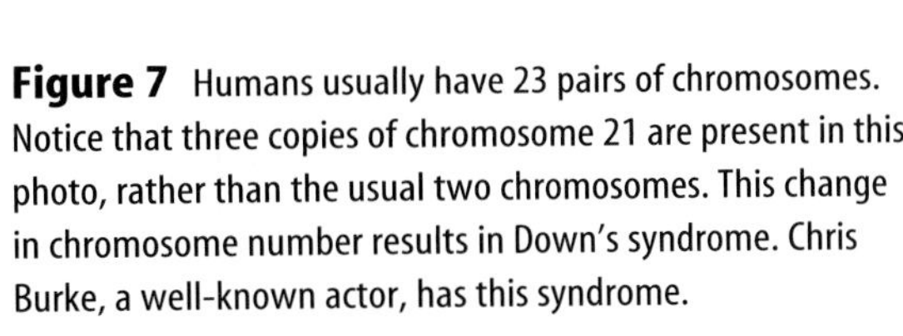

Figure 7 Humans usually have 23 pairs of chromosomes. Notice that three copies of chromosome 21 are present in this photo, rather than the usual two chromosomes. This change in chromosome number results in Down's syndrome. Chris Burke, a well-known actor, has this syndrome.

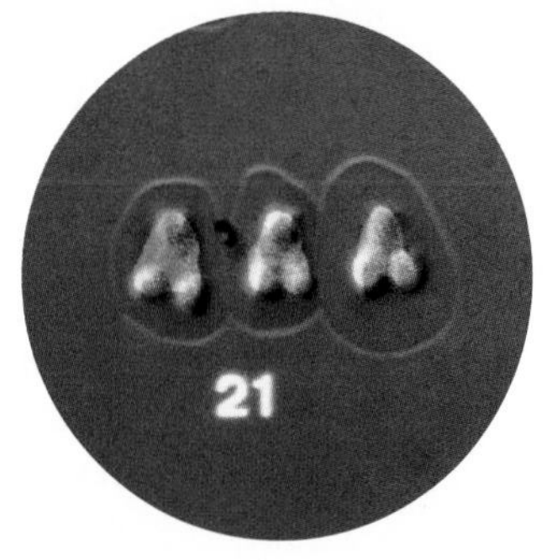

Teacher FYI

Mutations Somatic mutations occur in body cells and can produce a localized change—e.g., the streak of white sometimes found in the hair of an otherwise normal individual. All the cells descended from the mutant body cell will carry the mutation, but it cannot be passed on to offspring. Germ cell mutations affect the sex cells (eggs or sperm) and can be transmitted to the individual's offspring.

INTEGRATE Career

Genetic Counselor The field of genetic counseling is the communication process that deals with the probability that a genetic disorder will occur within a family. Medical professionals specialized in medical genetics and counseling are called genetic counselors. They can help educate the public and help families find support and treatment for genetic disorders. To become a genetic counselor, you must earn a master's level degree and a certification test.

LAB DEMONSTRATION

Purpose to show how mutations are passed to daughter cells

Materials blue and red overhead acetate, yarn, scissors, overhead projector

Preparation Cut out several 2-, 4-, and 6-cm long pairs of blue chromosomes. Cut one 4-cm long red chromosome.

Procedure Make a circle of yarn on the projector to represent a cell. Place the blue chromosome pairs in the cell. "Mutate" one chromosome from blue to red. Have the cell undergo mitosis.

Expected Outcome Daughter cells carry the mutation.

Assessment

What will happen when the cells carrying the mutation reproduce? The mutation will be reproduced. How might this explain a white stripe of hair on someone with black hair? The mutation is in the hair cells. It is passed along when the hair cells undergo mitosis.

SECTION 2 Genetics Since Mendel A ◆ 139

Discussion

Human Disorders Point out that about 600 simple recessive human disorders are presently known. Genetic disorders caused by dominant alleles are more common. An example is Huntington's disease, which usually does not express itself until the person is an adult. Why are fewer human genetic disorders recessive? Humans with recessive genetic disorders rarely live to a reproductive age.

Reading Check

Answer Cystic fibrosis is a recessive disorder.

Caption Answer

Figure 8 The X chromosome is larger than the Y, and looks like an X. The Y chromosome looks like the V part of a Y.

Activity

Genetic Disorders Have students work in pairs to research genetic disorders. Student pairs can create a table that lists the disorder, its pattern of inheritance, and what characteristics someone with the disorder would have.

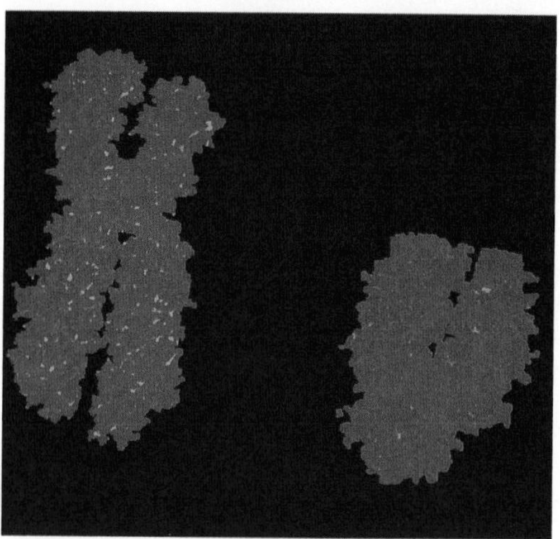

Color-enhanced SEM Magnification: 16000×

Figure 8 Sex in many organisms is determined by X and Y chromosomes.
Observe *How do the X (left) and Y (right) chromosomes differ from one another in shape and size?*

Recessive Genetic Disorders

Many human genetic disorders, such as cystic fibrosis, are caused by recessive genes. Some recessive genes are the result of a mutation within the gene. Many of these alleles are rare. Such genetic disorders occur when both parents have a recessive allele responsible for this disorder. Because the parents are heterozygous, they don't show any symptoms. However, if each parent passes the recessive allele to the child, the child inherits both recessive alleles and will have a recessive genetic disorder.

Reading Check *How is cystic fibrosis inherited?*

Cystic fibrosis is a homozygous recessive disorder. It is the most common genetic disorder that can lead to death among Caucasian Americans. In most people, a thin fluid is produced that lubricates the lungs and intestinal tract. People with cystic fibrosis produce thick mucus instead of this thin fluid. The thick mucus builds up in the lungs and makes it hard to breathe. This buildup often results in repeated bacterial respiratory infections. The thick mucus also reduces or prevents the flow of substances necessary for digesting food. Physical therapy, special diets, and new drug therapies have increased the life spans of patients with cystic fibrosis.

Sex Determination

What determines the sex of an individual? Much information on sex inheritance came from studies of fruit flies. Fruit flies have only four pairs of chromosomes. Because the chromosomes are large and few in number, they are easy to study. Scientists identified one pair that contains genes that determine the sex of the organism. They labeled the pair XX in females and XY in males. Geneticists use these labels when studying organisms, including humans. You can see human X and Y chromosomes in **Figure 8.**

Each egg produced by a female normally contains one X chromosome. Males produce sperm that normally have either an X or a Y chromosome. When a sperm with an X chromosome fertilizes an egg, the offspring is a female, XX. A male offspring, XY, is the result of a Y-containing sperm fertilizing an egg. What pair of sex chromosomes is in each of your cells? Sometimes chromosomes do not separate during meiosis. When this occurs, an individual can inherit an abnormal number of sex chromosomes.

Differentiated Instruction

English-Language Learners Have students work in pairs to create bookmarks using vocabulary and key terms from this section. Students can test each other's ability to pronounce and define each word. The bookmarks can be used to mark pages that contain words that students find difficult. L2

Teacher FYI

Genetic Disorders Most students will be aware of someone with a genetic disorder. Be sensitive to the possibility that students may have someone in their own family with a disorder.

Sex-Linked Disorders

Some inherited conditions are linked with the X and Y chromosomes. An allele inherited on a sex chromosome is called a **sex-linked gene.** Color blindness is a sex-linked disorder in which people cannot distinguish between certain colors, particularly red and green. This trait is a recessive allele on the X chromosome. Because males have only one X chromosome, a male with this allele on his X chromo-some is color-blind. However, a color-blind female occurs only when both of her X chromosomes have the allele for this trait.

The allele for the distinct patches of three different colors found in calico cats is recessive and carried on the X chromosome. As shown in **Figure 9,** calico cats have inherited two X chromosomes with this recessive allele—one from both parents.

Female carrier of calico gene (X^CX)

Male carrier of calico gene (X^CY)

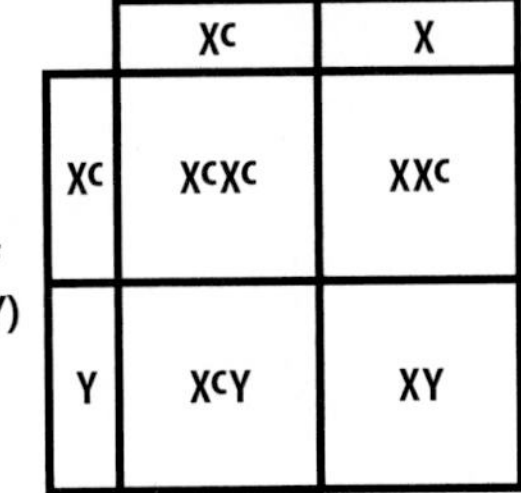

X^C
X
X^C
X^CX^C
XX^C
Y
X^CY
XY

Genotypes: X^CX^C, X^CX, X^CY, XY
Phenotypes: one calico female, one carrier female, one carrier male, one normal male

Figure 9 Calico cat fur is a homozygous recessive sex-linked trait. Female cats that are heterozygous are not calico but are only carriers. Two recessive alleles must be present for this allele to be expressed.
Determine *Why aren't all the females calico?*

Pedigrees Trace Traits

How can you trace a trait through a family? A pedigree is a visual tool for following a trait through generations of a family. Males are represented by squares and females by circles. A completely filled circle or square shows that the trait is seen in that person. Half-colored circles or squares indicate carriers. A carrier is heterozygous for the trait, and it is not seen. People represented by empty circles or squares do not have the trait and are not carriers. The pedigree in **Figure 10** shows how the trait for color blindness is carried through a family.

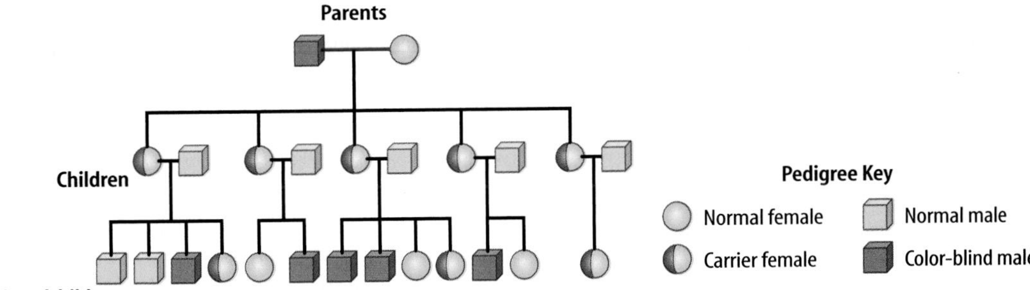

Figure 10 The symbols in this pedigree's key mean the same thing on all pedigree charts. The grandfather in this family was color-blind and married to a woman who was not a carrier of the color-blind allele.
Infer *why no women in this family are color-blind.*

Quick Demo

Punnett Squares

Materials blank transparency (or chalkboard), marker (or chalk)

Estimated Time 10 minutes

Procedure Demonstrate the inheritance patterns discussed in this section by using Punnett squares. Use the combination of X and Y chromosomes that determines the sex of the individual. Follow a sex-linked trait and show examples of the different patterns of inheritance.

Make a Model

Sex-linked Disorder Have students use a set of cutouts of X and Y chromosomes to model how a sex-linked disorder can be inherited. L2

Caption Answer

Figure 9 All the females aren't calico because some are heterozygous.

Visual Learning

Figure 10 Have students use this figure to answer the following questions. How many children are carriers for color blindness? 5 How many grandchildren? 3 What percent is this of each generation? 100% of children, 23% of grandchildren are carriers.

Caption Answer

Figure 10 Because color-blind women must inherit the allele from both mother and father, more women are carriers of color blindness than have the disorder.

Differentiated Instruction

Challenge Have students do research on the pros and cons of purebred dogs. Have them make a list of different breeds of purebred dogs and what kind of detrimental traits are propagated. They also can investigate the popularity of certain dog breeds. Students can design a pamphlet that provides information on how to pick out a dog and avoid breeds that have undesirable traits. L3

SECTION 2 Genetics Since Mendel **A** ◆ **141**

3 Assess

DAILY INTERVENTION

Check for Understanding

Visual-Spatial Using colored pencils or markers and white paper, have students draw the outcome of crossing pea plants heterozygous for purple flowers. Extend this by having them show the outcome if pea plants' inheritance showed incomplete dominance and if inheritance was polygenic. The student's results can be displayed in the classroom. L2

Reteach

Inheritance Patterns Have students compare the three inheritance patterns in this section by making a chart. L1 LS **Visual-Spatial**

Assessment

Process Have students prepare a table that lists types of inheritance, their descriptions, and examples of each. Use **Performance Assessment in the Science Classroom,** p. 109. L2

Shih Tzu

Black Labrador

Figure 11
A variety of traits are considered when breeding dogs.

Using Pedigrees A pedigree is a useful tool for a geneticist. Sometimes a geneticist needs to understand who has had a trait in a family over several generations to determine its pattern of inheritance. A geneticist determines if a trait is recessive, dominant, sex-linked, or has some other pattern of inheritance. When geneticists understand how a trait is inherited, they can predict the probability that a baby will be born with a specific trait.

Pedigrees also are important in breeding animals or plants. Because livestock and plant crops are used as sources of food, these organisms are bred to increase their yield and nutritional content. Breeders of pets and show animals, like the dogs pictured in **Figure 11,** also examine pedigrees carefully for possible desirable physical and ability traits. Issues concerning health also are considered when researching pedigrees.

section 2 review

Summary

Incomplete Dominance

- Incomplete dominance is when a dominant and recessive allele for a trait show an intermediate phenotype.
- Many traits are controlled by more than two alleles.
- A wide variety of phenotypes is produced by polygenic inheritance.

Human Genes and Mutations

- Errors can occur when DNA is copied.
- Mistakes in meiosis can result in an unequal number of chromosomes in sex cells.
- Recessive genes control many human genetic disorders.

Sex Determination

- An allele inherited on a sex chromosome is called a sex-linked gene.
- Pedigrees are visual tools to trace a trait through generations of a family.

Self Check

1. **Compare** how inheritance by multiple alleles and polygenic inheritance are similar.
2. **Explain** why a trait inherited by incomplete dominance is not a blend of two alleles.
3. **Discuss** Choose two genetic disorders and discuss how they are inherited.
4. **Apply** Using a Punnett square, explain why males are affected more often than females by sex-linked genetic disorders.
5. **Think Critically** Calico male cats are rare. Explain how such a cat can exist.

Applying Skills

6. **Predict** A man with blood type B marries a woman with blood type A. Their first child has blood type O. Use a Punnett square to predict what other blood types are possible for their offspring.
7. **Communicate** In your Science Journal, explain why offspring may or may not resemble either parent.

Science Online booka.msscience.com/self_check_quiz

section 2 review

1. both result in many phenotypes
2. The two alleles are present in the offspring and can be passed on. Their DNA remains separate; it does not mix.
3. Answers will vary. Sample response: cystic fibrosis is inherited as a simple recessive trait.
4. Males only need to inherit one allele for the disorder to be affected. Females must inherit two alleles.
5. Possible answer: A male cat could inherit an extra X chromosome. Both X chromosomes may carry the recessive calico trait.
6. The Punnett square should show heterozygous parents with the alleles AO and BO.
7. There are many genes and combinations, so an individual may look very different from either parent.

section 3

Advances in Genetics

Why is genetics important?

If Mendel were to pick up a daily newspaper in any country today, he'd probably be surprised. News articles about developments in genetic research appear almost daily. The term *gene* has become a common word. The principles of heredity are being used to change the world.

Genetic Engineering

You may know that chromosomes are made of DNA and are in the nucleus of a cell. Sections of DNA in chromosomes that direct cell activities are called genes. Through **genetic engineering,** scientists are experimenting with biological and chemical methods to change the arrangement of DNA that makes up a gene. Genetic engineering already is used to help produce large volumes of medicine. Genes also can be inserted into cells to change how those cells perform their normal functions, as shown in **Figure 12.** Other research is being done to find new ways to improve crop production and quality, including the development of plants that are resistant to disease.

as you read

What **You'll Learn**

- **Evaluate** the importance of advances in genetics.
- **Sequence** the steps in making genetically engineered organisms.

Why **It's Important**

Advances in genetics can affect your health, the foods that you eat, and your environment.

Review Vocabulary
DNA: deoxyribonucleic acid; the genetic material of all organisms

New Vocabulary
- genetic engineering

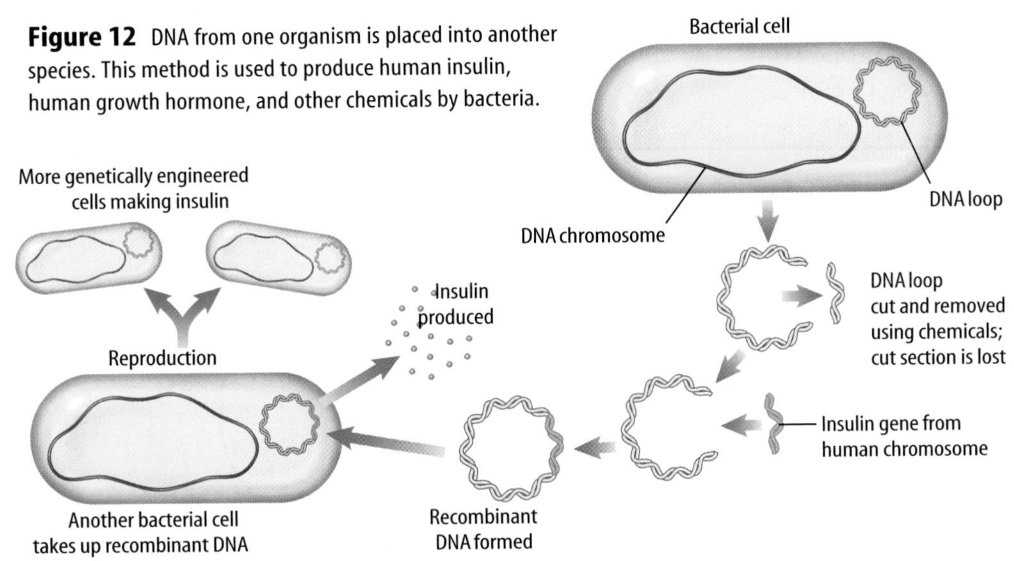

Figure 12 DNA from one organism is placed into another species. This method is used to produce human insulin, human growth hormone, and other chemicals by bacteria.

1 Motivate

Bellringer

Section Focus Transparencies also are available on the Interactive Chalkboard CD-ROM. L2 

Section Focus Transparency 3 — Two Quarts of Oil and a Side Salad, Please

For many years, scientists have looked for ways to raise plants and animals with traits that people want most. At the same time they try to take away unwanted traits. But how can they make a better bacteria? Recently, scientists learned how to put new parts of DNA directly into cells. By doing this, they gave certain bacteria an appetite for oil!

1. What other advantages might there be to changing an organism in this way?
2. Are there any dangers in making these sorts of changes?

Tie to Prior Knowledge

Selective Breeding Explain that in selective breeding, specific crosses are made to accentuate a desired trait in offspring. Discuss with students how this might be advantageous to a plant breeder trying to produce a corn plant that has higher yields. Then explain that scientists are trying to find new ways to change traits without the time involved in selective breeding. They will learn about these techniques in this section.

Section 3 Resource Manager 

Chapter *FAST FILE* Resources

Transparency Activity, p. 42

Directed Reading for Content Mastery, pp. 17, 18

Reinforcement, p. 25

Lab Worksheet, pp. 7–8

Enrichment, p. 28

Lab Management and Safety, p. 74

2 Teach

Genetically Engineered Crops Possible answer: The plants may pollinate other fields of the same crop unintentionally.

Career Have students research different careers in environmental science. They should discuss what type of study is required for the different careers and where an environmental scientist can find a job. Students should choose a specific environmental career and design a brochure that advertises how to become an environmental scientist. L2

Visual Learning

Figure 13 Explain that gene therapy is still in its infancy. As more is learned, the applications are likely to extend to many more genetic disorders. Remind students of the demonstration of a mutation in a cell being propagated by mitosis. How is gene therapy similar to the way a mutation is propagated through body cells? The mechanisms are similar, but in gene therapy, a mutation is corrected by the propagation, instead of spread.

Teacher FYI

Transferring a Gene Transgenesis is a genetic engineering process that involves transferring a gene from one organism into another. Using transgenesis, scientists have developed tomato plants that have increased resistance to disease and spoilage. Potato, cotton, and corn plants that have a natural resistance to insects, such as moth larvae and beetles, also have been developed.

Genetically Engineered Crops Crop plants are now being genetically engineered to produce chemicals that kill specific pests that feed on them. Some of the pollen from pesticide-resistant canola crops is capable of spreading up to 8 km from the plant, while corn and potato pollen can spread up to 1 km. What might be the effects of pollen landing on other plants?

Recombinant DNA Making recombinant DNA is one method of genetic engineering. Recombinant DNA is made by inserting a useful segment of DNA from one organism into a bacterium, as illustrated in **Figure 12.** Large quantities of human insulin are made by some genetically engineered organisms. People with Type 1 diabetes need this insulin because their pancreases produce too little or no insulin. Other uses include the production of growth hormone to treat dwarfism and chemicals to treat cancer.

Gene Therapy Gene therapy is a kind of genetic engineering. In gene therapy, a normal allele is placed in a virus, as shown in **Figure 13.** The virus then delivers the normal allele when it infects its target cell. The normal allele replaces the defective one. Scientists are conducting experiments that use this method to test ways of controlling cystic fibrosis and some kinds of cancer. More than 2,000 people already have taken part in gene therapy experiments. Gene therapy might be a method of curing several other genetic disorders in the future.

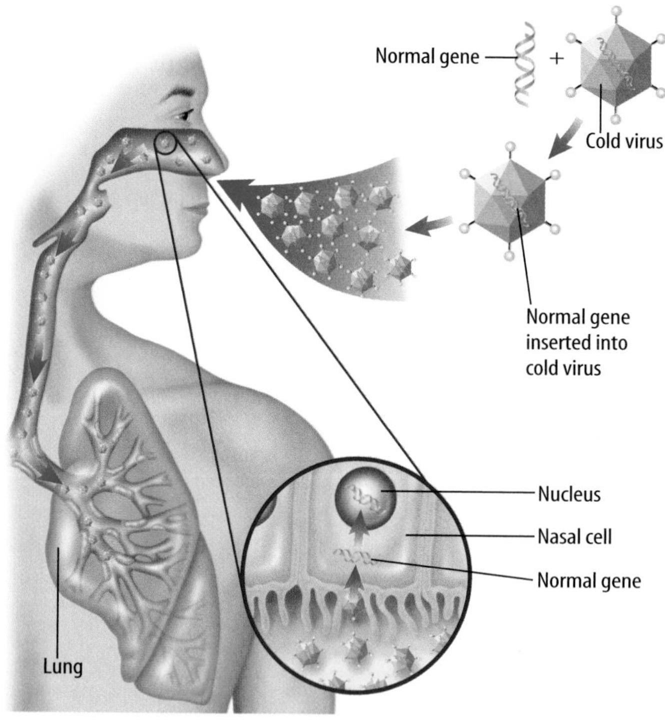

Figure 13 Gene therapy involves placing a normal allele into a cell that has a mutation. When the normal allele begins to function, a genetic disorder such as cystic fibrosis (CF) may be corrected.

Cultural Diversity

Genetic Engineering Research into genetic engineering, especially of crops, is taking place in many countries. Genetically engineered crops have already been planted in Europe, Canada, and the United States, though several countries in Europe have now banned the use of genetically engineered crops. Have students research to find out what countries could most benefit from agricultural advances involving genetic engineering. Have them research the staples of diets in those countries, and what, if any, research is being done on engineering those crops. Possible answer: Researchers at the International Rice Institute in the Philippines are working to produce new strains of rice. L2

Genetically Engineered Plants For thousands of years people have improved the plants they use for food and clothing even without the knowledge of genotypes. Until recently, these improvements were the results of selecting plants with the most desired traits to breed for the next generation. This process is called selective breeding. Recent advances in genetics have not replaced selective breeding. Although a plant can be bred for a particular phenotype, the genotype and pedigree of the plants also are considered.

Genetic engineering can produce improvements in crop plants, such as corn, wheat, and rice. One type of genetic engineering involves finding the genes that produce desired traits in one plant and then inserting those genes into a different plant. Scientists recently have made genetically engineered tomatoes with a gene that allows tomatoes to be picked green and transported great distances before they ripen completely. Ripe, firm tomatoes are then available in the local market. In the future, additional food crops may be genetically engineered so that they are not desirable food for insects.

 *What other types of traits would be considered desirable in plants?*

Because some people might prefer foods that are not changed genetically, some stores label such produce, as shown in **Figure 14.** The long-term effects of consuming genetically engineered plants are unknown.

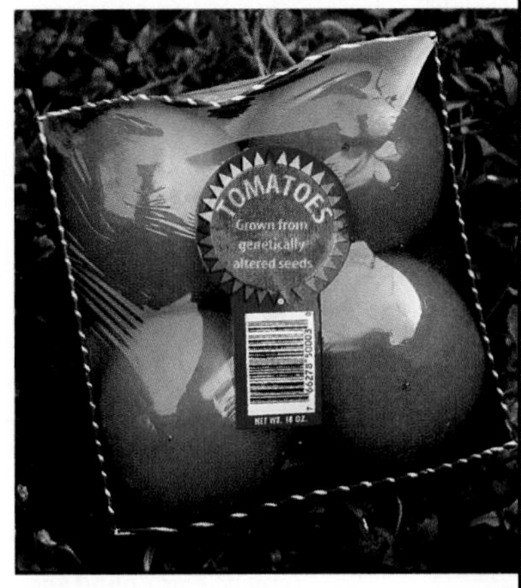

Figure 14 Genetically engineered produce is sometimes labeled. This allows consumers to make informed choices about their foods.

section 3 review

Summary

Why is genetics important?

- Developments in genetic research appear in newspapers almost daily.
- The world is being changed by the principles of heredity.

Genetic Engineering

- Scientists work with biological and chemical methods to change the arrangement of DNA that makes up a gene.
- One method of genetic engineering is making recombinant DNA.
- A normal allele is replaced in a virus and then delivers the normal allele when it infects its target cell.

Self Check

1. **Apply** Give examples of areas in which advances in genetics are important.
2. **Compare and contrast** the technologies of using recombinant DNA and gene therapy.
3. **Infer** What are some benefits of genetically engineered crops?
4. **Describe** how selective breeding differs from genetic engineering.
5. **Think Critically** Why might some people be opposed to genetically engineered plants?

Applying Skills

6. **Concept Map** Make an events-chain concept map of the steps used in making recombinant DNA.

Science Online booka.msscience.com/self_check_quiz

Reading Check

Answer Possible answers: increased growth rate, increased fruit size and production, reduced need for water, improved flavor, desirable flower color

3 Assess

DAILY INTERVENTION

Check for Understanding

Kinesthetic Have students make a time line for the future that shows their predictions about how advances in genetics might affect their life over the next ten years. They can include various gene therapies for genetic disorders and futuristic advancements in genetically engineered plants and crops. L2

Reteach

Flash Cards Have students make flash cards that illustrate steps in the process of genetic engineering. Have students practice identifying and ordering the steps using these cards. L2

Assessment

Performance Have students make a model that demonstrates the process of genetic engineering. Use **Performance Assessment in the Science Classroom,** p. 123. L2 P

section 3 review

1. Answers may include agriculture, health, and medicine.
2. Recombinant DNA inserts a segment of DNA from an organism into a bacterium to produce needed substances. Gene therapy places a normal allele into a virus, which delivers the allele to its target cell. There, it replaces the defective allele.
3. They may lead to increased crop production or be pest-resistant.
4. Selective breeding relies on natural, reproductive processes. Genetic engineering may take traits from one organism and place them into another.
5. Some people are concerned about pesticide resistance in weeds or other unforeseen consequences.
6. Answers should reflect steps shown in **Figure 12.**

Real-World Question

Purpose Students will devise a method to test for color blindness, and administer the test to determine the percentage of affected individuals.

Process Skills interpret data, design an experiment, form a hypothesis, communicate, use numbers

Time Required one class period

Possible Materials colored markers, blank white paper

Form a Hypothesis

Possible Hypothesis Students may hypothesize that color blindness will affect more males than females, because the allele for color blindness is carried on the X chromosome.

Test Your Hypothesis

Possible Procedures Students may choose to create a picture or number out of green circles. They can then use circles of red, orange, or yellow to surround the picture or number. Using this test, students would determine whether individuals could see the "hidden" picture or number.

Design Your Own

Tests for Color Blindness

Goals
- **Design** an experiment that tests for a specific type of color blindness in males and females.
- **Calculate** the percentage of males and females with the disorder.

Possible Materials
white paper or poster board
colored markers: red, orange, yellow, bright green, dark green, blue
computer and color printer
**Alternate materials*

Real-World Question

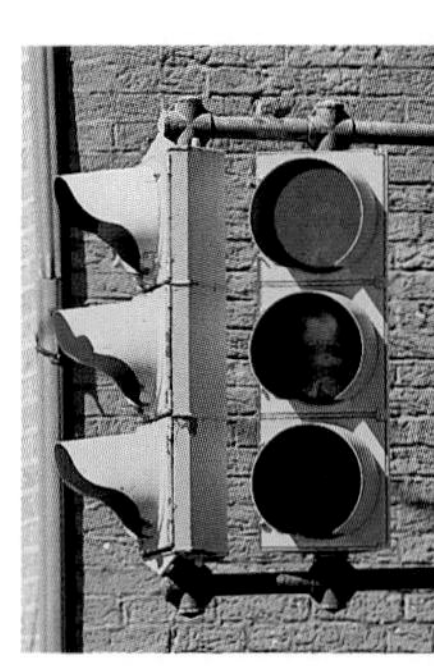

What do color-blind people see? People who have inherited color blindness can see most colors, but they have difficulty telling the difference between two specific colors. You have three genes that help you see color. One gene lets you see red, another blue, and the third gene allows you to see green. In the most common type of color blindness, red-green color blindness, the green gene does not work properly. What percentages of males and females in your school are color-blind?

Form a Hypothesis

Based on your reading and your own experiences, form a hypothesis about how common color blindness is among males and females.

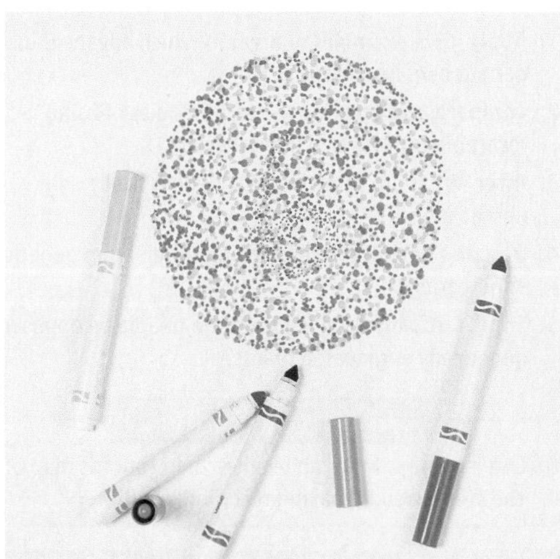

Test Your Hypothesis

Make a Plan

1. Decide what type of color blindness you will test for—the common green-red color blindness or the more rare green-blue color blindness.
2. **List** the materials you will need and describe how you will create test pictures. Tests for color blindness use many circles of red, orange, and yellow as a background, with circles of dark and light green to make a picture or number. List the steps you will take to test your hypothesis.
3. Prepare a data table in your Science Journal to record your test results.

Alternative Inquiry Lab

Test for Color Blindness To make this Lab an Inquiry Lab, have students investigate color blindness in terms of traffic lights. Explain to students that the most common form of color blindness is red-green color blindness. Have students relate this to driving and stopping at traffic lights. What percentage of people in the school are color blind? What percentage of males and females are color blind? They can design test pictures and collect data from within the school. If a larger study is needed, students can test individuals outside of the school.

Using Scientific Methods

4. **Examine** your experiment to make sure all steps are in logical order.
5. **Identify** which pictures you will use as a control and which pictures you will use as variables.

Follow Your Plan

1. Make sure your teacher approves your plan before you start.
2. **Draw** the pictures that you will use to test for color blindness.
3. Carry out your experiment as planned and record your results in your data table.

Analyze Your Data

1. **Calculate** the percentage of males and females that tested positive for color blindness.
2. **Compare** the frequency of color blindness in males with the frequency of color blindness in females.

Conclude and Apply

1. **Explain** whether or not the results supported your hypothesis.
2. **Explain** why color blindness is called a sex-linked disorder.
3. **Infer** how common the color-blind disorder is in the general population.
4. **Predict** your results if you were to test a larger number of people.

Communicating Your Data

Using a word processor, write a short article for the advice column of a fashion magazine about how a color-blind person can avoid wearing outfits with clashing colors. **For more help, refer to the Science Skill Handbook.**

Teaching Strategies Allow students to test individuals outside of class. Encourage them to test family, friends, and other teachers. Have them turn in their results after one week.

Expected Outcome More males than females will test positive for color blindness.

Analyze Your Data

Answers to Questions

1. More males should test positive than females.
2. Males are much more likely to be color blind than females.

Error Analysis Have students compare results to identify errors in data collection. Some possible sources of error are colors on the test pictures not being right or students overhearing the results of others so as not to give a true result.

Conclude and Apply

1. Answers will vary.
2. The allele for this trait is only located on the X chromosome. Because males only have one X chromosome, males with this allele will be color blind. A female will be color blind only when both of her X chromosomes have the color blind allele.
3. Color blindness afflicts 8 percent of males and 0.04 percent of females.
4. A larger sample will give more accurate results.

Communicating Your Data

Students might suggest that matching colors be grouped in different areas of the closet, or that a tagging system be developed so that one group of matching clothing is labeled *A*, a second group is labeled *B*, and so on.

Assessment

Process Have students create a similar test for another type of color blindness. After getting results, have students make a bar graph showing the percentages of individuals affected with each type of color blindness. Use **Performance Assessment in the Science Classroom,** p. 105. L2

Content Background

The human genome project is making continual contributions to our knowledge of human genetics. Scientists involved in the project are quick to point out the many things they don't know, even though the genome is complete. Students may be curious to know whose genome is being sequenced. The government and private companies working on genomes are using several anonymous donors of various racial and ethnic backgrounds.

Discussion

Similar Genes Mice and humans have many similar genes. What is one characteristic or function shared by mice and humans that might be coded for by similar genes? Possible answer: Both mice and humans have digestive enzymes that could be coded for by similar genes.

Activity

Gene's Story Have students write a story from the point of view of a human gene. Students should include details such as which chromosome the gene is located on, the function of the gene, and whether the gene functions all the time or is switched on and off. Students can either use an imaginary gene, or an actual human gene. L2 LS **Linguistic**

Applying Math

Answer about 3 gigabytes (1 million base pairs = 1 megabyte; 3 billion base pairs = 3,000 megabytes)

SCIENCE Stats

The Human Genome

Did you know...

. . . The biggest advance in genetics in years took place in February 2001. Scientists successfully mapped the human genome. There are 30,000 to 40,000 genes in the human genome. Genes are in the nucleus of each of the several trillion cells in your body.

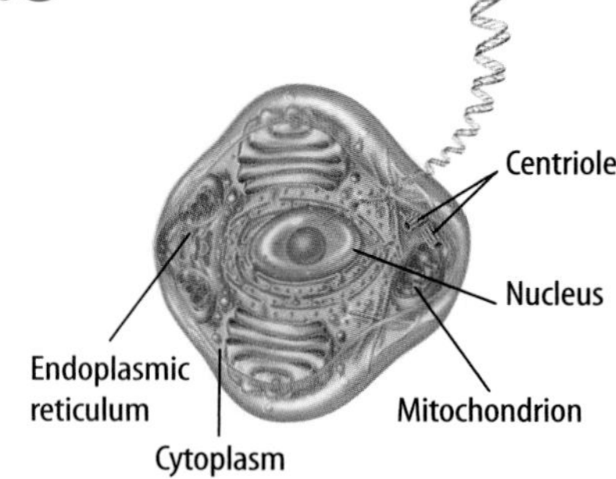

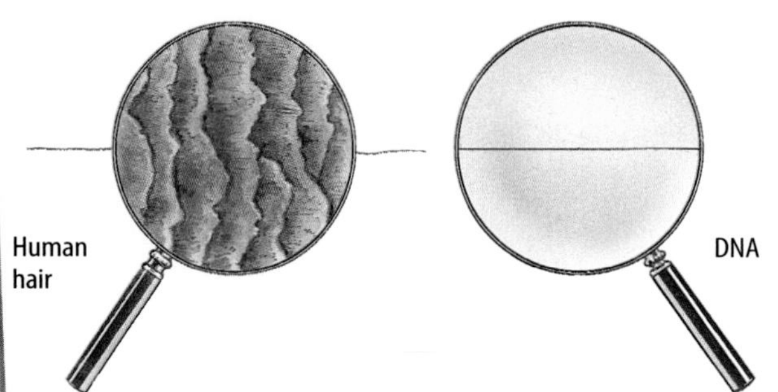

. . . The strands of DNA in the human genome, if unwound and connected end to end, would be more than 1.5 m long—but only about 130 trillionths of a centimeter wide. Even an average human hair is as much as 200,000 times wider than that.

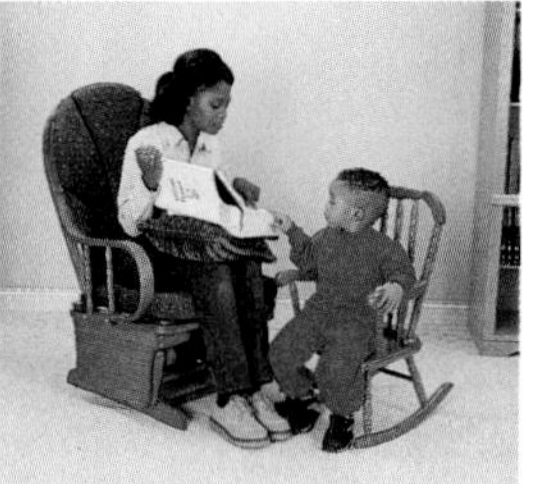

. . . It would take about nine and one-half years to read aloud without stopping the 3 billion bits of instructions (called base pairs) in your genome.

Applying Math If one million base pairs of DNA take up 1 megabyte of storage space on a computer, how many gigabytes (1,024 megabytes) would the whole genome fill?

Find Out About It

Human genome scientists hope to identify the location of disease-causing genes. Visit booka.msscience.com/science_stats to research a genetic disease and share your results with your class.

Curriculum Connection

Art Have students use the Internet or print sources to find the names of artists who have created drawings and paintings that depict a molecule of DNA. Students then can either create a collage of copies of the drawings or paintings they find, or they can create their own drawing using colored pencils, markers, or crayons. Display the collages and artwork. L2

Write About It

Organize Information Have students make a chart with information they learn about genetic diseases. They can include columns to show whether the disease is dominant or recessive, sex-linked, and how genetic therapy may help treat the disease. L2

Reviewing Main Ideas

Section 1 Genetics

1. Genetics is the study of how traits are inherited. Gregor Mendel determined the basic laws of genetics.
2. Traits are controlled by alleles on chromosomes.
3. Some alleles can be dominant or recessive.
4. When a pair of chromosomes separates during meiosis, the different alleles move into separate sex cells. Mendel found that he could predict the outcome of genetic crosses.

Section 2 Genetics Since Mendel

1. Inheritance patterns studied since Mendel include incomplete dominance, multiple alleles, and polygenic inheritance.
2. These inheritance patterns allow a variety of phenotypes to be produced.
3. Some disorders are the results of inheritance and can be harmful and even deadly.
4. Pedigree charts help reveal patterns of the inheritance of a trait in a family. Pedigrees show that sex-linked traits are expressed more often in males than in females.

Section 3 Advances in Genetics

1. Genetic engineering uses biological and chemical methods to change genes.
2. Recombinant DNA is one method of genetic engineering to make useful chemicals, including hormones.
3. Gene therapy shows promise for correcting many human genetic disorders by inserting normal alleles into cells.
4. Breakthroughs in the field of genetic engineering are allowing scientists to do many things, such as producing plants that are resistant to disease.

Visualizing Main Ideas

Examine the following pedigree for diabetes and explain the inheritance pattern.

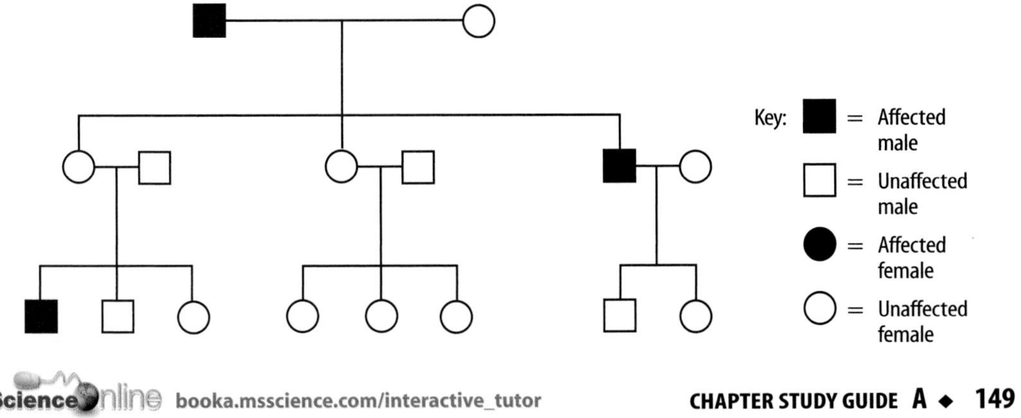

chapter 5 Study Guide

Reviewing Main Ideas

Summary statements can be used by students to review the major concepts of the chapter.

Visualizing Main Ideas

See student page.

Visit booka.msscience.com
/self_check_quiz
/interactive_tutor
/vocabulary_puzzlemaker
/chapter_review
/standardized_test

Assessment Transparency

For additional assessment questions, use the *Assessment Transparency* located in the transparency book.

Assessment

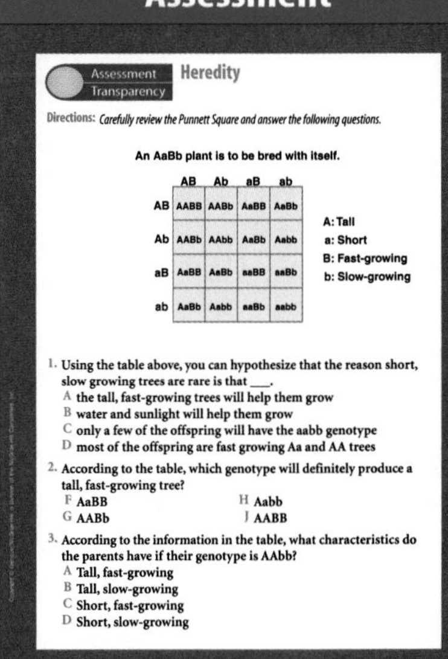

Assessment Transparency **Heredity**

Directions: *Carefully review the Punnett Square and answer the following questions.*

An AaBb plant is to be bred with itself.

	AB	Ab	aB	ab
AB	AABB	AABb	AaBB	AaBb
Ab	AABb	AAbb	AaBb	Aabb
aB	AaBB	AaBb	aaBB	aaBb
ab	AaBb	Aabb	aaBb	aabb

A: Tall
a: Short
B: Fast-growing
b: Slow-growing

1. Using the table above, you can hypothesize that the reason short, slow growing trees are rare is that ___.
   A the tall, fast-growing trees will help them grow
   B water and sunlight will help them grow
   C only a few of the offspring will have the aabb genotype
   D most of the offspring are fast growing Aa and AA trees
2. According to the table, which genotype will definitely produce a tall, fast-growing tree?
   F AaBB
   G AABb
   H Aabb
   J AABB
3. According to the information in the table, what characteristics do the parents have if their genotype is AAbb?
   A Tall, fast-growing
   B Tall, slow-growing
   C Short, fast-growing
   D Short, slow-growing

Heredity

Identifying Misconceptions

Assess

Use this assessment as follow-up to page F at the beginning of this chapter.

Procedure Repeat the question: If brown eyes are dominant over blue eyes, does this mean that someday all people will be brown eyed? Have students write and diagram their answer.

Expected Outcome Students should show that brown-eyed parents can have blue-eyed children if both parents have one blue-eyed allele. It does not disappear in the parent, then reappear in the child. Students should show that they understand that a dominant allele is not stronger or more frequently expressed than a recessive allele. L2

chapter 5 Review

Using Vocabulary

1. alleles
2. phenotype
3. polygenic inheritance
4. dominant
5. Genetics
6. genotype
7. Genetic engineering
8. Punnett square
9. Heredity
10. sex-linked gene

Checking Concepts

11. C	14. C
12. A	15. D
13. C	16. B

chapter 5 Review

Using Vocabulary

allele p. 128	hybrid p. 130
dominant p. 130	incomplete dominance p. 136
genetic engineering p. 143	phenotype p. 132
genetics p. 128	polygenic inheritance p. 138
genotype p. 132	Punnett square p. 132
heredity p. 128	recessive p. 130
heterozygous p. 132	sex-linked gene p. 141
homozygous p. 132	

Fill in the blanks with the correct word.

1. Alternate forms of a gene are called _________.
2. The outward appearance of a trait is a(n) _________.
3. Human height, eye color, and skin color are all traits controlled by _________.
4. An allele that produces a trait in the heterozygous condition is _________.
5. _________ is the branch of biology that deals with the study of heredity.
6. The actual combination of alleles of an organism is its _________.
7. _________ is moving fragments of DNA from one organism and inserting them into another organism.
8. A(n) _________ is a helpful device for predicting the proportions of possible genotypes.
9. _________ is the passing of traits from parents to offspring.
10. Red-green color blindness and hemophilia are two human genetic disorders that are caused by a(n) _________.

Checking Concepts

Choose the word or phrase that best answers the question.

11. Which of the following describes the allele that causes color blindness?
    A) dominant
    B) carried on the Y chromosome
    C) carried on the X chromosome
    D) present only in males
12. What is it called when the presence of two different alleles results in an intermediate phenotype?
    A) incomplete dominance
    B) polygenic inheritance
    C) multiple alleles
    D) sex-linked genes
13. What separates during meiosis?
    A) proteins
    B) phenotypes
    C) alleles
    D) pedigrees
14. What controls traits in organisms?
    A) cell membrane
    B) cell wall
    C) genes
    D) Punnett squares
15. What term describes the inheritance of cystic fibrosis?
    A) polygenic inheritance
    B) multiple alleles
    C) incomplete dominance
    D) recessive genes
16. What phenotype will the offspring represented in the Punnett square have?
    A) all recessive
    B) all dominant
    C) half recessive, half dominant
    D) Each will have a different phenotype.

	F	f
F	FF	Ff
F	FF	Ff

booka.msscience.com/vocabulary_puzzlemaker

Use the ExamView® Pro Testmaker CD-ROM to:

- create multiple versions of tests
- create modified tests with one mouse click for inclusion students
- edit existing questions and add your own questions
- build tests aligned with state standards using built-in State Curriculum Tags
- change English tests to Spanish with one mouse click and vice versa

Thinking Critically

17. **Explain** the relationship between DNA, genes, alleles, and chromosomes.

18. **Classify** the inheritance pattern for each of the following:
   a. many different phenotypes produced by one pair of alleles
   b. many phenotypes produced by more than one pair of alleles; two phenotypes from two alleles; three phenotypes from two alleles.

Use the illustration below to answer question 19.

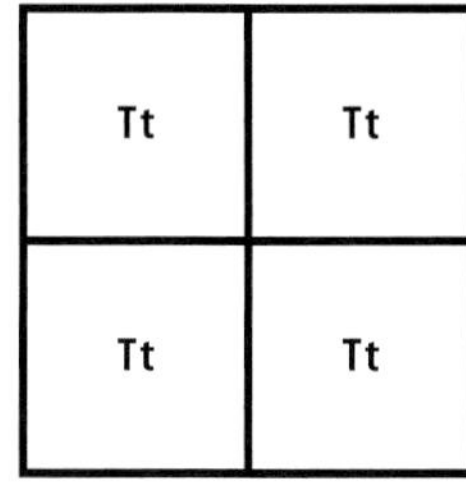

19. **Interpret Scientific Illustrations** What were the genotypes of the parents that produced the Punnett Square shown above?

20. **Explain** why two rabbits with the same genes might not be colored the same if one is raised in northern Maine and one is raised in southern Texas.

21. **Apply** Why would a person who receives genetic therapy for a disorder still be able to pass the disorder to his or her children?

22. **Predict** Two organisms were found to have different genotypes but the same phenotype. Predict what these phenotypes might be. Explain.

23. **Compare and contrast** Mendelian inheritance with incomplete dominance.

Performance Activities

24. **Newspaper Article** Write a newspaper article to announce a new, genetically engineered plant. Include the method of developing the plant, the characteristic changed, and the terms that you would expect to see. Read your article to the class.

25. **Predict** In humans, the widow's peak allele is dominant, and the straight hairline allele is recessive. Predict how both parents with widow's peaks could have a child without a widow's peak hairline.

26. **Use a word processor** or program to write predictions about how advances in genetics might affect your life in the next ten years.

Applying Math

27. **Human Genome** If you wrote the genetic information for each gene in the human genome on a separate sheet of 0.2-mm-thick paper and stacked the sheets, how tall would the stack be?

Use the table below to answer question 28.

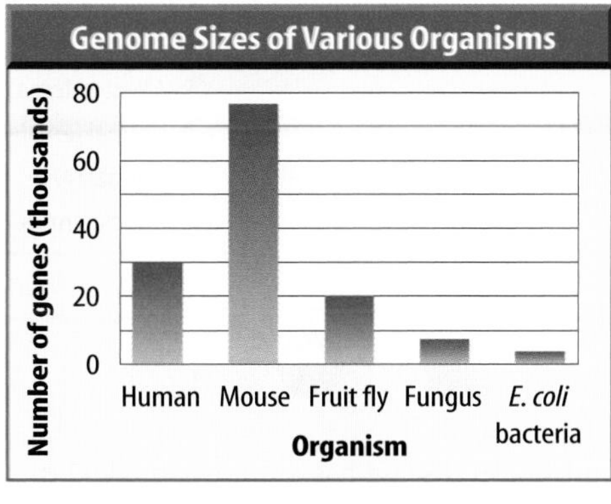

28. **Genes** Consult the graph above. How many more genes are in the human genome than the genome of the fruit fly?

Assessment Resources

Reproducible Masters

Chapter *Fast File* Resources
Chapter Review, pp. 33–34
Chapter Tests, pp. 35–38
Assessment Transparency Activity, p. 45

Glencoe Science Web site
Chapter Review Test
Standardized Test Practice

Glencoe Technology
Assessment Transparency
Exam*View*® Pro Testmaker
MindJogger Videoquiz
Interactive Chalkboard

Thinking Critically

17. DNA is a chemical; a gene contains DNA; an allele is a form of a gene specific for a trait; genes are located on chromosomes.
18. (a) multiple allele inheritance
(b) polygenic inheritance
19. TT and tt; both were purebred, one dominant, one recessive.
20. The coat colors of some rabbits are affected by temperature differences in the environment.
21. The normal allele is usually inserted only into the cells that cause the disorder. For this reason, the reproductive cells would not be changed by gene therapy.
22. The phenotypes would be the expression of a dominant trait.
23. Mendelian inheritance has two forms of an allele that produce only two phenotypes. Incomplete dominance also has two forms of an allele, but produces three phenotypes.

Performance Activities

24. Answers will vary, but should explain genetic engineering methods and how the methods can change the traits of organisms. Use **Performance Assessment in the Science Classroom,** p. 141.
25. Both parents would have to be heterozygous to produce children without the widow's peak trait.
26. Answers may include increased food production, curing genetic disorders, or providing new medicines.

Applying Math

National Math Standards
1, 5, 9

27. 20 m
28. about 10,000 genes

CHAPTER REVIEW A ◆ 151

FAST FILE

Answer Sheet A practice answer sheet can be found at booka.msscience.com/answer_sheet.

Student Recording Sheet

Standardized Test Practice

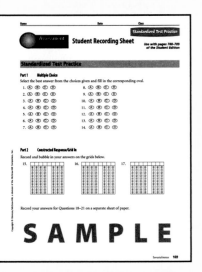

SAMPLE

Part 1 Multiple Choice

1. C
2. A
3. C
4. C
5. B
6. C
7. A
8. C
9. C

Part 2 Short Response

10. 50%—heterozygous; 50%—homozygous; 75%—same phenotype as the parents

	F	f
F	FF	Ff
f	Ff	ff

FF – full
ff – flat

11. If the flower color trait was an example of incomplete dominance, Mendel would have observed an intermediate phenotype when two purebred were crossed. Specifically, this phenotype would have been a light purple.
12. Heterozygous individuals are called carriers because they have or carry the recessive allele for a trait or disorder even though it is not present in their phenotype.
13. A—AO, AA; B—BO, BB
14. A body cell has a pair of alleles for each trait. Following meiosis, the sex cells only have one allele for each trait.

chapter 5 Standardized Test Practice

Part 1 Multiple Choice

Record your answers on the answer sheet provided by your teacher or on a sheet of paper.

1. Heredity includes all of the following except
   A. traits. **C.** nutrients.
   B. chromosomes. **D.** phenotype.

2. What is a mutation?
   A. A change in a gene which is harmful, beneficial, or has no effect at all.
   B. A change in a gene which is only beneficial.
   C. A change in a gene which is only harmful.
   D. No change in a gene.

3. Sex of the offspring is determined by
   A. only the mother, because she has two X chromosomes.
   B. only the father, because he has one X and one Y chromosome.
   C. an X chromosome from the mother and either an X or Y chromosome from the father.
   D. mutations.

Use the pedigree below to answer questions 4–6.

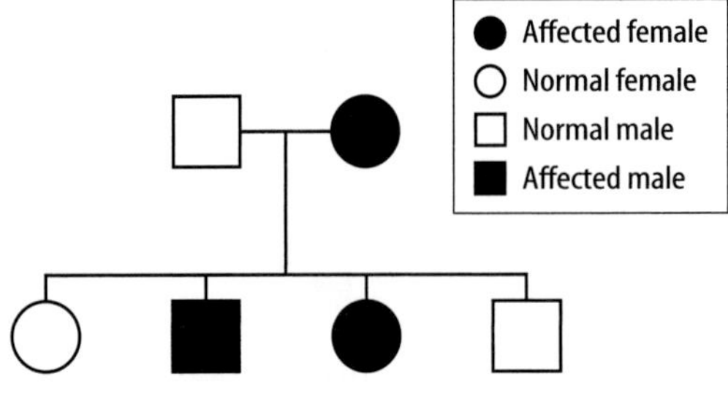

Huntington disease has a dominant (DD or Dd) inheritance pattern.

4. What is the genotype of the father?
   A. DD **C.** dd
   B. Dd **D.** D

5. What is the genotype of the mother?
   A. DD **C.** dd
   B. Dd **D.** D

6. The genotype of the unaffected children is
   A. DD. **C.** dd.
   B. Dd. **D.** D.

7. Manipulating the arrangement of DNA that makes up a gene is called
   A. genetic engineering.
   B. chromosomal migration.
   C. viral reproduction.
   D. cross breeding.

Use the Punnett square below to answer question 8.

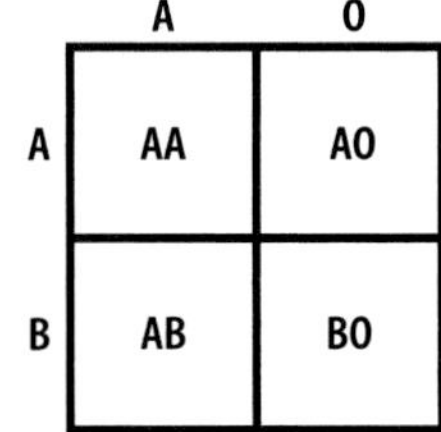

8. How many phenotypes would result from the following Punnett square?
   A. 1 **C.** 3
   B. 2 **D.** 4

9. Down's Syndrome is an example of
   A. incomplete dominance.
   B. genetic engineering.
   C. a chromosome disorder.
   D. a sex linked disorder.

Test-Taking Tip

Complete Charts Write directly on complex charts such as a Punnett square.

Question 10 Draw a Punnett square to answer all parts of the question.

Part 2 Short Response/Grid In

Record your answers on the answer sheet provided by your teacher or on a sheet of paper.

Use the table below to answer questions 10–11.

Some Traits Compared by Mendel			
Traits	Shape of Seeds	Shape of Pods	Flower Color
Dominant Trait	Round	Full	Purple
Recessive Trait	Wrinkled	Flat, constricted	White

10. Create a Punnett square using the *Shape of Pods* trait crossing heterozygous parents. What percentage of the offspring will be heterozygous? What percentage of the offspring will be homozygous? What percentage of the offspring will have the same phenotype as the parents?

11. Gregor Mendel studied traits in pea plants that were controlled by single genes. Explain what would have happened if the alleles for flower color were an example of incomplete dominance. What phenotypes would he have observed?

12. Why are heterozygous individuals called carriers for non-sex-linked and X-linked recessive patterns of inheritance?

13. How many alleles does a body cell have for each trait? What happens to the alleles during meiosis?

Part 3 Open Ended

Record your answers on a sheet of paper.

14. Genetic counseling helps individuals determine the genetic risk or probability a disorder will be passed to offspring. Why would a pedigree be a very important tool for the counselors? Which patterns of inheritance (dominant, recessive, x-linked) would be the easiest to detect?

15. Explain the process of gene therapy. What types of disorders would this therapy be best suited? How has this therapy helped patients with cystic fibrosis?

Refer to the figure below to answer question 16.

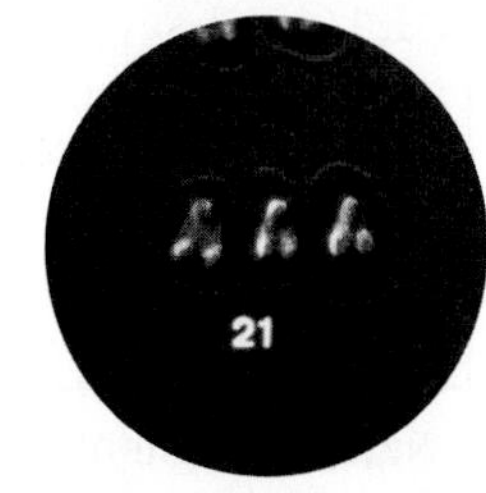

16. What is the disorder associated with the karyotype shown above? How does this condition occur? What are the characteristics of someone with this disorder?

17. Explain why the parents of someone with cystic fibrosis do not show any symptoms. How are the alleles for cystic fibrosis passed from parents to offspring?

18. What is recombinant DNA and how is it used to help someone with Type I diabetes?

19. If each kernel on an ear of corn represents a separate genetic cross, would corn be a good plant to use to study genetics? Why or why not? What process could be used to control pollination?

17. Down's syndrome; chromosomal disorders can be a result of mistakes in the process of meiosis. Individuals with Down's syndrome can be short, exhibit learning disabilities, and have heart problems.

18. Cystic fibrosis is caused by recessive genes. Such genetic disorders occur when both parents have a recessive allele for the disorder. Because the parents are heterozygous, they don't show any symptoms. However, if each parent passes the recessive allele to the child, the child inherits both recessive alleles and will have a recessive genetic disorder.

19. Recombinant DNA is made by inserting a segment of DNA from one organism into a bacterium. Large quantities of human insulin are made by some genetically engineered organisms. People with Type I diabetes need this insulin because they produce too little or no insulin.

20. Corn would be a good plant to study genetics because you could see the offspring of many crosses on just one ear of corn and a corn stalk produces several ears of corn. This makes producing a large number of results easier. Valid scientific conclusions need to be based on results that can be duplicated. The corn plants would need to be pollinated by hand rather than letting insects randomly pollinate plants.

Rubrics

For more help evaluating open-ended assessment questions, see the rubric on p. 10T.

Part 3 Open Ended

15. A pedigree is a very important tool for a genetic counselor because it is a visual means to trace a trait through a family. Any trait that has a dominant pattern of inheritance would be easy to detect because it would be present in every generation. Recessive disorders would be difficult to detect because the carriers would not display the phenotype. Environmental factors such as nutrition, lifestyle, habitat, and medical care would contribute to a person's phenotype.

16. Gene therapy is when a normal allele is placed in a virus and the virus delivers the normal allele when it infects its target cell. This type of therapy is best suited for single genes that are defective and would be very difficult to use with disorders that are polygenic. In cystic fibrosis patients, the normal allele is delivered into their lungs so it can begin to produce the normal thin fluid.

chapter 6 Organizer

<table>
<tr><th rowspan="2">Section/Objectives</th><th colspan="2">Standards</th><th rowspan="2">Labs/Features</th></tr>
<tr><th>National</th><th>State/Local</th></tr>
<tr><td>Chapter Opener</td><td>See pp. 16T–17T for a Key to Standards.</td><td></td><td>Launch Lab: Adaptation for a Hunter, p. 155
Foldables, p. 155</td></tr>
<tr><td>Section 1 Ideas About Evolution
2 sessions
1 block
1. Describe Lamarck's hypothesis of acquired characteristics and Darwin's theory of natural selection.
2. Identify why variations in organisms are important.
3. Compare and contrast gradualism and punctuated equilibrium.</td><td>National Content Standards: UCP.1–UCP.5, A.1, A.2, C.1, C.4, C.5, G.1–G.3</td><td></td><td>Science Online, p. 158
Applying Science: Does natural selection take place in a fish tank?, p. 159
Integrate Language Arts, p. 160
MiniLAB: Relating Evolution to Species, p. 161
Lab: Hidden Frogs, p. 164</td></tr>
<tr><td>Section 2 Clues About Evolution
2 sessions
1.5 blocks
4. Identify the importance of fossils as evidence of evolution.
5. Explain how relative and radiometric dating are used to estimate the age of fossils.
6. List examples of five types of evidence for evolution.</td><td>National Content Standards: UCP.1–UCP.5, A.1, A.2, F.1, G.2</td><td></td><td>Science Online, p. 167
Visualizing the Geologic Time Scale, p. 168
Integrate Earth Science, p. 169</td></tr>
<tr><td>Section 3 The Evolution of Primates
3 sessions
2 blocks
7. Describe the differences among living primates.
8. Identify the adaptations of primates.
9. Discuss the evolutionary history of modern primates.</td><td>National Content Standards: UCP.1–UCP.5, A.1, A.2, C.1, C.5, G.1–G.3</td><td></td><td>MiniLAB: Living Without Thumbs, p. 173
Lab: Recognizing Variation in a Population, p. 176
Science and History: Fighting HIV, p. 178</td></tr>
</table>

Lab Materials	Reproducible Resources	Section Assessment	Technology
Launch Lab: classified ads from the newspaper, white paper, black paper, hole punch, watch or clock with second hand	**Chapter *Fast File* Resources** Foldables Worksheet, p. 15 Directed Reading Overview, p. 17 Note-taking Worksheets, pp. 31–32	Glencoe's Assessment Advantage	TeacherWorks includes: • Interactive Teacher Edition • Lesson Planner with calendar • Access to all program blacklines • Correlations to standards • Web links
MiniLAB: lined paper **Lab:** cardboard form of a frog, colored markers, crayons, colored pencils, glue, beads, sequins, modeling clay	**Chapter *Fast File* Resources** Transparency Activity, p. 42 MiniLAB, p. 3 Enrichment, p. 28 Reinforcement, p. 25 Directed Reading, p. 18 Lab Activities, pp. 9–10, 11–14 Lab Worksheet, pp. 5–6 **Cultural Diversity,** p. 19 **Mathematics Skill Activities,** p. 1 **Science Inquiry Lab,** pp. 21–22	**Portfolio** Curriculum Connection, p. 161 **Performance** Applying Science, p. 159 MiniLAB, p. 161 Applying Math, p. 163 **Content** Section Review, p. 163	Section Focus Transparency Virtual Labs CD-ROM Guided Reading Audio Program Interactive Chalkboard CD-ROM
Need materials? Contact Science Kit at 1-800-828-7777 or www.sciencekit.com on the Internet.	**Chapter *Fast File* Resources** Transparency Activity, p. 43 Enrichment, p. 29 Reinforcement, p. 26 Directed Reading, p. 19 Transparency Activity, pp. 45–46 **Life Science Critical Thinking/ Problem Solving,** p. 3	**Portfolio** Science Journal, p. 166 **Performance** Applying Math, p. 171 **Content** Section Review, p. 171	Section Focus Transparency Teaching Transparency Virtual Labs CD-ROM Guided Reading Audio Program Interactive Chalkboard CD-ROM
MiniLAB: tape **Lab:** fruit and seeds from one plant species, metric ruler, magnifying lens, graph paper	**Chapter *Fast File* Resources** Transparency Activity, p. 44 MiniLAB, p. 4 Enrichment, p. 30 Reinforcement, p. 27 Directed Reading, pp. 19, 20 Lab Worksheet, pp. 7–8 **Lab Management and Safety,** p. 71	**Portfolio** MiniLAB Assessment, p. 173 **Performance** MiniLAB, p. 173 Applying Skills, p. 175 **Content** Section Review, p. 175	Section Focus Transparency Virtual Labs CD-ROM Guided Reading Audio Program Interactive Chalkboard CD-ROM Video Lab

End of Chapter Assessment

Glencoe's Assessment Advantage

Blackline Masters	Technology	Professional Series
Chapter *Fast File* Resources Chapter Review, pp. 35–36 Chapter Tests, pp. 37–40 **Standardized Test Practice,** pp. 27–30	MindJogger Videoquiz Virtual Labs CD-ROM Exam*View*® Pro Testmaker TeacherWorks CD-ROM Interactive Chalkboard CD-ROM	**Performance Assessment in the Science Classroom (PASC)**

Transparencies

Section Focus

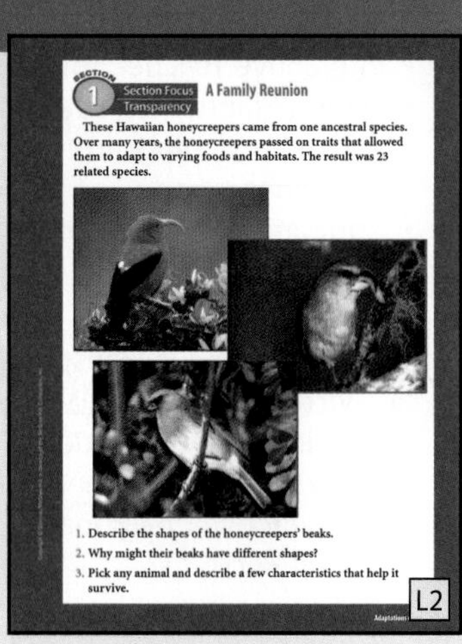
Section 1 Section Focus Transparency — A Family Reunion

These Hawaiian honeycreepers came from one ancestral species. Over many years, the honeycreepers passed on traits that allowed them to adapt to varying foods and habitats. The result was 23 related species.

1. Describe the shapes of the honeycreepers' beaks.
2. Why might their beaks have different shapes?
3. Pick any animal and describe a few characteristics that help it survive.

L2

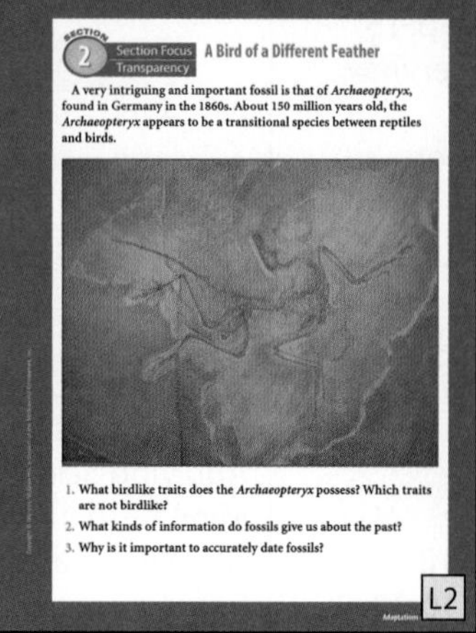
Section 2 Section Focus Transparency — A Bird of a Different Feather

A very intriguing and important fossil is that of *Archaeopteryx*, found in Germany in the 1860s. About 150 million years old, the *Archaeopteryx* appears to be a transitional species between reptiles and birds.

1. What birdlike traits does the *Archaeopteryx* possess? Which traits are not birdlike?
2. What kinds of information do fossils give us about the past?
3. Why is it important to accurately date fossils?

L2

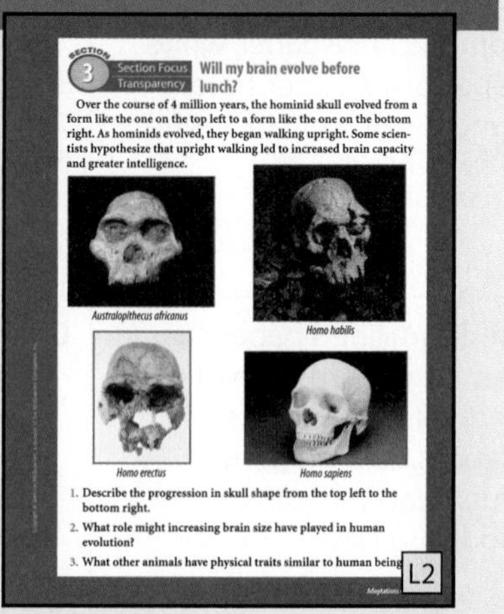
Section 3 Section Focus Transparency — Will my brain evolve before lunch?

Over the course of 4 million years, the hominid skull evolved from a form like the one on the top left to a form like the one on the bottom right. As hominids evolved, they began walking upright. Some scientists hypothesize that upright walking led to increased brain capacity and greater intelligence.

1. Describe the progression in skull shape from the top left to the bottom right.
2. What role might increasing brain size have played in human evolution?
3. What other animals have physical traits similar to human beings?

L2

This is a representation of key blackline masters available in the Teacher Classroom Resources. See Resource Manager boxes within the chapter for additional information.

Assessment

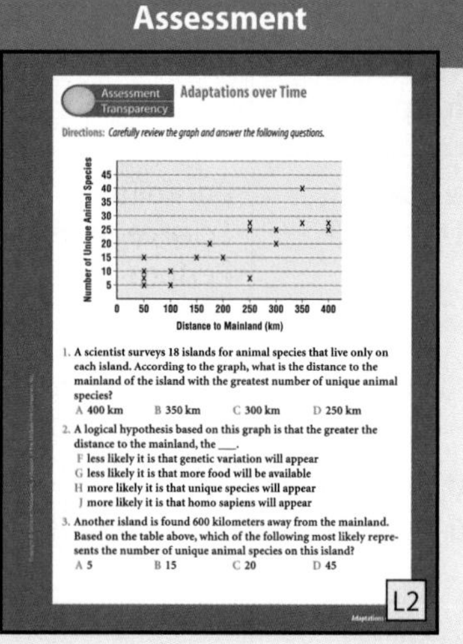
Assessment Transparency — Adaptations over Time

Directions: *Carefully review the graph and answer the following questions.*

1. A scientist surveys 18 islands for animal species that live only on each island. According to the graph, what is the distance to the mainland of the island with the greatest number of unique animal species?
   A 400 km B 350 km C 300 km D 250 km
2. A logical hypothesis based on this graph is that the greater the distance to the mainland, the ___.
   F less likely it is that genetic variation will appear
   G less likely it is that more food will be available
   H more likely it is that unique species will appear
   J more likely it is that homo sapiens will appear
3. Another island is found 600 kilometers away from the mainland. Based on the table above, which of the following most likely represents the number of unique animal species on this island?
   A 5 B 15 C 20 D 45

L2

Teaching

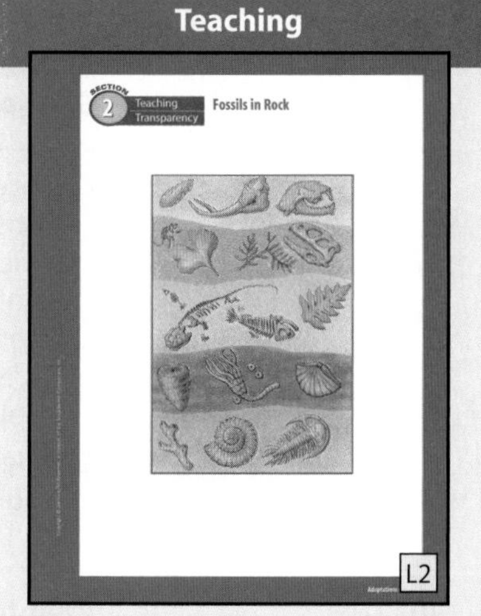
Section 2 Teaching Transparency — Fossils in Rock

L2

Key to Teaching Strategies

The following designations will help you decide which activities are appropriate for your students.

- **L1** Level 1 activities should be appropriate for students with learning difficulties.
- **L2** Level 2 activities should be within the ability range of all students.
- **L3** Level 3 activities are designed for above-average students.
- **ELL** ELL activities should be within the ability range of English-Language Learners.
- **COOP LEARN** Cooperative Learning activities are designed for small group work.
- **LS** Multiple Learning Styles logos, as described on page 12T, are used throughout to indicate strategies that address different learning styles.
- **P** These strategies represent student products that can be placed into a best-work portfolio.
- **PBL** Problem-Based Learning activities apply real-world situations to learning.

Hands-on Activities

Student Text Lab Worksheet

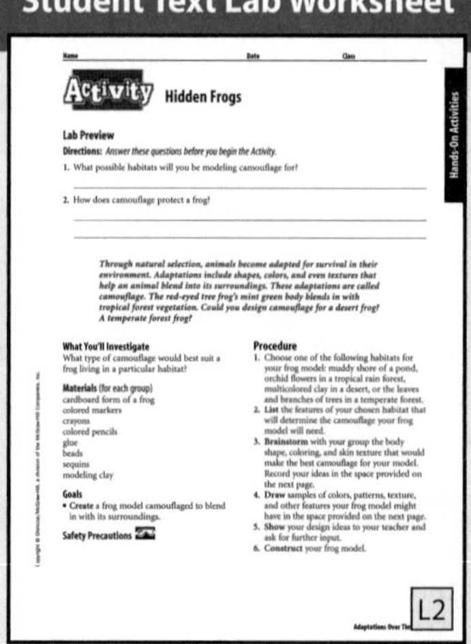
Name Date Class

Activity — Hidden Frogs

Lab Preview

Directions: *Answer these questions before you begin the Activity.*

1. What possible habitats will you be modeling camouflage for?
2. How does camouflage protect a frog?

Through natural selection, animals become adapted for survival in their environment. Adaptations include shapes, colors, and even textures that help an animal blend into its surroundings. These adaptations are called camouflage. The red-eyed tree frog's mint green body blends in with tropical forest vegetation. Could you design camouflage for a desert frog? A temperate forest frog?

What You'll Investigate

What type of camouflage would best suit a frog living in a particular habitat?

Materials (for each group)

cardboard form of a frog
colored markers
crayons
colored pencils
glue
beads
sequins
modeling clay

Goals

- **Create** a frog model camouflaged to blend in with its surroundings.

Safety Precautions

Procedure

1. Choose one of the following habitats for your frog model: muddy shore of a pond, orchid flowers in a tropical rain forest, multicolored clay in a desert, or the leaves and branches of trees in a temperate forest.
2. **List** the features of your chosen habitat that will determine the camouflage your frog model will need.
3. **Brainstorm** with your group the body shape, coloring, and skin texture that would make the best camouflage for your model. Record your ideas in the space provided on the next page.
4. **Draw** samples of colors, patterns, texture, and other features your frog model might have in the space provided on the next page.
5. **Show** your design ideas to your teacher and ask for further input.
6. **Construct** your frog model.

Hands-On Activities

Adaptations Over Time

L2

Laboratory Activities

Name Date Class

Lab 1 Laboratory Activity — Modeling Geographic Isolation

The traits of a species can change over time. Individuals moving into or out of an area can add variation to the genetic makeup of a species in a particular area. When a small part of a population is isolated, they will usually have fewer variations of traits than exist in a large population. You can model the frequency at which different variations of traits might occur in different sizes of populations.

Strategy

You will model the effect of geographic isolation on the frequency of variations of a trait in a population.
You will infer the risks and benefits of geographic isolation.

Materials

index cards paper bags
markers—10 different colors

Procedure

1. The class will be divided into groups. *Geographically isolated populations:* groups containing 2 students *Large populations:* groups containing 3–8 students
2. Assign a number to each member of the group. Start with one, and continue until every member of the group has a number. Your teacher will distribute 5 index cards to each student.
3. Mark your index cards according to your assigned number:
   one—red five—orange
   two—blue six—yellow
   three—green seven—purple
   four—black eight—brown
4. Shuffle all marked index cards and place them into one paper bag.
5. The color on each card represents a variation of one trait. Without looking, pull 10 index cards from the bag to represent 10 individuals. Record the percent of your group's population that has each of the chosen variations in the data table. Return all cards to the bag. Repeat five times, recording your results each time.
6. Meet with a member of a different group and share results, so that everyone has information about both types of populations.

Data and Observations

Trials	Red	Blue	Green	Black	Orange	Yellow	Purple	Brown
1								
2								
3								
4								
5								

Hands-On Activities

Adaptations Over Time

L2

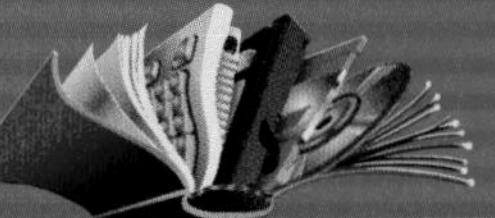

Resource Manager

Meeting Different Ability Levels

Content Outline

Note-taking Worksheet — Adaptations Over Time

Section 1 Ideas About Evolution

L2

Reinforcement

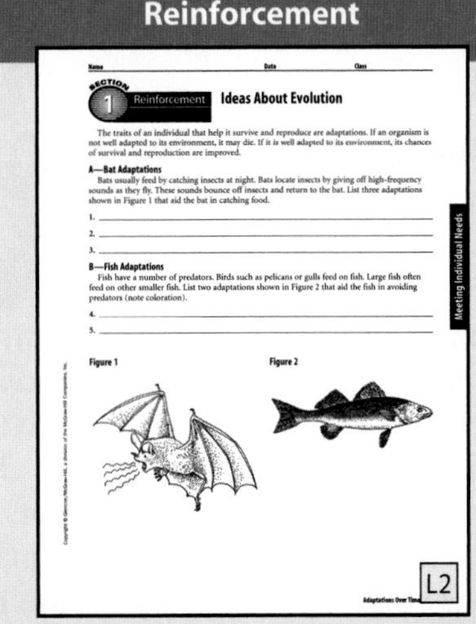

Section 1 Reinforcement — Ideas About Evolution

A—Bat Adaptations

B—Fish Adaptations

Figure 1 Figure 2

L2

Enrichment

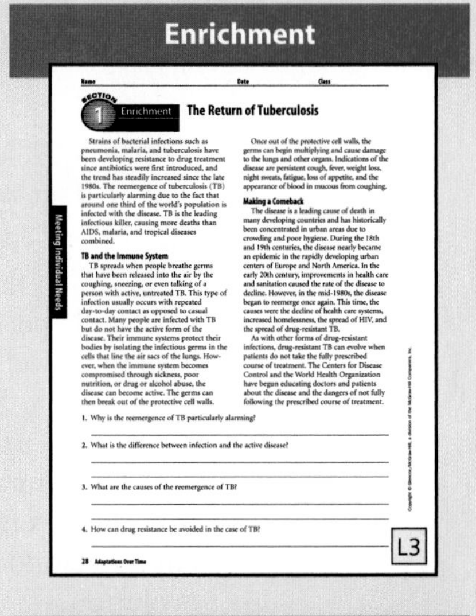

Section 1 Enrichment — The Return of Tuberculosis

Making a Comeback

TB and the Immune System

L3

Directed Reading (English/Spanish)

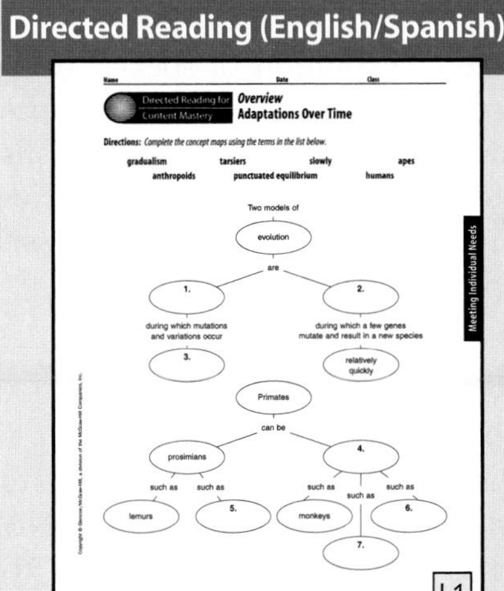

Directed Reading for Content Mastery — Overview — Adaptations Over Time

Directions: Complete the concept maps using the terms in the list below.

gradualism, tarsiers, slowly, apes, anthropoids, punctuated equilibrium, humans

L1

Study Guide

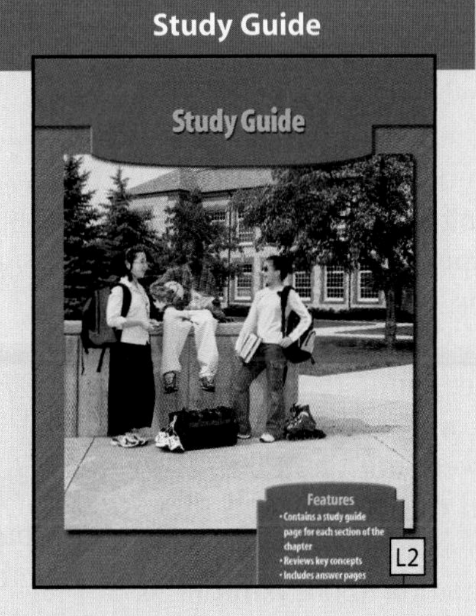

Study Guide
Features
• Condensed core content
• Actively involves students in reading
• Contains a study guide page for each section of the chapter
• Reviews key concepts
• Includes answer pages

L2

Reading Essentials

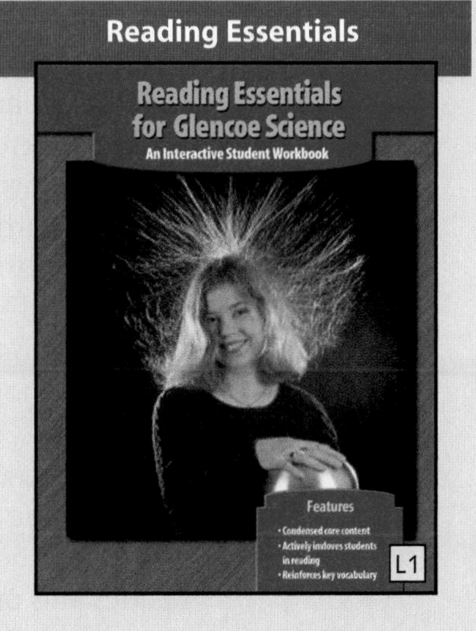

L1

Assessment

Test Practice Workbook

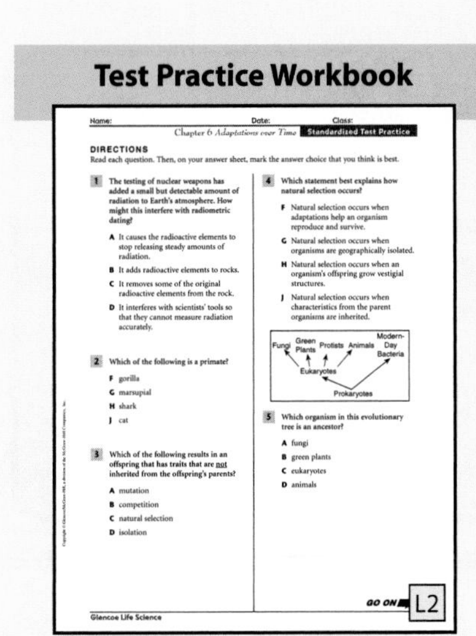

Chapter 6 Adaptations over Time — Standardized Test Practice

DIRECTIONS

Read each question. Then, on your answer sheet, mark the answer choice that you think is best.

Glencoe Life Science

L2

Chapter Review

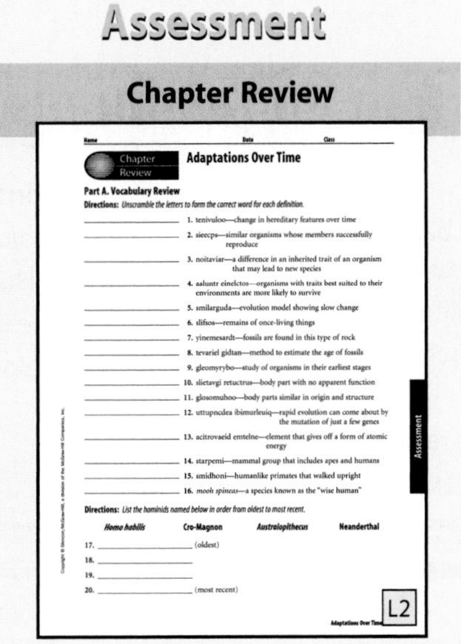

Chapter Review — Adaptations Over Time

Part A. Vocabulary Review

L2

Chapter Tests

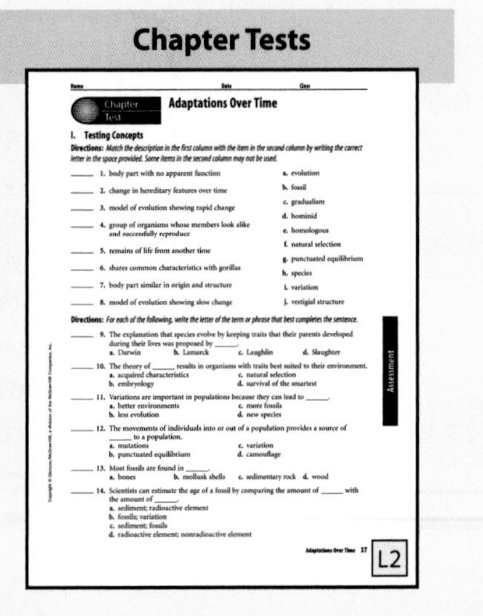

Chapter Test — Adaptations Over Time

I. Testing Concepts

L2

Science Content Background

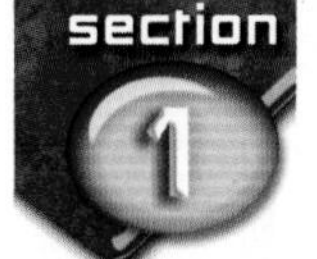

Ideas About Evolution

Before Evolutionary Theories

Aristotle, a Greek philosopher, held a view that species were essentially perfect. Because species were considered to be well adapted, there was no discussion of evolution. Special Creation, with all species fixed, was the prevailing view. In addition, Carolus Linnaeus, father of taxonomy, organized the diversity of living things into a hierarchy of taxonomic categories that did not imply evolution.

Evolution by Natural Selection

In 1858, Charles Darwin and Alfred Wallace provided enough evidence to convince many scientists that evolution occurs. Their ideas differed from the prevailing views of their time in two important ways—species change, or evolve, and natural selection is the process by which this evolution occurs.

An important point about the discussions on natural selection and evolution is that Darwin's observations were not limited to those made during his trip on the HMS *Beagle.* Even as a young boy, Darwin was an avid collector of beetles and other information about natural history. Much of the evidence for his theory came from his own study of pigeons.

Clues About Evolution

The Fossil Record

Some organisms which lived for only a short time in a certain environment formed fossils called index fossils. Index fossils are used by geologists to correlate rock strata across large areas.

Radioactive isotopes have half-lives that are not affected by environmental factors such as temperature or atmospheric pressure. Because the lengths of half-lives for radioactive isotopes of elements are known, an age estimate can be assigned to many rocks or fossils.

The evidence of evolution of species from the fossils record is compatible with other types of evidence for evolution. Transitional fossils have been located for some species, and species such as echinoderms have extensive fossil records that appear mostly complete.

The Evolution of Primates

Ongoing Research

Discoveries regarding primate evolution occur regularly. DNA comparisons have been done in an attempt to establish a date for the evolution of modern humans. Results of these tests are currently being debated, repeated, and extended.

chapter content resources

Internet Resources

For additional content background, visit booka.msscience.com to:

- access your book online
- find references to related articles in popular science magazines
- access Web links with related content background
- access current events with science journal topics

Print Resources

Evolution: The Triumph of an Idea, by Carl Zimmer, Harper Collins Publishers, 2001

The Beak of the Finch, by Jonathan Weiner, Vintage Books, 1994

Misconceptions

Find Out What Students Think

Students may think that . . .

Environmental changes cause changes in traits that help organisms cope with the new environment.

Students often form a magical view of natural selection. They know that if pesticides are applied to a crop, some insects will survive and reproduce. However, rather than understanding that the insects that survived did so because of pre-exisiting traits, students often believe that the pesticide itself caused the insects to become resistant. In the same way they may believe that antibiotics cause bacteria to form antibiotic resistance, or that organisms develop new traits because they need them to survive in a new environment (e.g., giraffes having long necks).

Activity

Have students read the section in the text that describes how bacteria become resistant to penicillin. If possible, bring in an article from a popular science journal describing the problem of antibiotic resistance. Ask students to imagine a situation in which they were required to clean their desks and the counters of the room daily with antibiotic soap to kill *Salmonella* and *Staphylococcus* bacteria. Have students write a paragraph describing what would happen to the bacteria in the room. Students should understand that resistant strains of these bacteria could be selected for and become a problem in the room. Some students, however, may persist in believing that the resistant bacteria form because of the antibacterial soaps. L2

Promote Understanding

Activity

Divide the class into small groups, and give each group a bowl containing 10 beans of various, distinct colors (i.e., white, black, spotted, red). Only one bean should be red. Supply each group with bags of various colors of beans. Tell students that the beans represent a colony of bacteria, and the colors represent minor genetic variations in the same species. L2

- On your signal have each group "multiply" their beans. Since bacteria reproduce by cell division, have students simply add one new black bean for each black bean in the bowl, one red bean for every red bean in the bowl, and so on. Have students "multiply" their beans twice (for a total of 40 beans in the bowl).
- Next, tell students that an antibiotic has been spilled in the environment. The antibiotic works by destroying the bacterial cell wall. The genes that gave the red bacteria their color also gave them a cell wall that was particularly thick and resists the action of the antibiotic. All other bacteria were killed.
- Have students remove all beans from the bowl except the red beans. Now have them "multiply" the remaining (red) beans for two or three more generations. Point out that because the red "bacteria" already had a feature that allowed them to survive the antibiotic, only red "bacteria" remain.

Assess

After completing the chapter, see *Identifying Misconceptions* in the Study Guide at the end of the chapter.

Chapter Vocabulary

species, p. 156
evolution, p. 156
natural selection, p. 159
variation, p. 160
adaptation, p. 160
gradualism, p. 162
punctuated equilibrium, p. 162
sedimentary rock, p. 166
radioactive element, p. 167
embryology, p. 169
homologous, p. 170
vestigial structure, p. 170
primate, p. 172
hominid, p. 173
Homo sapiens, p. 174

Science Journal Answers will vary. Check that students understand that an adaptation is anything that helps an organism survive and reproduce in its environment. Also note that especially because of humans, many organisms are not well-adapted to their current habitats.

PowerPoint® Presentations

This CD-ROM is an editable Microsoft® PowerPoint® presentation that includes:

- a pre-made presentation for every chapter
- interactive graphics
- animations
- audio clips
- image bank
- all new section and chapter questions
- Standardized Test Practice
- transparencies
- pre-lab questions for all labs
- Foldables directions
- links to booka.msscience.com

chapter 6

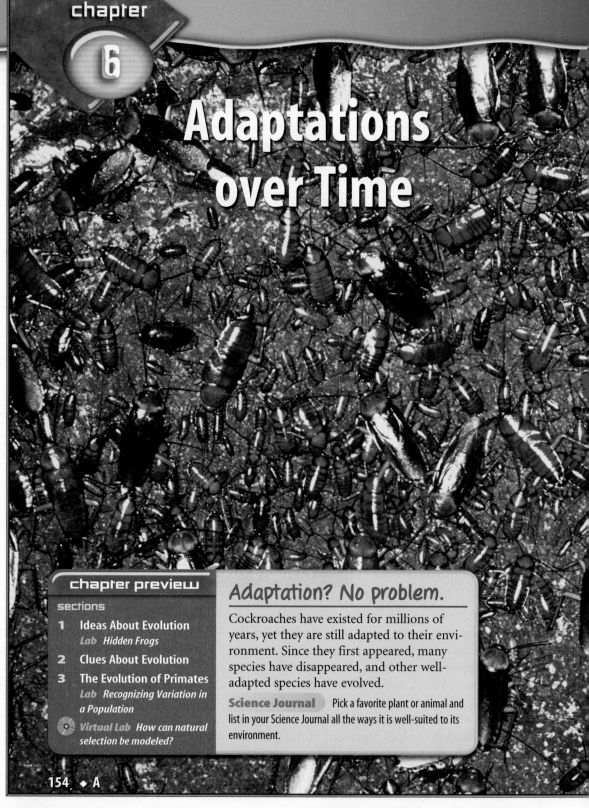

Adaptations over Time

chapter preview

sections

Adaptation? No problem.

Cockroaches have existed for millions of years, yet they are still adapted to their environment. Since they first appeared, many species have disappeared, and other well-adapted species have evolved.

Science Journal Pick a favorite plant or animal and list in your Science Journal all the ways it is well-suited to its environment.

154 ◆ A

Theme Connection

Stability and Change Changes that occur during evolution can bring about stability by increasing variation within a population.

About the Photo

Successful Insects Cockroaches, and insects in general, are well-adapted to their environments. Separation of life stages reduces competition. Their body plan is particularly flexible for adaptation. By sheer numbers, insects are the most successful organisms on Earth.

Start-Up Activities

Adaptation for a Hunter

The cheetah is nature's fastest hunter, but it can run swiftly for only short distances. Its fur blends in with tall grass, making it almost invisible as it hides and waits for prey. Then the cheetah pounces, capturing the prey before it can run away.

1. Spread a sheet of newspaper classified ads on the floor.
2. Using a hole puncher, make 100 circles from each of the following types of paper: white paper, black paper, and classified ads.
3. Scatter all the circles on the newspaper on the floor. For 10 s, pick up as many circles as possible, one at a time. Have a partner time you.
4. Count the number of each kind of paper circle that you picked up. Record your results in your Science Journal.
5. **Think Critically** Which paper circles were most difficult to find? What can you infer about a cheetah's coloring from this activity? Enter your responses to these questions in your Science Journal.

Principles of Natural Selection Make the following Foldable to help you understand the process of natural selection.

STEP 1 **Fold** a sheet of paper in half lengthwise.

STEP 2 **Fold** paper down 2.5 cm from the top. (Hint: From the tip of your index finger to your middle knuckle is about 2.5 cm.)

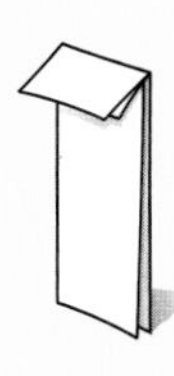

STEP 3 **Open and draw** lines along the 2.5-cm fold and the center fold. **Label** as shown.

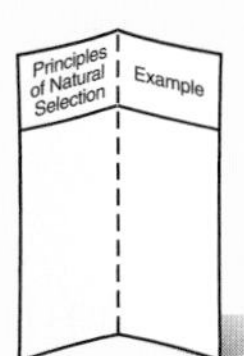

Summarize in a Table As you read, list the five principles of natural selection in the left-hand column. In the right-hand column, briefly write an example for each principle.

Preview this chapter's content and activities at booka.msscience.com

Purpose Students model camouflage coloration and its role in survival. L1 ELL COOP LEARN

IS **Kinesthetic**

Preparation Accumulate classified ads from the newspaper. Clear space for partners to work.

Materials newspaper classified ads, black and white paper, stopwatch or clock, hole punch

Teaching Strategies

- Show students photographs of a cheetah crouched in tall grass, and ask them to explain how the animal's markings enable it to blend in with its surroundings.
- If you find that students are picking up most of the circles within the time limit, add more circles or use less time.

Think Critically

Printed circles are most difficult to find. The cheetah's spotted fur blends in with the shadows and shades of dried vegetation found in tall grass.

Assessment

Process Provide students with photographs of animals that exhibit concealing coloration or patterns and have them describe how these features benefit each animal. Use **Performance Assessment in the Science Classroom,** p. 89. L1

Dinah Zike Study Fold

Student preparation materials for this Foldable are available in the **Chapter *Fast File* Resources.**

section 1 Ideas About Evolution

1 Motivate

Bellringer

Section Focus Transparencies also are available on the Interactive Chalkboard CD-ROM.

Tie to Prior Knowledge

Hypothesis v. Theory Reinforce the differences between the terms *hypothesis* and *theory.* A hypothesis is a testable prediction based on observations. Explain that a theory is not a guess, but rather an accepted explanation based on a large number of tests. Most scientists consider theories to be the best current explanation.

Caption Answer

Figure 1 Answers will vary.

---

as you read

What You'll Learn

- **Describe** Lamarck's hypothesis of acquired characteristics and Darwin's theory of natural selection.
- **Identify** why variations in organisms are important.
- **Compare and contrast** gradualism and punctuated equilibrium.

Why It's Important

The theory of evolution suggests why there are so many different living things.

Review Vocabulary
gene: a section of DNA that contains instructions for making specific proteins

New Vocabulary
- species
- evolution
- natural selection
- variation
- adaptation
- gradualism
- punctuated equilibrium

Early Models of Evolution

Millions of species of plants, animals, and other organisms live on Earth today. Do you suppose they are exactly the same as they were when they first appeared—or have any of them changed? A **species** is a group of organisms that share similar characteristics and can reproduce among themselves to produce fertile offspring. Many characteristics of a species are inherited when they pass from parent to offspring. Change in these inherited characteristics over time is **evolution. Figure 1** shows how the characteristics of the camel have changed over time.

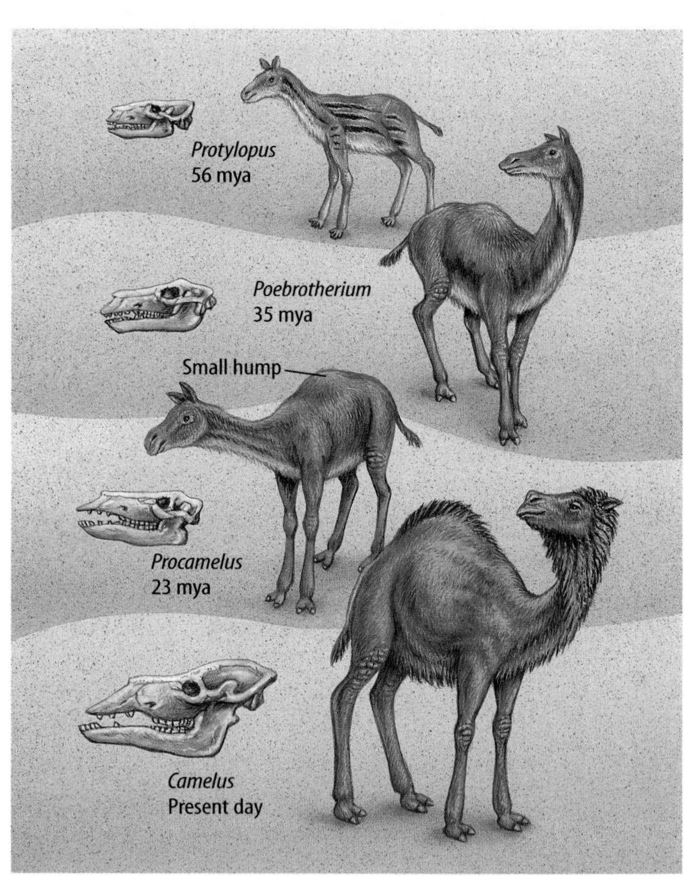

Figure 1 By studying fossils, scientists have traced the hypothesized evolution of the camel.
Discuss *the changes you observe in camels over time.*

Section 1 Resource Manager

Chapter *FAST FILE* Resources
- Transparency Activity, p. 42
- Directed Reading for Content Mastery, pp. 17, 18
- Note-taking Worksheets, pp. 31–32
- MiniLAB, p. 3
- Enrichment, p. 28
- Reinforcement, p. 26
- Lab Worksheet, pp. 5–6
- Lab Activities, pp. 9–10, 11–14

Mathematics Skill Activities, p. 1
Science Inquiry Labs, pp. 21–22

156 ◆ A CHAPTER 6 Adaptations over Time

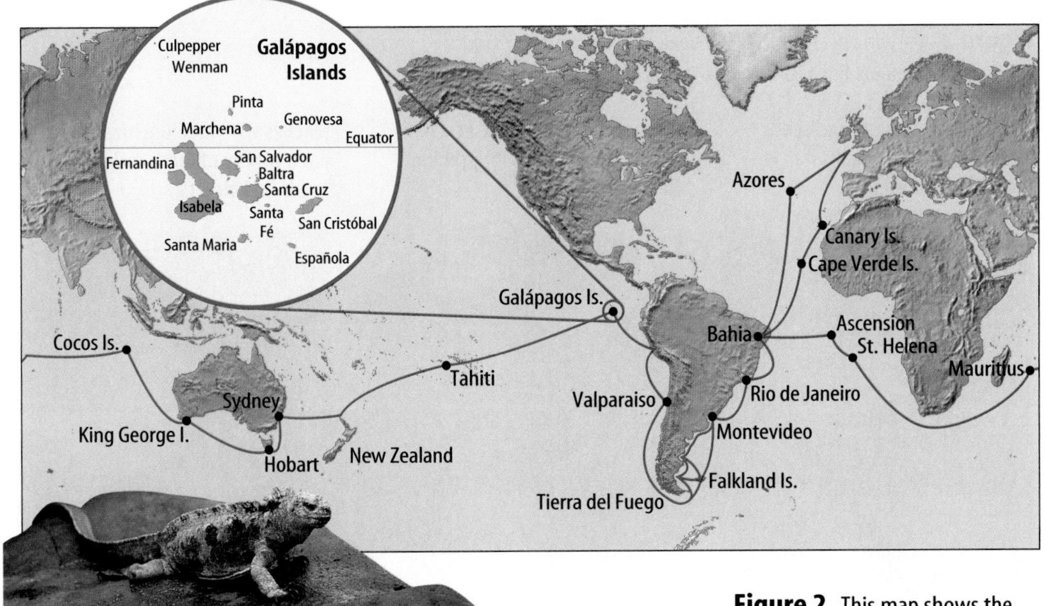

Figure 2 This map shows the route of Darwin's voyage on the HMS *Beagle*. Darwin noticed many species on the Galápagos Islands that he had not seen along the coast of South America, including the marine iguana. This species is the only lizard in the world known to enter the ocean and feed on seaweed.

Hypothesis of Acquired Characteristics In 1809, Jean Baptiste de Lamarck proposed a hypothesis to explain how species change over time. He suggested that characteristics, or traits, developed during a parent organism's lifetime are inherited by its offspring. His hypothesis is called the inheritance of acquired characteristics. Scientists collected data on traits that are passed from parents to offspring. The data showed that traits developed during a parent's lifetime, such as large muscles built by hard work or exercise, are not passed on to offspring. The evidence did not support Lamarck's hypothesis.

Reading Check *What was Lamarck's explanation of evolution?*

Darwin's Model of Evolution

In December 1831, the HMS *Beagle* sailed from England on a journey to explore the South American coast. On board was a young naturalist named Charles Darwin. During the journey, Darwin recorded observations about the plants and animals he saw. He was amazed by the variety of life on the Galápagos Islands, which are about 1,000 km from the coast of Ecuador. Darwin hypothesized that the plants and animals on the Galápagos Islands originally must have come from Central and South America. But the islands were home to many species he had not seen in South America, including giant cactus trees, huge land tortoises, and the iguana shown in **Figure 2.**

2 Teach

Reading Check

Answer Traits developed during a parent organism's lifetime are inherited by its offspring.

IDENTIFYING Misconceptions

Lamarck's Hypothesis Ask students to list the inadequacies of Lamarck's hypothesis. Students may agree with Lamarck until they critically examine the failures of this explanation. The primary failure of Lamarck's explanation is that acquired characteristics are not inherited. L3

Visual Learning

Figure 2 Ask students to explain why Darwin was able to use evidence from his voyage to develop his theory of evolution by natural selection. Many of the species in the Galápagos are unique to the islands but are similar to forms found on the mainland of South America.

Differentiated Instruction

Learning Disabled Allow students to use clay to make impressions of various items such as a comb, a key, etc. Plaster-of-paris can be poured into the impressions to form fossils. Place the plaster casts into a box. Allow students to try to identify the objects by reaching into the box without looking. You may use blindfolds if some students cannot resist the temptation to look. L1
LS **Kinesthetic**

Discussion

Genetics and Evolution How are genetics and the theory of evolution related? Genetics provides the inheritance mechanism for evolution to work in a population. If traits were not inherited, there could be no evolution.

Quick Demo

Adaptations

Materials photos of animals

Estimated Time 5–10 minutes

Procedure Show students photographs of different organisms and have them list the adaptations they think are most needed for each species to survive. L2 LS **Visual-Spatial**

Reading Check

Answer Darwin suggested that they all evolved from a common ancestral species in South America.

Activity

Unique Adaptations Display photographs of organisms that have unique adaptations such as the eye spots on the wings of moths or the thickness of a coconut husk. Have students identify the usefulness of each adaptation. Eye spots on moth wings may startle predators. Coconut husks protect the seed and allow it to travel by floating in salt water. L2 LS **Visual-Spatial**

Teacher FYI

Galápagos Tortoises In addition to finches, the tortoises also vary. Each island has a tortoise with a unique shell pattern.

Figure 3 Darwin observed that the beak shape of each species of Galápagos finch is related to its eating habits.

Finches that eat nuts and seeds have short, strong beaks for breaking hard shells.

Finches that feed on insects have long, slender beaks for probing beneath tree bark.

Finches with medium-sized beaks eat a variety of foods including seeds and insects.

Topic: Darwin's Finches
Visit booka.msscience.com for Web links to information about the finches Darwin observed.

Activity In your Science Journal, describe the similarities and differences of any two species of Galápagos finches.

Darwin's Observations Darwin observed 13 species of finches on the Galápagos Islands. He noticed that all 13 species were similar, except for differences in body size, beak shape, and eating habits, as shown in **Figure 3.** He also noticed that all the Galápagos finch species were similar to one finch species he had seen on the South American coast.

Darwin reasoned that the Galápagos finches must have had to compete for food. Finches with beak shapes that allowed them to eat available food survived longer and produced more offspring than finches without those beak shapes. After many generations, these groups of finches became separate species.

How did Darwin explain the evolution of the different species of Galápagos finches?

Natural Selection

After the voyage, Charles Darwin returned to England and continued to think about his observations. He collected more evidence on inherited traits by breeding racing pigeons. He also studied breeds of dogs and varieties of flowers. In the mid 1800s, Darwin developed a theory of evolution that is accepted by most scientists today. He described his ideas in a book called *On the Origin of Species,* which was published in 1859.

Differentiated Instruction

Challenge Students can invent their own species. They can draw it, describe its habitat and diet, and give the species a history. They should describe evolutionary changes that may have occurred within the species. Have students make a timeline showing major physical changes and ecological events that resulted in changes in the species. The species may be from the past or the future. L3 LS **Visual-Spatial**

Science Journal

Darwin and Wallace Have students research and describe in their Science Journal how the work of Alfred Wallace complemented that of Charles Darwin. Wallace and Darwin came to the same conclusion about evolution. The work of both men was presented in the same year. L2 LS **Linguistic**

Darwin's Theory Darwin's observations led many other scientists to conduct experiments on inherited characteristics. After many years, Darwin's ideas became known as the theory of evolution by natural selection. **Natural selection** means that organisms with traits best suited to their environment are more likely to survive and reproduce. Their traits are passed to more offspring. All living organisms produce more offspring than survive. Galápagos finches lay several eggs every few months. Darwin realized that in just a few years, several pairs of finches could produce a large population. A population is all of the individuals of a species living in the same area. Members of a large population compete for living space, food, and other resources. Those that are best able to survive are more likely to reproduce and pass on their traits to the next generation.

The principles that describe how natural selection works are listed in **Table 1.** Over time, as new data was gathered and reported, changes were made to Darwin's original ideas about evolution by natural selection. His theory remains one of the most important ideas in the study of life science.

Table 1 The Principles of Natural Selection
1. Organisms produce more offspring than can survive.
2. Differences, or variations, occur among individuals of a species.
3. Some variations are passed to offspring.
4. Some variations are helpful. Individuals with helpful variations survive and reproduce better than those without these variations.
5. Over time, the offspring of individuals with helpful variations make up more of a population and eventually may become a separate species.

Applying Science

Does natural selection take place in a fish tank?

Alejandro raises tropical fish as a hobby. Could the observations that he makes over several weeks illustrate the principles of natural selection?

Identifying the Problem

Alejandro keeps a detailed journal of his observations, some of which are given in the table to the right.

Fish Tank Observations

Date	Observation
June 6	6 fish are placed in aquarium tank.
July 22	16 new young appear.
July 24	3 young have short or missing tail fins. 13 young have normal tail fins.
July 28	Young with short or missing tail fins die.
August 1	2 normal fish die—from overcrowding?
August 12	30 new young appear.
August 15	5 young have short or missing tail fins. 25 young have normal tail fins.
August 18	Young with short or missing tail fins die.
August 20	Tank is overcrowded. Fish are divided equally into two tanks.

Solving the Problem

Refer to **Table 1** and match each of Alejandro's journal entries with the principle(s) it demonstrates. Here's a hint: *Some entries may not match any of the principles of natural selection. Some entries may match more than one principle.*

Applying Science

Teaching Strategy

Emphasize to students that there may be several correct answers for each journal entry.

Solving the Problem

June 6: none
July 22: 1 or none
July 24: 2, 3, or 4
July 28: 4 or 5
August 1: 1, 4, or none
August 12: 1 or none
August 15: 2, 3, or 5
August 18: 2, 3, or 4
August 20: 1 or none

Visual Learning

Table 1 Emphasize the importance of the principles of natural selection as mechanisms for evolution. Why is overproduction of offspring important? Overproduction results in a lack of resources, forcing animals to compete with one another. L2 IS **Logical-Mathematical**

Differentiated Instruction

Learning Disabled Write the five principles of natural selection on a piece of colored paper. Cut the pieces apart to make a puzzle. Allow students to put the puzzle together to reinforce what they learn about natural selection. L1 IS **Visual-Spatial**

Fun Fact

Albinism occurs in almost all species of mammals and has also been observed in other groups of plants and animals.

Caption Answers

Figure 4 Left Neither predators nor prey can detect the scorpion fish in its natural environment.

Figure 4 Right Predators might find it easily. Other lemurs might avoid it, preventing it from reproducing.

Evolution of English Etymology, the study of words, is in many ways a study of evolution. Discuss with students how their slang differs from yours and that of your parents.

Research Have students use the *Oxford English Dictionary* to investigate the history of words like house, man, nice, girl, brave, and hurry. They can then report to the class on the evolution of these words.

Evolution of English
If someone from Shakespeare's time were to speak to you today, you probably would not understand her. Languages, like species, change over time. In your Science Journal, discuss some words or phrases that you use that your parents or teachers do not use correctly.

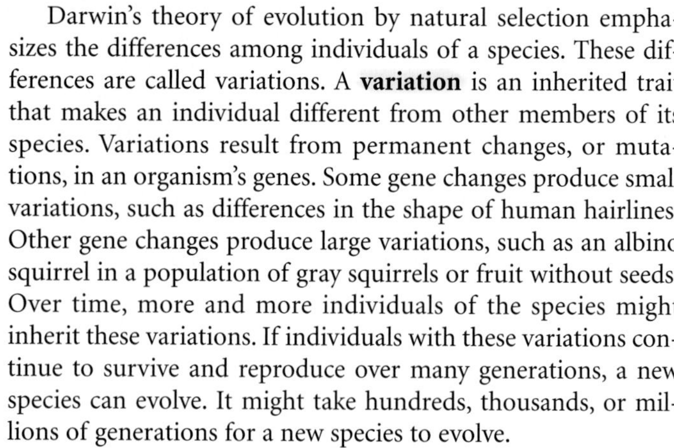

Variation and Adaptation

Darwin's theory of evolution by natural selection emphasizes the differences among individuals of a species. These differences are called variations. A **variation** is an inherited trait that makes an individual different from other members of its species. Variations result from permanent changes, or mutations, in an organism's genes. Some gene changes produce small variations, such as differences in the shape of human hairlines. Other gene changes produce large variations, such as an albino squirrel in a population of gray squirrels or fruit without seeds. Over time, more and more individuals of the species might inherit these variations. If individuals with these variations continue to survive and reproduce over many generations, a new species can evolve. It might take hundreds, thousands, or millions of generations for a new species to evolve.

Some variations are more helpful than others. An **adaptation** is any variation that makes an organism better suited to its environment. The variations that result in an adaptation can involve an organism's color, shape, behavior, or chemical makeup. Camouflage (KA muh flahj) is an adaptation. A camouflaged organism, like the one shown in **Figure 4,** blends into its environment and is more likely to survive and reproduce.

Figure 4 Variations that provide an advantage tend to increase in a population over time. Variations that result in a disadvantage tend to decrease in a population over time.

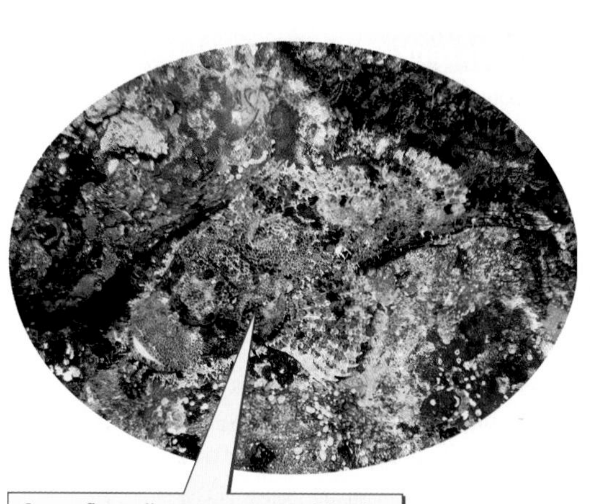

Camouflage allows organisms to blend into their environments.
Infer *how its coloration gives this scorpion fish a survival advantage.*

Albinism can prevent an organism from blending into its environment.
Infer *what might happen to an albino lemur in its natural environment.*

LAB DEMONSTRATION

Purpose to observe variations

Materials pictures of various animal groups (i.e., cows, antelope, horses, wolves, rabbits), overhead projector

Preparation Make transparencies of pictures. Try to find pictures that show obvious differences (such as animals of different colors).

Procedure Have students observe each picture and list variations among the individuals in a group.

Expected Outcome Students will observe variations within a species.

Assessment

What causes differences between animals in the same species? genetic variations Do any of these variations aid in survival? If so, how? Answers will vary. Accept all reasonable answers.

European rabbits, like the one above, feed during the day and are fairly large.

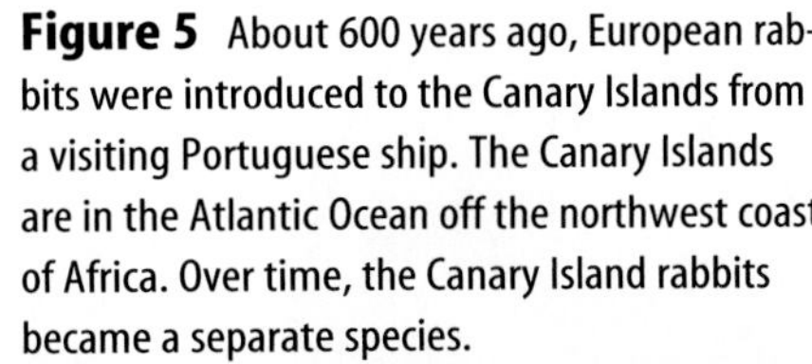

Figure 5 About 600 years ago, European rabbits were introduced to the Canary Islands from a visiting Portuguese ship. The Canary Islands are in the Atlantic Ocean off the northwest coast of Africa. Over time, the Canary Island rabbits became a separate species.

Canary Island rabbits feed during the night. **Explain** *why large eyes might be considered a helpful adaptation in Canary Island rabbits.*

Changes in the Sources of Genes Over time, the genetic makeup of a species might change its appearance. For example, as the genetic makeup of a species of seed-eating Galápagos finch changed, so did the size and shape of its beak. Many kinds of environmental factors help bring about changes. When individuals of the same species move into or out of an area, they might bring in or remove genes and variations. Suppose a family from another country moves to your neighborhood. They might bring different foods, customs, and ways of speaking with them. In a similar way, when new individuals enter an existing population, they can bring in different genes and variations.

Geographic Isolation Sometimes mountains, lakes, or other geologic features isolate a small number of individuals from the rest of a population. Over several generations, variations that do not exist in the larger population might begin to be more common in the isolated population. Also, gene mutations can occur that add variations to populations. Over time, the two populations can become so different that they no longer can breed with each other. The two populations of rabbits shown in **Figure 5** have been geographically isolated from each other for thousands of generations.

Relating Evolution to Species

Procedure

1. On a piece of **paper,** print the word *train.*
2. Add, subtract, or change one letter to make a new word.
3. Repeat step 2 with the new word.
4. Repeat steps 2 and 3 two more times.
5. Make a "family tree" that shows how your first word changed over time.

Analysis

1. Compare your tree to those of other people. Did you produce the same words?
2. How is this process similar to evolution by natural selection?

Caption Answer

Figure 5 Their large eyes help the rabbits see in the dark.

Purpose Students practice classifying and sequencing. L2 LS **Visual-Spatial**

Teaching Strategy Have students think of each word as a species with the English language as the environment. Only useful changes that make other words will survive.

Analysis

1. Answers will vary. The same words will appear, but often in different places.
2. Answers will vary. Accept those that point out change over time, mutation, or adaptation.

Assessment

Performance To further assess students' understanding of evolution, have them make up and explain another hypothetical evolutionary schema using whatever shapes or materials they choose. Use **Performance Assessment in the Science Classroom,** p. 103.

Curriculum Connection

History Direct students to research the mid-nineteenth century to determine what daily life was like for Darwin and his peers. Students should make posters showing technologies used, dress of the period, and religious or political events. L2 LS **Visual-Spatial** P

SECTION 1 Ideas About Evolution A ◆ 161

Use Science Words

Word Origin Scientists once accepted that organisms evolve according to the gradualism model. *Gradus,* meaning a step, is the Latin word from which gradualism is derived. Ask students why this word is used. Gradualism seems to occur step by step. L2 LS **Linguistic**

Caption Answer

Figure 6 Many changes occurred in a short time. Gradualism predicts slower changes.

Inquiry Lab

Investigating Selection

Purpose Help students see how natural selection works with preexisting variation.

Possible Materials

- Iron nails, pennies, marbles, popcorn seeds, cereal
- Tweezers, fingers, magnets, spoons, clothespins

Estimated Time 25–30 minutes

Teaching Strategies

- Have students try to pick up as many nails as possible in 15s using the above materials.
- Then have them try to get popcorn with the same materials.
- How does this relate to natural selection?
- Allow students to think of other comparisons to natural selection. Discuss them as time allows. L2

For additional inquiry activities, see *Science Inquiry Labs.*

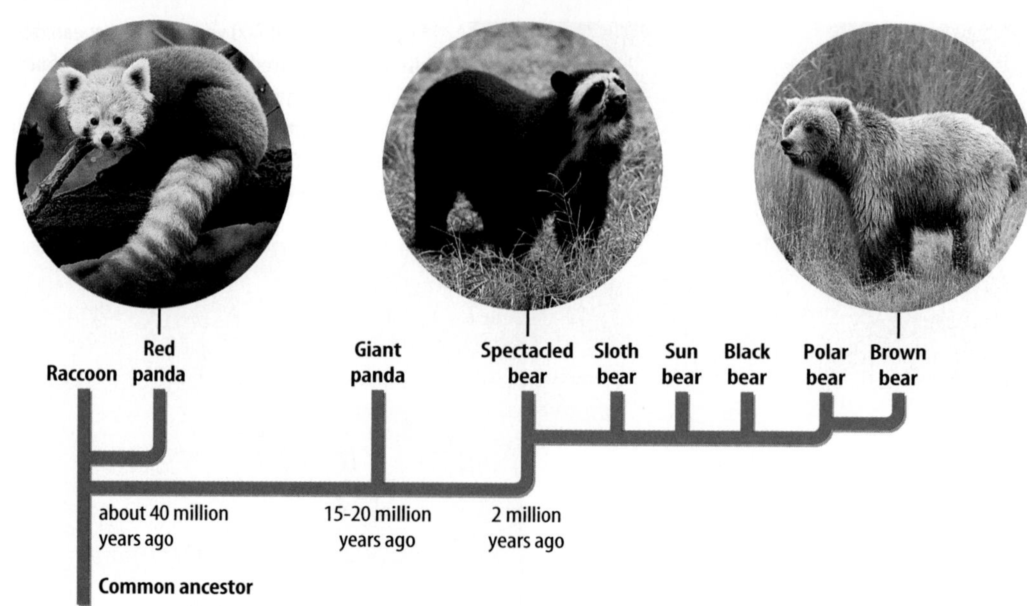

Figure 6 The hypothesized evolution of bears illustrates the punctuated equilibrium model of evolution.
Discuss *how the six species on the far right are explained better by punctuated equlibrium.*

The Speed of Evolution

Scientists do not agree on how quickly evolution occurs. Many scientists hypothesize that evolution occurs slowly, perhaps over tens or hundreds of millions of years. Other scientists hypothesize that evolution can occur quickly. Most scientists agree that evidence supports both of these models.

Gradualism Darwin hypothesized that evolution takes place slowly. The model that describes evolution as a slow, ongoing process by which one species changes to a new species is known as **gradualism.** According to the gradualism model, a continuing series of mutations and variations over time will result in a new species. Look back at **Figure 1,** which shows the evolution of the camel over tens of millions of years. Fossil evidence shows a series of intermediate forms that indicate a gradual change from the earliest camel species to today's species.

Punctuated Equilibrium Gradualism doesn't explain the evolution of all species. For some species, the fossil record shows few intermediate forms—one species suddenly changes to another. According to the **punctuated equilibrium** model, rapid evolution comes about when the mutation of a few genes results in the appearance of a new species over a relatively short period of time. The fossil record gives examples of this type of evolution, as you can see in **Figure 6.**

Curriculum Connection

Art Have students make a piece of art that shows their understanding of gradualism (i.e., a drawing that shows the slow evolution of one organism to another). In art, this process is called morphing. L2 LS **Visual-Spatial**

Punctuated Equilibrium Today Evolution by the punctuated equilibrium model can occur over a few thousand or million years, and sometimes even faster. For example, many bacteria have changed in a few decades. The antibiotic penicillin originally came from the fungus shown in **Figure 7.** But many bacteria species that were once easily killed by penicillin no longer are harmed by it. These bacteria have developed resistance to the drug. Penicillin has been in use since 1943. Just four years later, in 1947, a species of bacteria that causes pneumonia and other infections already had developed resistance to the drug. By the 1990s, several disease-producing bacteria had become resistant to penicillin and many other antibiotics.

How did penicillin-resistant bacteria evolve so quickly? As in any population, some organisms have variations that allow them to survive unfavorable living conditions when other organisms cannot. When penicillin was used to kill bacteria, those with the penicillin-resistant variation survived, reproduced, and passed this trait to their offspring. Over a period of time, this bacteria population became penicillin-resistant.

Figure 7 The fungus growing in this petri dish is *Penicillium,* the original source of penicillin. It produces an antibiotic substance that prevents the growth of certain bacteria.

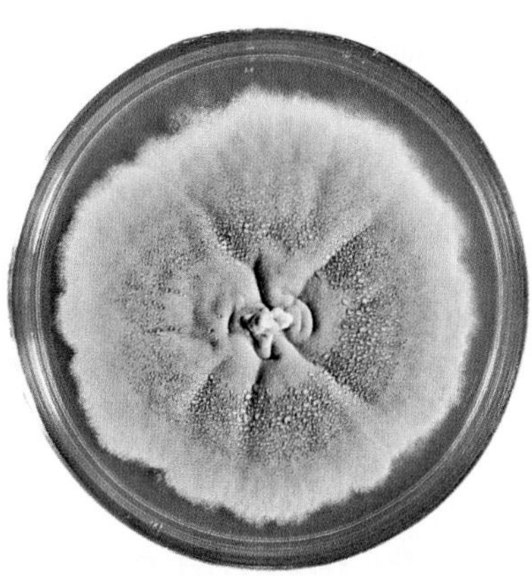

section 1 review

Summary

Early Models of Evolution
- Evolution is change in the characteristics of a species over time.
- Lamarck proposed the hypothesis of inherited acquired characteristics.

Natural Selection
- Darwin proposed evolution by natural selection, a process by which organisms best suited to their environments are most likely to survive and reproduce.
- Organisms have more offspring than can survive, individuals of a species vary, and many of these variations are passed to offspring.

Variation and Adaptation
- Adaptations are variations that help an organism survive or reproduce in its environment.
- Mutations are the source of new variations.

The Speed of Evolution
- Evolution may be a slow or fast process depending on the species under study.

Self Check

1. **Compare** Lamarck's and Darwin's ideas about how evolution takes place.
2. **Explain** why variations are important to understanding change in a population over time.
3. **Discuss** how the gradualism model of evolution differs from the punctuated equilibrium model of evolution.
4. **Describe** how geographic isolation contributes to evolution.
5. **Think Critically** What adaptations would be helpful for an animal species that was moved to the Arctic?
6. **Concept Map** Use information given in **Figure 6** to make a map that shows how raccoons, red pandas, giant pandas, polar bears, and black bears are related to a common ancestor.

Applying Math

7. **Use Percentages** The evolution of the camel can be traced back at least 56 million years. Use **Figure 1** to estimate the percent of this time that the modern camel has existed.

Science Online booka.msscience.com/self_check_quiz

IDENTIFYING Misconceptions

Environmental Changes Many students think that environmental changes cause changes in traits that help organisms cope with the new environment. Refer to page F at the beginning of this chapter for teaching strategies that address this misconception.

3 Assess

DAILY INTERVENTION

Check for Understanding

Interpersonal Have students discuss why Darwin was impressed with the ability of humans to produce new breeds of plants and animals through artificial selection. He saw this as an analogy to the mechanism of evolution by natural selection. L2 COOP LEARN IN

Reteach

Types of Selection Have students list similarities between artificial selection, such as dog breeding, and natural selection. In both, specific traits are selected. L2

Assessment

Performance To assess students' abilities to classify organisms by their variations, ask them to classify two species of birds that eat different types of foods. Use **Performance Assessment in the Science Classroom,** p. 121. L2

section 1 review

1. Lamarck thought acquired traits were passed to offspring; Darwin concluded that only inherited traits were passed to offspring.
2. If a population were genetically uniform, any harmful factor that affected one of them would affect all of them. Because of variation, some individuals in a population would not be affected by the adverse factor and would survive and reproduce.
3. Gradualism—species slowly evolve to become other species; punctuated equilibrium—species suddenly become other species in a relatively short amount of time.
4. Populations with different variations evolve independently, producing greater variation.
5. Possible answers: lighter coat color; traits for surviving extreme cold
6. The concept map should illustrate several species evolving from a common ancestor.
7. 2 million years/56 million years $\times$ 100% = approximately 4%

Real-World Question

Purpose Students will explore how natural selection equips organisms for survival in their environment.

Process Skills observe, analyze, infer, formulate, model

Time Required 40 minutes

Procedure

Teaching Strategies

- Obtain color photographs of frogs in natural settings to present examples of camouflage to students.
- Obtain color photographs of other camouflaged animals and ask students how natural selection has prepared them for survival in their environment.

Troubleshooting Provide students with pictures of different environments to serve as a reference.

Conclude and Apply

1. Answer will vary, but students should consider the colors, patterns, and textures of the habitat.
2. Color patterns, textures, and body shapes that provide the best camouflage in an environment help those frogs avoid predators, and, through natural selection, these characteristics become dominant in a frog population.
3. The frog may not be properly camouflaged from predators in its new environment.

Hidden Frogs

Through natural selection, animals become adapted for survival in their environment. Adaptations include shapes, colors, and even textures that help an animal blend into its surroundings. These adaptations are called camouflage. The red-eyed tree frog's mint green body blends in with tropical forest vegetation as shown in the photo on the right. Could you design camouflage for a desert frog? A temperate forest frog?

Real-World Question

What type of camouflage would best suit a frog living in a particular habitat?

Goals

- **Create** a frog model camouflaged to blend in with its surroundings.

Materials (for each group)

cardboard form of a frog
colored markers
crayons
colored pencils
glue
beads
sequins
modeling clay

Safety Precautions

Procedure

1. Choose one of the following habitats for your frog model: muddy shore of a pond, orchid flowers in a tropical rain forest, multicolored clay in a desert, or the leaves and branches of trees in a temperate forest.
2. **List** the features of your chosen habitat that will determine the camouflage your frog model will need.
3. **Brainstorm** with your group the body shape, coloring, and skin texture that would make the best camouflage for your model. Record your ideas in your Science Journal.
4. **Draw** in your Science Journal samples of colors, patterns, texture, and other features your frog model might have.
5. Show your design ideas to your teacher and ask for further input.
6. **Construct** your frog model.

Conclude and Apply

1. **Explain** how the characteristics of the habitat helped you decide on the specific frog features you chose.
2. **Infer** how the color patterns and other physical features of real frogs develop in nature.
3. **Explain** why it might be harmful to release a frog into a habitat for which it is not adapted.

Communicating Your Data

Create a poster or other visual display that represents the habitat you chose for this activity. Use your display to show classmates how your design helps camouflage your frog model. **For more help, refer to the Science Skill Handbook.**

164 ◆ A CHAPTER 6 Adaptations over Time

Assessment

Process Ask students to explain why the frog they have modeled would not be equipped to survive in a different environment. Use **Performance Assessment in the Science Classroom,** p. 89. L2

Have students do library researches about their chosen habitats.

section 2

Clues About Evolution

Clues from Fossils

Imagine going on a fossil hunt in Wyoming. Your companions are paleontologists—scientists who study the past by collecting and examining fossils. As you climb a low hill, you notice a curved piece of stone jutting out of the sandy soil. One of the paleontologists carefully brushes the soil away and congratulates you on your find. You've discovered part of the fossilized shell of a turtle like the one shown in **Figure 8.**

The Green River Formation covers parts of Wyoming, Utah, and Colorado. On your fossil hunt, you learn that about 50 million years ago, during the Eocene Epoch, this region was covered by lakes. The water was home to fish, crocodiles, lizards, and turtles. Palms, fig trees, willows, and cattails grew on the lakeshores. Insects and birds flew through the air. How do scientists know all this? After many of the plants and animals of that time died, they were covered with silt and mud. Over millions of years, they became the fossils that have made the Green River Formation one of the richest fossil deposits in the world.

as you read

What You'll Learn

- **Identify** the importance of fossils as evidence of evolution.
- **Explain** how relative and radiometric dating are used to estimate the age of fossils.
- **List** examples of five types of evidence for evolution.

Why It's Important

The scientific evidence for evolution helps you understand why this theory is so important to the study of biology.

Review Vocabulary
epoch: next-smaller division of geological time after a period; is characterized by differences in life-forms that may vary regionally

New Vocabulary
- sedimentary rock
- radioactive element
- embryology
- homologous
- vestigial structure

The turtle *Cistemum undatum* is from the same fossil formation.

The most abundant fossils are of a freshwater herring, *Knightia oecaena*, which is Wyoming's state fossil.

Figure 8 The desert of the Green River Formation is home to pronghorn antelope, elks, coyotes, and eagles. Fossil evidence shows that about 50 million years ago the environment was much warmer and wetter than it is today.

1 Motivate

Bellringer

Section Focus Transparencies also are available on the Interactive Chalkboard CD-ROM.

L2 ELL

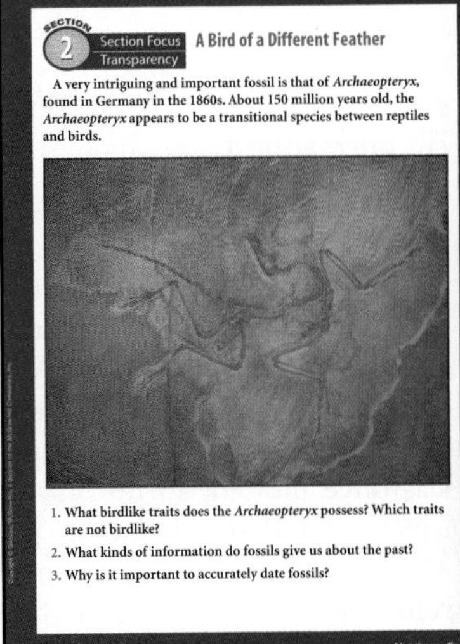

Section 2 Section Focus Transparency **A Bird of a Different Feather**

A very intriguing and important fossil is that of *Archaeopteryx*, found in Germany in the 1860s. About 150 million years old, the *Archaeopteryx* appears to be a transitional species between reptiles and birds.

1. What birdlike traits does the *Archaeopteryx* possess? Which traits are not birdlike?
2. What kinds of information do fossils give us about the past?
3. Why is it important to accurately date fossils?

Adaptation over Time

Tie to Prior Knowledge

DNA Changes Review the structure and function of DNA with students while they study the evidence for evolution. Emphasize that changes in DNA provide the basis for evolution.

Section 2 Resource Manager

Chapter *FAST FILE* Resources

Transparency Activity, pp. 43, 45–46
Directed Reading for Content Mastery, p. 19
Enrichment, p. 29
Reinforcement, p. 26

2 Teach

Caption Answer

Figure 9 Imprint fossils, mineralized fossils, and cast fossils are the most common.

Activity

Collect Rocks Have groups of students collect rocks and fossils from your area. Allow them to research the types of rocks and fossils they find. If students will donate their finds to the school, you can quickly build a school collection of fossils and rocks to display. L2 ELL COOP LEARN LS **Interpersonal**

Activity

Rock Characteristics Bring in samples of igneous, metamorphic, and sedimentary rocks. Ask students to observe the differences. Explain that igneous rock was once molten, so no organism could have lived in it. Metamorphic rock has been reheated, so its structure has changed from the original. Any fossils contained in it are usually lost. Sedimentary rock has the best characteristics for the preservation of a fossil record. L2 ELL LS **Visual-Spatial**

Fun Fact

Scientists have successfully extracted DNA from frozen mammoths and used the information to evaluate the evolutionary relationships between living elephants and extinct species.

Figure 9 Examples of several different types of fossils are shown here.
Infer *which of these would most likely be found in a layer of sedimentary rock.*

Imprint fossils A leaf, feather, bones, or even the entire body of an organism can leave an imprint on sediment that later hardens to become rock.

Mineralized fossils Minerals can replace wood or bone to create a piece of petrified wood as shown to the left or a mineralized bone fossil.

Frozen fossils The remains of organisms like this mammoth can be trapped in ice that remains frozen for thousands of years.

Cast Fossils Minerals can fill in the hollows of animal tracks, as shown to the right, a mollusk shell, or other parts of an organism to create a cast.

Fossils in amber When the sticky resin of certain cone-bearing plants hardens over time, amber forms. It can contain the remains of trapped insects.

Types of Fossils

Most of the evidence for evolution comes from fossils. A fossil is the remains, an imprint, or a trace of a prehistoric organism. Several types of fossils are shown in **Figure 9.** Most fossils are found in sedimentary rock. **Sedimentary rock** is formed when layers of sand, silt, clay, or mud are compacted and cemented together, or when minerals are deposited from a solution. Limestone, sandstone, and shale are all examples of sedimentary rock. Fossils are found more often in limestone than in any other kind of sedimentary rock. The fossil record provides evidence that living things have evolved.

Teacher FYI

Incomplete Fossil Record The fossil record has always been incomplete because most organisms never become fossils. They are either decomposed or eaten before they have an opportunity to become fossilized.

Science Journal

The Grand Canyon Few places on Earth have as many layers of exposed sedimentary rock as the Grand Canyon. Have students visit the U.S. National Park Service at nps.gov/grca and research the Grand Canyon. Have them prepare an essay on what they would expect to see if they visited it. L2 LS **Linguistic** P

166 ◆ A CHAPTER 6 Adaptations over Time

Determining a Fossil's Age

Paleontologists use detective skills to determine the age of dinosaur fossils or the remains of other ancient organisms. They can use clues provided by unique rock layers and the fossils they contain. The clues provide information about the geology, weather, and life-forms that must have been present during each geologic time period. Two basic methods—relative dating and radiometric dating—can be used, alone or together, to estimate the ages of rocks and fossils.

Relative Dating One way to find the approximate age of fossils found within a rock layer is relative dating. Relative dating is based on the idea that in undisturbed areas, younger rock layers are deposited on top of older rock layers, as shown in **Figure 10.** Relative dating provides only an estimate of a fossil's age. The estimate is made by comparing the ages of rock layers found above and below the fossil layer. For example, suppose a 50-million-year-old rock layer lies below a fossil, and a 35-million-year-old layer lies above it. According to relative dating, the fossil is between 35 million and 50 million years old.

Reading Check *Why can relative dating be used only to estimate the age of a fossil?*

Radiometric Dating Scientists can obtain a more accurate estimate of the age of a rock layer by using radioactive elements. A **radioactive element** gives off a steady amount of radiation as it slowly changes to a nonradioactive element. Each radioactive element gives off radiation at a different rate. Scientists can estimate the age of the rock by comparing the amount of radioactive element with the amount of nonradioactive element in the rock. This method of dating does not always produce exact results, because the original amount of radioactive element in the rock can never be determined for certain.

Science Online

Topic: Fossil Finds
Visit booka.msscience.com for Web links to information about recent fossil discoveries.

Activity Prepare a newspaper article describing how one of these discoveries was made, what it reveals about past life on Earth, and how it has impacted our understanding of what the past environments of Earth were like.

Figure 10 In Bryce Canyon, erosion by water and wind has cut through the sedimentary rock, exposing the layers.
Infer *the relative age of rocks in the lowest layers compared to the top layer.*

Quick Demo

Half-Lives

Materials two sets of jelly beans of different colors

Estimated Time five minutes

Procedure Take 40 beans of one color. Tell the class that they represent atoms of a radioactive isotope. After 30 seconds, replace 20 beans with beans of the other color. After another 30 seconds, replace half of the remaining beans of the first color. Repeat until all of the beans are of the new color. Ask students how many half-lives that took, and have them calculate how long decay would have taken with different half-lives. L2

Reading Check

Answer Relative dating can only give a range, not an exact age.

Make a Model

Relative Dating Have students make a model showing how relative dating is used. Their model can show layers of sand, dirt, salt, cornmeal, or other materials in a plastic drink bottle or glass container. Several "fossils" should be placed in the model to explain their relative ages. Have each student present his or her model to the group. L2 **Kinesthetic and Visual-Spatial**

Caption Answer

Figure 10 Assuming no disturbance, the bottom layers are older than the top layers.

Differentiated Instruction

Visually Impaired You can explain relative dating to visually impaired students by creating layers of different materials that the student can differentiate by touch. Use stiff cardboard or foam board and glue the materials in layers. Glue easily identifiable objects as analogies to fossils. L1 **Kinesthetic and Visual-Spatial**

Visualizing The Geologic Time Scale

Have students examine the pictures and read the captions. Then ask the following questions.

In the geologic time scale, which is longer—an era or a period? Students should note that an era is a longer time than a period.

The names of the geologic eras have Greek roots. *Ceno* means "recent" and *zoic* means "life." *Paleo* means "ancient." Infer the meaning of the Greek prefix *meso.* Meso means "middle," so mesozoic means "middle life."

Activity

Geologic Periods Have students work in teams to create a poster about one of the geologic periods shown in the feature. The poster should contain facts about the plants and animals that were alive during the period, as well as illustrations depicting the landforms and bodies of water that were present. The teams of students should present their findings to the class. L2

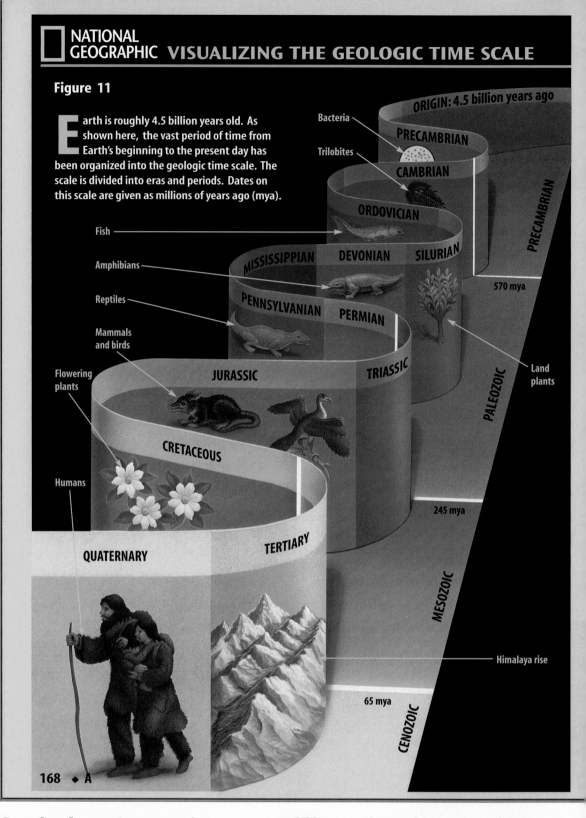

NATIONAL GEOGRAPHIC **VISUALIZING THE GEOLOGIC TIME SCALE**

Figure 11

Earth is roughly 4.5 billion years old. As shown here, the vast period of time from Earth's beginning to the present day has been organized into the geologic time scale. The scale is divided into eras and periods. Dates on this scale are given as millions of years ago (mya).

ORIGIN: 4.5 billion years ago
PRECAMBRIAN
CAMBRIAN
ORDOVICIAN
SILURIAN
DEVONIAN
MISSISSIPPIAN
PENNSYLVANIAN
PERMIAN
TRIASSIC
JURASSIC
CRETACEOUS
TERTIARY
QUATERNARY
Bacteria
Trilobites
Fish
Amphibians
Reptiles
Mammals and birds
Flowering plants
Humans
Land plants
Himalaya rise
PRECAMBRIAN
570 mya
PALEOZOIC
245 mya
MESOZOIC
65 mya
CENOZOIC

168 ◆ A

Curriculum Connection

Math Explain the vastness of geological, or "deep" time. A million years is only 0.02 percent of the total. Have students convert the eras and periods into percentages of the entire scale. L2
LS **Logical-Mathematical**

Differentiated Instruction

Challenge Have interested students research the Precambrian era, which accounts for about 90% of geologic time. Students should use a word processing program to prepare a short report of their findings. L3

Fossils and Evolution

Fossils provide a record of organisms that lived in the past. However, the fossil record is incomplete, or has gaps, much like a book with missing pages. The gaps exist because most organisms do not become fossils. By looking at fossils, scientists conclude that many simpler forms of life existed earlier in Earth's history, and more complex forms of life appeared later, as shown in **Figure 11.** Fossils provide indirect evidence that evolution has occurred on Earth.

Almost every week, fossil discoveries are made somewhere in the world. When fossils are found, they are used to help scientists understand the past. Scientists can use fossils to make models that show what the organisms might have looked like. From fossils, scientists can sometimes determine whether the organisms lived in family groups or alone, what types of food they ate, what kind of environment they lived in, and many other things about them. Most fossils represent extinct organisms. From a study of the fossil record, scientists have concluded that more than 99 percent of all organisms that have ever existed on Earth are now extinct.

Evolution in Fossils Many organisms have a history that has been preserved in sedimentary rock. Fossils show that the bones of animals such as horses and whales have become reduced in size or number over geologic time, as the species has evolved. In your Science Journal, explain what information can be gathered from changes in structures that occur over time.

More Clues About Evolution

Besides fossils, what other clues do humans have about evolution? Sometimes, evolution can be observed directly. Plant breeders observe evolution when they use cross-breeding to produce genetic changes in plants. The development of antibiotic resistance in bacteria is another direct observation of evolution. Entomologists have noted similar rapid evolution of pesticide-resistant insect species. These observations provide direct evidence that evolution occurs. Also, many examples of indirect evidence for evolution exist. They include similarities in embryo structures, the chemical makeup of organisms including DNA, and the way organisms develop into adults. Indirect evidence does not provide proof of evolution, but it does support the idea that evolution takes place over time.

Embryology The study of embryos and their development is called **embryology** (em bree AH luh jee). An embryo is the earliest growth stage of an organism. A tail and pharyngeal pouches are found at some point in the embryos of fish, reptiles, birds, and mammals, as **Figure 12** shows. Fish develop gills, but the other organisms develop other structures as their development continues. Fish, birds, and reptiles keep their tails, but many mammals lose theirs. These similarities suggest an evolutionary relationship among all vertebrate species.

Figure 12 Similarities in the embryos of fish, chickens, and rabbits show evidence of evolution.
Evaluate *these embryos as evidence for evolution.*

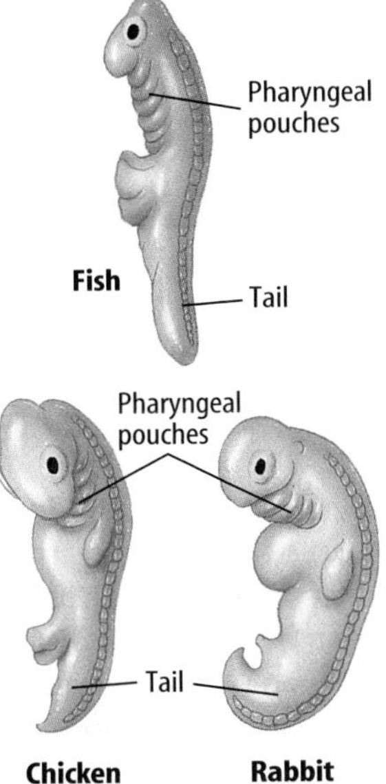

Use an Analogy

Geologic Time Use a length of rope or kite string as an analogy for the geologic time scale. Make knots to illustrate where the eras begin and end, and paint sections different colors to illustrate the periods. Another analogy for the geologic time scale is a clock. Use a wall clock and talk about the eras and periods as you advance the clock from 12:00. Make your conversion calculations before you begin.

Evolution in Fossils Changes in structures often mirror changes in the environment.

Teacher FYI

Family Trees Morphological and molecular studies indicate that marine mammals (e.g., whales, dolphins, porpoises) and some even-toed ungulates (e.g., hippos and cattle) share a common ancestor not shared by any other group. This implies that cattle and whales are more closely related than cattle and horses.

Caption Answer

Figure 12 Answers will vary. Accept answers that point out similarities.

Active Reading

Double Entry Journal In this strategy, the student takes notes and adds his or her own reflections while reading the text. Students are encouraged to explore ideas, make responses, and take risks in giving opinions about the reading. Have them divide a sheet of paper in half. On the left, have students identify a particular passage or quotation of significance in the reading. The reader records anything luminous, enigmatic, stimulating, or disturbing. On the right, the reader responds, questions, elaborates, makes personal connections, evaluates, reflects, analyzes, or interprets. Have students make a Double Entry Journal about evolution. L2

SECTION 2 Clues About Evolution A ◆ 169

Visual Learning

Figure 13 Have students compare the wing of a bat and the flipper of a porpoise with a human hand. Ask students what similarities they have. Possible answers: number of bones, muscle, and blood vessels; type of bones; they are homologous. L2 LS **Visual-Spatial**

Answer These structures often indicate that two or more species share common ancestors.

Teacher FYI

Evolution Evidence Pesticide resistance in insects, antibiotic resistance in bacteria, and observed differences in salamanders, frogs, and birds are all examples of direct evidence for evolution.

Discussion

Analogous Structures Structures that do not have a common origin but do appear similar are called analogous structures. What kinds of information would similar structures without a common origin provide? Such structures might indicate similar evolutionary solutions to similar environmental conditions.

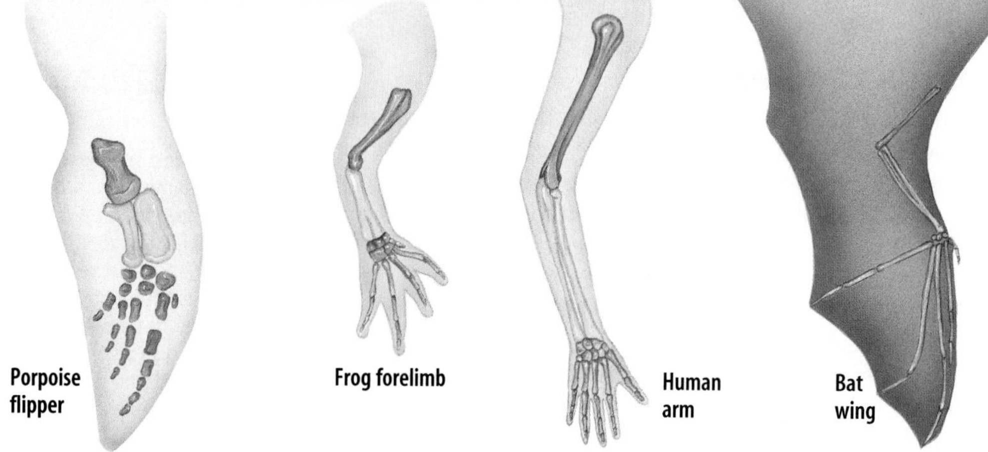

Figure 13 A porpoise flipper, frog forelimb, human arm, and bat wing are homologous. These structures show different arrangements and shapes of the bones of the forelimb. They have the same number of bones, muscles, and blood vessels, and they developed from similar tissues.

Homologous Structures What do the structures shown in **Figure 13** have in common? Although they have different functions, each of these structures is made up of the same kind of bones. Body parts that are similar in origin and structure are called **homologous** (hoh MAH luh gus). Homologous structures also can be similar in function. They often indicate that two or more species share common ancestors.

Reading Check *What do homologous structures indicate?*

Vestigial Structures The bodies of some organisms include **vestigial** (veh STIH jee ul) **structures**—structures that don't seem to have a function. Vestigial structures also provide evidence for evolution. For example, manatees, snakes, and whales no longer have back legs, but, like all animals with legs, they still have pelvic bones. The human appendix is a vestigial structure. The appendix appears to be a small version of the cecum, which is an important part of the digestive tract of many mammals. Scientists hypothesize that vestigial structures, like those shown in **Figure 14,** are body parts that once functioned in an ancestor.

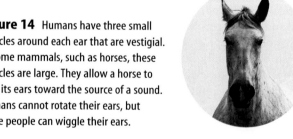

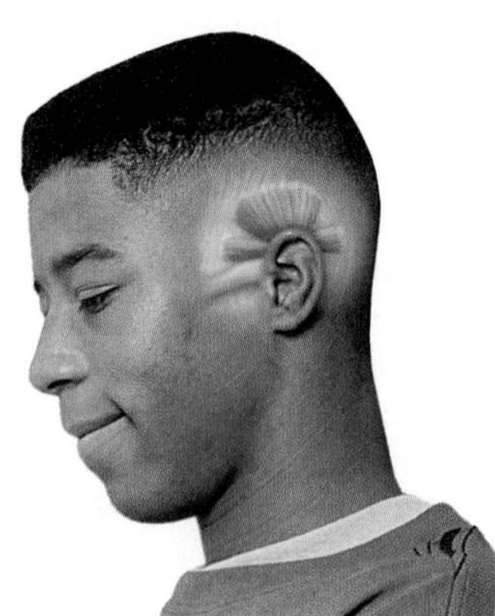

Figure 14 Humans have three small muscles around each ear that are vestigial. In some mammals, such as horses, these muscles are large. They allow a horse to turn its ears toward the source of a sound. Humans cannot rotate their ears, but some people can wiggle their ears.

Cultural Diversity

Evolving Viruses The flu is an example of a sickness caused by a virus whose DNA evolves in order for it to survive. Every major flu epidemic has come from South China, where ducks, pigs, and humans are brought into daily contact. An avian flu transfers to pigs, as does a human flu variety. The viruses exchange pieces of genetic code to form a new flu strain. When the virus reinfects humans, it is different enough that antibodies made to fight the first form do not stop the new virus. That is why flu shots do not protect against all varieties.

Figure 15 Gorillas have DNA and proteins that are similar to humans and other primates.

DNA If you enjoy science fiction, you probably have read books or seen movies in which scientists re-create dinosaurs and other extinct organisms from DNA taken from fossils. DNA is the molecule that controls heredity and directs the development of every organism. In a cell with a nucleus, DNA is found in genes that make up the chromosomes. Scientists compare DNA from living organisms to identify similarities among species. Examinations of ancient DNA often provide additional evidence of how some species evolved from their extinct ancestors. By looking at DNA, scientists also can determine how closely related organisms are. For example, DNA studies indicate that dogs are the closest relatives of bears.

Similar DNA also can suggest common ancestry. Apes such as the gorillas shown in **Figure 15,** chimpanzees, and orangutans have 24 pairs of chromosomes. Humans have 23 pairs. When two of an ape's chromosomes are laid end to end, a match for human chromosome number 2 is formed. Also, similar proteins such as hemoglobin—the oxygen-carrying protein in red blood cells—are found in many primates. This can be further evidence that primates have a common ancestor.

section 2 review

Summary

Clues from Fossils

- Scientists learn about past life by studying fossils.

Determining a Fossil's Age

- The relative date of a fossil can be estimated from the ages of rocks in nearby layers.
- Radiometric dating using radioactive elements gives more accurate dates for fossils.

Fossils and Evolution

- The fossil record has gaps which may yet be filled with later discoveries.

More Clues About Evolution

- Homologous structures, similar embryos, or vestigial structures can show evolutionary relationships.
- Evolutionary relationships among organisms can be inferred from DNA comparisons.

Self Check

1. **Compare and contrast** relative dating and radiometric dating.
2. **Discuss** the importance of fossils as evidence of evolution and describe five different kinds of fossils.
3. **Explain** how DNA can provide some evidence of evolution.
4. **List** three examples of direct evidence for evolution.
5. **Interpret Scientific Illustrations** According to data in **Figure 11,** what was the longest geologic era? What was the shortest era? In what period did mammals appear?
6. **Think Critically** Compare and contrast the five types of evidence that support the theory of evolution.

Applying Math

7. **Use Percentages** The Cenozoic Era represents about 65 million years. Approximately what percent of Earth's 4.5-billion-year history does this era represent?

3 Assess

DAILY INTERVENTION

Check for Understanding

Visual-Spatial Prepare a display of several lines of evidence that support evolution by natural selection.

Reteach

Fossils Show students examples of as many kinds of fossils as possible. Have students identify each type of fossil. L1

LS **Naturalist**

Assessment

Performance Have students prepare a poster showing the time periods in which fish, amphibians, reptiles, birds, and mammals first appeared. Use **Performance Assessment in the Science Classroom,** p. 145. L2

section 2 review

1. Relative dating is used to find the approximate age of a rock layer by its position relative to other layers. Radiometric dating is used to date rocks by measuring relative amounts of radioactive and non-radioactive elements.
2. Fossils provide evidence of how species changed over time. Organisms can be frozen in ice or trapped in amber. Minerals can replace wood or bone. There are also cast fossils and imprint fossils.
3. Organisms with similar DNA may have a common ancestor.
4. antibiotic resistance in bacteria, pesticide resistance in insects, and genetic changes in plants
5. Precambrian; Cenozoic; Jurassic
6. Students should compare and contrast vestigial structures, DNA, homologous structures, fossils, and embryology.
7. 65 million years/4,500 million years $\times$ 100 = 1.44%

1 Motivate

Bellringer

Section Focus Transparencies also are available on the Interactive Chalkboard CD-ROM.  

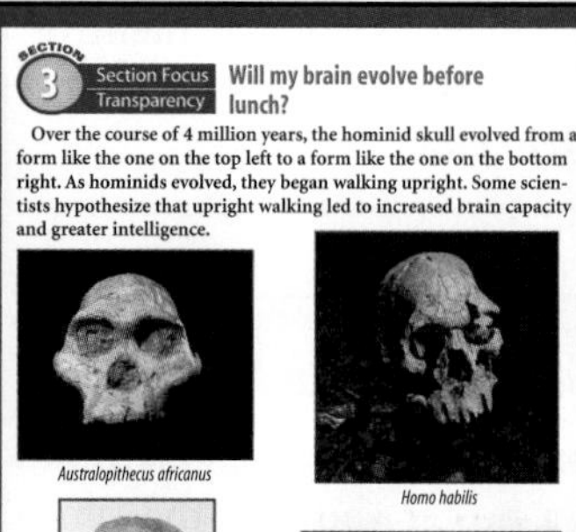

SECTION 3 Section Focus Transparency **Will my brain evolve before lunch?**

Over the course of 4 million years, the hominid skull evolved from a form like the one on the top left to a form like the one on the bottom right. As hominids evolved, they began walking upright. Some scientists hypothesize that upright walking led to increased brain capacity and greater intelligence.

Australopithecus africanus

Homo habilis

Homo erectus

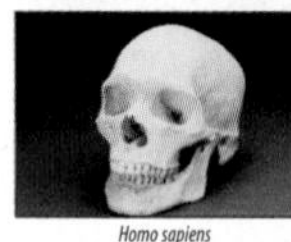

Homo sapiens

1. Describe the progression in skull shape from the top left to the bottom right.
2. What role might increasing brain size have played in human evolution?
3. What other animals have physical traits similar to human beings?

Adaptations over Time

Tie to Prior Knowledge

Primate Relationships Students may have questions about the relationship between species of primates. Remind students that species are classified into groups based on similarities, such as structure and DNA sequences.

Visual Learning

Figure 16 Have students identify other uses for rotating forelimbs in primates. Possible answers: opening doors, swinging a baseball bat, throwing a football Use the photos to discuss other common characteristics of primates. L2

LS **Visual-Spatial**

section 3

The Evolution of Primates

as you read

What **You'll Learn**

- **Describe** the differences among living primates.
- **Identify** the adaptations of primates.
- **Discuss** the evolutionary history of modern primates.

Why **It's Important**

Studying primate evolution will help you appreciate the differences among primates.

Review Vocabulary

opposable: can be placed against another digit of a hand or foot

New Vocabulary

- primate
- hominid
- *Homo sapiens*

Primates

Humans, monkeys, and apes belong to the group of mammals known as the **primates.** All primates have opposable thumbs, binocular vision, and flexible shoulders that allow the arms to rotate. These shared characteristics indicate that all primates may have evolved from a common ancestor.

Having an opposable thumb allows you to cross your thumb over your palm and touch your fingers. This means that you can grasp and hold things with your hands. An opposable thumb allows tree-dwelling primates to hold on to branches.

Binocular vision permits you to judge depth or distance with your eyes. In a similar way, it allows tree-dwelling primates to judge the distances as they move between branches. Flexible shoulders and rotating forelimbs also help tree-dwelling primates move from branch to branch. They also allow humans to do the backstroke, as shown in **Figure 16.**

Primates are divided into two major groups. The first group, the strepsirhines (STREP suh rines), includes lemurs and tarsiers like those shown in **Figure 17.** The second group, haplorhines (HAP luh rines), includes monkeys, apes, and humans.

Figure 16 The ability to rotate the shoulder in a complete circle allows humans to swim through water and tree-dwelling primates to travel through treetops.

Section 3 Resource Manager

Chapter *FAST FILE* Resources

Transparency Activity, p. 44

Directed Reading for Content Mastery, pp. 19, 20

MiniLAB, p. 4

Enrichment, p. 30

Reinforcement, p. 27

Lab Worksheet, pp. 7–8

Home and Community Involvement, p. 48

Lab Management and Safety, p. 71

Figure 17 Tarsiers and lemurs are active at night. Tarsiers are commonly found in the rain forests of Southeast Asia. Lemurs live on Madagascar and other nearby islands.
List *the traits that distinguish these animals as primates.*

Hominids About 4 million to 6 million years ago, humanlike primates appeared that were different from the other primates. These ancestors, called **hominids,** ate both meat and plants and walked upright on two legs. Hominids shared some characteristics with gorillas, orangutans, and chimpanzees, but a larger brain separated them from the apes.

African Origins In the early 1920s, a fossil skull was discovered in a quarry in South Africa. The skull had a small space for the brain, but it had a humanlike jaw and teeth. The fossil, named *Australopithecus,* was one of the oldest hominids discovered. An almost-complete skeleton of *Australopithecus* was found in northern Africa in 1974. This hominid fossil, shown in **Figure 18,** was called Lucy and had a small brain but is thought to have walked upright. This fossil indicates that modern hominids might have evolved from similar ancestors.

Figure 18 The fossil remains of Lucy are estimated to be 2.9 million to 3.4 million years old.

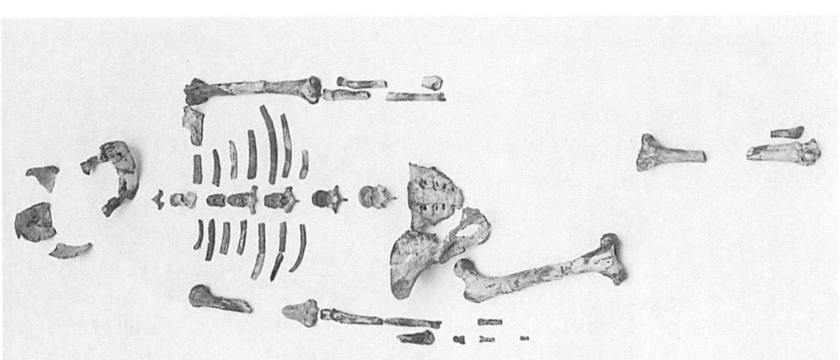

Mini LAB: Living Without Thumbs

Procedure

1. Using **tape,** fasten down each of your thumbs next to the palm of each hand.
2. Leave your thumbs taped down for at least 1 h. During this time, do the following activities: eat a meal, change clothes, and brush your teeth. Be careful not to try anything that could be dangerous.
3. Untape your thumbs, then write about your experiences in your **Science Journal.**

Analysis

1. Did not having use of your thumbs significantly affect the way you did anything? Explain.
2. Infer how having opposable thumbs could have influenced primate evolution.

Try at Home

2 Teach

Caption Answer

Figure 17 binocular vision, opposable thumbs

Purpose Students observe the function of opposable thumbs, and infer how they may have influenced primate evolution. L1 ELL IN **Kinesthetic**

Materials tape

Teaching Strategy Tell students it will be easier for them to tape both thumbs down if they use a roll of tape, rather than tape from a dispenser.

Safety Precautions Tell students not to try anything during this lab that could be dangerous without manual dexterity.

Analysis

1. Answers should indicate that students were negatively affected.
2. Possible answer: Opposable thumbs would allow for the use of tools, and tools are a foundation of modern civilization and technology.

Assessment

Performance Have students design a house with features that could be easily used by someone without thumbs. Use **Performance Assessment in the Science Classroom,** p. 123. P

Teacher FYI

Primate Existence Many types of primates existed in the Paleocene epoch. More modern forms are thought to have evolved during the Eocene epoch. There are presently about 200 species of primates, although there were more in the past.

Differentiated Instruction

English-Language Learners Have students look through old books and magazines for pictures or depictions of current primates and fossil hominids. Have them assemble these into a family tree that shows the relationships among these primates. L2 ELL **Visual-Spatial**

Teacher FYI

Rift Valley Fossils The African Rift Valley is an area of Africa where many human and hominid fossils have been uncovered. A rift valley occurs between geologic faults.

Activity

The Neanderthal News Using what they know about Neanderthals, have students write and illustrate an advertisement in their Science Journals for a fictional newspaper, *The Neanderthal News.* The ad should be for a modern product that Neanderthals might have been able to use. Student ads may emphasize tools for hammering and cutting. L2
LS **Linguistic**

Reading Check

Answer because tools were found near *Homo habilis* fossils, and *Homo habilis* means "handy human"

Caption Answer

Figure 20 Neanderthal skulls have a heavier brow ridge and a smaller brain cavity.

Discussion

African Origins What kinds of evidence might support the hypothesis that hominids first appeared in Africa? Fossils with established radioactive isotope dates may be oldest in Africa. Also, the most primitive fossil forms may be found only in Africa. L2

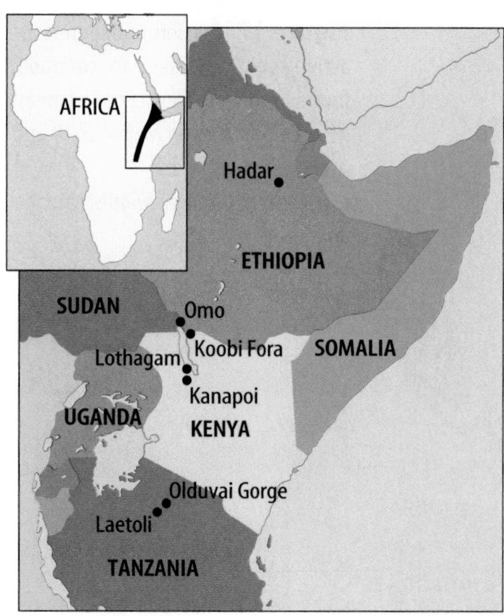

Figure 19 Many of the oldest humanlike skeletons have been found in this area of east Africa.

Early Humans In the 1960s in the region of Africa shown in **Figure 19,** a hominid fossil, which was more like present-day humans than *Australopithecus,* was discovered. The hominid was named *Homo habilis,* meaning "handy man," because simple stone tools were found near him. *Homo habilis* is estimated to be 1.5 million to 2 million years old. Based upon many fossil comparisons, scientists have suggested that *Homo habilis* gave rise to another species, *Homo erectus,* about 1.6 million years ago. This hominid had a larger brain than *Homo habilis. Homo erectus* traveled from Africa to Southeast Asia, China, and possibly Europe. *Homo habilis* and *Homo erectus* are thought to be ancestors of humans because they had larger brains and more humanlike features than *Australopithecus.*

Reading Check *Why was* Homo habilis *given that name?*

Humans

The fossil record indicates that ***Homo sapiens*** evolved about 400,000 years ago. By about 125,000 years ago, two early human groups, Neanderthals (nee AN dur tawlz) and Cro-Magnon humans, as shown in **Figure 20,** probably lived at the same time in parts of Africa and Europe.

Neanderthals Short, heavy bodies with thick bones, small chins, and heavy browridges were physical characteristics of Neanderthals. Family groups lived in caves and used well-made stone tools to hunt large animals. Neanderthals disappeared from the fossil record about 30,000 years ago. They probably are not direct ancestors of modern humans, but represent a side branch of human evolution.

Figure 20 Compare the skull of a Neanderthal with the skull of a Cro-Magnon. **Describe** *what differences you can see between these two skulls.*

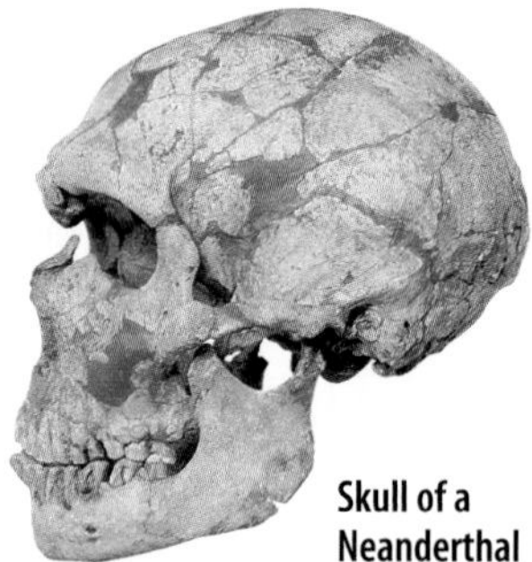

Skull of a Neanderthal

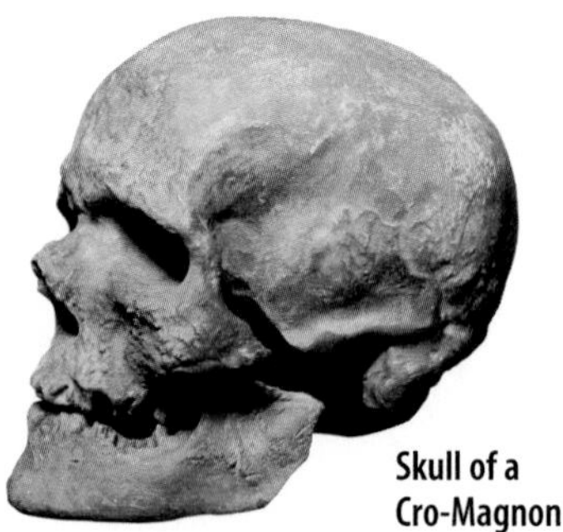

Skull of a Cro-Magnon

Cultural Diversity

Tribal Customs Use the information about fossil sites in Africa to increase students' awareness of African geography and the rich cultural heritage found there. Have students research African tribes, such as the Masai, and report on their way of life, customs, and rituals. L2

Differentiated Instruction

Challenge Show examples of art from the caves of France and other European countries. Ask students to write a paragraph in their Science Journal explaining why this art is important to us today. Art provides insight and understanding of the artists and their lives. L3 LS **Visual-Spatial**

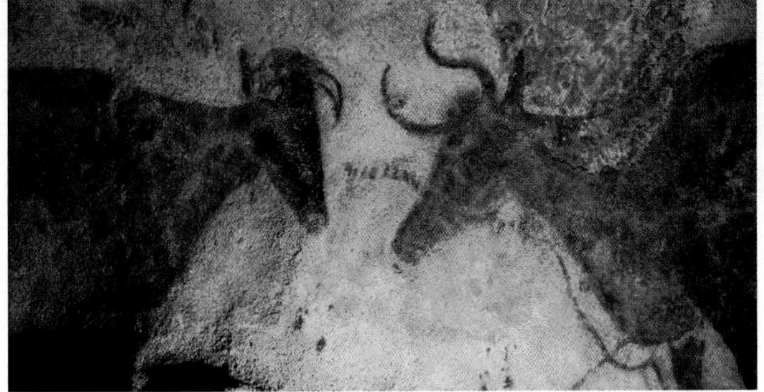

Figure 21 Paintings on cave walls have led scientists to hypothesize that Cro-Magnon humans had a well-developed culture.

Cro-Magnon Humans Cro-Magnon fossils have been found in Europe, Asia, and Australia and date from 10,000 to about 40,000 years in age. Standing about 1.6 m to 1.7 m tall, the physical appearance of Cro-Magnon people was almost the same as that of modern humans. They lived in caves, made stone carvings, and buried their dead. As shown in **Figure 21,** the oldest recorded art has been found on the walls of caves in France, where Cro-Magnon humans first painted bison, horses, and people carrying spears. Cro-Magnon humans are thought to be direct ancestors of early humans, *Homo sapiens,* which means "wise human." Evidence indicates that modern humans, *Homo sapiens sapiens,* evolved from *Homo sapiens.*

section 3 review

Summary

Primates

- Primates are an order of mammals characterized by opposable thumbs, binocular vision, and flexible shoulder joints.
- Primates are divided into strepsirrhines and haplorhines.
- Hominids are human ancestors that first appeared in Africa 4–6 million years ago.
- Hominids in the genus *Homo* first used tools and had larger brains than previous primates.

Humans

- *Homo sapiens* first appeared about 400,000 years ago.
- Cro-Magnon humans and Neanderthals coexisted in many places until Neanderthals disappeared about 30,000 years ago.
- *Homo sapiens* looked like modern humans and are believed to be our direct ancestors.

Self Check

1. **Describe** three kinds of evidence suggesting that all primates might have shared a common ancestor.
2. **Discuss** the importance of *Australopithecus.*
3. **Compare and contrast** Neanderthals, Cro-Magnon humans, and early humans.
4. **Identify** three groups most scientists consider to be direct ancestors of modern humans.
5. **Think Critically** Propose a hypothesis to explain why teeth are the most abundant fossil of hominids.

Applying Skills

6. **Concept Map** Make a concept map to show in what sequence hominids appeared. Use the following: *Homo sapiens sapiens,* Neanderthal, *Homo habilis, Australopithecus, Homo sapiens,* and Cro-Magnon human.
7. **Write** a story in your Science Journal about what life might have been like when both Neanderthals and Cro-Magnon humans were alive.

Science Online booka.msscience.com/self_check_quiz

Fun Fact

Most animals depicted in cave art no longer live anywhere near those caves today. Some are extinct, but scientists have fossil evidence of their existence. A few, however, are unknown to modern science as either living or fossil animals.

3 Assess

DAILY INTERVENTION

Check for Understanding

Interpersonal Have students work in groups to identify the traits of primates that are important for human evolution. Each group should then present their ideas to the whole class. L2

Reteach

Primates Have students prepare a list on the board of characteristics common to primates. L1 COOP LEARN IS **Interpersonal**

Assessment

Portfolio Have students make a timeline of the sequence of hominid evolution. Use **Performance Assessment in the Science Classroom,** p. 163. L2

section 3 review

1. homologous structures; similar DNA; fossils
2. *Australopithecus,* an early hominid, had a small brain case but human-like jaws and teeth.
3. Neanderthals had short bodies with massive bones and heavy brow ridges. Cro-Magnon humans were taller, invented art, and made stone carvings. Cro-Magnon humans were very similar to early humans.
4. *Homo sapiens, Homo erectus,* and *Homo habilis*
5. Teeth are the hardest parts of an organism.
6. The concept map should be an events chain in the following order: *Australopithecus, Homo habilis,* Neanderthals, Cro-Magnon humans, *Homo sapiens,* and *Homo sapiens sapiens.*
7. Stories should indicate hardships that might result from being maladapted to their environment.

Real-World Question

Purpose Students design and carry out an experiment showing the variation in a population. L2 ELL COOP LEARN LS **Logical-Mathematical**

Process Skills form a hypothesis, measure in SI, use numbers, interpret data, communicate, make and use tables, design an experiment

Time Required 45 minutes to plan the investigation, 45 minutes to complete the investigation

Safety Precautions Caution students not to put any materials into their mouths. Be sure students are not allergic to any plants used.

Form a Hypothesis

Possible Hypotheses Student hypotheses will vary. Possible hypotheses include: "A sample of peanuts will exhibit variations in numbers of seeds," or "A sample of peanuts will exhibit variations in length of seeds."

Test Your Hypothesis

Possible Procedures Procedures will vary. Most students will choose width or length to measure. Others may choose volume, number of seeds, or some other variable. Volume of fruit can be measured by water displacement. Students may want to design color charts to compare differences in fruit coloration.

Design Your Own

Recognizing Variation in a Population

Goals

- **Design** an experiment that will allow you to collect data about variation in a population.
- **Observe, measure, and analyze** variations in a population.

Possible Materials

fruit and seeds from one plant species
metric ruler
magnifying lens
graph paper

Safety Precautions

WARNING: *Do not put any fruit or seeds in your mouth.*

Real-World Question

When you first observe a flock of pigeons, you might think all the birds look alike. However, if you look closer, you will notice minor differences, or variations, among the individuals. Different pigeons might have different color markings, or some might be smaller or larger than others. Individuals of the same species—whether they're birds, plants, or worms—might look alike at first, but some variations undoubtedly exist. According to the principles of natural selection, evolution could not occur without variations. What kinds of variations have you noticed among species of plants or animals? How can you measure variation in a plant or animal population?

Form a Hypothesis

Make a hypothesis about the amount of variation in the fruit and seeds of one species of plant.

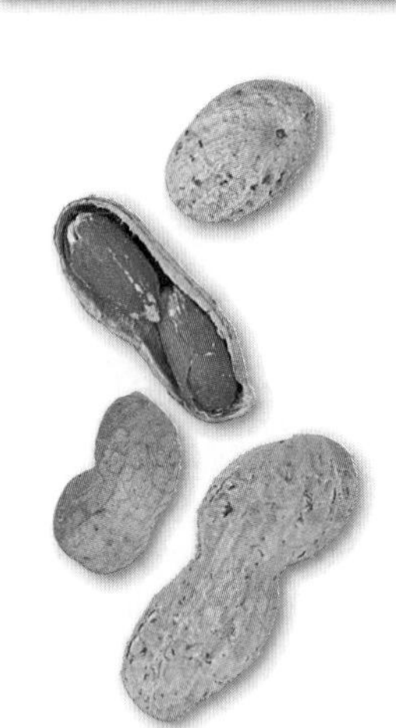

Alternative Inquiry Lab

Plant Variation Allow students to choose a plant species to grow from seeds. When the plants flower, have them investigate variation in assorted plant traits. How do plants vary when flowering? Does that relate to variation in seeds? L3

Using Scientific Methods

Test a Hypothesis

Make a Plan

1. As a group, agree upon and write out the prediction.
2. **List** the steps you need to take to test your prediction. Be specific. Describe exactly what you will do at each step. List your materials.
3. **Decide** what characteristic of fruit and seeds you will study. For example, you could measure the length of fruit and seeds or count the number of seeds per fruit.
4. **Design** a data table in your Science Journal to collect data about two variations. Use the table to record the data your group collects.
5. **Identify** any constants, variables, and controls of the experiment.
6. How many fruit and seeds will you examine? Will your data be more accurate if you examine larger numbers?
7. **Summarize** your data in a graph or chart.

Follow Your Plan

1. Make sure your teacher approves your plan before you start.
2. Carry out the experiment as planned.
3. While the experiment is going on, write down any observations you make and complete the data table in your Science Journal.

Analyze Your Data

1. **Calculate** the mean and range of variation in your experiment. The range is the difference between the largest and the smallest measurements. The mean is the sum of all the data divided by the sample size.
2. **Graph** your group's results by making a line graph for the variations you measured. Place the range of variation on the *x*-axis and the number of organisms that had that measurement on the *y*-axis.

Conclude and Apply

1. **Explain** your results in terms of natural selection.
2. **Discuss** the factors you used to determine the amount of variation present.
3. **Infer** why one or more of the variations you observed in this activity might be helpful to the survival of the individual.

Create a poster or other exhibit that illustrates the variations you and your classmates observed.

Teaching Strategies

- Guide students as they decide what trait to measure. Length or width of seeds will be most easily measured with the materials suggested.
- For most students, larger seeds will be easier to work with. Peanuts, lima beans, sunflower seeds, pinto beans, and peas are large enough.
- If students are physically incapable of measuring the seeds, have them work with a partner who can help.

Expected Outcome Most students will collect data that results in a bell-shaped curve when graphed.

Analyze Your Data

Answers to Questions

1. Mean and range will vary depending on the seeds used and the variables measured.
2. Graphs will be a bell-shaped curve for most variables studied.

Error Analysis Have students who measure the same trait share their results and explain any differences they observe.

Conclude and Apply

1. Natural selection may result in a variation that is found in many organisms within a population, but variations in the trait may also be found in smaller numbers.
2. by determining what the "norm" is and how often seeds vary from it
3. Answers will vary. Accept all reasonable answers. Possible response: Small, lightweight fruit is more easily dispersed to other areas by birds than heavier fruit.

Assessment

Performance Ask students to infer the natural selection advantage of fruits producing larger quantities of seeds. Larger seed quantities increase the chances that at least a few seeds will germinate and grow to maturity. Use **Performance Assessment in the Science Classroom,** p. 89. L2

Discuss the variations observed by the class. Have students discuss why some variations are more advantageous than others.

TIME

Content Background

About the time of the 12th International Conference on AIDS in 1998, it had become clear that the powerful new drugs being used to attack HIV, called the protease inhibitors or the triple cocktail, would not bring the miracle that many had hoped they would. Between 10 and 50 percent of patients with AIDS who took protease inhibitors were later diagnosed with more virulent forms of HIV. As many as 4.5 percent of newly infected patients had drug-resistant strains of the virus.

If a person contracts HIV from another person with a resistant strain, it could be as if the person got infected in 1983 when there were no anti-retroviral drugs.

Discussion

New Approaches How would Wong-Stall's research avoid the pitfalls of the new drugs and vaccines to treat HIV and AIDS? Possible answer: Instead of depending on suppressing the virus with drugs, this new research would prevent the virus from multiplying by changing existing cell structure. This could eliminate the daily regimen of drugs.

Historical Significance

Have students research tuberculosis, or TB. Have students answer these questions:

- When and where was the first known outbreak of TB?
- At the height of the disease, how many people were infected with the disease?
- When was the TB vaccine introduced?

Explain that even though there is a TB vaccine, new drug-resistant strains of TB have recently been discovered. Because of these resistant strains, scientists are interested in the TB vaccine again.

TIME SCIENCE AND HISTORY

SCIENCE CAN CHANGE THE COURSE OF HISTORY!

Fighting HIV

The first cases of AIDS, or acquired immune deficiency syndrome, in humans were reported in the early 1980s. AIDS is caused by the human immunodeficiency virus, or HIV.

A major problem in AIDS research is the rapid evolution of HIV. When HIV multiplies inside a host cell, new versions of the virus are produced as well as identical copies of the virus that invaded the cell. New versions of the virus soon can outnumber the original version. A treatment that works against today's HIV might not work against tomorrow's version.

These rapid changes in HIV also mean that different strains of the virus exist in different places around the world. Treatments developed in the United States work only for people who contracted the virus in the United States. This leaves people in some parts of the world without effective treatments. So, researchers such as geneticist Flossie Wong-Staal at the University of California in San Diego, must look for new ways to fight the evolving virus.

Working Backwards

Flossie Wong-Staal is taking a new approach. First, her team identifies the parts of a human cell that HIV depends on and the parts of the human cell that HIV needs but the human cell doesn't need. Then the team looks for a way to remove—or inactivate—those unneeded parts. This technique limits the virus's ability to multiply.

Wong-Staal's research combines three important aspects of science—a deep understanding of how cells and genes operate, great skill in the techniques of genetics, and great ideas. Understanding, skill, and great ideasare the best weapons so far in the fight to conquer HIV.

Wong-Staal was on one of the two teams that first identified HIV as the virus that causes AIDS.

Research Use the link to the right and other sources to determine which nations have the highest rates of HIV infection. Which nation has the highest rate? Where does the U.S. rank? Next, find data from ten years ago. Have the rankings changed?

For more information, visit booka.msscience.com/time

Research What might account for the difference in numbers of people infected in different countries? Possible answers: The rates vary with the availability of medicine and access to health care and with education about how HIV is transmitted. Explain that the largest number of new infections of HIV in the U.S. are among young people. Have students discuss possible reasons for this.

Resources for Teachers and Students

AIDS and STDs: Global Perspectives, Rachel Donatelle, Pearson Custom Publishing, New York, 1999

Global Responses to AIDS, by Cristiana Bestos, Indiana University Press, Bloomington, Indiana, 1999

Reviewing Main Ideas

Section 1 Ideas About Evolution

1. Evolution is one of the central ideas of biology. It explains how living things have changed in the past and is a basis for predicting how they might change in the future.
2. Charles Darwin developed the theory of evolution by natural selection to explain how evolutionary changes account for the diversity of organisms on Earth.
3. Natural selection includes concepts of variation, overproduction, and competition.
4. According to natural selection, organisms with traits best suited to their environment are more likely to survive and reproduce.

Section 2 Clues About Evolution

1. Fossils provide evidence for evolution.
2. Relative dating and radiometric dating can be used to estimate the age of fossils.
3. The evolution of antibiotic-resistant bacteria, pesticide-resistant insects, and rapid genetic changes in plant species provides direct evidence that evolution occurs.
4. Homologous structures, vestigial structures, comparative embryology, and similarities in DNA provide indirect evidence of evolution.

Section 3 The Evolution of Primates

1. Primates include monkeys, apes, and humans. Hominids are humanlike primates.
2. The earliest known hominid fossil is *Australopithecus.*
3. *Homo sapiens* are thought to have evolved from Cro-Magnon humans about 400,000 years ago.

Visualizing Main Ideas

Copy and complete the following spider map on evolution.

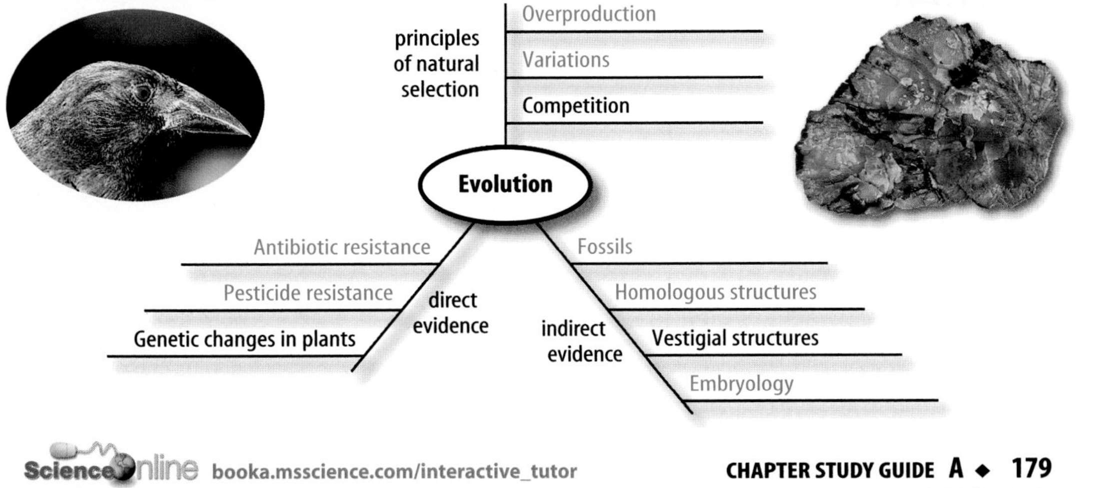

Identifying Misconceptions

Assess

Use this assessment as follow-up to page F at the beginning of this chapter.

Discussion After students complete the bean/bacteria activity, ask the following questions:

- Why did the red "bacteria" survive?
- Did the antibiotic cause the bacteria to have a thicker cell wall?
- When did the red bacteria's thick cell wall develop—before or after the antibiotic?

Expected Outcome Students should understand that the red bacteria's trait of a thicker cell wall existed before the antibiotic was introduced. The trait gave the bacterium an advantage that helped it survive. L2

chapter 6 Study Guide

Reviewing Main Ideas

Summary statements can be used by students to review the major concepts of the chapter.

Visualizing Main Ideas

See student page.

Science Online

Visit booka.msscience.com
/self_check_quiz
/interactive_tutor
/vocabulary_puzzlemaker
/chapter_review
/standardized_test

Assessment Transparency

For additional assessment questions, use the *Assessment Transparency* located in the transparency book.

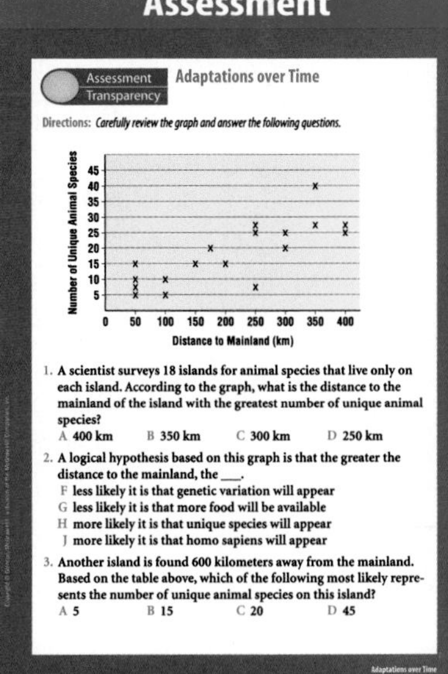

Assessment

Assessment Transparency **Adaptations over Time**

Directions: *Carefully review the graph and answer the following questions.*

1. A scientist surveys 18 islands for animal species that live only on each island. According to the graph, what is the distance to the mainland of the island with the greatest number of unique animal species?
   A 400 km B 350 km C 300 km D 250 km
2. A logical hypothesis based on this graph is that the greater the distance to the mainland, the ____.
   F less likely it is that genetic variation will appear
   G less likely it is that more food will be available
   H more likely it is that unique species will appear
   J more likely it is that homo sapiens will appear
3. Another island is found 600 kilometers away from the mainland. Based on the table above, which of the following most likely represents the number of unique animal species on this island?
   A 5 B 15 C 20 D 45

Adaptations over Time

chapter 6 Review

Using Vocabulary

1. sedimentary rock
2. vestigial structures
3. homologous
4. primates
5. embryology, species, or variation
6. natural selection
7. *Homo sapiens*

Checking Concepts

8. C
9. B
10. D
11. D
12. A
13. C
14. D

Thinking Critically

15. The foot is from an aquatic bird with webbed feet for swimming.
16. Lamarck: Owls hunt at night and their eyes grow larger with use. The trait is passed on. Darwin: Larger owls' eyes were an advantage to survival. This inherited feature was passed on to offspring over many generations until owls became adapted for seeing prey at night with large eyes.
17. Answers will vary. Possible answer: Geographical isolation as a result of a volcanic eruption can divide a population. Two species may evolve.
18. Chameleons blend into their environment. This ability to change color helps protect them from predators.
19. Predators and competition for resources will eliminate many frogs. Only the most adapted will survive.

chapter 6 Review

Using Vocabulary

adaptation p. 160
embryology p. 169
evolution p. 156
gradualism p. 162
hominid p. 173
Homo sapiens p. 174
homologous p. 170
natural selection p. 159
primate p. 172
punctuated equilibrium p. 162
radioactive element p. 167
sedimentary rock p. 166
species p. 156
variation p. 160
vestigial structure p. 170

Fill in the blanks with the correct vocabulary word or words.

1. _________ contains many different kinds of fossils.
2. The muscles that move the human ear appear to be _________.
3. Forelimbs of bats, humans, and seals are _________.
4. Opposable thumbs are a characteristic of _________.
5. The study of _________ can provide evidence of evolution.
6. The principles of _________ include variation and competition.
7. _________ likely evolved directly from Cro-Magnons.

Checking Concepts

Choose the word or phrase that best answers the question.

8. What is an example of adaptation?
   - **A)** a fossil
   - **B)** gradualism
   - **C)** camouflage
   - **D)** embryo
9. What method provides the most accurate estimate of a fossil's age?
   - **A)** natural selection
   - **B)** radiometric dating
   - **C)** relative dating
   - **D)** camouflage
10. What do homologous structures, vestigial structures, and fossils provide evidence of?
    - **A)** gradualism
    - **B)** food choice
    - **C)** populations
    - **D)** evolution
11. Which model of evolution shows change over a relatively short period of time?
    - **A)** embryology
    - **B)** adaptation
    - **C)** gradualism
    - **D)** punctuated equilibrium
12. What might a series of helpful variations in a species result in?
    - **A)** adaptation
    - **B)** fossils
    - **C)** embryology
    - **D)** climate change

Use the following chart to answer question 13.

Homo habilis
↓
Homo erectus
↓
?
↓
Homo sapiens

13. Which of the following correctly fills the gap in the line of descent from *Homo habilis?*
    - **A)** Neanderthal
    - **B)** *Australopithecus*
    - **C)** Cro-Magnon human
    - **D)** chimpanzee
14. What is the study of an organism's early development called?
    - **A)** adaptation
    - **B)** relative dating
    - **C)** natural selection
    - **D)** embryology

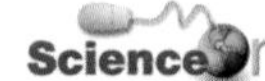

booka.msscience.com/vocabulary_puzzlemaker

Use the Exam*View*® Pro Testmaker CD-ROM to:

- create multiple versions of tests
- create modified tests with one mouse click for inclusion students
- edit existing questions and add your own questions
- build tests aligned with state standards using built-in State Curriculum Tags
- change English tests to Spanish with one mouse click and vice versa

Thinking Critically

15. Predict what type of bird the foot pictured at right would belong to. Explain your reasoning.

16. Discuss how Lamarck and Darwin would have explained the large eyes of an owl.

17. Explain, using an example, how a new species of organism could evolve.

18. Identify how the color-changing ability of chameleons is an adaptation.

19. Form a hypothesis as to why ponds are not overpopulated by frogs in summer. Use the concept of natural selection to help you.

20. Sequence Make an events-chain concept map of the events that led Charles Darwin to his theory of evolution by natural selection.

Use the table below to answer question 21.

Chemicals Present in Bacteria	
Species 1	A, G, T, C, L, E, S, H
Species 2	A, G, T, C, L, D, H
Species 3	A,G, T, C, L, D, P, U, S, R, I, V
Species 4	A, G, T, C, L, D, H

21. Interpret Data Each letter above represents a chemical found in a species of bacteria. Which species are most closely related?

22. Discuss the evidence you would use to determine whether the evolution of a group were best explained by gradualism. How would this differ from a group that followed a punctuated equilibrium model?

23. Describe the processes a scientist would use to figure out the age of a fossil.

24. Evaluate the possibility for each of the five types of fossils in **Figure 9** to yield a DNA sample. Remember that only biological tissue will contain DNA.

Performance Activities

25. Collection With permission, collect fossils from your area and identify them. Show your collection to your class.

26. Brochure Assume that you are head of an advertising company. Develop a brochure to explain Darwin's theory of evolution by natural selection.

Applying Math

27. Relative Age The rate of radioactive decay is measured in half-lives—the amount of time it takes for one half of a radioactive element to decay. Determine the relative age of a fossil given the following information:

- Rock layers are undisturbed.
- The layer below the fossil has potassium-40 with a half-life of 1 million years and only one half of the original potassium is left.
- The layer above the fossil has carbon-14 with a half-life of 5,730 years and one-sixteenth of the carbon isotope remains.

Use the graph below to answer question 28.

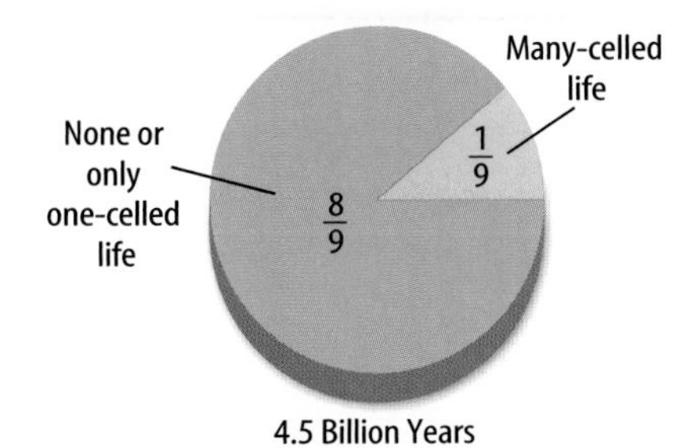

28. First Appearances If Earth is 4.5 billion years old, how long ago did the first many-celled life-forms appear?

Thinking Critically

20. Darwin did amateur studies in natural history as a boy. He became a naturalist aboard the *Beagle* and gathered information for five years. After returning to England, Darwin worked for the rest of his life to develop his theory.

21. Species 2 and 4 are the closest in relation; they have the same chemicals.

22. The best evidence will be from the fossil record. If species show slow changes over a long time, this would suggest gradualism. Punctuated equilibrium would be indicated if rapid change occurred in a short time followed by long periods with no change.

23. The layer of rock where it was formed would be noted. Radiometric dating would be done. Comparisons to other fossils would be made.

24. imprint fossils—the fossil is only an impression of an organism, no DNA will be present; mineralized fossils—minerals replace tissues, no DNA left to analyze; cast fossils—the DNA has been replaced; fossils in amber—if the DNA has not degraded, it might be available; frozen fossil—DNA has been extracted from frozen organisms (mammoths).

Performance Activities

25. Fossil collections will vary, depending on location. Students may get help from experts at a nearby university. Use **PASC,** p. 121.

26. The brochures should include the principles of natural selection, as found in **Table 1.** Use **PASC,** p. 129.

Applying Math

National Math Standards

1, 2, 5, 9

27. between 22,920 and 1 million years old

28. about 500 million years ago

Assessment Resources

Reproducible Masters

Chapter *Fast File* Resources
Chapter Review, pp. 35–36
Chapter Tests, pp. 37–40
Assessment Transparency Activity, p. 47

Glencoe Science Web site
Chapter Review Test
Standardized Test Practice

Glencoe Technology
Assessment Transparency
Exam*View*® Pro Testmaker
MindJogger Videoquiz
Interactive Chalkboard

Answer Sheet A practice answer sheet can be found at booka.msscience.com/answer_sheet.

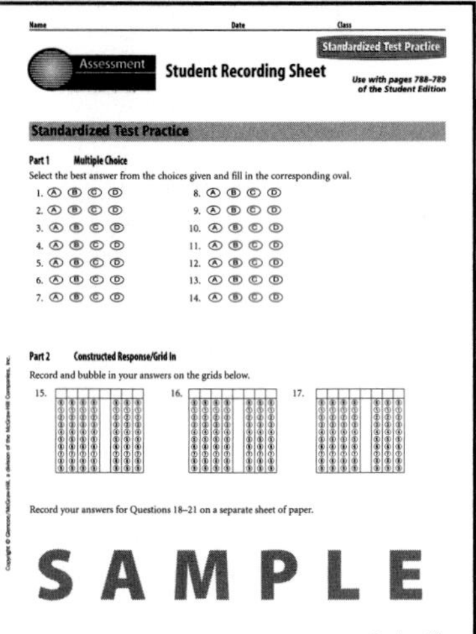

Part 1 Multiple Choice

1. B
2. B
3. D
4. A
5. D
6. B

chapter 6 Standardized Test Practice

Part 1 Multiple Choice

Record your answers on the answer sheet provided by your teacher or on a sheet of paper.

1. A species is a group of organisms
   A. that lives together with similar characteristics.
   B. that shares similar characteristics and can reproduce among themselves to produce fertile offspring.
   C. across a wide area that cannot reproduce.
   D. that chooses mates from among themselves.

2. Which of the following is considered an important factor in natural selection?
   A. limited reproduction
   B. competition for resources
   C. no variations within a population
   D. plentiful food and other resources

3. The marine iguana of the Galápagos Islands enters the ocean and feeds on seaweed. What is this an example of?
   A. adaptation
   B. gradualism
   C. survival of the fittest
   D. acquired characteristic

Use the illustration below to answer question 4.

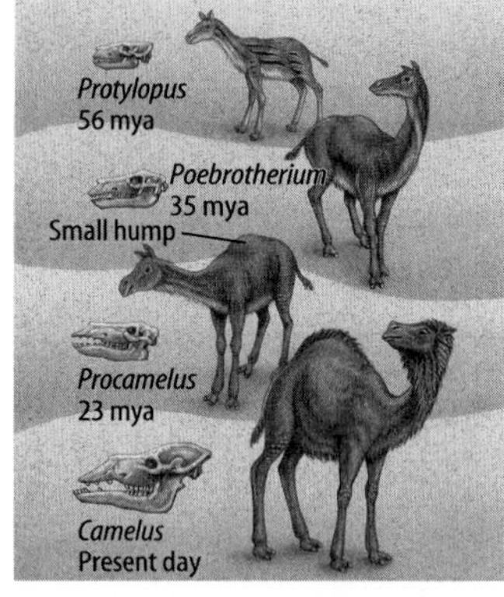

4. According to Lamarck's hypothesis of acquired characteristics, which statement best explains the changes in the camel over time?
   A. All characteristics developed during an individual's lifetime are passed on to offspring.
   B. Characteristics that do not help the animal survive are passed to offspring.
   C. Variation of the species leads to adaptation.
   D. Individuals moving from one area to another carry with them new characteristics.

Use the illustrations below to answer question 5.

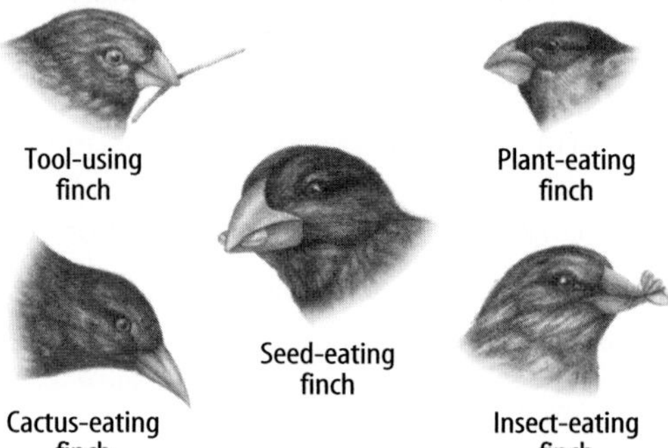

5. What, besides competition for food, contributed to the evolution of the species of Darwin's finches?
   A. predation
   B. natural disaster
   C. DNA
   D. variation in beak shapes

6. Some harmless species imitate or mimic a poisonous species as a means for increased survival. What is this an example of?
   A. acquired characteristics
   B. adaptation
   C. variation
   D. geographic isolation

182 ◆ A STANDARDIZED TEST PRACTICE

Part 2 Short Response/Grid In

7. Camouflage is beneficial to a species because it helps the organism escape predation, which increases the chances of survival and reproduction.
8. The albino lemur would not be at a disadvantage in an environment with a lot of snow.
9. The level of variation is lower with an endangered species because the number of individuals is so low.
10. A variation that provides an advantage for an endangered species will increase the number of individuals and help the species to thrive again. A disadvantageous variation might cause the extinction of a species.
11. The Cro-Magnon humans had an adaptation that made them better suited for their environment thus allowing them to survive. The Neanderthals did not adapt to their environment over time and could not survive as a species.

Part 2 Short Response/Grid In

Record your answers on the answer sheet provided by your teacher or on a sheet of paper.

7. How does camouflage benefit a species?

Use the photo below to answer question 8.

8. Describe an environment where the albino lemur would not be at a disadvantage.
9. Variation between members of a species plays an important role in Darwin's theory of evolution. What happens to variation in endangered species where the number of individuals is very low?
10. Describe what happens to an endangered species if a variation provides an advantage for the species. What would happen if the variation resulted in a disadvantage?
11. Using the theory of natural selection, hypothesize why the Cro-Magnon humans survived and the Neanderthals disappeared.

Test-Taking Tip

Never Leave Any Answer Blank Answer each question as best you can. You can receive partial credit for partially correct answers.

Question 16 If you cannot remember all primate characteristics, list as many as you can.

Part 3 Open Ended

Record your answers on a sheet of paper.

12. What are the two groups of early humans that lived about 125,000 years ago in Africa and Europe? Describe their general appearance and characteristics. Compare these characteristics to modern humans.
13. Explain how bacterial resistance to antibiotics is an example of punctuated equilibrium.
14. Why are radioactive elements useful in dating fossils? Does this method improve accuracy over relative dating?

Use the illustrations below to answer question 15.

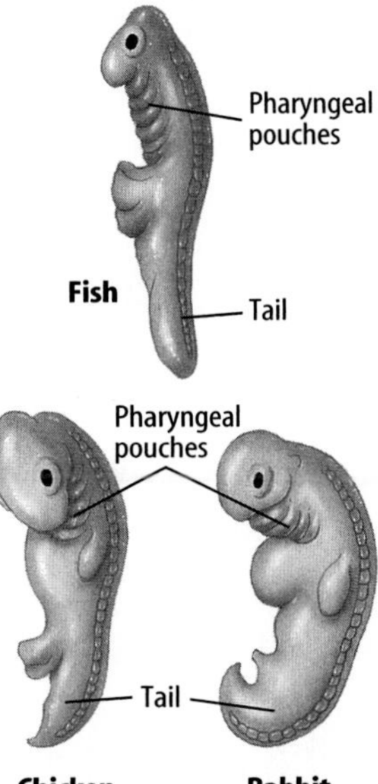

15. Why would scientists study embryos? What features of these three embryos support evolution?
16. How does DNA evidence provide support that primates have a common ancestor?

which is based on the theory that older rock layers are underneath younger rock layers.

15. Scientists would study embryos because they are the earliest growth stage of an organism. The fish, chicken and rabbit embryos all have gill slits and tail at this stage. These similarities at this stage support an evolutionary relationship between all vertebrate species.
16. Scientists have compared the DNA of primates and it suggests common ancestry. Specifically the apes have 24 pairs of chromosomes and humans have 23 pairs of chromosomes. Two of the apes' chromosomes can be laid end to end and it will match with a human's number 2 chromosomes.

Rubrics

For more help evaluating open-ended assessment questions, see the rubric on p. 10T.

Part 3 Open Ended

12. Neanderthals and Cro-Magnons. The Neanderthals had short, heavy bodies with thick bones, small chins and heavy brow ridges. They lived in family groups in caves and used well-made tools to hunt large animals. The Cro-Magnon people were similar to modern humans in appearance. They lived in caves, made stone carvings and buried their dead. Comparing the Neanderthals and Cro-Magnons to modern day humans could have a vast number of responses.
13. Punctuated equilibrium is when a species changes in a relatively short period of time. Bacteria became resistant to antibiotics over several decades.
14. Radioactive elements are useful in dating fossils because they decay at a constant rate. Each radioactive element gives off radiation at a different rate. Scientists can use the ratio of radioactive to nonradioactive elements in the rock to estimate the age. This method is much more accurate than relative dating

Student Resources

CONTENTS

Scientific Methods

Scientists use an orderly approach called scientific methods to solve problems. These include organizing and recording data so others can understand them. Scientists use many variations in these methods when they solve problems.

Identify a Question

The first step in a scientific investigation or experiment is to identify a question to be answered or a problem to be solved. For example, you might ask which gasoline is the most efficient.

Gather and Organize Information

After you have identified your question, begin gathering and organizing information. There are many ways to gather information, such as researching in a library, interviewing those knowledgeable about the subject, testing and working in the laboratory and field. Fieldwork is investigations and observations done outside of a laboratory.

Researching Information Before moving in a new direction, it is important to gather the information that already is known about the subject. Start by asking yourself questions to determine exactly what you need to know. Then you will look for the information in various reference sources, like the student is doing in **Figure 1.** Some sources may include textbooks, encyclopedias, government documents, professional journals, science magazines, and the Internet. Always list the sources of your information.

Figure 1 The Internet can be a valuable research tool.

Evaluate Sources of Information Not all sources of information are reliable. You should evaluate all of your sources of information, and use only those you know to be dependable. For example, if you are researching ways to make homes more energy efficient, a site written by the U.S. Department of Energy would be more reliable than a site written by a company that is trying to sell a new type of weatherproofing material. Also, remember that research always is changing. Consult the most current resources available to you. For example, a 1985 resource about saving energy would not reflect the most recent findings.

Sometimes scientists use data that they did not collect themselves, or conclusions drawn by other researchers. This data must be evaluated carefully. Ask questions about how the data were obtained, if the investigation was carried out properly, and if it has been duplicated exactly with the same results. Would you reach the same conclusion from the data? Only when you have confidence in the data can you believe it is true and feel comfortable using it.

Interpret Scientific Illustrations As you research a topic in science, you will see drawings, diagrams, and photographs to help you understand what you read. Some illustrations are included to help you understand an idea that you can't see easily by yourself, like the tiny particles in an atom in **Figure 2.** A drawing helps many people to remember details more easily and provides examples that clarify difficult concepts or give additional information about the topic you are studying. Most illustrations have labels or a caption to identify or to provide more information.

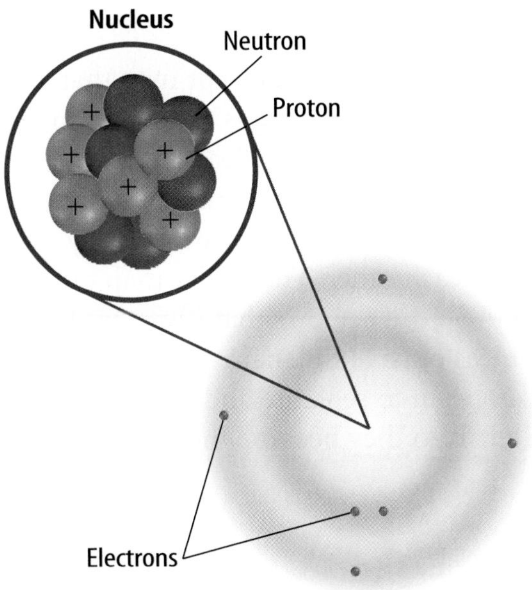

Figure 2 This drawing shows an atom of carbon with its six protons, six neutrons, and six electrons.

Concept Maps One way to organize data is to draw a diagram that shows relationships among ideas (or concepts). A concept map can help make the meanings of ideas and terms more clear, and help you understand and remember what you are studying. Concept maps are useful for breaking large concepts down into smaller parts, making learning easier.

Network Tree A type of concept map that not only shows a relationship, but how the concepts are related is a network tree, shown in **Figure 3.** In a network tree, the words are written in the ovals, while the description of the type of relationship is written across the connecting lines.

When constructing a network tree, write down the topic and all major topics on separate pieces of paper or notecards. Then arrange them in order from general to specific. Branch the related concepts from the major concept and describe the relationship on the connecting line. Continue to more specific concepts until finished.

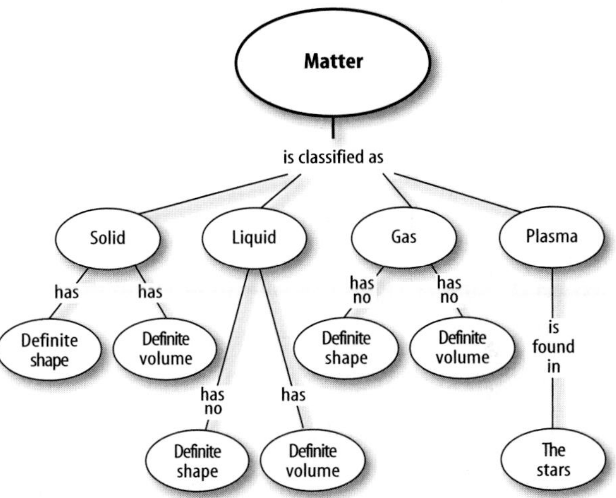

Figure 3 A network tree shows how concepts or objects are related.

Events Chain Another type of concept map is an events chain. Sometimes called a flow chart, it models the order or sequence of items. An events chain can be used to describe a sequence of events, the steps in a procedure, or the stages of a process.

When making an events chain, first find the one event that starts the chain. This event is called the initiating event. Then, find the next event and continue until the outcome is reached, as shown in **Figure 4.**

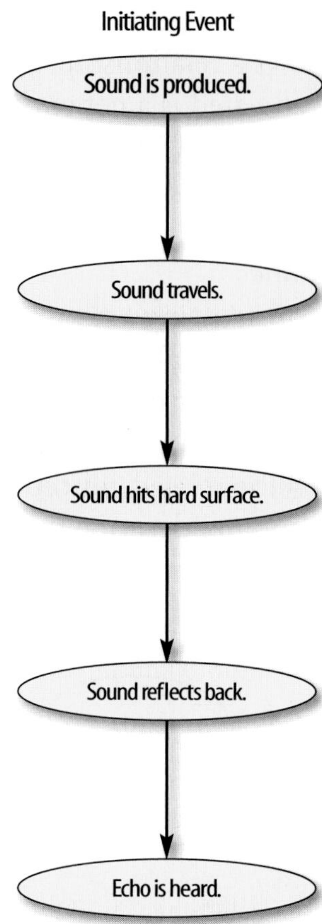

Figure 4 Events-chain concept maps show the order of steps in a process or event. This concept map shows how a sound makes an echo.

Cycle Map A specific type of events chain is a cycle map. It is used when the series of events do not produce a final outcome, but instead relate back to the beginning event, such as in **Figure 5.** Therefore, the cycle repeats itself.

To make a cycle map, first decide what event is the beginning event. This is also called the initiating event. Then list the next events in the order that they occur, with the last event relating back to the initiating event. Words can be written between the events that describe what happens from one event to the next. The number of events in a cycle map can vary, but usually contain three or more events.

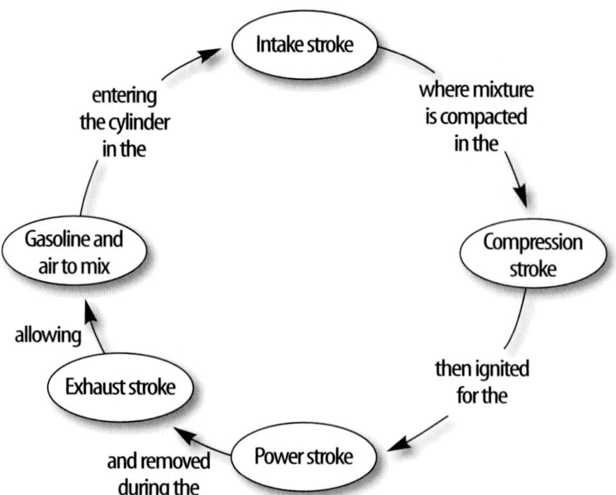

Figure 5 A cycle map shows events that occur in a cycle.

Spider Map A type of concept map that you can use for brainstorming is the spider map. When you have a central idea, you might find that you have a jumble of ideas that relate to it but are not necessarily clearly related to each other. The spider map on sound in **Figure 6** shows that if you write these ideas outside the main concept, then you can begin to separate and group unrelated terms so they become more useful.

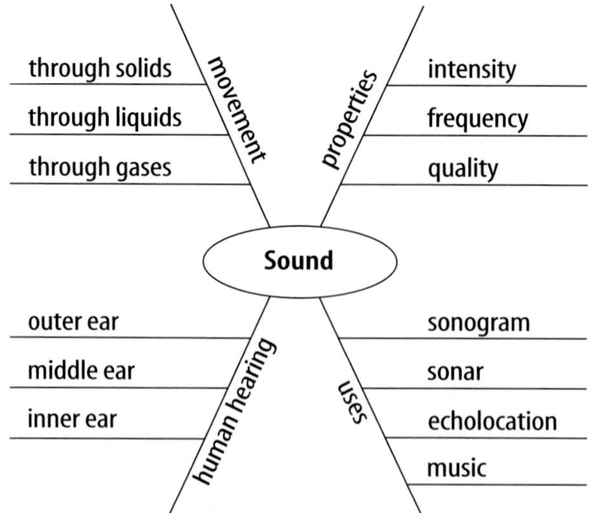

Figure 6 A spider map allows you to list ideas that relate to a central topic but not necessarily to one another.

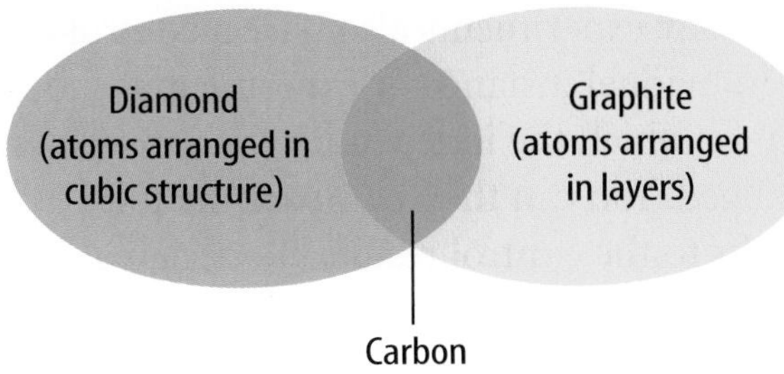

Figure 7 This Venn diagram compares and contrasts two substances made from carbon.

Venn Diagram To illustrate how two subjects compare and contrast you can use a Venn diagram. You can see the characteristics that the subjects have in common and those that they do not, shown in **Figure 7.**

To create a Venn diagram, draw two overlapping ovals that that are big enough to write in. List the characteristics unique to one subject in one oval, and the characteristics of the other subject in the other oval. The characteristics in common are listed in the overlapping section.

Make and Use Tables One way to organize information so it is easier to understand is to use a table. Tables can contain numbers, words, or both.

To make a table, list the items to be compared in the first column and the characteristics to be compared in the first row. The title should clearly indicate the content of the table, and the column or row heads should be clear. Notice that in **Table 1** the units are included.

Table 1 Recyclables Collected During Week

Day of Week	Paper (kg)	Aluminum (kg)	Glass (kg)
Monday	5.0	4.0	12.0
Wednesday	4.0	1.0	10.0
Friday	2.5	2.0	10.0

Make a Model One way to help you better understand the parts of a structure, the way a process works, or to show things too large or small for viewing is to make a model. For example, an atomic model made of a plastic-ball nucleus and pipe-cleaner electron shells can help you visualize how the parts of an atom relate to each other. Other types of models can by devised on a computer or represented by equations.

Form a Hypothesis

A possible explanation based on previous knowledge and observations is called a hypothesis. After researching gasoline types and recalling previous experiences in your family's car you form a hypothesis—our car runs more efficiently because we use premium gasoline. To be valid, a hypothesis has to be something you can test by using an investigation.

Predict When you apply a hypothesis to a specific situation, you predict something about that situation. A prediction makes a statement in advance, based on prior observation, experience, or scientific reasoning. People use predictions to make everyday decisions. Scientists test predictions by performing investigations. Based on previous observations and experiences, you might form a prediction that cars are more efficient with premium gasoline. The prediction can be tested in an investigation.

Design an Experiment A scientist needs to make many decisions before beginning an investigation. Some of these include: how to carry out the investigation, what steps to follow, how to record the data, and how the investigation will answer the question. It also is important to address any safety concerns.

Test the Hypothesis

Now that you have formed your hypothesis, you need to test it. Using an investigation, you will make observations and collect data, or information. This data might either support or not support your hypothesis. Scientists collect and organize data as numbers and descriptions.

Follow a Procedure In order to know what materials to use, as well as how and in what order to use them, you must follow a procedure. **Figure 8** shows a procedure you might follow to test your hypothesis.

Procedure

1. Use regular gasoline for two weeks.
2. Record the number of kilometers between fill-ups and the amount of gasoline used.
3. Switch to premium gasoline for two weeks.
4. Record the number of kilometers between fill-ups and the amount of gasoline used.

Figure 8 A procedure tells you what to do step by step.

Identify and Manipulate Variables and Controls In any experiment, it is important to keep everything the same except for the item you are testing. The one factor you change is called the independent variable. The change that results is the dependent variable. Make sure you have only one independent variable, to assure yourself of the cause of the changes you observe in the dependent variable. For example, in your gasoline experiment the type of fuel is the independent variable. The dependent variable is the efficiency.

Many experiments also have a control—an individual instance or experimental subject for which the independent variable is not changed. You can then compare the test results to the control results. To design a control you can have two cars of the same type. The control car uses regular gasoline for four weeks. After you are done with the test, you can compare the experimental results to the control results.

Collect Data

Whether you are carrying out an investigation or a short observational experiment, you will collect data, as shown in **Figure 9.** Scientists collect data as numbers and descriptions and organize it in specific ways.

Observe Scientists observe items and events, then record what they see. When they use only words to describe an observation, it is called qualitative data. Scientists' observations also can describe how much there is of something. These observations use numbers, as well as words, in the description and are called quantitative data. For example, if a sample of the element gold is described as being "shiny and very dense" the data are qualitative. Quantitative data on this sample of gold might include "a mass of 30 g and a density of 19.3 g/cm^3."

Figure 9 Collecting data is one way to gather information directly.

Figure 10 Record data neatly and clearly so it is easy to understand.

When you make observations you should examine the entire object or situation first, and then look carefully for details. It is important to record observations accurately and completely. Always record your notes immediately as you make them, so you do not miss details or make a mistake when recording results from memory. Never put unidentified observations on scraps of paper. Instead they should be recorded in a notebook, like the one in **Figure 10.** Write your data neatly so you can easily read it later. At each point in the experiment, record your observations and label them. That way, you will not have to determine what the figures mean when you look at your notes later. Set up any tables that you will need to use ahead of time, so you can record any observations right away. Remember to avoid bias when collecting data by not including personal thoughts when you record observations. Record only what you observe.

Estimate Scientific work also involves estimating. To estimate is to make a judgment about the size or the number of something without measuring or counting. This is important when the number or size of an object or population is too large or too difficult to accurately count or measure.

Sample Scientists may use a sample or a portion of the total number as a type of estimation. To sample is to take a small, representative portion of the objects or organisms of a population for research. By making careful observations or manipulating variables within that portion of the group, information is discovered and conclusions are drawn that might apply to the whole population. A poorly chosen sample can be unrepresentative of the whole. If you were trying to determine the rainfall in an area, it would not be best to take a rainfall sample from under a tree.

Measure You use measurements everyday. Scientists also take measurements when collecting data. When taking measurements, it is important to know how to use measuring tools properly. Accuracy also is important.

Length To measure length, the distance between two points, scientists use meters. Smaller measurements might be measured in centimeters or millimeters.

Length is measured using a metric ruler or meter stick. When using a metric ruler, line up the 0-cm mark with the end of the object being measured and read the number of the unit where the object ends. Look at the metric ruler shown in **Figure 11.** The centimeter lines are the long, numbered lines, and the shorter lines are millimeter lines. In this instance, the length would be 4.50 cm.

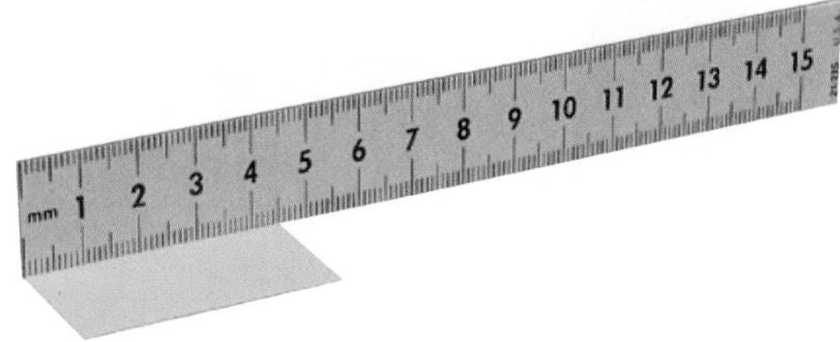

Figure 11 This metric ruler has centimeter and millimeter divisions.

Mass The SI unit for mass is the kilogram (kg). Scientists can measure mass using units formed by adding metric prefixes to the unit gram (g), such as milligram (mg). To measure mass, you might use a triple-beam balance similar to the one shown in **Figure 12.** The balance has a pan on one side and a set of beams on the other side. Each beam has a rider that slides on the beam.

When using a triple-beam balance, place an object on the pan. Slide the largest rider along its beam until the pointer drops below zero. Then move it back one notch. Repeat the process for each rider proceeding from the larger to smaller until the pointer swings an equal distance above and below the zero point. Sum the masses on each beam to find the mass of the object. Move all riders back to zero when finished.

Instead of putting materials directly on the balance, scientists often take a tare of a container. A tare is the mass of a container into which objects or substances are placed for measuring their masses. To mass objects or substances, find the mass of a clean container. Remove the container from the pan, and place the object or substances in the container. Find the mass of the container with the materials in it. Subtract the mass of the empty container from the mass of the filled container to find the mass of the materials you are using.

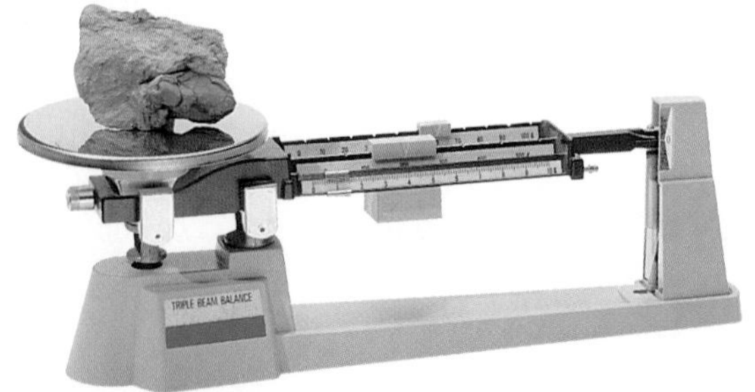

Figure 12 A triple-beam balance is used to determine the mass of an object.

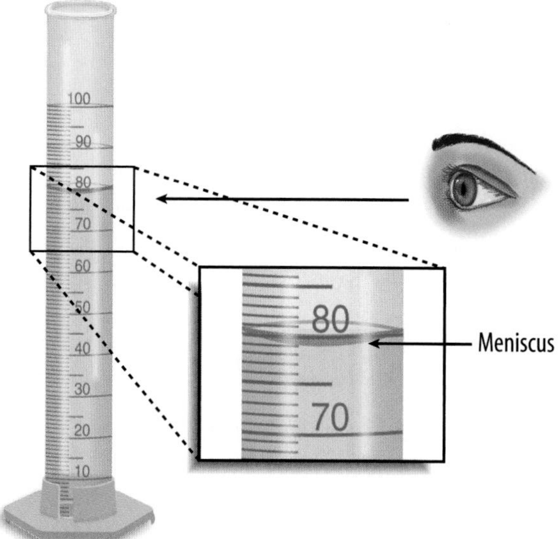

Figure 13 Graduated cylinders measure liquid volume.

Liquid Volume To measure liquids, the unit used is the liter. When a smaller unit is needed, scientists might use a milliliter. Because a milliliter takes up the volume of a cube measuring 1 cm on each side it also can be called a cubic centimeter ($cm^3 = cm \times cm \times cm$).

You can use beakers and graduated cylinders to measure liquid volume. A graduated cylinder, shown in **Figure 13,** is marked from bottom to top in milliliters. In lab, you might use a 10-mL graduated cylinder or a 100-mL graduated cylinder. When measuring liquids, notice that the liquid has a curved surface. Look at the surface at eye level, and measure the bottom of the curve. This is called the meniscus. The graduated cylinder in **Figure 13** contains 79.0 mL, or 79.0 cm^3, of a liquid.

Temperature Scientists often measure temperature using the Celsius scale. Pure water has a freezing point of 0°C and boiling point of 100°C. The unit of measurement is degrees Celsius. Two other scales often used are the Fahrenheit and Kelvin scales.

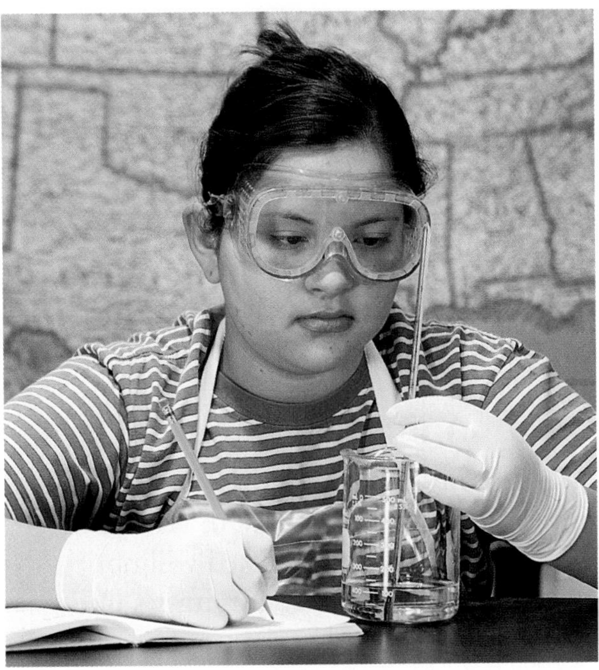

Figure 14 A thermometer measures the temperature of an object.

Scientists use a thermometer to measure temperature. Most thermometers in a laboratory are glass tubes with a bulb at the bottom end containing a liquid such as colored alcohol. The liquid rises or falls with a change in temperature. To read a glass thermometer like the thermometer in **Figure 14,** rotate it slowly until a red line appears. Read the temperature where the red line ends.

Form Operational Definitions An operational definition defines an object by how it functions, works, or behaves. For example, when you are playing hide and seek and a tree is home base, you have created an operational definition for a tree.

Objects can have more than one operational definition. For example, a ruler can be defined as a tool that measures the length of an object (how it is used). It can also be a tool with a series of marks used as a standard when measuring (how it works).

Analyze the Data

To determine the meaning of your observations and investigation results, you will need to look for patterns in the data. Then you must think critically to determine what the data mean. Scientists use several approaches when they analyze the data they have collected and recorded. Each approach is useful for identifying specific patterns.

Interpret Data The word *interpret* means "to explain the meaning of something." When analyzing data from an experiement, try to find out what the data show. Identify the control group and the test group to see whether or not changes in the independent variable have had an effect. Look for differences in the dependent variable between the control and test groups.

Classify Sorting objects or events into groups based on common features is called classifying. When classifying, first observe the objects or events to be classified. Then select one feature that is shared by some members in the group, but not by all. Place those members that share that feature in a subgroup. You can classify members into smaller and smaller subgroups based on characteristics. Remember that when you classify, you are grouping objects or events for a purpose. Keep your purpose in mind as you select the features to form groups and subgroups.

Compare and Contrast Observations can be analyzed by noting the similarities and differences between two more objects or events that you observe. When you look at objects or events to see how they are similar, you are comparing them. Contrasting is looking for differences in objects or events.

Science Skill Handbook

Recognize Cause and Effect A cause is a reason for an action or condition. The effect is that action or condition. When two events happen together, it is not necessarily true that one event caused the other. Scientists must design a controlled investigation to recognize the exact cause and effect.

Draw Conclusions

When scientists have analyzed the data they collected, they proceed to draw conclusions about the data. These conclusions are sometimes stated in words similar to the hypothesis that you formed earlier. They may confirm a hypothesis, or lead you to a new hypothesis.

Infer Scientists often make inferences based on their observations. An inference is an attempt to explain observations or to indicate a cause. An inference is not a fact, but a logical conclusion that needs further investigation. For example, you may infer that a fire has caused smoke. Until you investigate, however, you do not know for sure.

Apply When you draw a conclusion, you must apply those conclusions to determine whether the data supports the hypothesis. If your data do not support your hypothesis, it does not mean that the hypothesis is wrong. It means only that the result of the investigation did not support the hypothesis. Maybe the experiment needs to be redesigned, or some of the initial observations on which the hypothesis was based were incomplete or biased. Perhaps more observation or research is needed to refine your hypothesis. A successful investigation does not always come out the way you originally predicted.

Avoid Bias Sometimes a scientific investigation involves making judgments. When you make a judgment, you form an opinion. It is important to be honest and not to allow any expectations of results to bias your judgments. This is important throughout the entire investigation, from researching to collecting data to drawing conclusions.

Communicate

The communication of ideas is an important part of the work of scientists. A discovery that is not reported will not advance the scientific community's understanding or knowledge. Communication among scientists also is important as a way of improving their investigations.

Scientists communicate in many ways, from writing articles in journals and magazines that explain their investigations and experiments, to announcing important discoveries on television and radio. Scientists also share ideas with colleagues on the Internet or present them as lectures, like the student is doing in **Figure 15.**

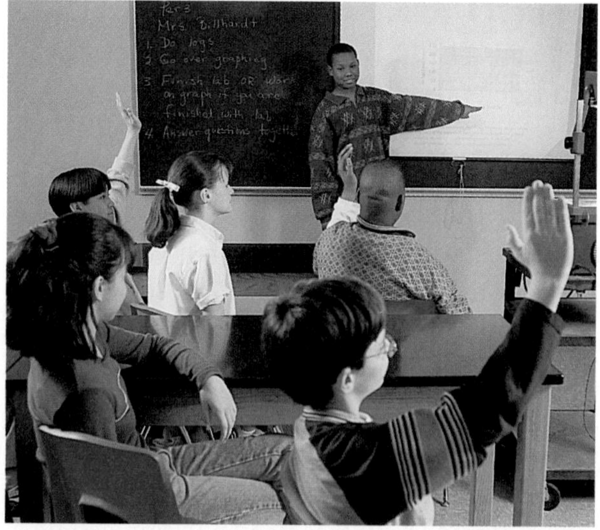

Figure 15 A student communicates to his peers about his investigation.

SAFETY SYMBOLS	HAZARD	EXAMPLES	PRECAUTION	REMEDY
DISPOSAL	Special disposal procedures need to be followed.	certain chemicals, living organisms	Do not dispose of these materials in the sink or trash can.	Dispose of wastes as directed by your teacher.
BIOLOGICAL	Organisms or other biological materials that might be harmful to humans	bacteria, fungi, blood, unpreserved tissues, plant materials	Avoid skin contact with these materials. Wear mask or gloves.	Notify your teacher if you suspect contact with material. Wash hands thoroughly.
EXTREME TEMPERATURE	Objects that can burn skin by being too cold or too hot	boiling liquids, hot plates, dry ice, liquid nitrogen	Use proper protection when handling.	Go to your teacher for first aid.
SHARP OBJECT	Use of tools or glassware that can easily puncture or slice skin	razor blades, pins, scalpels, pointed tools, dissecting probes, broken glass	Practice common-sense behavior and follow guidelines for use of the tool.	Go to your teacher for first aid.
FUME	Possible danger to respiratory tract from fumes	ammonia, acetone, nail polish remover, heated sulfur, moth balls	Make sure there is good ventilation. Never smell fumes directly. Wear a mask.	Leave foul area and notify your teacher immediately.
ELECTRICAL	Possible danger from electrical shock or burn	improper grounding, liquid spills, short circuits, exposed wires	Double-check setup with teacher. Check condition of wires and apparatus.	Do not attempt to fix electrical problems. Notify your teacher immediately.
IRRITANT	Substances that can irritate the skin or mucous membranes of the respiratory tract	pollen, moth balls, steel wool, fiberglass, potassium permanganate	Wear dust mask and gloves. Practice extra care when handling these materials.	Go to your teacher for first aid.
CHEMICAL	Chemicals can react with and destroy tissue and other materials	bleaches such as hydrogen peroxide; acids such as sulfuric acid, hydrochloric acid; bases such as ammonia, sodium hydroxide	Wear goggles, gloves, and an apron.	Immediately flush the affected area with water and notify your teacher.
TOXIC	Substance may be poisonous if touched, inhaled, or swallowed.	mercury, many metal compounds, iodine, poinsettia plant parts	Follow your teacher's instructions.	Always wash hands thoroughly after use. Go to your teacher for first aid.
FLAMMABLE	Flammable chemicals may be ignited by open flame, spark, or exposed heat.	alcohol, kerosene, potassium permanganate	Avoid open flames and heat when using flammable chemicals.	Notify your teacher immediately. Use fire safety equipment if applicable.
OPEN FLAME	Open flame in use, may cause fire.	hair, clothing, paper, synthetic materials	Tie back hair and loose clothing. Follow teacher's instruction on lighting and extinguishing flames.	Notify your teacher immediately. Use fire safety equipment if applicable.

Eye Safety
Proper eye protection should be worn at all times by anyone performing or observing science activities.

Clothing Protection
This symbol appears when substances could stain or burn clothing.

Animal Safety
This symbol appears when safety of animals and students must be ensured.

Handwashing
After the lab, wash hands with soap and water before removing goggles.

Safety in the Science Laboratory

The science laboratory is a safe place to work if you follow standard safety procedures. Being responsible for your own safety helps to make the entire laboratory a safer place for everyone. When performing any lab, read and apply the caution statements and safety symbol listed at the beginning of the lab.

General Safety Rules

1. Obtain your teacher's permission to begin all investigations and use laboratory equipment.
2. Study the procedure. Ask your teacher any questions. Be sure you understand safety symbols shown on the page.
3. Notify your teacher about allergies or other health conditions which can affect your participation in a lab.
4. Learn and follow use and safety procedures for your equipment. If unsure, ask your teacher.

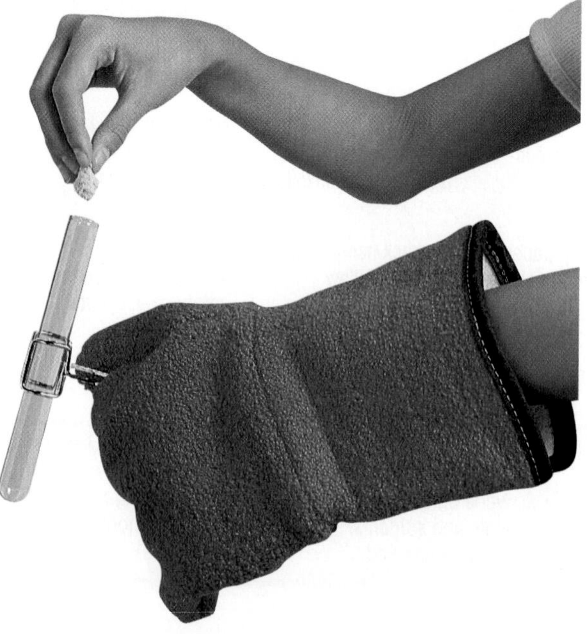

5. Never eat, drink, chew gum, apply cosmetics, or do any personal grooming in the lab. Never use lab glassware as food or drink containers. Keep your hands away from your face and mouth.
6. Know the location and proper use of the safety shower, eye wash, fire blanket, and fire alarm.

Prevent Accidents

1. Use the safety equipment provided to you. Goggles and a safety apron should be worn during investigations.
2. Do NOT use hair spray, mousse, or other flammable hair products. Tie back long hair and tie down loose clothing.
3. Do NOT wear sandals or other open-toed shoes in the lab.
4. Remove jewelry on hands and wrists. Loose jewelry, such as chains and long necklaces, should be removed to prevent them from getting caught in equipment.
5. Do not taste any substances or draw any material into a tube with your mouth.
6. Proper behavior is expected in the lab. Practical jokes and fooling around can lead to accidents and injury.
7. Keep your work area uncluttered.

Laboratory Work

1. Collect and carry all equipment and materials to your work area before beginning a lab.
2. Remain in your own work area unless given permission by your teacher to leave it.

3. Always slant test tubes away from yourself and others when heating them, adding substances to them, or rinsing them.
4. If instructed to smell a substance in a container, hold the container a short distance away and fan vapors towards your nose.
5. Do NOT substitute other chemicals/substances for those in the materials list unless instructed to do so by your teacher.
6. Do NOT take any materials or chemicals outside of the laboratory.
7. Stay out of storage areas unless instructed to be there and supervised by your teacher.

Laboratory Cleanup

1. Turn off all burners, water, and gas, and disconnect all electrical devices.
2. Clean all pieces of equipment and return all materials to their proper places.
3. Dispose of chemicals and other materials as directed by your teacher. Place broken glass and solid substances in the proper containers. Never discard materials in the sink.
4. Clean your work area.
5. Wash your hands with soap and water thoroughly BEFORE removing your goggles.

Emergencies

1. Report any fire, electrical shock, glassware breakage, spill, or injury, no matter how small, to your teacher immediately. Follow his or her instructions.
2. If your clothing should catch fire, STOP, DROP, and ROLL. If possible, smother it with the fire blanket or get under a safety shower. NEVER RUN.
3. If a fire should occur, turn off all gas and leave the room according to established procedures.
4. In most instances, your teacher will clean up spills. Do NOT attempt to clean up spills unless you are given permission and instructions to do so.
5. If chemicals come into contact with your eyes or skin, notify your teacher immediately. Use the eyewash or flush your skin or eyes with large quantities of water.
6. The fire extinguisher and first-aid kit should only be used by your teacher unless it is an extreme emergency and you have been given permission.
7. If someone is injured or becomes ill, only a professional medical provider or someone certified in first aid should perform first-aid procedures.

 Your Daily Drink

Time required one day (no class time)

Materials
- Purchase inexpensive measuring cups at a discount department store.
- Students can make inexpensive measuring cups by using a new graduated cylinder to fill up a clear plastic cup 50 mL at a time. They can mark the 50 mL increments on the outside of the cup with a permanent marker.

Safety Precaution Students should make certain their measuring cups are clean and have never contained toxic substances.

Teaching Strategy Students can convert the number of milliliters of liquid they drank in one day to liters by dividing their total number of milliliters by 1,000.

Conclude and Apply
1. Answers should include the units of milliliters or liters.
2. The mass in grams of individually wrapped foods is printed on the packaging, and a balance could be used to measure the mass of fresh foods or foods poured from a larger container.

EXTRA Try at Home Labs

From Your Kitchen, Junk Drawer, or Yard

1 Your Daily Drink

Real-World Question
How much liquid do you consume in a day?

Possible Materials
- 500-mL measuring cup
- calculator

Procedure
1. When you drink a bottle or can of juice, soda, water, or other beverage, look on the label of the container to find the volume in milliliters.
2. Record the volumes of all the canned and bottled drinks you consume in one day in your Science Journal.
3. Use a measuring cup to measure the liquids that you pour from larger containers. Record these volumes in your Science Journal.
4. Add up the volumes of all the drinks you consumed during the day.

Conclude and Apply
1. How much liquid did you drink during the day?
2. Infer how you would measure the mass of the foods you ate in one day.

2 Cell Sizes

Real-World Question
How do different cells compare in size?

Possible Materials
- meterstick
- metric ruler
- white paper
- pencil
- pen
- masking tape

Procedure
1. Make a dot on a white sheet of paper with a pencil.
2. Use a metric ruler to make a second dot 1 mm away from the first dot. This distance represents the average length of a bacteria cell.
3. Measure a distance 8 mm away from the first dot and make a third dot. This distance represents the average length of a red blood cell.
4. Mark a spot on the floor with a piece of tape and use the meterstick to measure a distance of 7 m. Mark this distance with a second piece of tape. This distance represents the average length of an amoeba cell.

Conclude and Apply
1. The distance between the first and second dot is 1,000 times longer than the actual size of a bacterium cell. Calculate the length of an actual bacterium cell.
2. A large chicken egg is just one cell, and it is 100 times longer than an amoeba cell. Using your measurement from step 4, calculate the distance you would have to measure to represent the average length of a hen's egg.

Adult supervision required for all labs.

These labs are available at booka.msscience.com.

 Cell Sizes

Time required 15 minutes

Materials Students can complete this lab by using only metersticks.

Safety Precaution Caution students to use metersticks with care. Metal metersticks bend easily and can harm others if used carelessly.

Teaching Strategies
- Clear away space on the classroom floor for this lab or have students complete it outside.
- Students can research the length of other types of cells and measure their relative distances on the white sheet of paper or on the floor.

Conclude and Apply
1. 0.001 mm or 1 micrometer
2. 700 m

3 Expanding Eggs

Real-World Question

How can you observe liquids passing through a cell membrane?

Possible Materials

- glass jar with lid
- white vinegar
- medium chicken egg
- tape measure or string and ruler
- tongs
- measuring cup

Procedure

1. Obtain a glass jar with a lid and a medium egg.
2. Make certain your egg easily fits into your jar.
3. Measure the circumference of your egg.
4. Pour 250 mL of white vinegar into the jar.
5. Carefully place your egg in the jar so that it is submerged in the vinegar. Be careful not to crack or break the egg.
6. Observe your egg each day for three days. Measure the circumference of the egg after three days.

Conclude and Apply

1. Describe the changes that happened to your egg.
2. Infer why the egg's circumference changed. *HINT: A hen's egg is a single cell.*

4 Putting Down Roots

Real-World Question

Can cells from a plant's stem produce root cells for a new plant?

Possible Materials

- houseplant
- scissors
- metric ruler
- glasses or jars (3)
- water
- magnifying lens

Procedure

1. Examine the stems of a houseplant, such as *Pothos,* and locate a node on three different stems. A node looks like a small bump.
2. Cut 3 stems off the plant at a 45° angle about 3–4 mm below the node.
3. Place the end of each stem into a separate glass of water and observe them for a week.

Conclude and Apply

1. Describe what happened to the ends of the stems.
2. Infer how plant stem cells can produce root cells.

Adult supervision required for all labs.

3 Expanding Eggs

Time Required five minutes for set-up; five-minute observation periods for three days

Materials

- Make certain the egg will fit into the jar both before and after the lab is completed. Avoid using large or extra large eggs.
- Spaghetti sauce or pickle jars work well for this lab.
- Students also can measure egg circumferences with lengths of string and metric rulers.

Safety Precaution

Students should wash their hands thoroughly after handling eggs.

Teaching Strategy The eggshell is made of calcium carbonate and has the same chemical composition as limestone. Vinegar dissolves the calcium carbonate, producing bubbles of carbon dioxide during the reaction.

Conclude and Apply

1. The egg's shell will dissolve. The outer membrane of the egg will become rubbery, and the egg will increase in circumference by about 15 percent.
2. The water in the vinegar passes through the membrane of the egg cell expanding the egg's size. The particles inside the egg are too large to move out through the membrane.

4 Putting Down Roots

Time Required several two-to-three minute observation periods for a week

Materials The plant roots will grow more quickly when dipped in rooting hormone, but the hormone is not necessary to complete the lab.

Safety Precaution Students should wash their hands thoroughly after the lab.

Teaching Strategies

- Not all the cuttings will grow roots. Roots will be more easily visible when viewed under a hand lens.
- Consider having students plant their cuttings in soil once roots have grown.

Conclude and Apply

1. Tiny roots should grow on one or more stems.
2. Flowers and buds consume energy for growth. Cuttings can conserve more energy without them.
3. The DNA of each plant cell contains all the information needed to make every type of plant cell.

5 Do Your Ears Hang Low?

Time Required 25 minutes (additional time out of class may be needed)

Material Consider supplying students with clipboards to use when interviewing other classmates.

Safety Precaution Caution students to be polite and respectful when they interview people.

Teaching Strategy To gather a large sample, students can interview friends and family members before class and then interview each other during class.

Conclude and Apply

1. Answers will vary but about 70 to 90 percent of people have free earlobes.
2. Free earlobes is a dominant trait.
3. Since both parents carry a recessive gene for attached earlobes, none of the children will have free earlobes.

Extra Try at Home Labs

Extra Try at Home Labs

5 Do your ears hang low?

Real-World Question

Is ear lobe attachment a dominant or recessive trait?

Possible Materials
- Science Journal
- pencil
- pen
- calculator

Procedure

1. Ask your friends, family members, and other people you know if their ear lobes are attached or free.
2. Try to interview as many people as possible to collect a large sample of data.
3. Record the number of people who have attached ear lobes and the number with free ear lobes in your Science Journal.

Conclude and Apply

1. Calculate the percentage of people who have attached ear lobes and the percentage of people who have free ear lobes.
2. Infer whether or not attached ear lobes is a dominant or recessive trait. Do research to confirm your results.
3. Infer how many children in a family would have free ear lobes if their parents had attached ear lobes.

6 Frozen Fossils

Real-World Question

How can we model the formation of an amber fossil?

Possible Materials 
- small glass jar with lid
- honey
- ruler
- dead insect or spider or small rubber insect or spider
- freezer

Procedure

1. Thoroughly wash and dry a small glass jar and its lid.
2. Pour 3 cm of honey into the jar. Do not pour honey down the sides of the jar.
3. Search for a dead insect or spider around your home or school and drop it into the center of the honey's surface.
4. Pour another 3 cm of honey into the jar to cover the organism.
5. Place the jar in the freezer overnight.

Conclude and Apply

1. Explain how you modeled the formation of an amber fossil.
2. Infer how amber fossils help scientists observe adaptations of organisms over time.

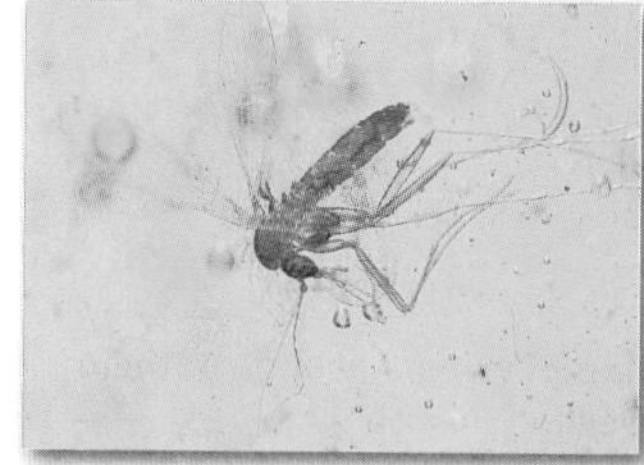

Adult supervision required for all labs.

These labs are available at booka.msscience.com.

6 Frozen Fossils

Time Required 20 minutes

Materials

- Baby food jars work best for this lab.
- Encourage students to search windowsills for dead insects and spiders.
- Clear away space in the classroom freezer for the jars.

Safety Precaution Students should thoroughly wash their hands after handling the insects.

Teaching Strategy Set up a display of the amber fossil models for your class and group the fossils by taxonomic phyla and classes.

Conclude and Apply

1. Amber fossils formed when insects became trapped and covered in tree sap. Over time, the tree sap hardened into amber. The freezing honey modeled the hardening of tree sap.
2. These fossils can be compared with modern day descendents of the organisms.

Computer Skills

People who study science rely on computers, like the one in **Figure 16,** to record and store data and to analyze results from investigations. Whether you work in a laboratory or just need to write a lab report with tables, good computer skills are a necessity.

Using the computer comes with responsibility. Issues of ownership, security, and privacy can arise. Remember, if you did not author the information you are using, you must provide a source for your information. Also, anything on a computer can be accessed by others. Do not put anything on the computer that you would not want everyone to know. To add more security to your work, use a password.

Use a Word Processing Program

A computer program that allows you to type your information, change it as many times as you need to, and then print it out is called a word processing program. Word processing programs also can be used to make tables.

Figure 16 A computer will make reports neater and more professional looking.

Learn the Skill To start your word processing program, a blank document, sometimes called "Document 1," appears on the screen. To begin, start typing. To create a new document, click the *New* button on the standard tool bar. These tips will help you format the document.

- The program will automatically move to the next line; press *Enter* if you wish to start a new paragraph.
- Symbols, called non-printing characters, can be hidden by clicking the *Show/Hide* button on your toolbar.
- To insert text, move the cursor to the point where you want the insertion to go, click on the mouse once, and type the text.
- To move several lines of text, select the text and click the *Cut* button on your toolbar. Then position your cursor in the location that you want to move the cut text and click *Paste.* If you move to the wrong place, click *Undo.*
- The spell check feature does not catch words that are misspelled to look like other words, like "cold" instead of "gold." Always reread your document to catch all spelling mistakes.
- To learn about other word processing methods, read the user's manual or click on the *Help* button.
- You can integrate databases, graphics, and spreadsheets into documents by copying from another program and pasting it into your document, or by using desktop publishing (DTP). DTP software allows you to put text and graphics together to finish your document with a professional look. This software varies in how it is used and its capabilities.

Use a Database

A collection of facts stored in a computer and sorted into different fields is called a database. A database can be reorganized in any way that suits your needs.

Learn the Skill A computer program that allows you to create your own database is a database management system (DBMS). It allows you to add, delete, or change information. Take time to get to know the features of your database software.

- Determine what facts you would like to include and research to collect your information.
- Determine how you want to organize the information.
- Follow the instructions for your particular DBMS to set up fields. Then enter each item of data in the appropriate field.
- Follow the instructions to sort the information in order of importance.
- Evaluate the information in your database, and add, delete, or change as necessary.

Use the Internet

The Internet is a global network of computers where information is stored and shared. To use the Internet, like the students in **Figure 17,** you need a modem to connect your computer to a phone line and an Internet Service Provider account.

Learn the Skill To access internet sites and information, use a "Web browser," which lets you view and explore pages on the World Wide Web. Each page is its own site, and each site has its own address, called a URL. Once you have found a Web browser, follow these steps for a search (this also is how you search a database).

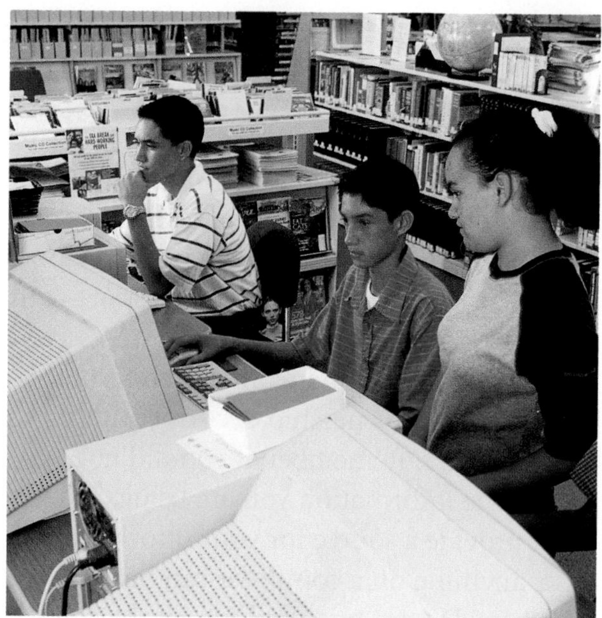

Figure 17 The Internet allows you to search a global network for a variety of information.

- Be as specific as possible. If you know you want to research "gold," don't type in "elements." Keep narrowing your search until you find what you want.
- Web sites that end in *.com* are commercial Web sites; *.org*, *.edu*, and *.gov* are non-profit, educational, or government Web sites.
- Electronic encyclopedias, almanacs, indexes, and catalogs will help locate and select relevant information.
- Develop a "home page" with relative ease. When developing a Web site, NEVER post pictures or disclose personal information such as location, names, or phone numbers. Your school or community usually can host your Web site. A basic understanding of HTML (hypertext mark-up language), the language of Web sites, is necessary. Software that creates HTML code is called authoring software, and can be downloaded free from many Web sites. This software allows text and pictures to be arranged as the software is writing the HTML code.

Use a Spreadsheet

A spreadsheet, shown in **Figure 18,** can perform mathematical functions with any data arranged in columns and rows. By entering a simple equation into a cell, the program can perform operations in specific cells, rows, or columns.

Learn the Skill Each column (vertical) is assigned a letter, and each row (horizontal) is assigned a number. Each point where a row and column intersect is called a cell, and is labeled according to where it is located—Column A, Row 1 (A1).

- Decide how to organize the data, and enter it in the correct row or column.
- Spreadsheets can use standard formulas or formulas can be customized to calculate cells.
- To make a change, click on a cell to make it activate, and enter the edited data or formula.
- Spreadsheets also can display your results in graphs. Choose the style of graph that best represents the data.

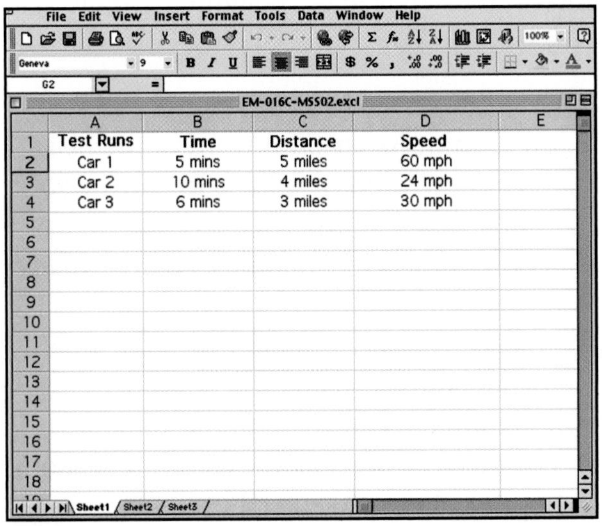

	A	B	C	D	E
1	Test Runs	Time	Distance	Speed	
2	Car 1	5 mins	5 miles	60 mph	
3	Car 2	10 mins	4 miles	24 mph	
4	Car 3	6 mins	3 miles	30 mph	

Figure 18 A spreadsheet allows you to perform mathematical operations on your data.

Use Graphics Software

Adding pictures, called graphics, to your documents is one way to make your documents more meaningful and exciting. This software adds, edits, and even constructs graphics. There is a variety of graphics software programs. The tools used for drawing can be a mouse, keyboard, or other specialized devices. Some graphics programs are simple. Others are complicated, called computer-aided design (CAD) software.

Learn the Skill It is important to have an understanding of the graphics software being used before starting. The better the software is understood, the better the results. The graphics can be placed in word-processing document.

- Clip art can be found on a variety of internet sites, and on CDs. These images can be copied and pasted into your document.
- When beginning, try editing existing drawings, then work up to creating drawings.
- The images are made of tiny rectangles of color called pixels. Each pixel can be altered.
- Digital photography is another way to add images. The photographs in the memory of a digital camera can be downloaded into a computer, then edited and added to the document.
- Graphics software also can allow animation. The software allows drawings to have the appearance of movement by connecting basic drawings automatically. This is called in-betweening, or tweening.
- Remember to save often.

Presentation Skills

Develop Multimedia Presentations

Most presentations are more dynamic if they include diagrams, photographs, videos, or sound recordings, like the one shown in **Figure 19.** A multimedia presentation involves using stereos, overhead projectors, televisions, computers, and more.

Learn the Skill Decide the main points of your presentation, and what types of media would best illustrate those points.

- Make sure you know how to use the equipment you are working with.
- Practice the presentation using the equipment several times.
- Enlist the help of a classmate to push play or turn lights out for you. Be sure to practice your presentation with him or her.
- If possible, set up all of the equipment ahead of time, and make sure everything is working properly.

Figure 19 These students are engaging the audience using a variety of tools.

Computer Presentations

There are many different interactive computer programs that you can use to enhance your presentation. Most computers have a compact disc (CD) drive that can play both CDs and digital video discs (DVDs). Also, there is hardware to connect a regular CD, DVD, or VCR. These tools will enhance your presentation.

Another method of using the computer to aid in your presentation is to develop a slide show using a computer program. This can allow movement of visuals at the presenter's pace, and can allow for visuals to build on one another.

Learn the Skill In order to create multimedia presentations on a computer, you need to have certain tools. These may include traditional graphic tools and drawing programs, animation programs, and authoring systems that tie everything together. Your computer will tell you which tools it supports. The most important step is to learn about the tools that you will be using.

- Often, color and strong images will convey a point better than words alone. Use the best methods available to convey your point.
- As with other presentations, practice many times.
- Practice your presentation with the tools you and any assistants will be using.
- Maintain eye contact with the audience. The purpose of using the computer is not to prompt the presenter, but to help the audience understand the points of the presentation.

Math Review

Use Fractions

A fraction compares a part to a whole. In the fraction $\frac{2}{3}$, the 2 represents the part and is the numerator. The 3 represents the whole and is the denominator.

Reduce Fractions To reduce a fraction, you must find the largest factor that is common to both the numerator and the denominator, the greatest common factor (GCF). Divide both numbers by the GCF. The fraction has then been reduced, or it is in its simplest form.

Example Twelve of the 20 chemicals in the science lab are in powder form. What fraction of the chemicals used in the lab are in powder form?

Step 1 Write the fraction.

$$\frac{\text{part}}{\text{whole}} = \frac{12}{20}$$

Step 2 To find the GCF of the numerator and denominator, list all of the factors of each number.

Factors of 12: 1, 2, 3, 4, 6, 12 (the numbers that divide evenly into 12)

Factors of 20: 1, 2, 4, 5, 10, 20 (the numbers that divide evenly into 20)

Step 3 List the common factors.

1, 2, 4.

Step 4 Choose the greatest factor in the list.

The GCF of 12 and 20 is 4.

Step 5 Divide the numerator and denominator by the GCF.

$$\frac{12 \div 4}{20 \div 4} = \frac{3}{5}$$

In the lab, $\frac{3}{5}$ of the chemicals are in powder form.

Practice Problem At an amusement park, 66 of 90 rides have a height restriction. What fraction of the rides, in its simplest form, has a height restriction?

Add and Subtract Fractions To add or subtract fractions with the same denominator, add or subtract the numerators and write the sum or difference over the denominator. After finding the sum or difference, find the simplest form for your fraction.

Example 1 In the forest outside your house, $\frac{1}{8}$ of the animals are rabbits, $\frac{3}{8}$ are squirrels, and the remainder are birds and insects. How many are mammals?

Step 1 Add the numerators.

$$\frac{1}{8} + \frac{3}{8} = \frac{(1 + 3)}{8} = \frac{4}{8}$$

Step 2 Find the GCF.

$$\frac{4}{8} \text{ (GCF, 4)}$$

Step 3 Divide the numerator and denominator by the GCF.

$$\frac{4}{4} = 1, \ \frac{8}{4} = 2$$

$\frac{1}{2}$ of the animals are mammals.

Example 2 If $\frac{7}{16}$ of the Earth is covered by freshwater, and $\frac{1}{16}$ of that is in glaciers, how much freshwater is not frozen?

Step 1 Subtract the numerators.

$$\frac{7}{16} - \frac{1}{16} = \frac{(7 - 1)}{16} = \frac{6}{16}$$

Step 2 Find the GCF.

$$\frac{6}{16} \text{ (GCF, 2)}$$

Step 3 Divide the numerator and denominator by the GCF.

$$\frac{6}{2} = 3, \ \frac{16}{2} = 8$$

$\frac{3}{8}$ of the freshwater is not frozen.

Practice Problem A bicycle rider is going 15 km/h for $\frac{4}{9}$ of his ride, 10 km/h for $\frac{2}{9}$ of his ride, and 8 km/h for the remainder of the ride. How much of his ride is he going over 8 km/h?

Reduce Fractions

$$\frac{66 \div 6}{90 \div 6} = \frac{11}{15}$$

Add and Subtract Fractions

$$\frac{4}{9} + \frac{2}{9} = \frac{6}{9}$$

$$\frac{6 \div 3}{9 \div 3} = \frac{2}{3}$$

Math Skill Handbook

MATH SKILL HANDBOOK A ◆ 205

Unlike Denominators

Problem 1

$1 \times 5 = 5, 8 \times 5 = 40$

$1 \times 4 = 4, 10 \times 4 = 40$

$\frac{5}{40} + \frac{4}{40} = \frac{9}{40}$

Problem 2

If $\frac{7}{10}$ are involuntary, the remainder are voluntary.

$\frac{10}{10} - \frac{7}{10} = \frac{3}{10}$

Unlike Denominators To add or subtract fractions with unlike denominators, first find the least common denominator (LCD). This is the smallest number that is a common multiple of both denominators. Rename each fraction with the LCD, and then add or subtract. Find the simplest form if necessary.

Example 1 A chemist makes a paste that is $\frac{1}{2}$ table salt (NaCl), $\frac{1}{3}$ sugar ($C_6H_{12}O_6$), and the rest water (H_2O). How much of the paste is a solid?

Step 1 Find the LCD of the fractions.

$\frac{1}{2} + \frac{1}{3}$ (LCD, 6)

Step 2 Rename each numerator and each denominator with the LCD.

$1 \times 3 = 3, \; 2 \times 3 = 6$

$1 \times 2 = 2, \; 3 \times 2 = 6$

Step 3 Add the numerators.

$\frac{3}{6} + \frac{2}{6} = \frac{(3 + 2)}{6} = \frac{5}{6}$

$\frac{5}{6}$ of the paste is a solid.

Example 2 The average precipitation in Grand Junction, CO, is $\frac{7}{10}$ inch in November, and $\frac{3}{5}$ inch in December. What is the total average precipitation?

Step 1 Find the LCD of the fractions.

$\frac{7}{10} + \frac{3}{5}$ (LCD, 10)

Step 2 Rename each numerator and each denominator with the LCD.

$7 \times 1 = 7, \; 10 \times 1 = 10$

$3 \times 2 = 6, \; 5 \times 2 = 10$

Step 3 Add the numerators.

$\frac{7}{10} + \frac{6}{10} = \frac{(7 + 6)}{10} = \frac{13}{10}$

$\frac{13}{10}$ inches total precipitation, or $1\frac{3}{10}$ inches.

Practice Problem On an electric bill, about $\frac{1}{8}$ of the energy is from solar energy and about $\frac{1}{10}$ is from wind power. How much of the total bill is from solar energy and wind power combined?

Example 3 In your body, $\frac{7}{10}$ of your muscle contractions are involuntary (cardiac and smooth muscle tissue). Smooth muscle makes $\frac{3}{15}$ of your muscle contractions. How many of your muscle contractions are made by cardiac muscle?

Step 1 Find the LCD of the fractions.

$\frac{7}{10} - \frac{3}{15}$ (LCD, 30)

Step 2 Rename each numerator and each denominator with the LCD.

$7 \times 3 = 21, \; 10 \times 3 = 30$

$3 \times 2 = 6, \; 15 \times 2 = 30$

Step 3 Subtract the numerators.

$\frac{21}{30} - \frac{6}{30} = \frac{(21 - 6)}{30} = \frac{15}{30}$

Step 4 Find the GCF.

$\frac{15}{30}$ (GCF, 15)

$\frac{1}{2}$

$\frac{1}{2}$ of all muscle contractions are cardiac muscle.

Example 4 Tony wants to make cookies that call for $\frac{3}{4}$ of a cup of flour, but he only has $\frac{1}{3}$ of a cup. How much more flour does he need?

Step 1 Find the LCD of the fractions.

$\frac{3}{4} - \frac{1}{3}$ (LCD, 12)

Step 2 Rename each numerator and each denominator with the LCD.

$3 \times 3 = 9, \; 4 \times 3 = 12$

$1 \times 4 = 4, \; 3 \times 4 = 12$

Step 3 Subtract the numerators.

$\frac{9}{12} - \frac{4}{12} = \frac{(9 - 4)}{12} = \frac{5}{12}$

$\frac{5}{12}$ of a cup of flour.

Practice Problem Using the information provided to you in Example 3 above, determine how many muscle contractions are voluntary (skeletal muscle).

Math Skill Handbook

206 ◆ A STUDENT RESOURCES

Multiply Fractions To multiply with fractions, multiply the numerators and multiply the denominators. Find the simplest form if necessary.

Example Multiply $\frac{3}{5}$ by $\frac{1}{3}$.

Step 1 Multiply the numerators and denominators.

$$\frac{3}{5} \times \frac{1}{3} = \frac{(3 \times 1)}{(5 \times 3)} = \frac{3}{15}$$

Step 2 Find the GCF.

$\frac{3}{15}$ (GCF, 3)

Step 3 Divide the numerator and denominator by the GCF.

$\frac{3}{3} = 1$, $\frac{15}{3} = 5$

$\frac{1}{5}$

$\frac{3}{5}$ multiplied by $\frac{1}{3}$ is $\frac{1}{5}$.

Practice Problem Multiply $\frac{3}{14}$ by $\frac{5}{16}$.

Find a Reciprocal Two numbers whose product is 1 are called multiplicative inverses, or reciprocals.

Example Find the reciprocal of $\frac{3}{8}$.

Step 1 Inverse the fraction by putting the denominator on top and the numerator on the bottom.

$\frac{8}{3}$

The reciprocal of $\frac{3}{8}$ is $\frac{8}{3}$.

Practice Problem Find the reciprocal of $\frac{4}{9}$.

Divide Fractions To divide one fraction by another fraction, multiply the dividend by the reciprocal of the divisor. Find the simplest form if necessary.

Example 1 Divide $\frac{1}{9}$ by $\frac{1}{3}$.

Step 1 Find the reciprocal of the divisor.

The reciprocal of $\frac{1}{3}$ is $\frac{3}{1}$.

Step 2 Multiply the dividend by the reciprocal of the divisor.

$$\frac{\frac{1}{9}}{\frac{1}{3}} = \frac{1}{9} \times \frac{3}{1} = \frac{(1 \times 3)}{(9 \times 1)} = \frac{3}{9}$$

Step 3 Find the GCF.

$\frac{3}{9}$ (GCF, 3)

Step 4 Divide the numerator and denominator by the GCF.

$\frac{3}{3} = 1$, $\frac{9}{3} = 3$

$\frac{1}{3}$

$\frac{1}{9}$ divided by $\frac{1}{3}$ is $\frac{1}{3}$.

Example 2 Divide $\frac{3}{5}$ by $\frac{1}{4}$.

Step 1 Find the reciprocal of the divisor.

The reciprocal of $\frac{1}{4}$ is $\frac{4}{1}$.

Step 2 Multiply the dividend by the reciprocal of the divisor.

$$\frac{\frac{3}{5}}{\frac{1}{4}} = \frac{3}{5} \times \frac{4}{1} = \frac{(3 \times 4)}{(5 \times 1)} = \frac{12}{5}$$

$\frac{3}{5}$ divided by $\frac{1}{4}$ is $\frac{12}{5}$ or $2\frac{2}{5}$.

Practice Problem Divide $\frac{3}{11}$ by $\frac{7}{10}$.

Multiply Fractions

$$\frac{3}{14} \times \frac{5}{16} = \frac{(3 \times 5)}{(14 \times 16)} = \frac{15}{224}$$

Find a Reciprocal

$\frac{9}{4}$

Divide Fractions

The reciprocal of $\frac{7}{10}$ is $\frac{10}{7}$.

$$\frac{3}{11} \times \frac{10}{7} = \frac{(3 \times 10)}{(11 \times 7)} = \frac{30}{77}$$

Math Skill Handbook

MATH SKILL HANDBOOK A ◆ 207

Use Ratios

$$\frac{100\text{ cm}}{144\text{ cm}} = \frac{100 \div 4}{144 \div 4} = \frac{25}{36}$$

25:36

Add or Subtract Decimals

$$\begin{array}{r} {\scriptstyle 1} \\ 1.245 \\ +\,3.842 \\ \hline 5.087 \end{array}$$

Use Ratios

When you compare two numbers by division, you are using a ratio. Ratios can be written 3 to 5, 3:5, or $\frac{3}{5}$. Ratios, like fractions, also can be written in simplest form.

Ratios can represent probabilities, also called odds. This is a ratio that compares the number of ways a certain outcome occurs to the number of outcomes. For example, if you flip a coin 100 times, what are the odds that it will come up heads? There are two possible outcomes, heads or tails, so the odds of coming up heads are 50:100. Another way to say this is that 50 out of 100 times the coin will come up heads. In its simplest form, the ratio is 1:2.

Example 1 A chemical solution contains 40 g of salt and 64 g of baking soda. What is the ratio of salt to baking soda as a fraction in simplest form?

Step 1 Write the ratio as a fraction.

$$\frac{\text{salt}}{\text{baking soda}} = \frac{40}{64}$$

Step 2 Express the fraction in simplest form.

The GCF of 40 and 64 is 8.

$$\frac{40}{64} = \frac{40 \div 8}{64 \div 8} = \frac{5}{8}$$

The ratio of salt to baking soda in the sample is 5:8.

Example 2 Sean rolls a 6-sided die 6 times. What are the odds that the side with a 3 will show?

Step 1 Write the ratio as a fraction.

$$\frac{\text{number of sides with a 3}}{\text{number of sides}} = \frac{1}{6}$$

Step 2 Multiply by the number of attempts.

$$\frac{1}{6} \times 6 \text{ attempts} = \frac{6}{6} \text{ attempts} = 1 \text{ attempt}$$

1 attempt out of 6 will show a 3.

Practice Problem Two metal rods measure 100 cm and 144 cm in length. What is the ratio of their lengths in simplest form?

Use Decimals

A fraction with a denominator that is a power of ten can be written as a decimal. For example, 0.27 means $\frac{27}{100}$. The decimal point separates the ones place from the tenths place.

Any fraction can be written as a decimal using division. For example, the fraction $\frac{5}{8}$ can be written as a decimal by dividing 5 by 8. Written as a decimal, it is 0.625.

Add or Subtract Decimals When adding and subtracting decimals, line up the decimal points before carrying out the operation.

Example 1 Find the sum of 47.68 and 7.80.

Step 1 Line up the decimal places when you write the numbers.

$$\begin{array}{r} 47.68 \\ +\,7.80 \\ \hline \end{array}$$

Step 2 Add the decimals.

$$\begin{array}{r} 47.68 \\ +\,7.80 \\ \hline 55.48 \end{array}$$

The sum of 47.68 and 7.80 is 55.48.

Example 2 Find the difference of 42.17 and 15.85.

Step 1 Line up the decimal places when you write the number.

$$\begin{array}{r} 42.17 \\ -\,15.85 \\ \hline \end{array}$$

Step 2 Subtract the decimals.

$$\begin{array}{r} 42.17 \\ -\,15.85 \\ \hline 26.32 \end{array}$$

The difference of 42.17 and 15.85 is 26.32.

Practice Problem Find the sum of 1.245 and 3.842.

Math Skill Handbook

208 ◆ A STUDENT RESOURCES

Multiply Decimals To multiply decimals, multiply the numbers like any other number, ignoring the decimal point. Count the decimal places in each factor. The product will have the same number of decimal places as the sum of the decimal places in the factors.

Example Multiply 2.4 by 5.9.

Step 1 Multiply the factors like two whole numbers.
$24 \times 59 = 1416$

Step 2 Find the sum of the number of decimal places in the factors. Each factor has one decimal place, for a sum of two decimal places.

Step 3 The product will have two decimal places.
14.16

The product of 2.4 and 5.9 is 14.16.

Practice Problem Multiply 4.6 by 2.2.

Divide Decimals When dividing decimals, change the divisor to a whole number. To do this, multiply both the divisor and the dividend by the same power of ten. Then place the decimal point in the quotient directly above the decimal point in the dividend. Then divide as you do with whole numbers.

Example Divide 8.84 by 3.4.

Step 1 Multiply both factors by 10.
$3.4 \times 10 = 34,\ 8.84 \times 10 = 88.4$

Step 2 Divide 88.4 by 34.

$$\begin{array}{r} 2.6 \\ 34\overline{)88.4} \\ -68 \\ \hline 20\,4 \\ -20\,4 \\ \hline 0 \end{array}$$

8.84 divided by 3.4 is 2.6.

Practice Problem Divide 75.6 by 3.6.

Use Proportions

An equation that shows that two ratios are equivalent is a proportion. The ratios $\frac{2}{4}$ and $\frac{5}{10}$ are equivalent, so they can be written as $\frac{2}{4} = \frac{5}{10}$. This equation is a proportion.

When two ratios form a proportion, the cross products are equal. To find the cross products in the proportion $\frac{2}{4} = \frac{5}{10}$, multiply the 2 and the 10, and the 4 and the 5. Therefore $2 \times 10 = 4 \times 5$, or $20 = 20$.

Because you know that both proportions are equal, you can use cross products to find a missing term in a proportion. This is known as solving the proportion.

Example The heights of a tree and a pole are proportional to the lengths of their shadows. The tree casts a shadow of 24 m when a 6-m pole casts a shadow of 4 m. What is the height of the tree?

Step 1 Write a proportion.
$$\frac{\text{height of tree}}{\text{height of pole}} = \frac{\text{length of tree's shadow}}{\text{length of pole's shadow}}$$

Step 2 Substitute the known values into the proportion. Let h represent the unknown value, the height of the tree.
$$\frac{h}{6} = \frac{24}{4}$$

Step 3 Find the cross products.
$h \times 4 = 6 \times 24$

Step 4 Simplify the equation.
$4h = 144$

Step 5 Divide each side by 4.
$$\frac{4h}{4} = \frac{144}{4}$$
$h = 36$

The height of the tree is 36 m.

Practice Problem The ratios of the weights of two objects on the Moon and on Earth are in proportion. A rock weighing 3 N on the Moon weighs 18 N on Earth. How much would a rock that weighs 5 N on the Moon weigh on Earth?

Math Skill Handbook

Multiply Decimals

Multiply 4.6 and 2.2 by 10.

$46 \times 22 = 1012$

Each factor had one decimal place.

10.12

Divide Decimals

Multiply both factors by 10.

Divide 756 by 36.

$$\begin{array}{r} 21 \\ 36\overline{)756} \\ 72 \\ \hline 36 \\ 36 \\ \hline 0 \end{array}$$

Use Proportions

$$\frac{3}{18} = \frac{5}{w}$$

$w \times 3 = 5 \times 18$

$$\frac{3w}{3} = \frac{90}{3}$$

$w = 30$

Math Skill Handbook

MATH SKILL HANDBOOK A ◆ 209

Use Percentages

$\frac{73}{365} = \frac{x}{100}$

$\frac{7300}{365} = \frac{365x}{365}$

$20\% = x$

Solve One-Step Equations

$h = gd$

$\frac{17.4}{12.3} = \frac{12.3d}{12.3}$

$1.41 = d$

Use Percentages

The word *percent* means "out of one hundred." It is a ratio that compares a number to 100. Suppose you read that 77 percent of the Earth's surface is covered by water. That is the same as reading that the fraction of the Earth's surface covered by water is $\frac{77}{100}$. To express a fraction as a percent, first find the equivalent decimal for the fraction. Then, multiply the decimal by 100 and add the percent symbol.

Example Express $\frac{13}{20}$ as a percent.

Step 1 Find the equivalent decimal for the fraction.

```
   0.65
20)13.00
   12 0
    1 00
    1 00
       0
```

Step 2 Rewrite the fraction $\frac{13}{20}$ as 0.65.

Step 3 Multiply 0.65 by 100 and add the % sign.

$0.65 \times 100 = 65 = 65\%$

So, $\frac{13}{20} = 65\%$.

This also can be solved as a proportion.

Example Express $\frac{13}{20}$ as a percent.

Step 1 Write a proportion.

$\frac{13}{20} = \frac{x}{100}$

Step 2 Find the cross products.

$1300 = 20x$

Step 3 Divide each side by 20.

$\frac{1300}{20} = \frac{20x}{20}$

$65\% = x$

Practice Problem In one year, 73 of 365 days were rainy in one city. What percent of the days in that city were rainy?

Solve One-Step Equations

A statement that two things are equal is an equation. For example, $A = B$ is an equation that states that A is equal to B.

An equation is solved when a variable is replaced with a value that makes both sides of the equation equal. To make both sides equal the inverse operation is used. Addition and subtraction are inverses, and multiplication and division are inverses.

Example 1 Solve the equation $x - 10 = 35$.

Step 1 Find the solution by adding 10 to each side of the equation.

$x - 10 = 35$

$x - 10 + 10 = 35 + 10$

$x = 45$

Step 2 Check the solution.

$x - 10 = 35$

$45 - 10 = 35$

$35 = 35$

Both sides of the equation are equal, so $x = 45$.

Example 2 In the formula $a = bc$, find the value of c if $a = 20$ and $b = 2$.

Step 1 Rearrange the formula so the unknown value is by itself on one side of the equation by dividing both sides by b.

$a = bc$

$\frac{a}{b} = \frac{bc}{b}$

$\frac{a}{b} = c$

Step 2 Replace the variables a and b with the values that are given.

$\frac{a}{b} = c$

$\frac{20}{2} = c$

$10 = c$

Step 3 Check the solution.

$a = bc$

$20 = 2 \times 10$

$20 = 20$

Both sides of the equation are equal, so $c = 10$ is the solution when $a = 20$ and $b = 2$.

Practice Problem In the formula $h = gd$, find the value of d if $g = 12.3$ and $h = 17.4$.

Math Skill Handbook

210 ◆ A STUDENT RESOURCES

Use Statistics

The branch of mathematics that deals with collecting, analyzing, and presenting data is statistics. In statistics, there are three common ways to summarize data with a single number—the mean, the median, and the mode.

The **mean** of a set of data is the arithmetic average. It is found by adding the numbers in the data set and dividing by the number of items in the set.

The **median** is the middle number in a set of data when the data are arranged in numerical order. If there were an even number of data points, the median would be the mean of the two middle numbers.

The **mode** of a set of data is the number or item that appears most often.

Another number that often is used to describe a set of data is the range. The **range** is the difference between the largest number and the smallest number in a set of data.

A **frequency table** shows how many times each piece of data occurs, usually in a survey. **Table 2** below shows the results of a student survey on favorite color.

Table 2 Student Color Choice

Color	Tally	Frequency
red	𝍷𝍷𝍷𝍷	4
blue	𝍸	5
black	𝍷𝍷	2
green	𝍷𝍷𝍷	3
purple	𝍸 𝍷𝍷	7
yellow	𝍸 𝍷	6

Based on the frequency table data, which color is the favorite?

Example The speeds (in m/s) for a race car during five different time trials are 39, 37, 44, 36, and 44.

To find the mean:

Step 1 Find the sum of the numbers.
$39 + 37 + 44 + 36 + 44 = 200$

Step 2 Divide the sum by the number of items, which is 5.
$200 \div 5 = 40$

The mean is 40 m/s.

To find the median:

Step 1 Arrange the measures from least to greatest.
36, 37, 39, 44, 44

Step 2 Determine the middle measure.
36, 37, 39, 44, 44

The median is 39 m/s.

To find the mode:

Step 1 Group the numbers that are the same together.
44, 44, 36, 37, 39

Step 2 Determine the number that occurs most in the set.
44, 44, 36, 37, 39

The mode is 44 m/s.

To find the range:

Step 1 Arrange the measures from largest to smallest.
44, 44, 39, 37, 36

Step 2 Determine the largest and smallest measures in the set.
44, 44, 39, 37, 36

Step 3 Find the difference between the largest and smallest measures.
$44 - 36 = 8$

The range is 8 m/s.

Practice Problem Find the mean, median, mode, and range for the data set 8, 4, 12, 8, 11, 14, 16.

Math Skill Handbook

Use Statistics

mean
$8 + 4 + 12 + 8 + 11 + 14 + 16 = 73$
$73 \div 7 = 10.4$

median
4, 8, 8, 11, 12, 14, 16

mode
4, 8, 8, 11, 12, 14, 16

range
4, 8, 8, 11, 12, 14, 16
$16 - 4 = 12$

Math Skill Handbook

MATH SKILL HANDBOOK A ◆ 211

Perimeter

Problem 1

$P = 2(18 \text{ m} + 7 \text{ m})$

$P = 2(25 \text{ m})$

$P = 50 \text{ m}$

Problem 2

$P = 1.6 \text{ cm} + 2.4 \text{ cm} + 2.4 \text{ cm}$

$P = 6.4 \text{ cm}$

Area of a Rectangle

$A = (4 \text{ m} \times 4 \text{ m})$

$A = 16 \text{ m}^2$

Area of a Triangle

$A = \frac{1}{2}(27 \text{ cm} \times 17 \text{ cm})$

$A = \frac{1}{2}(459 \text{ cm}^2)$

$A = 229.5 \text{ cm}^2$

Math Skill Handbook

Use Geometry

The branch of mathematics that deals with the measurement, properties, and relationships of points, lines, angles, surfaces, and solids is called geometry.

Perimeter The **perimeter** (P) is the distance around a geometric figure. To find the perimeter of a rectangle, add the length and width and multiply that sum by two, or $2(l + w)$. To find perimeters of irregular figures, add the length of the sides.

Example 1 Find the perimeter of a rectangle that is 3 m long and 5 m wide.

Step 1 You know that the perimeter is 2 times the sum of the width and length.
$P = 2(3 \text{ m} + 5 \text{ m})$

Step 2 Find the sum of the width and length.
$P = 2(8 \text{ m})$

Step 3 Multiply by 2.
$P = 16 \text{ m}$

The perimeter is 16 m.

Example 2 Find the perimeter of a shape with sides measuring 2 cm, 5 cm, 6 cm, 3 cm.

Step 1 You know that the perimeter is the sum of all the sides.
$P = 2 + 5 + 6 + 3$

Step 2 Find the sum of the sides.
$P = 2 + 5 + 6 + 3$
$P = 16$

The perimeter is 16 cm.

Practice Problem Find the perimeter of a rectangle with a length of 18 m and a width of 7 m.

Practice Problem Find the perimeter of a triangle measuring 1.6 cm by 2.4 cm by 2.4 cm.

Area of a Rectangle The **area** (A) is the number of square units needed to cover a surface. To find the area of a rectangle, multiply the length times the width, or $l \times w$. When finding area, the units also are multiplied. Area is given in square units.

Example Find the area of a rectangle with a length of 1 cm and a width of 10 cm.

Step 1 You know that the area is the length multiplied by the width.
$A = (1 \text{ cm} \times 10 \text{ cm})$

Step 2 Multiply the length by the width. Also multiply the units.
$A = 10 \text{ cm}^2$

The area is 10 cm^2.

Practice Problem Find the area of a square whose sides measure 4 m.

Area of a Triangle To find the area of a triangle, use the formula:

$$A = \frac{1}{2}(\text{base} \times \text{height})$$

The base of a triangle can be any of its sides. The height is the perpendicular distance from a base to the opposite endpoint, or vertex.

Example Find the area of a triangle with a base of 18 m and a height of 7 m.

Step 1 You know that the area is $\frac{1}{2}$ the base times the height.
$A = \frac{1}{2}(18 \text{ m} \times 7 \text{ m})$

Step 2 Multiply $\frac{1}{2}$ by the product of 18×7. Multiply the units.
$A = \frac{1}{2}(126 \text{ m}^2)$
$A = 63 \text{ m}^2$

The area is 63 m^2.

Practice Problem Find the area of a triangle with a base of 27 cm and a height of 17 cm.

Math Skill Handbook

212 ◆ A STUDENT RESOURCES

Circumference of a Circle The **diameter** (d) of a circle is the distance across the circle through its center, and the **radius** (r) is the distance from the center to any point on the circle. The radius is half of the diameter. The distance around the circle is called the **circumference** (C). The formula for finding the circumference is:

$C = 2\pi r$ *or* $C = \pi d$

The circumference divided by the diameter is always equal to 3.1415926... This nonterminating and nonrepeating number is represented by the Greek letter π (pi). An approximation often used for π is 3.14.

Example 1 Find the circumference of a circle with a radius of 3 m.

Step 1 You know the formula for the circumference is 2 times the radius times π.
$C = 2\pi(3)$

Step 2 Multiply 2 times the radius.
$C = 6\pi$

Step 3 Multiply by π.
$C = 19$ m

The circumference is 19 m.

Example 2 Find the circumference of a circle with a diameter of 24.0 cm.

Step 1 You know the formula for the circumference is the diameter times π.
$C = \pi(24.0)$

Step 2 Multiply the diameter by π.
$C = 75.4$ cm

The circumference is 75.4 cm.

Practice Problem Find the circumference of a circle with a radius of 19 cm.

Area of a Circle The formula for the area of a circle is:
$A = \pi r^2$

Example 1 Find the area of a circle with a radius of 4.0 cm.

Step 1 $A = \pi(4.0)^2$

Step 2 Find the square of the radius.
$A = 16\pi$

Step 3 Multiply the square of the radius by π.
$A = 50 \text{ cm}^2$

The area of the circle is 50 cm^2.

Example 2 Find the area of a circle with a radius of 225 m.

Step 1 $A = \pi(225)^2$

Step 2 Find the square of the radius.
$A = 50625\pi$

Step 3 Multiply the square of the radius by π.
$A = 158962.5$

The area of the circle is 158,962 m^2.

Example 3 Find the area of a circle whose diameter is 20.0 mm.

Step 1 You know the formula for the area of a circle is the square of the radius times π, and that the radius is half of the diameter.
$A = \pi\left(\frac{20.0}{2}\right)^2$

Step 2 Find the radius.
$A = \pi(10.0)^2$

Step 3 Find the square of the radius.
$A = 100\pi$

Step 4 Multiply the square of the radius by π.
$A = 314 \text{ mm}^2$

The area is 314 mm^2.

Practice Problem Find the area of a circle with a radius of 16 m.

Circumference of a Circle

$C = 2\pi r$
$C = 2\pi(19)$
$C = 38\pi$
$C = 119.3$

Area of a Circle

$A = \pi r^2$
$A = \pi(16 \text{ m})^2$
$A = \pi\ 256 \text{ m}^2$
$A = 803.8 \text{ m}^2$

Math Skill Handbook

MATH SKILL HANDBOOK A ◆ 213

Volume

Problem 1

$V = 8\text{ m} \times 4\text{ m} \times 4\text{ m}$

$V = 128\text{ m}^3$

Problem 2

$V = \pi r^2 \times \text{height}$

$V = \left[\pi\left(\frac{1}{2} \times 7\right)^2\right] \times 16$

$V = [\pi(3.5)^2] \times 16$

$V = [\pi(12.25)] \times 16$

$V = 38.46 \times 16$

$V = 615.36$

Volume The measure of space occupied by a solid is the **volume** (V). To find the volume of a rectangular solid multiply the length times width times height, or $V = l \times w \times h$. It is measured in cubic units, such as cubic centimeters (cm^3).

Example Find the volume of a rectangular solid with a length of 2.0 m, a width of 4.0 m, and a height of 3.0 m.

Step 1 You know the formula for volume is the length times the width times the height.

$V = 2.0\text{ m} \times 4.0\text{ m} \times 3.0\text{ m}$

Step 2 Multiply the length times the width times the height.

$V = 24\text{ m}^3$

The volume is 24 m^3.

Practice Problem Find the volume of a rectangular solid that 8 m long, 4 m wide, and 4 m high.

To find the volume of other solids, multiply the area of the base times the height.

Example 1 Find the volume of a solid that has a triangular base with a length of 8.0 m and a height of 7.0 m. The height of the entire solid is 15.0 m.

Step 1 You know that the base is a triangle, and the area of a triangle is $\frac{1}{2}$ the base times the height, and the volume is the area of the base times the height.

$V = \left[\frac{1}{2}(b \times h)\right] \times 15$

Step 2 Find the area of the base.

$V = \left[\frac{1}{2}(8 \times 7)\right] \times 15$

$V = \left(\frac{1}{2} \times 56\right) \times 15$

Step 3 Multiply the area of the base by the height of the solid.

$V = 28 \times 15$

$V = 420\text{ m}^3$

The volume is 420 m^3.

Example 2 Find the volume of a cylinder that has a base with a radius of 12.0 cm, and a height of 21.0 cm.

Step 1 You know that the base is a circle, and the area of a circle is the square of the radius times π, and the volume is the area of the base times the height.

$V = (\pi r^2) \times 21$

$V = (\pi 12^2) \times 21$

Step 2 Find the area of the base.

$V = 144\pi \times 21$

$V = 452 \times 21$

Step 3 Multiply the area of the base by the height of the solid.

$V = 9490\text{ cm}^3$

The volume is 9490 cm^3.

Example 3 Find the volume of a cylinder that has a diameter of 15 mm and a height of 4.8 mm.

Step 1 You know that the base is a circle with an area equal to the square of the radius times π. The radius is one-half the diameter. The volume is the area of the base times the height.

$V = (\pi r^2) \times 4.8$

$V = \left[\pi\left(\frac{1}{2} \times 15\right)^2\right] \times 4.8$

$V = (\pi 7.5^2) \times 4.8$

Step 2 Find the area of the base.

$V = 56.25\pi \times 4.8$

$V = 176.63 \times 4.8$

Step 3 Multiply the area of the base by the height of the solid.

$V = 847.8$

The volume is 847.8 mm^3.

Practice Problem Find the volume of a cylinder with a diameter of 7 cm in the base and a height of 16 cm.

Science Applications

Measure in SI

The metric system of measurement was developed in 1795. A modern form of the metric system, called the International System (SI), was adopted in 1960 and provides the standard measurements that all scientists around the world can understand.

The SI system is convenient because unit sizes vary by powers of 10. Prefixes are used to name units. Look at **Table 3** for some common SI prefixes and their meanings.

Table 3 Some SI Prefixes

Prefix	Symbol	Meaning	
kilo-	k	1,000	thousand
hecto-	h	100	hundred
deka-	da	10	ten
deci-	d	0.1	tenth
centi-	c	0.01	hundredth
milli-	m	0.001	thousandth

Example How many grams equal one kilogram?

Step 1 Find the prefix *kilo* in **Table 3.**

Step 2 Using **Table 3,** determine the meaning of *kilo.* According to the table, it means 1,000. When the prefix *kilo* is added to a unit, it means that there are 1,000 of the units in a "*kilo*unit."

Step 3 Apply the prefix to the units in the question. The units in the question are grams. There are 1,000 grams in a kilogram.

Practice Problem Is a milligram larger or smaller than a gram? How many of the smaller units equal one larger unit? What fraction of the larger unit does one smaller unit represent?

Dimensional Analysis

Convert SI Units In science, quantities such as length, mass, and time sometimes are measured using different units. A process called dimensional analysis can be used to change one unit of measure to another. This process involves multiplying your starting quantity and units by one or more conversion factors. A conversion factor is a ratio equal to one and can be made from any two equal quantities with different units. If 1,000 mL equal 1 L then two ratios can be made.

$$\frac{1{,}000 \text{ mL}}{1 \text{ L}} = \frac{1 \text{ L}}{1{,}000 \text{ mL}} = 1$$

One can covert between units in the SI system by using the equivalents in **Table 3** to make conversion factors.

Example 1 How many cm are in 4 m?

Step 1 Write conversion factors for the units given. From **Table 3,** you know that 100 cm = 1 m. The conversion factors are

$$\frac{100 \text{ cm}}{1 \text{ m}} \textit{ and } \frac{1 \text{ m}}{100 \text{ cm}}$$

Step 2 Decide which conversion factor to use. Select the factor that has the units you are converting from (m) in the denominator and the units you are converting to (cm) in the numerator.

$$\frac{100 \text{ cm}}{1 \text{ m}}$$

Step 3 Multiply the starting quantity and units by the conversion factor. Cancel the starting units with the units in the denominator. There are 400 cm in 4 m.

$$4 \cancel{\text{m}} \times \frac{100 \text{ cm}}{1 \cancel{\text{m}}} = 400 \text{ cm}$$

Practice Problem How many milligrams are in one kilogram? (Hint: You will need to use two conversion factors from **Table 3.**)

Measure in SI

smaller; 1000; one thousandth

Dimensional Analysis

$$x \text{ mg} = 1 \cancel{\text{kg}} \times \frac{1000 \cancel{\text{g}}}{1 \cancel{\text{kg}}} \times \frac{1000 \text{ mg}}{1 \cancel{\text{g}}} =$$

1,000,000 mg

1,000,000 mg = 1 kg

Math Skill Handbook

MATH SKILL HANDBOOK A ◆ 215

Convert Between Unit Systems

$$\frac{(1\text{ in})^3}{(2.54\text{ cm})^3}$$

$$= \frac{1\text{ in} \times 1\text{ in} \times 1\text{ in}}{2.54\text{ cm} \times 2.54\text{ cm} \times 2.54\text{ cm}}$$

$$= \frac{1\text{ in}^3}{16.39\text{ cm}^3}$$

Table 4 Unit System Equivalents

Type of Measurement	Equivalent
Length	1 in = 2.54 cm 1 yd = 0.91 m 1 mi = 1.61 km
Mass and Weight*	1 oz = 28.35 g 1 lb = 0.45 kg 1 ton (short) = 0.91 tonnes (metric tons) 1 lb = 4.45 N
Volume	1 in^3 = 16.39 cm^3 1 qt = 0.95 L 1 gal = 3.78 L
Area	1 in^2 = 6.45 cm^2 1 yd^2 = 0.83 m^2 1 mi^2 = 2.59 km^2 1 acre = 0.40 hectares
Temperature	$°C = \frac{(°F - 32)}{1.8}$ K = °C + 273

*Weight is measured in standard Earth gravity.

Convert Between Unit Systems **Table 4** gives a list of equivalents that can be used to convert between English and SI units.

Example If a meterstick has a length of 100 cm, how long is the meterstick in inches?

Step 1 Write the conversion factors for the units given. From **Table 4,** 1 in = 2.54 cm.

$$\frac{1\text{ in}}{2.54\text{ cm}} \textit{ and } \frac{2.54\text{ cm}}{1\text{ in}}$$

Step 2 Determine which conversion factor to use. You are converting from cm to in. Use the conversion factor with cm on the bottom.

$$\frac{1\text{ in}}{2.54\text{ cm}}$$

Step 3 Multiply the starting quantity and units by the conversion factor. Cancel the starting units with the units in the denominator. Round your answer based on the number of significant figures in the conversion factor.

$$100\ \cancel{\text{cm}} \times \frac{1\text{ in}}{2.54\ \cancel{\text{cm}}} = 39.37\text{ in}$$

The meterstick is 39.4 in long.

Practice Problem A book has a mass of 5 lbs. What is the mass of the book in kg?

Practice Problem Use the equivalent for in and cm (1 in = 2.54 cm) to show how 1 in^3 = 16.39 cm^3.

Math Skill Handbook

Math Skill Handbook

Precision and Significant Digits

When you make a measurement, the value you record depends on the precision of the measuring instrument. This precision is represented by the number of significant digits recorded in the measurement. When counting the number of significant digits, all digits are counted except zeros at the end of a number with no decimal point such as 2,050, and zeros at the beginning of a decimal such as 0.03020. When adding or subtracting numbers with different precision, round the answer to the smallest number of decimal places of any number in the sum or difference. When multiplying or dividing, the answer is rounded to the smallest number of significant digits of any number being multiplied or divided.

Example The lengths 5.28 and 5.2 are measured in meters. Find the sum of these lengths and record your answer using the correct number of significant digits.

Step 1 Find the sum.

5.28 m	2 digits after the decimal
+ 5.2 m	1 digit after the decimal
10.48 m	

Step 2 Round to one digit after the decimal because the least number of digits after the decimal of the numbers being added is 1.

The sum is 10.5 m.

Practice Problem How many significant digits are in the measurement 7,071,301 m? How many significant digits are in the measurement 0.003010 g?

Practice Problem Multiply 5.28 and 5.2 using the rule for multiplying and dividing. Record the answer using the correct number of significant digits.

Scientific Notation

Many times numbers used in science are very small or very large. Because these numbers are difficult to work with scientists use scientific notation. To write numbers in scientific notation, move the decimal point until only one non-zero digit remains on the left. Then count the number of places you moved the decimal point and use that number as a power of ten. For example, the average distance from the Sun to Mars is 227,800,000,000 m. In scientific notation, this distance is 2.278×10^{11} m. Because you moved the decimal point to the left, the number is a positive power of ten.

The mass of an electron is about 0.000 000 000 000 000 000 000 000 000 000 911 kg. Expressed in scientific notation, this mass is 9.11×10^{-31} kg. Because the decimal point was moved to the right, the number is a negative power of ten.

Example Earth is 149,600,000 km from the Sun. Express this in scientific notation.

Step 1 Move the decimal point until one non-zero digit remains on the left.

1.496 000 00

Step 2 Count the number of decimal places you have moved. In this case, eight.

Step 3 Show that number as a power of ten, 10^8.

The Earth is 1.496×10^8 km from the Sun.

Practice Problem How many significant digits are in 149,600,000 km? How many significant digits are in 1.496×10^8 km?

Practice Problem Parts used in a high performance car must be measured to 7×10^{-6} m. Express this number as a decimal.

Practice Problem A CD is spinning at 539 revolutions per minute. Express this number in scientific notation.

Precision and Significant Digits

Problem 1
7; 4

Problem 2
$5.28 \times 5.2 = 27.456$

5.28 has 3 significant digits.

5.2 has 2 significant digits.

When multiplying and dividing, the answer is rounded to the smallest number of significant digits of the numbers being multiplied or divided—in this case, 2.

27.456 is rounded to 27.

Scientific Notation

Problem 1
4; 4

Problem 2
0.000007

Problem 3
5.39×10^2

Math Skill Handbook

MATH SKILL HANDBOOK A ◆ 217

Make and Use Graphs

Data in tables can be displayed in a graph—a visual representation of data. Common graph types include line graphs, bar graphs, and circle graphs.

Line Graph A line graph shows a relationship between two variables that change continuously. The independent variable is changed and is plotted on the x-axis. The dependent variable is observed, and is plotted on the y-axis.

Example Draw a line graph of the data below from a cyclist in a long-distance race.

Table 5 Bicycle Race Data

Time (h)	Distance (km)
0	0
1	8
2	16
3	24
4	32
5	40

Step 1 Determine the x-axis and y-axis variables. Time varies independently of distance and is plotted on the x-axis. Distance is dependent on time and is plotted on the y-axis.

Step 2 Determine the scale of each axis. The x-axis data ranges from 0 to 5. The y-axis data ranges from 0 to 40.

Step 3 Using graph paper, draw and label the axes. Include units in the labels.

Step 4 Draw a point at the intersection of the time value on the x-axis and corresponding distance value on the y-axis. Connect the points and label the graph with a title, as shown in **Figure 20.**

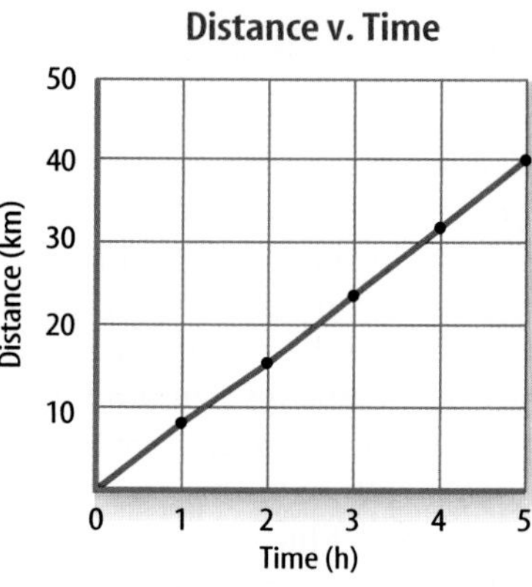

Figure 20 This line graph shows the relationship between distance and time during a bicycle ride.

Practice Problem A puppy's shoulder height is measured during the first year of her life. The following measurements were collected: (3 mo, 52 cm), (6 mo, 72 cm), (9 mo, 83 cm), (12 mo, 86). Graph this data.

Find a Slope The slope of a straight line is the ratio of the vertical change, rise, to the horizontal change, run.

$$\text{Slope} = \frac{\text{vertical change (rise)}}{\text{horizontal change (run)}} = \frac{\text{change in } y}{\text{change in } x}$$

Example Find the slope of the graph in **Figure 20.**

Step 1 You know that the slope is the change in y divided by the change in x.

$$\text{Slope} = \frac{\text{change in } y}{\text{change in } x}$$

Step 2 Determine the data points you will be using. For a straight line, choose the two sets of points that are the farthest apart.

$$\text{Slope} = \frac{(40-0)\text{ km}}{(5-0)\text{ hr}}$$

Step 3 Find the change in y and x.

$$\text{Slope} = \frac{40\text{ km}}{5\text{h}}$$

Step 4 Divide the change in y by the change in x.

$$\text{Slope} = \frac{8\text{ km}}{\text{h}}$$

The slope of the graph is 8 km/h.

Line Graph

x	y
3	52
6	72
9	83
12	86

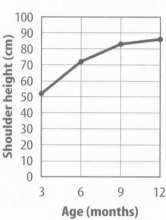

Puppy Growth

Shoulder height (cm)

Age (months)

Math Skill Handbook

218 ◆ A STUDENT RESOURCES

Bar Graph To compare data that does not change continuously you might choose a bar graph. A bar graph uses bars to show the relationships between variables. The x-axis variable is divided into parts. The parts can be numbers such as years, or a category such as a type of animal. The y-axis is a number and increases continuously along the axis.

Example A recycling center collects 4.0 kg of aluminum on Monday, 1.0 kg on Wednesday, and 2.0 kg on Friday. Create a bar graph of this data.

Step 1 Select the x-axis and y-axis variables. The measured numbers (the masses of aluminum) should be placed on the y-axis. The variable divided into parts (collection days) is placed on the x-axis.

Step 2 Create a graph grid like you would for a line graph. Include labels and units.

Step 3 For each measured number, draw a vertical bar above the x-axis value up to the y-axis value. For the first data point, draw a vertical bar above Monday up to 4.0 kg.

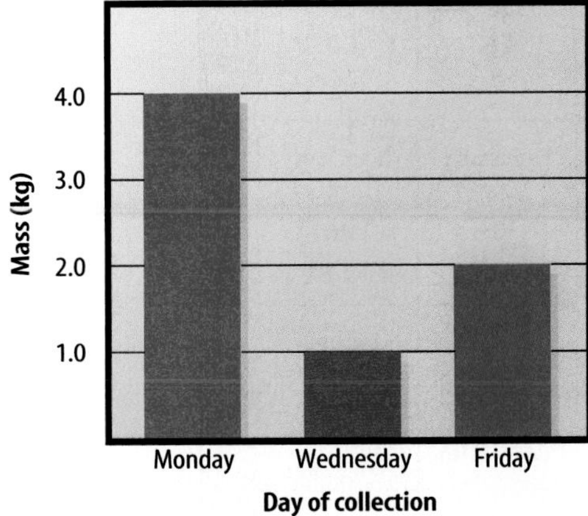

Practice Problem Draw a bar graph of the gases in air: 78% nitrogen, 21% oxygen, 1% other gases.

Circle Graph To display data as parts of a whole, you might use a circle graph. A circle graph is a circle divided into sections that represent the relative size of each piece of data. The entire circle represents 100%, half represents 50%, and so on.

Example Air is made up of 78% nitrogen, 21% oxygen, and 1% other gases. Display the composition of air in a circle graph.

Step 1 Multiply each percent by 360° and divide by 100 to find the angle of each section in the circle.

$$78\% \times \frac{360°}{100} = 280.8°$$

$$21\% \times \frac{360°}{100} = 75.6°$$

$$1\% \times \frac{360°}{100} = 3.6°$$

Step 2 Use a compass to draw a circle and to mark the center of the circle. Draw a straight line from the center to the edge of the circle.

Step 3 Use a protractor and the angles you calculated to divide the circle into parts. Place the center of the protractor over the center of the circle and line the base of the protractor over the straight line.

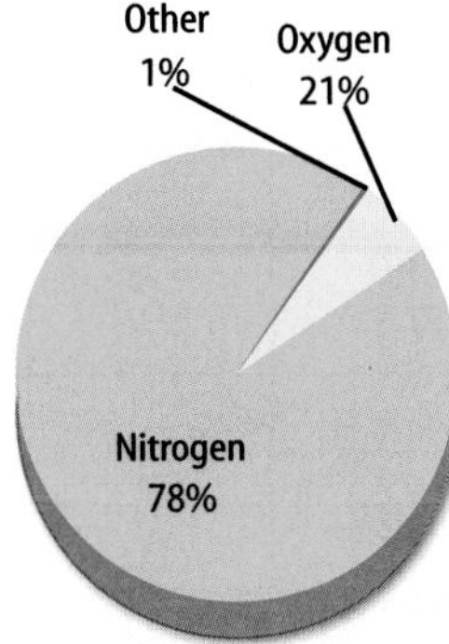

Practice Problem Draw a circle graph to represent the amount of aluminum collected during the week shown in the bar graph to the left.

Bar Graph

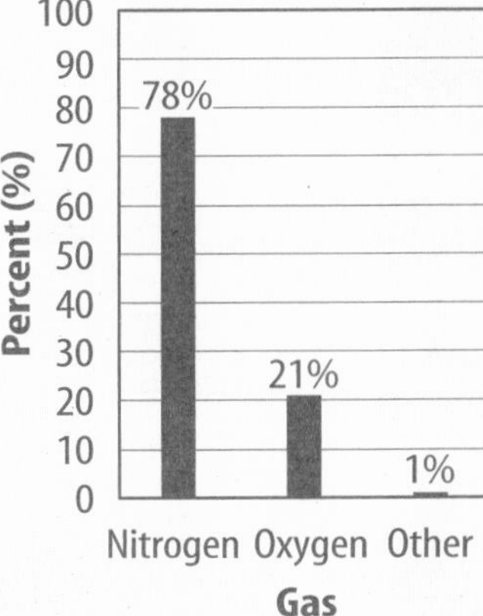

Circle Graph

The total amount of aluminum collected is:

$$4.0\text{ kg} + 1.0\text{ kg} + 2.0\text{ kg} = 7.0\text{ kg}$$

$$\frac{4.0\text{ kg}}{7.0\text{ kg}} = \frac{x}{360°};\ x = 206°$$

$$\frac{1.0\text{ kg}}{7.0\text{ kg}} = \frac{x}{360°};\ x = 51°$$

$$\frac{2.0\text{ kg}}{7.0\text{ kg}} = \frac{x}{360°};\ x = 103°$$

PERIODIC TABLE OF THE ELEMENTS

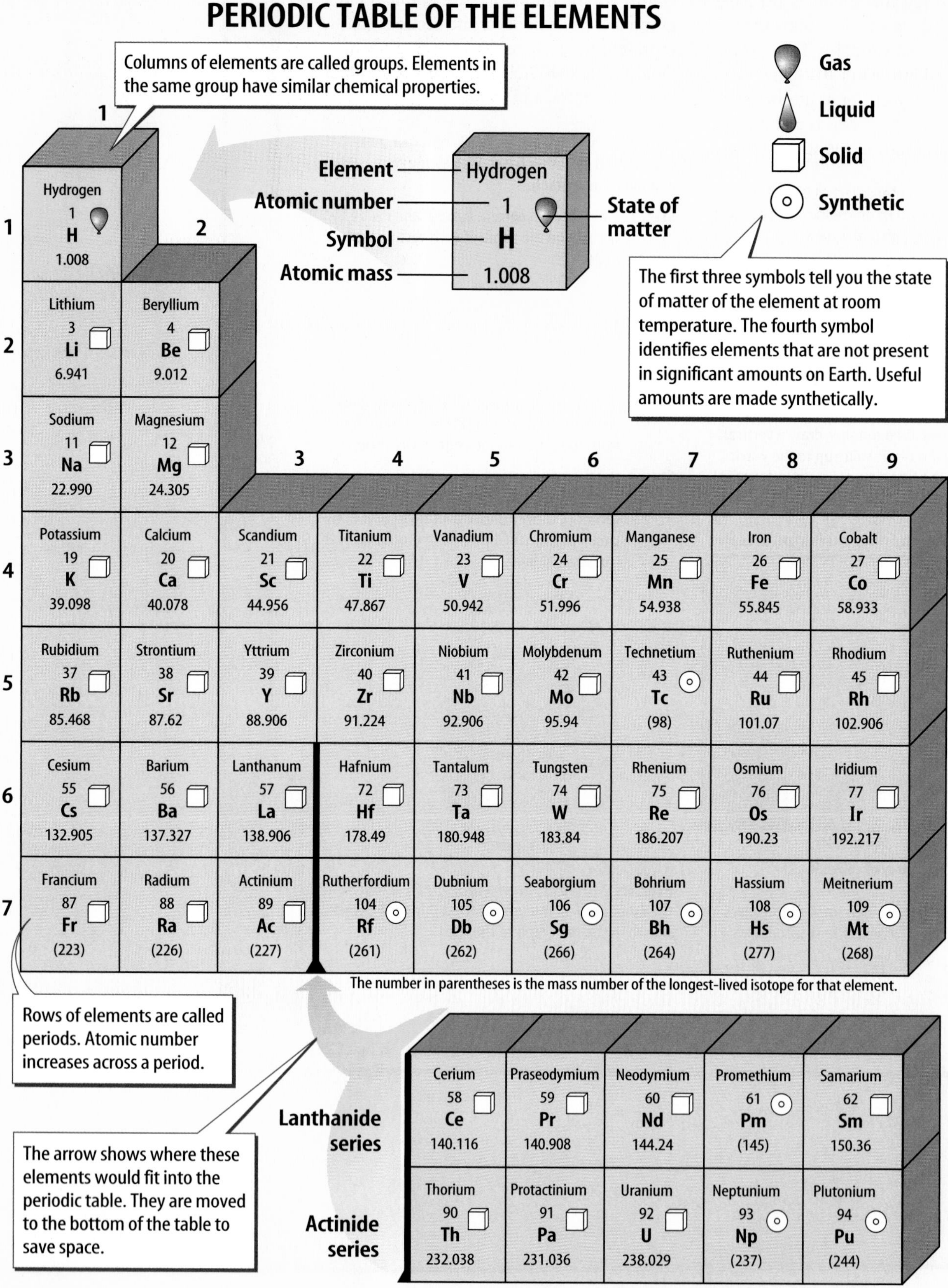

Columns of elements are called groups. Elements in the same group have similar chemical properties.
Element — Hydrogen
Atomic number — 1
Symbol — H
Atomic mass — 1.008
State of matter
Gas
Liquid
Solid
Synthetic
The first three symbols tell you the state of matter of the element at room temperature. The fourth symbol identifies elements that are not present in significant amounts on Earth. Useful amounts are made synthetically.
Rows of elements are called periods. Atomic number increases across a period.
The arrow shows where these elements would fit into the periodic table. They are moved to the bottom of the table to save space.

	1	2	3	4	5	6	7	8	9
1	Hydrogen 1 H (gas) 1.008								
2	Lithium 3 Li (solid) 6.941	Beryllium 4 Be (solid) 9.012							
3	Sodium 11 Na (solid) 22.990	Magnesium 12 Mg (solid) 24.305							
4	Potassium 19 K (solid) 39.098	Calcium 20 Ca (solid) 40.078	Scandium 21 Sc (solid) 44.956	Titanium 22 Ti (solid) 47.867	Vanadium 23 V (solid) 50.942	Chromium 24 Cr (solid) 51.996	Manganese 25 Mn (solid) 54.938	Iron 26 Fe (solid) 55.845	Cobalt 27 Co (solid) 58.933
5	Rubidium 37 Rb (solid) 85.468	Strontium 38 Sr (solid) 87.62	Yttrium 39 Y (solid) 88.906	Zirconium 40 Zr (solid) 91.224	Niobium 41 Nb (solid) 92.906	Molybdenum 42 Mo (solid) 95.94	Technetium 43 Tc (synthetic) (98)	Ruthenium 44 Ru (solid) 101.07	Rhodium 45 Rh (solid) 102.906
6	Cesium 55 Cs (solid) 132.905	Barium 56 Ba (solid) 137.327	Lanthanum 57 La (solid) 138.906	Hafnium 72 Hf (solid) 178.49	Tantalum 73 Ta (solid) 180.948	Tungsten 74 W (solid) 183.84	Rhenium 75 Re (solid) 186.207	Osmium 76 Os (solid) 190.23	Iridium 77 Ir (solid) 192.217
7	Francium 87 Fr (solid) (223)	Radium 88 Ra (solid) (226)	Actinium 89 Ac (solid) (227)	Rutherfordium 104 Rf (synthetic) (261)	Dubnium 105 Db (synthetic) (262)	Seaborgium 106 Sg (synthetic) (266)	Bohrium 107 Bh (synthetic) (264)	Hassium 108 Hs (synthetic) (277)	Meitnerium 109 Mt (synthetic) (268)

The number in parentheses is the mass number of the longest-lived isotope for that element.

Lanthanide series	Cerium 58 Ce (solid) 140.116	Praseodymium 59 Pr (solid) 140.908	Neodymium 60 Nd (solid) 144.24	Promethium 61 Pm (synthetic) (145)	Samarium 62 Sm (solid) 150.36
Actinide series	Thorium 90 Th (solid) 232.038	Protactinium 91 Pa (solid) 231.036	Uranium 92 U (solid) 238.029	Neptunium 93 Np (synthetic) (237)	Plutonium 94 Pu (synthetic) (244)

Metal

Metalloid

Nonmetal

The color of an element's block tells you if the element is a metal, nonmetal, or metalloid.

Science Online

Visit booka.msscience.com for the updates to the periodic table.

10	11	12	13	14	15	16	17	18
								Helium 2 He 4.003
			Boron 5 B 10.811	Carbon 6 C 12.011	Nitrogen 7 N 14.007	Oxygen 8 O 15.999	Fluorine 9 F 18.998	Neon 10 Ne 20.180
			Aluminum 13 Al 26.982	Silicon 14 Si 28.086	Phosphorus 15 P 30.974	Sulfur 16 S 32.065	Chlorine 17 Cl 35.453	Argon 18 Ar 39.948
Nickel 28 Ni 58.693	Copper 29 Cu 63.546	Zinc 30 Zn 65.409	Gallium 31 Ga 69.723	Germanium 32 Ge 72.64	Arsenic 33 As 74.922	Selenium 34 Se 78.96	Bromine 35 Br 79.904	Krypton 36 Kr 83.798
Palladium 46 Pd 106.42	Silver 47 Ag 107.868	Cadmium 48 Cd 112.411	Indium 49 In 114.818	Tin 50 Sn 118.710	Antimony 51 Sb 121.760	Tellurium 52 Te 127.60	Iodine 53 I 126.904	Xenon 54 Xe 131.293
Platinum 78 Pt 195.078	Gold 79 Au 196.967	Mercury 80 Hg 200.59	Thallium 81 Tl 204.383	Lead 82 Pb 207.2	Bismuth 83 Bi 208.980	Polonium 84 Po (209)	Astatine 85 At (210)	Radon 86 Rn (222)
Darmstadtium 110 Ds (281)	Unununium * 111 Uuu (272)	Ununbium * 112 Uub (285)		Ununquadium * 114 Uuq (289)		** 116		** 118

* The names and symbols for elements 111–114 are temporary. Final names will be selected when the elements' discoveries are verified.

** Elements 116 and 118 were thought to have been created. The claim was retracted because the experimental results could not be repeated.

Europium 63 Eu 151.964	Gadolinium 64 Gd 157.25	Terbium 65 Tb 158.925	Dysprosium 66 Dy 162.500	Holmium 67 Ho 164.930	Erbium 68 Er 167.259	Thulium 69 Tm 168.934	Ytterbium 70 Yb 173.04	Lutetium 71 Lu 174.967
Americium 95 Am (243)	Curium 96 Cm (247)	Berkelium 97 Bk (247)	Californium 98 Cf (251)	Einsteinium 99 Es (252)	Fermium 100 Fm (257)	Mendelevium 101 Md (258)	Nobelium 102 No (259)	Lawrencium 103 Lr (262)

Use and Care of a Microscope

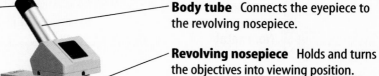

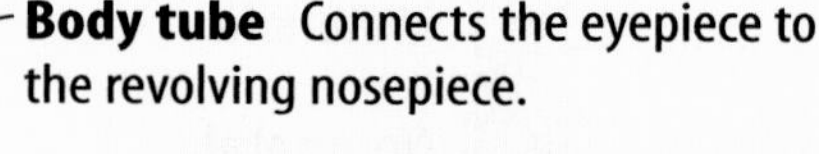

Eyepiece Contains magnifying lenses you look through.

Arm Supports the body tube.

Low-power objective Contains the lens with the lowest power magnification.

Stage clips Hold the microscope slide in place.

Coarse adjustment Focuses the image under low power.

Fine adjustment Sharpens the image under high magnification.

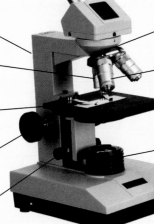

Body tube Connects the eyepiece to the revolving nosepiece.

Revolving nosepiece Holds and turns the objectives into viewing position.

High-power objective Contains the lens with the highest magnification.

Stage Supports the microscope slide.

Light source Provides light that passes upward through the diaphragm, the specimen, and the lenses.

Base Provides support for the microscope.

Caring for a Microscope

1. Always carry the microscope holding the arm with one hand and supporting the base with the other hand.
2. Don't touch the lenses with your fingers.
3. The coarse adjustment knob is used only when looking through the lowest-power objective lens. The fine adjustment knob is used when the high-power objective is in place.
4. Cover the microscope when you store it.

Using a Microscope

1. Place the microscope on a flat surface that is clear of objects. The arm should be toward you.
2. Look through the eyepiece. Adjust the diaphragm so light comes through the opening in the stage.
3. Place a slide on the stage so the specimen is in the field of view. Hold it firmly in place by using the stage clips.
4. Always focus with the coarse adjustment and the low-power objective lens first. After the object is in focus on low power, turn the nosepiece until the high-power objective is in place. Use ONLY the fine adjustment to focus with the high-power objective lens.

Making a Wet-Mount Slide

1. Carefully place the item you want to look at in the center of a clean, glass slide. Make sure the sample is thin enough for light to pass through.
2. Use a dropper to place one or two drops of water on the sample.
3. Hold a clean coverslip by the edges and place it at one edge of the water. Slowly lower the coverslip onto the water until it lies flat.
4. If you have too much water or a lot of air bubbles, touch the edge of a paper towel to the edge of the coverslip to draw off extra water and draw out unwanted air.

Diversity of Life: Classification of Living Organisms

A six-kingdom system of classification of organisms is used today. Two kingdoms—Kingdom Archaebacteria and Kingdom Eubacteria—contain organisms that do not have a nucleus and that lack membrane-bound structures in the cytoplasm of their cells. The members of the other four kingdoms have a cell or cells that contain a nucleus and structures in the cytoplasm, some of which are surrounded by membranes. These kingdoms are Kingdom Protista, Kingdom Fungi, Kingdom Plantae, and Kingdom Animalia.

Kingdom Archaebacteria

one-celled; some absorb food from their surroundings; some are photosynthetic; some are chemosynthetic; many are found in extremely harsh environments including salt ponds, hot springs, swamps, and deep-sea hydrothermal vents

Kingdom Eubacteria

one-celled; most absorb food from their surroundings; some are photosynthetic; some are chemosynthetic; many are parasites; many are round, spiral, or rod-shaped; some form colonies

Kingdom Protista

Phylum Euglenophyta one-celled; photosynthetic or take in food; most have one flagellum; euglenoids

Phylum Bacillariophyta one-celled; photosynthetic; have unique double shells made of silica; diatoms

Phylum Dinoflagellata one-celled; photosynthetic; contain red pigments; have two flagella; dinoflagellates

Phylum Chlorophyta one-celled, many-celled, or colonies; photosynthetic; contain chlorophyll; live on land, in freshwater, or salt water; green algae

Phylum Rhodophyta most are many-celled; photosynthetic; contain red pigments; most live in deep, saltwater environments; red algae

Phylum Phaeophyta most are many-celled; photosynthetic; contain brown pigments; most live in saltwater environments; brown algae

Phylum Rhizopoda one-celled; take in food; are free-living or parasitic; move by means of pseudopods; amoebas

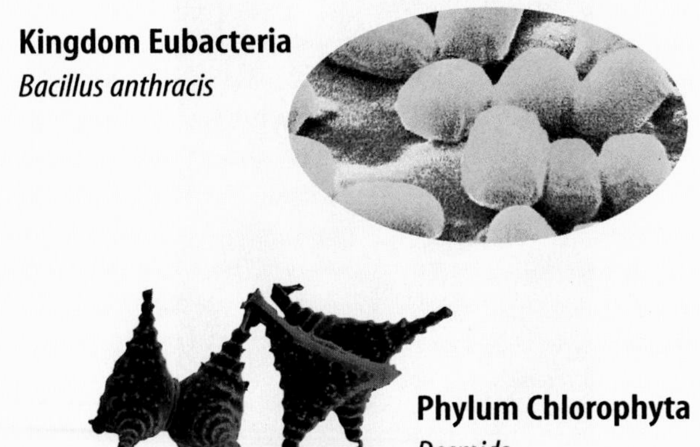

Kingdom Eubacteria
Bacillus anthracis

Phylum Chlorophyta
Desmids

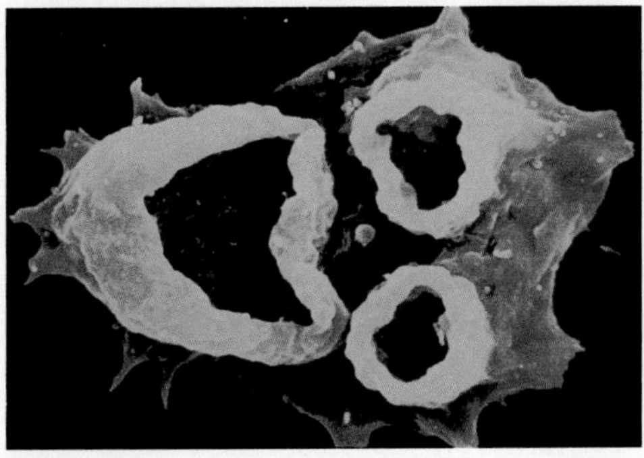

Amoeba

Phylum Zoomastigina one-celled; take in food; free-living or parasitic; have one or more flagella; zoomastigotes

Phylum Ciliophora one-celled; take in food; have large numbers of cilia; ciliates

Phylum Sporozoa one-celled; take in food; have no means of movement; are parasites in animals; sporozoans

Phylum Myxomycota
Slime mold

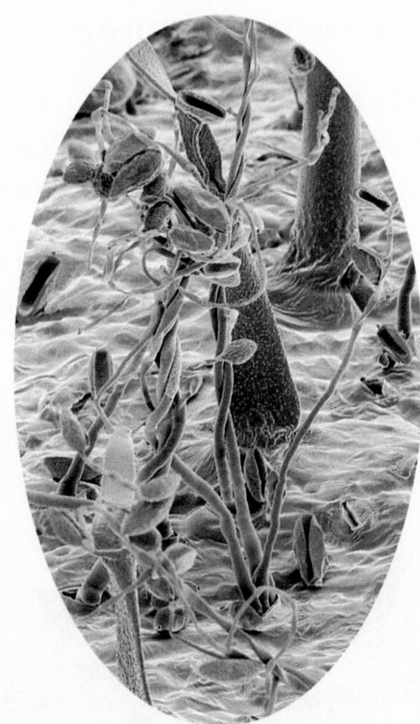

Phylum Oomycota
Phytophthora infestans

Phyla Myxomycota and Acrasiomycota one- or many-celled; absorb food; change form during life cycle; cellular and plasmodial slime molds

Phylum Oomycota many-celled; are either parasites or decomposers; live in freshwater or salt water; water molds, rusts and downy mildews

Kingdom Fungi

Phylum Zygomycota many-celled; absorb food; spores are produced in sporangia; zygote fungi; bread mold

Phylum Ascomycota one- and many-celled; absorb food; spores produced in asci; sac fungi; yeast

Phylum Basidiomycota many-celled; absorb food; spores produced in basidia; club fungi; mushrooms

Phylum Deuteromycota members with unknown reproductive structures; imperfect fungi; *Penicillium*

Phylum Mycophycota organisms formed by symbiotic relationship between an ascomycote or a basidiomycote and green alga or cyanobacterium; lichens

Lichens

Kingdom Plantae

Divisions Bryophyta (mosses), **Anthocerophyta** (hornworts), **Hepaticophyta** (liverworts), **Psilophyta** (whisk ferns) many-celled nonvascular plants; reproduce by spores produced in capsules; green; grow in moist, land environments

Division Lycophyta many-celled vascular plants; spores are produced in conelike structures; live on land; are photosynthetic; club mosses

Division Arthrophyta vascular plants; ribbed and jointed stems; scalelike leaves; spores produced in conelike structures; horsetails

Division Pterophyta vascular plants; leaves called fronds; spores produced in clusters of sporangia called sori; live on land or in water; ferns

Division Ginkgophyta deciduous trees; only one living species; have fan-shaped leaves with branching veins and fleshy cones with seeds; ginkgoes

Division Cycadophyta palmlike plants; have large, featherlike leaves; produces seeds in cones; cycads

Division Coniferophyta deciduous or evergreen; trees or shrubs; have needlelike or scale-like leaves; seeds produced in cones; conifers

Division Gnetophyta shrubs or woody vines; seeds are produced in cones; division contains only three genera; gnetum

Division Anthophyta dominant group of plants; flowering plants; have fruits with seeds

Kingdom Animalia

Phylum Porifera aquatic organisms that lack true tissues and organs; are asymmetrical and sessile; sponges

Phylum Cnidaria radially symmetrical organisms; have a digestive cavity with one opening; most have tentacles armed with stinging cells; live in aquatic environments singly or in colonies; includes jellyfish, corals, hydra, and sea anemones

Phylum Platyhelminthes bilaterally symmetrical worms; have flattened bodies; digestive system has one opening; parasitic and free-living species; flatworms

Division Anthophyta
Tomato plant

Division Bryophyta
Liverwort

Phylum Platyhelminthes
Flatworm

Phylum Chordata

Phylum Nematoda round, bilaterally symmetrical body; have digestive system with two openings; free-living forms and parasitic forms; roundworms

Phylum Mollusca soft-bodied animals, many with a hard shell and soft foot or footlike appendage; a mantle covers the soft body; aquatic and terrestrial species; includes clams, snails, squid, and octopuses

Phylum Annelida bilaterally symmetrical worms; have round, segmented bodies; terrestrial and aquatic species; includes earthworms, leeches, and marine polychaetes

Phylum Arthropoda largest animal group; have hard exoskeletons, segmented bodies, and pairs of jointed appendages; land and aquatic species; includes insects, crustaceans, and spiders

Phylum Echinodermata marine organisms; have spiny or leathery skin and a water-vascular system with tube feet; are radially symmetrical; includes sea stars, sand dollars, and sea urchins

Phylum Chordata organisms with internal skeletons and specialized body systems; most have paired appendages; all at some time have a notochord, nerve cord, gill slits, and a post-anal tail; include fish, amphibians, reptiles, birds, and mammals

Cómo usar el glosario en español:
1. Busca el término en inglés que desees encontrar.
2. El término en español, junto con la definición, se encuentran en la columna de la derecha.

Pronunciation Key

Use the following key to help you sound out words in the glossary.

a	**back** (BAK)	**ew**	**food** (FEWD)
ay	**day** (DAY)	**yoo**	**pure** (PYOOR)
ah	**father** (FAH thur)	**yew**	**few** (FYEW)
ow	**flower** (FLOW ur)	**uh**	**comma** (CAH muh)
ar	**car** (CAR)	**u** (+ con)	**rub** (RUB)
e	**less** (LES)	**sh**	**shelf** (SHELF)
ee	**leaf** (LEEF)	**ch**	**nature** (NAY chur)
ih	**trip** (TRIHP)	**g**	**gift** (GIHFT)
i (i + con + e)	**idea** (i DEE uh)	**j**	**gem** (JEM)
oh	**go** (GOH)	**ing**	**sing** (SING)
aw	**soft** (SAWFT)	**zh**	**vision** (VIH zhun)
or	**orbit** (OR buht)	**k**	**cake** (KAYK)
oy	**coin** (COYN)	**s**	**seed, cent** (SEED, SENT)
oo	**foot** (FOOT)	**z**	**zone, raise** (ZOHN, RAYZ)

English — A — Español

active transport: energy-requiring process in which transport proteins bind with particles and move them through a cell membrane. (p. 79)

adaptation: any variation that makes an organism better suited to its environment. (p. 160)

allele (uh LEEL): an alternate form that a gene may have for a single trait; can be dominant or recessive. (p. 128)

asexual reproduction: a type of reproduction—fission, budding, and regeneration—in which a new organism is produced from one organism and has DNA identical to the parent organism. (p. 103)

transporte activo: proceso que requiere energía y en el cual las proteínas de transporte se unen con partículas y las trasladan a través de la membrana celular. (p. 79)

adaptación: cualquier variación que haga que un organismo se adapte mejor a su medio ambiente. (p. 160)

alelo: forma alternativa que un gen puede tener para un rasgo único; puede ser dominante o recesivo. (p. 128)

reproducción asexual: tipo de reproducción –fisión, gemación y regeneración– en el que un organismo da origen a uno nuevo de ADN idéntico al organismo progenitor. (p. 103)

B

binomial nomenclature (bi NOH mee ul • NOH mun klay chur): two-word naming system that gives all organisms their scientific name. (p. 26)

biogenesis (bi oh JEH nuh sus): theory that living things come only from other living things. (p. 21)

nomenclatura binomial: sistema de denominación de dos palabras que da a todos los organismos su nombre científico. (p. 26)

biogénesis: teoría que sostiene que los seres vivos sólo provienen de otros seres vivos. (p. 21)

C

cell: smallest unit of an organism that can carry on life functions. (p. 16)

cell membrane: protective outer covering of all cells that regulates the interaction between the cell and the environment. (p. 40)

cell theory: states that all organisms are made up of one or more cells, the cell is the basic unit of life, and all cells come from other cells. (p. 53)

cell wall: rigid structure that encloses, supports, and protects the cells of plants, algae, fungi, and most bacteria. (p. 41)

chloroplast: green, chlorophyll-containing, plant-cell organelle that uses light energy to produce sugar from carbon dioxide and water. (p. 44)

chromosome: structure in a cell's nucleus that contains hereditary material. (p. 100)

control: standard to which the outcome of a test is compared. (p. 11)

cytoplasm: constantly moving gel-like mixture inside the cell membrane that contains heredity material and is the location of most of a cell's life processes. (p. 40)

célula: la unidad más pequeña de un organismo que puede continuar con sus funciones vitales. (p. 16)

membrana celular: capa externa protectora de todas las células y reguladora de la interacción entre la célula y su entorno. (p. 40)

teoría celular: establece que todos los organismos están formados por una o más células, que la célula es la unidad básica de la vida y que las células provienen de otras células. (p. 53)

pared celular: estructura rígida que envuelve, sostiene y protege a las células de las plantas, algas, hongos y de la mayoría de las bacterias. (p. 41)

cloroplasto: organelo de las células vegetales, de color verde, que contiene clorofila y que usa la luz solar para convertir el dióxido de carbono y el agua en azúcar. (p. 44)

cromosoma: estructura en el núcleo celular que contiene el material hereditario. (p. 100)

control: estándar contra el que se compara el resultado de una prueba. (p. 11)

citoplasma: mezcla parecida al gel y que está en constante movimiento dentro de la membrana celular, contiene material hereditario y es en donde tiene lugar la mayor parte de los procesos vitales de la célula. (p. 40)

D

diffusion: a type of passive transport in cells in which molecules move from areas where there are more of them to areas where there are fewer of them. (p. 77)

diploid (DIHP loyd): cell whose similar chromosomes occur in pairs. (p. 106)

DNA: deoxyribonucleic acid; the genetic material of all organisms; made up of two twisted strands of sugar-phosphate molecules and nitrogen bases. (p. 112)

dominant (DAH muh nunt): describes a trait that covers over, or dominates, another form of that trait. (p. 130)

difusión: tipo de transporte pasivo en las células en el que las moléculas se mueven de áreas de mayor concentración de éstas hacia áreas de menor concentración. (p. 77)

diploide: célula cuyos cromosomas similares están en pares. (p. 106)

ADN: ácido desoxirribonucleico; material genético de todos los organismos constituido por dos cadenas trenzadas de moléculas de azúcar-fosfato y bases de nitrógeno (p. 112)

dominante: describe un rasgo que encubre o domina a otra forma de ese rasgo. (p. 130)

E

egg: haploid sex cell formed in the female reproductive organs. (p. 106)

embryology (em bree AH luh jee): study of embryos and their development. (p. 169)

óvulo: célula sexual haploide que se forma en los órganos reproductivos femeninos. (p. 106)

embriología: el estudio de los embriones y su desarrollo. (p. 169)

endocytosis (en duh si TOH sus): process by which a cell takes in a substance by surrounding it with the cell membrane. (p. 80)

endoplasmic reticulum (ER): cytoplasmic organelle that moves materials around in a cell and is made up of a complex series of folded membranes; can be rough (with attached ribosomes) or smooth (without attached ribosomes). (p. 45)

enzyme: a type of protein that regulates nearly all chemical reactions in cells. (p. 73)

equilibrium: occurs when molecules of one substance are spread evenly throughout another substance. (p. 77)

evolution: change in inherited characteristics over time. (p. 156)

exocytosis (ek soh si TOH sus): process by which vesicles release their contents outside the cell. (p. 80)

endocitosis: proceso mediante el cual una célula capta una sustancia rodeándola con su membrana celular. (p. 80)

retículo endoplásmático (RE): organelo citoplasmático que transporta materiales dentro de una célula y está formado por una serie compleja de membranas plegadas; puede ser rugoso (con ribosomas adosados) o liso (sin ribosomas adosados). (p. 45)

enzima: tipo de proteína que regula casi todas las clases de reacciones químicas en las células. (p. 73)

equilibrio: ocurre cuando las moléculas de una sustancia están diseminadas completa y uniformemente a lo largo de otra sustancia. (p. 77)

evolución: cambio en las características heredadas a través del tiempo. (p. 156)

exocitosis: proceso mediante el cual las vesículas liberan su contenido fuera de la célula. (p. 80)

F

fermentation: process by which oxygen-lacking cells and some one-celled organisms release small amounts of energy from glucose molecules and produce wastes such as alcohol, carbon dioxide, and lactic acid. (p. 86)

fertilization: in sexual reproduction, the joining of a sperm and egg. (p. 106)

fermentación: proceso mediante el cual las células carentes de oxígeno y algunos organismos unicelulares liberan pequeñas cantidades de energía a partir de moléculas de glucosa y producen desechos como alcohol, dióxido de carbono y ácido láctico. (p. 86)

fertilización: en la reproducción sexual, la unión de un óvulo y un espermatozoide. (p. 106)

G

gene: section of DNA on a chromosome that contains instructions for making specific proteins. (p. 114)

genetic engineering: biological and chemical methods to change the arrangement of a gene's DNA to improve crop production, produce large volumes of medicine, and change how cells perform their normal functions. (p. 143)

genetics (juh NEH tihks): the study of how traits are inherited through the actions of alleles. (p. 128)

genotype (JEE nuh tipe): the genetic makeup of an organism. (p. 132)

genus: first word of the two-word scientific name used to identify a group of similar species. (p. 26)

Golgi bodies: organelles that package cellular materials and transport them within the cell or out of the cell. (p. 45)

gen: sección de ADN en un cromosoma, el cual contiene instrucciones para la formación de proteínas específicas. (p. 114)

ingeniería genética: métodos biológicos y químicos para cambiar la disposición del ADN de un gen y así mejorar la producción de cosechas, producir grandes volúmenes de un medicamento, o cambiar la forma en que las células realizan sus funciones normales. (p. 143)

genética: estudio de la forma como se heredan los rasgos a través de las acciones de los alelos. (p. 128)

genotipo: composición genética de un organismo. (p. 132)

género: primera palabra, de las dos palabras del nombre científico, que se usa para identificar a un grupo de especies similares. (p. 26)

aparato de Golgi: organelo que concentra los materiales celulares y los transporta hacia adentro o afuera de la célula. (p. 45)

Glossary/Glosario

gradualism: model describing evolution as a slow process by which one species changes into a new species through a continuing series of mutations and variations over time. (p. 162)

gradualismo: modelo que describe la evolución como un proceso lento mediante el cual una especie existente se convierte en una especie nueva a través de series continuas de mutaciones y variaciones a través del tiempo. (p. 162)

H

haploid (HAP loyd): cell that has half the number of chromosomes as body cells. (p. 107)

haploide: célula que posee la mitad del número de cromosomas que tienen las células somáticas. (p. 107)

heredity (huh REH duh tee): the passing of traits from parent to offspring. (p. 128)

herencia: transferencia de rasgos de un progenitor a su descendencia. (p. 128)

heterozygous (he tuh roh ZI gus): describes an organism with two different alleles for a trait. (p. 132)

heterocigoto: describe a un organismo con dos alelos diferentes para un rasgo. (p. 132)

homeostasis: regulation of an organism's internal, life-maintaining conditions. (p. 17)

homeostasis: control de las condiciones internas que mantienen la vida de un organismo. (p. 17)

hominid: humanlike primate that appeared about 4 million to 6 million years ago, ate both plants and meat, and walked upright on two legs. (p. 173)

homínido: primate con forma de humano que apareció entre 4 y 6 millones de años atrás, se alimentaba de plantas y carne, y caminaba erguido sobre sus dos pies. (p. 173)

Homo sapiens: early humans that likely evolved from Cro-Magnons. (p. 175)

Homo sapiens: humanos primitivos que probablemente evolucionaron a partir de los CroMagnon. (p. 175)

homologous (huh MAH luh gus): body parts that are similar in structure and origin and can be similar in function. (p. 170)

homólogos: partes del cuerpo que son similares en estructura y origen y que pueden tener funciones similares. (p. 170)

homozygous (hoh muh ZI gus): describes an organism with two alleles that are the same for a trait. (p. 132)

homocigoto: describe a un organismo con dos alelos iguales para un rasgo. (p. 132)

host cell: living cell in which a virus can actively multiply or in which a virus can hide until activated by environmental stimuli. (p. 54)

célula huésped: célula viva en la que un virus puede reproducirse activamente o en la que un virus puede ocultarse hasta que es activado por estímulos del medio ambiente. (p. 54)

hybrid (HI brud): an offspring that was given different genetic information for a trait from each parent. (p. 130)

híbrido: un descendiente que recibe de cada progenitor información genética diferente para un rasgo. (p. 130)

hypothesis: prediction that can be tested. (p. 10)

hipótesis: predicción que puede probarse. (p. 10)

I

incomplete dominance: production of a phenotype that is intermediate between the two homozygous parents. (p. 136)

dominancia incompleta: producción de un fenotipo intermedio entre dos progenitores homocigotos. (p. 136)

inorganic compound: compound, such as H_2O, that is made from elements other than carbon and whose atoms usually can be arranged in only one structure. (p. 73)

compuesto inorgánico: compuesto, como H_2O, formado por elementos distintos al carbono y cuyos átomos generalmente pueden estar organizados en sólo una estructura. (p. 73)

K

kingdom: first and largest category used to classify organisms. (p. 25)

reino: la primera y más grande categoría utilizada para clasificar a los organismos. (p. 25)

L

law: statement about how things work in nature that seems to be true consistently. (p. 12)

ley: enunciado acerca de cómo funciona todo en la naturaleza y que constantemente parece ser verdadero. (p. 12)

M

meiosis (mi OH sus): reproductive process that produces four haploid sex cells from one diploid cell and ensures offspring will have the same number of chromosomes as the parent organisms. (p. 107)

metabolism: the total of all chemical reactions in an organism. (p. 83)

mitochondrion: cell organelle that breaks down food and releases energy. (p. 44)

mitosis (mi TOH sus): cell process in which the nucleus divides to form two nuclei identical to each other, and identical to the original nucleus, in a series of steps (prophase, metaphase, anaphase, and telophase). (p. 100)

mixture: a combination of substances in which the individual substances do not change or combine chemically but instead retain their own individual properties; can be gases, solids, liquids, or any combination of them. (p. 71)

mutation: any permanent change in a gene or chromosome of a cell; may be beneficial, harmful, or have little effect on an organism. (p. 116)

meiosis: proceso reproductivo que produce cuatro células sexuales haploides a partir de una célula diploide y asegura que la descendencia tendrá el mismo número de cromosomas que los organismos progenitores. (p. 107)

metabolismo: el conjunto de todas las reacciones químicas en un organismo. (p. 83)

mitocondria: organelo celular que degrada nutrientes y libera energía. (p. 44)

mitosis: proceso celular en el que el núcleo se divide para formar dos núcleos idénticos entre sí e idénticos al núcleo original, a través de varias etapas (profase, metafase, anafase y telofase). (p. 100)

mezcla: una combinación de sustancias en la que las sustancias individuales no cambian ni se combinan químicamente pero mantienen sus propiedades individuales; pueden ser gases, sólidos, líquidos o una combinación de ellos. (p. 71)

mutación: cualquier cambio permanente en un gen o cromosoma de una célula; puede ser benéfica, perjudicial o tener un pequeño efecto sobre un organismo. (p. 116)

N

natural selection: a process by which organisms with traits best suited to their environment are more likely to survive and reproduce; includes concepts of variation, overproduction, and competition. (p. 158)

nucleus: organelle that controls all the activities of a cell and contains hereditary material made of proteins and DNA. (p. 42)

selección natural: proceso mediante el cual los organismos con rasgos mejor adaptados a su ambiente tienen mayor probabilidad de sobrevivir y reproducirse; incluye los conceptos de variación, sobreproducción y competencia. (p. 158)

núcleo: organelo que controla todas las actividades de una célula y que contiene el material hereditario formado por proteínas y ADN. (p. 42)

O

organ: structure, such as the heart, made up of different types of tissues that all work together. (p. 47)

organelle: structure in the cytoplasm of a eukaryotic cell that can act as a storage site, process energy, move materials, or manufacture substances. (p. 42)

organic compounds: compounds that always contain hydrogen and carbon; carbohydrates, lipids, proteins, and nucleic acids are organic compounds found in living things. (p. 72)

organism: any living thing. (p. 16)

osmosis: a type of passive transport that occurs when water diffuses through a cell membrane. (p. 78)

órgano: estructura, como el corazón, que consiste en diferentes tipos de tejidos que trabajan conjuntamente. (p. 47)

organelo: estructura del citoplasma de una célula eucariota que puede actuar como sitio de almacenamiento, procesamiento de energía, movimiento de materiales o elaboración de sustancias. (p. 42)

compuestos orgánicos: compuestos que siempre contienen hidrógeno y carbono; los carbohidratos, lípidos, proteínas y ácidos nucleicos son compuestos orgánicos que se encuentran en los seres vivos. (p. 72)

organismo: cualquier ser vivo. (p. 16)

ósmosis: tipo de transporte pasivo que ocurre cuando el agua se difunde a través de una membrana celular. (p. 78)

P

passive transport: movement of substances through a cell membrane without the use of cellular energy; includes diffusion, osmosis, and facilitated diffusion. (p. 76)

phenotype (FEE nuh tipe): outward physical appearance and behavior of an organism as a result of its genotype. (p. 132)

photosynthesis: process by which plants and many other producers use light energy to produce a simple sugar from carbon dioxide and water and give off oxygen. (p. 84)

phylogeny (fi LAH juh nee): evolutionary history of an organism; used today to group organisms into six kingdoms. (p. 25)

polygenic (pah lih JEH nihk) inheritance: occurs when a group of gene pairs acts together and produces a specific trait, such as human eye color, skin color, or height. (p. 138)

primates: group of mammals including humans, monkeys, and apes that share characteristics such as opposable thumbs, binocular vision, and flexible shoulders. (p. 172)

punctuated equilibrium: model describing the rapid evolution that occurs when mutation of a few genes results in a species suddenly changing into a new species. (p. 162)

transporte pasivo: movimiento de sustancias a través de la membrana celular sin usar energía celular; incluye difusión, ósmosis y difusión facilitada. (p. 76)

fenotipo: apariencia física externa y comportamiento de un organismo como resultado de su genotipo. (p. 132)

fotosíntesis: proceso mediante el cual las plantas y muchos otros organismos productores usan la energía solar para producir azúcares simples a partir de dióxido de carbono y agua y desprender oxígeno. (p. 84)

filogenia: historia evolutiva de un organismo; usada hoy para agrupar a los organismos en seis reinos. (p. 25)

herencia poligénica: ocurre cuando un grupo de pares de genes actúa conjuntamente y produce un rasgo específico, tal como el color de los ojos , el color de la piel, o la estatura en los humanos. (p. 138)

primates: grupo de mamíferos que incluye a los humanos, monos y simios, los cuales comparten características como pulgares opuestos, visión binocular y hombros flexibles. (p. 172)

equilibrio punteado: modelo que describe la evolución rápida que ocurre cuando la mutación de unos pocos genes resulta en que una especie cambie rápidamente para convertirse en otra especie. (p. 162)

Punnett (PUH nut) square: a tool to predict the probability of certain traits in offspring that shows the different ways alleles can combine. (p. 132)

Cuadrado de Punnett: herramienta para predecir la probabilidad de ciertos rasgos en la descendencia mostrando las diferentes formas en que los alelos pueden combinarse. (p. 132)

R

radioactive element: element that gives off a steady amount of radiation as it slowly changes to a nonradioactive element. (p. 167)

recessive (rih SE sihv): describes a trait that is covered over, or dominated, by another form of that trait and seems to disappear. (p. 130)

respiration: process by which producers and consumers release stored energy from food molecules. (p. 85)

ribosome: small cytoplasmic structure on which cells make their own proteins. (p. 44)

RNA: ribonucleic acid; a type of nucleic acid that carries codes for making proteins from the nucleus to the ribosomes. (p. 114)

elemento radiactivo: elemento que emite una cantidad estable de radiación mientras se convierte lentamente en un elemento no radiactivo. (p. 167)

recesivo: describe un rasgo que está encubierto, o que es dominado, por otra forma del mismo rasgo y que parece no estar presente. (p. 130)

respiración: proceso mediante el cual los organismos productores y consumidores liberan la energía almacenada en las moléculas de los alimentos. (p. 85)

ribosoma: estructura citoplasmática pequeña en la que las células producen sus propias proteínas. (p. 44)

ARN: ácido ribonucleico; tipo de ácido nucleico que transporta los códigos para la formación de proteínas del núcleo a los ribosomas. (p. 114)

S

scientific methods: procedures used to solve problems and answer questions that can include stating the problem, gathering information, forming a hypothesis, testing the hypothesis with an experiment, analyzing data, and drawing conclusions. (p. 9)

sedimentary rock: a type of rock, such as limestone, that is most likely to contain fossils and is formed when layers of sand, silt, clay, or mud are cemented and compacted together or when minerals are deposited from a solution. (p. 166)

sex-linked gene: an allele inherited on a sex chromosome and that can cause human genetic disorders such as color blindness and hemophilia. (p. 141)

sexual reproduction: a type of reproduction in which two sex cells, usually an egg and a sperm, join to form a zygote, which will develop into a new organism with a unique identity. (p. 106)

species: group of organisms that share similar characteristics and can reproduce among themselves producing fertile offspring. (p. 156)

métodos científicos: procedimientos utilizados para solucionar problemas y responder a preguntas; puede incluir el establecimiento de un problema, recopilación de información, formulación de una hipótesis, comprobación de la hipótesis con un experimento, análisis de la información y presentación de conclusiones. (p. 9)

roca sedimentaria: tipo de roca, como la piedra caliza, con alta probabilidad de contener fósiles y que se forma cuando las capas de arena, sedimento, arcilla o lodo son cementadas y compactadas o cuando los minerales de una solución son depositados. (p. 166)

gen ligado al sexo: un alelo heredado en un cromosoma sexual y que puede causar desórdenes genéticos humanos como daltonismo y hemofilia. (p. 141)

reproducción sexual: tipo de reproducción en la que dos células sexuales, generalmente un óvulo y un espermatozoide, se unen para formar un zigoto, el cual se desarrollará para formar un nuevo organismo con identidad única. (p. 106)

especie: grupo de organismos que comparten características similares entre sí y que pueden reproducirse entre ellos dando lugar a una descendencia fértil. (p. 156)

sperm: haploid sex cell formed in the male reproductive organs. (p. 106)

espermatozoides: células sexuales haploides que se forman en los órganos reproductores masculinos. (p. 106)

spontaneous generation: idea that living things come from nonliving things. (p. 21)

generación espontánea: idea que sostiene que los seres vivos proceden de seres inertes. (p. 21)

T

theory: explanation of things or events based on scientific knowledge resulting from many observations and experiments. (p. 12)

tissue: group of similar cells that work together to do one job. (p. 47)

teoría: explicación de cosas o eventos basándose en el conocimiento científico resultante de muchas observaciones y experimentos. (p. 12)

tejido: grupo de células similares que trabajan conjuntamente para hacer una tarea. (p. 47)

variable: something in an experiment that can change. (p. 11)

variation: inherited trait that makes an individual different from other members of the same species and results from a mutation in the organism's genes. (p. 160)

vestigial (veh STIH jee ul) structure: structure, such as the human appendix, that doesn't seem to have a function and may once have functioned in the body of an ancestor. (p. 170)

virus: a strand of hereditary material surrounded by a protein coating. (p. 54)

variable: condición que puede cambiar en un experimento. (p. 11)

variación: rasgo heredado que hace que un individuo sea diferente a otros miembros de su misma especie como resultado de una mutación de sus genes. (p. 160)

estructura vestigial: estructura, como el apéndice humano, que no parece tener alguna función pero que pudo haber funcionado en el cuerpo de un antepasado. (p. 170)

virus: cadena de material hereditario rodeada por una membrana proteica. (p. 54)

Z

zygote: new diploid cell formed when a sperm fertilizes an egg; will divide by mitosis and develop into a new organism. (p. 106)

zigoto: célula diploide nueva formada cuando un espermatozoide fertiliza a un óvulo; se dividirá por mitosis y se desarrollará para formar un nuevo organismo. (p. 106)

Italic numbers = illustration/photo **Bold numbers = vocabulary term**
lab = indicates a page on which the entry is used in a lab
act = indicates a page on which the entry is used in an activity

A

B

C

Index

Index

Index

M

Index

Magnification Key: Magnifications listed are the magnifications at which images were originally photographed.
LM–Light Microscope
SEM–Scanning Electron Microscope
TEM–Transmission Electron Microscope

Acknowledgments: Glencoe would like to acknowledge the artists and agencies who participated in illustrating this program: Absolute Science Illustration; Andrew Evansen; Argosy; Articulate Graphics; Craig Attebery represented by Frank & Jeff Lavaty; CHK America; John Edwards and Associates; Gagliano Graphics; Pedro Julio Gonzalez represented by Melissa Turk & The Artist Network; Robert Hynes represented by Mendola Ltd.; Morgan Cain & Associates; JTH Illustration; Laurie O'Keefe; Matthew Pippin represented by Beranbaum Artist's Representative; Precision Graphics; Publisher's Art; Rolin Graphics, Inc.; Wendy Smith represented by Melissa Turk & The Artist Network; Kevin Torline represented by Berendsen and Associates, Inc.; WILDlife ART; Phil Wilson represented by Cliff Knecht Artist Representative; Zoo Botanica.

Photo Credits

Cover Andrew Syred/Science Photo Library/Photo Researchers; **i ii** Andrew Syred/Science Photo Library/Photo Researchers; **iv** (bkgd)John Evans, (inset)Andrew Syred/Science Photo Library/Photo Researchers; **v** (t)PhotoDisc, (b)John Evans; **vi** (l)John Evans, (r)Geoff Butler; **vii** (l)John Evans, (r)PhotoDisc; **viii** PhotoDisc; **ix** Aaron Haupt Photography; **x** Dave B. Fleetham/Tom Stack & Assoc.; **xi** (t)Archivo Iconografico, S.A./CORBIS, (b)John Reader/Science Photo Library/Photo Researchers; **1** Glencoe photo; **2–3** Bob Jacobson/International Stock; **3** Richard Hutchings/PhotoEdit; **4** courtesy of ABI PRISM; **5** (t)Dominic Oldershaw, (c)Dr. John Carpten, (b)Aaron Haupt; **6–7** A. Witte/C. Mahaney/Getty Images; **8** Kjell B. Sandved/Visuals Unlimited; **10 11** Mark Burnett; **13** Tek Image/Science Photo Library/Photo Researchers; **14 15** Mark Burnett; **16** (t)Michael Abbey/Science Source/Photo Researchers, (bl)Aaron Haupt, (br)Michael Delannoy/Visuals Unlimited; **17** Mark Burnett; **18** (tcr)A. Glauberman/Photo Researchers, (tr)Mark Burnett, (bl bcl br)Runk/Schoenberger from Grant Heilman, (others)Dwight Kuhn; **19** (t)Bill Beaty/Animals Animals, (bl)Tom & Therisa Stack/Tom Stack & Assoc., (br)Michael Fogden/Earth Scenes; **20** Aaron Haupt; **21** Geoff Butler; **24** (t)Arthur C. Smith III From Grant Heilman, (bl)Hal Beral/Visuals Unlimited, (br)Larry L. Miller/Photo Researchers; **25** Doug Perrine/Innerspace Visions; **26** (l)Brandon D. Cole, (r)Gregory Ochocki/Photo Researchers; **27** (l)Zig Leszczynski/Animals Animals, (r)R. Andrew Odum/Peter Arnold, Inc.; **28** Alvin E. Staffan; **29** Geoff Butler; **30** (t)Jan Hinsch/Science Photo Library/Photo Researchers, (b)Mark Burnett; **31** Mark Burnett; **32** Marc Von Roosmalen/AP; **33** (l)Mark Burnet, (r)Will & Deni McIntyre/Photo Researchers; **34** KS Studios/Mullenix; **35** Jeff Greenberg/Rainbow; **36** Dwight Kuhn; **37** Dave Spier/Visuals Unlimited; **38–39** Nancy Kedersha/Science Photo Library/Photo Researchers; **41** David M. Phillips/Visuals Unlimited; **42** (t)Don Fawcett/Photo Researchers, (b)M. Schliwa/Visuals Unlimited; **44** (t)George B. Chapman/Visuals Unlimited, (b)P. Motta & T. Naguro/Science Photo Library/Photo Researchers; **45** (t)Don Fawcett/Photo Researchers, (b)Biophoto Associates/Photo Researchers; **49** (l)Biophoto Associates/Photo Researchers, (r)Matt Meadows; **50–51** (bkgd)David M. Phillips/Visuals Unlimited; **50** (cw from top)Kathy Talaro/Visuals Unlimited, Michael Abbey/Visuals Unlimited, Michael Gabridge/Visuals Unlimited, David M. Phillips/Visuals Unlimited, David M. Phillips/Visuals Unlimited, courtesy Nikon Instruments Inc.; **51** (tl)Michael Abbey/Visuals Unlimited, (tr)Bob Krist/CORBIS, (cl)courtesy Olympus Corporation, (cr)James W. Evarts, (bl)Karl Aufderheide/Visuals Unlimited, (br)Lawrence Migdale/Stock Boston/PictureQuest; **54** (l)Richard J. Green/Photo Researchers, (c)Dr. J.F.J.M. van der Heuvel, (r)Gelderblom/Eye of Science/Photo Researchers; **57** Pam Wilson/Texas Dept. of Health; **58 59** Matt Meadows; **60** (t)Quest/Science Photo Library/Photo (b)courtesy California University; **61** (l)Keith Porter/Photo Researchers, (r)NIBSC/Science Photo Library/Photo Researchers; **63** Biophoto Associates/Science Source/Photo Researchers; **64** P. Motta & T. Naguro/Science Photo Library/Photo Researchers; **66–67** Jane Grushow/Grant Heilman Photography; **69** Bob Daemmrich; **71** (t)Runk/Schoenberger from Grant Heilman, (b)Klaus Guldbrandsen/Science Photo Library/Photo Researchers; **76** (l)John Fowler, (r)Richard Hamilton Smith/CORBIS; **77** KS Studios; **78** Aaron Haupt; **79** Visuals Unlimited; **80** Biophoto Associates/Science Source/Photo Researchers; **82** Matt Meadows; **84** Craig Lovell/CORBIS; **85** John Fowler; **86** David M. Phillips/Visuals Unlimited; **87** (l)Grant Heilman Photography, (r)Bios (Klein/Hubert)/Peter Arnold; **88** (t)Runk/Schoenberger from Grant Heilman, (b)Matt Meadows; **89** Matt Meadows; **90** Lappa/Marquart; **91** CNRI/Science Photo Library/Photo Researchers; **92** Biophoto Associates/Science Source/Photo Researchers; **96–97** Zig Leszcynski/Animals Animals; **98** (l)Dave B. Fleetham/Tom Stack & Assoc., (r)Cabisco/Visuals Unlimited; **100** Cabisco/Visuals Unlimited; **101** (tl)Michael Abbey/Visuals Unlimited, (others)John D. Cunningham/Visuals Unlimited; **102** (l)Matt Meadows, (r)Nigel Cattlin/Photo Researchers; **103** (l)Barry L. Runk from Grant Heilman, (r)Runk/Schoenberger from Grant Heilman; **104** (l)Walker England/Photo Researchers, (r)Tom Stack & Assoc.; **105** Runk/Schoenberger from Grant Heilman; **106** Dr. Dennis Kunkel/PhotoTake NYC; **107** (tl)Gerald & Buff Corsi/Visuals Unlimited, (bl)Susan McCartney/Photo Researchers, (r)Fred Bruenner/Peter Arnold, Inc.; **109** (l)John D. Cunningham/Visuals Unlimited, (c)Jen & Des Bartlett/Bruce Coleman, Inc., (r)Breck P. Kent; **110** (tl)Artville, (tr)Tim Fehr, (c)Bob Daemmrich/Stock Boston/PictureQuest, (bl)Troy Mary Parlee/Index Stock/PictureQuest, (br)Jeffery Myers/Southern Stock/PictureQuest; **116** Stewart Cohen/Stone/Getty Images; **118** (t)Tom McHugh/Photo Researchers, (b)file photo; **119** Monica Dalmasso/Stone/Getty Images; **120** (t)Philip Lee Harvey/Stone, (b)Lester V. Bergman/CORBIS; **122** Walker England/Photo Researchers; **124** Barry L. Runk from Grant Heilman; **125** Cabisco/Visuals Unlimited; **126–127** Ron Chapple/Getty Images; **127** Geoff Butler; **128** Stewart Cohen/Stone/Getty Images; **131** (bkgd)Jane Grushow from Grant Heilman, (others)Special Collections, National Agriculture Library; **132** Barry L. Runk From Grant Heilman; **134** Richard Hutchings/Photo Researchers; **136** (l)Robert Maier/Animals Animals, (r)Gemma Giannini from Grant Heilman; **137** Raymond Gehman/CORBIS; **138** Dan McCoy from Rainbow; **139** (l)Phil Roach/Ipol, Inc., (r)CNRI/Science Photo Library/Photo Researchers; **140** Gopal Murti/

PhotoTake, NYC; **141** Tim Davis/Photo Researchers; **142** (t)Renee Stockdale/Animals Animals, (b)Alan & Sandy Carey/Photo Researchers; **145** Tom Meyers/Photo Researchers; **146** (t)Runk/Schoenberger from Grant Heilman, (b)Mark Burnett; **147** Richard Hutchings; **148** KS Studios; **153** CNRI/Science Photo Library/Photo Researchers; **154–155** B.G. Thomson/Photo Researchers; **157** Barbera Cushman/DRK Photo; **158** (l c)Tui De Roy/Minden Pictures, (r)Tim Davis/Photo Researchers; **160** (l)Gregory G. Dimijian, M.D./Photo Researchers, (r)Patti Murray/Animals Animals; **161** (l)Darek Karp/Animals Animals, (r)Vonorla Photography; **162** (l)Joe McDonald/Animals Animals, (c)Tom McHugh/Photo Researchers, (r)Tim Davis/Photo Researchers; **163** James Richardson/Visuals Unlimited; **164** Frans Lanting/Minden Pictures; **165** (l)Dominique Braud/Earth Scenes, (c)Carr Clifton/Minden Pictures, (r)John Cancalosi/DRK Photo; **166** (t)Larry Ulrich/DRK Photo, (cl)Ken Lucas/Visuals Unlimited, (cr)John Cancalosi/Peter Arnold, Inc., (bl)John Cancalosi/DRK Photo, (br)Sinclair Stammers/Science Photo Library/Photo Researchers; **167** John Kieffer/Peter Arnold, Inc.; **170** (l)Kees Van Den Berg/Photo Researchers, (r)Doug Martin; **171** Peter Veit/DRK Photo; **172** (l)Mark E. Gibson, (r)Gerard Lacz/Animals Animals; **173** (l)Michael Dick/Animals Animals, (r)Carolyn A. McKeone/Photo Researchers; **174** (l)John Reader/Science Photo Library/Photo Researchers, (r)Archivo Iconografico, S.A./CORBIS; **175** Francois Ducasse/Rapho/Photo Researchers; **176–177** Aaron Haupt; **176** Kenneth W. Fink/Photo Researchers; **178** (t)Oliver Meckes/E.O.S/Gelderblom/Photo Researchers, (b)Lara Jo Regan/Saba; **179** (l)Koster-Survival/Animals Animals, (r)Stephen J. Keasemann/DRK Photo; **181** Tom Tietz/Stone/Getty Images; **182** Gregory G. Dimijian, M.D./Photo Researchers; **183** Patti Murray/Animals Animals; **184** PhotoDisc; **186** Tom Pantages; **190** Michell D. Bridwell/PhotoEdit, Inc.; **191** (t)Mark Burnett, (b)Dominic Oldershaw; **192** StudiOhio; **193** Timothy Fuller; **194** Aaron Haupt; **196** KS Studios; **197** Matt Meadows; **198 199** Aaron Haupt; **200** Sinclair Stammers/Science Photo Library/Photo Researchers; **201** Amanita Pictures; **202** Bob Daemmrich; **204** Davis Barber/PhotoEdit, Inc.; **222** Matt Meadows; **223** (l)Dr. Richard Kessel, (c)NIBSC/Science Photo Library/Photo Researchers, (r)David John/Visuals Unlimited; **224** (t)Runk/Schoenberger from Grant Heilman, (bl)Andrew Syred/Science Photo Library/Photo Researchers, (br)Rich Brommer; **225** (tr)G.R. Roberts, (l)Ralph Reinhold/Earth Scenes, (br)Scott Johnson/Animals Animals; **226** Martin Harvey/DRK Photo.

PERIODIC TABLE OF THE ELEMENTS

Columns of elements are called groups. Elements in the same group have similar chemical properties.

Gas

Liquid

Solid

Synthetic

The first three symbols tell you the state of matter of the element at room temperature. The fourth symbol identifies elements that are not present in significant amounts on Earth. Useful amounts are made synthetically.

Element — Hydrogen
Atomic number — 1
Symbol — H
Atomic mass — 1.008
State of matter

	1	2	3	4	5	6	7	8	9
1	Hydrogen 1 **H** 1.008								
2	Lithium 3 **Li** 6.941	Beryllium 4 **Be** 9.012							
3	Sodium 11 **Na** 22.990	Magnesium 12 **Mg** 24.305							
4	Potassium 19 **K** 39.098	Calcium 20 **Ca** 40.078	Scandium 21 **Sc** 44.956	Titanium 22 **Ti** 47.867	Vanadium 23 **V** 50.942	Chromium 24 **Cr** 51.996	Manganese 25 **Mn** 54.938	Iron 26 **Fe** 55.845	Cobalt 27 **Co** 58.933
5	Rubidium 37 **Rb** 85.468	Strontium 38 **Sr** 87.62	Yttrium 39 **Y** 88.906	Zirconium 40 **Zr** 91.224	Niobium 41 **Nb** 92.906	Molybdenum 42 **Mo** 95.94	Technetium 43 **Tc** (98)	Ruthenium 44 **Ru** 101.07	Rhodium 45 **Rh** 102.906
6	Cesium 55 **Cs** 132.905	Barium 56 **Ba** 137.327	Lanthanum 57 **La** 138.906	Hafnium 72 **Hf** 178.49	Tantalum 73 **Ta** 180.948	Tungsten 74 **W** 183.84	Rhenium 75 **Re** 186.207	Osmium 76 **Os** 190.23	Iridium 77 **Ir** 192.217
7	Francium 87 **Fr** (223)	Radium 88 **Ra** (226)	Actinium 89 **Ac** (227)	Rutherfordium 104 **Rf** (261)	Dubnium 105 **Db** (262)	Seaborgium 106 **Sg** (266)	Bohrium 107 **Bh** (264)	Hassium 108 **Hs** (277)	Meitnerium 109 **Mt** (268)

The number in parentheses is the mass number of the longest-lived isotope for that element.

Rows of elements are called periods. Atomic number increases across a period.

The arrow shows where these elements would fit into the periodic table. They are moved to the bottom of the table to save space.

Lanthanide series	Cerium 58 **Ce** 140.116	Praseodymium 59 **Pr** 140.908	Neodymium 60 **Nd** 144.24	Promethium 61 **Pm** (145)	Samarium 62 **Sm** 150.36
Actinide series	Thorium 90 **Th** 232.038	Protactinium 91 **Pa** 231.036	Uranium 92 **U** 238.029	Neptunium 93 **Np** (237)	Plutonium 94 **Pu** (244)